Ready®
Common Core

1 **Mathematics**
INSTRUCTION
Teacher Resource Book

$3 \text{ tens} + ? \text{ tens} = 8 \text{ tens}$

Teacher Advisors

Crystal Bailey, Math Impact Teacher, Eastern Guilford Middle School, Guilford County Schools, Gibsonville, NC

Max Brand, Reading Specialist, Indian Run Elementary, Dublin City School District, Dublin, OH

Helen Comba, Supervisor of Basic Skills & Language Arts, School District of the Chathams, Chatham, NJ

Cindy Dean, Classroom Teacher, Mt. Diablo Unified School District, Concord, CA

Randall E. Groth, Ph.D, Associate Professor of Mathematics Education, Salisbury University, Salisbury, MD

Bill Laraway, Classroom Teacher, Silver Oak Elementary, Evergreen School District, San Jose, CA

Jennifer Lerner, Classroom Teacher, PS 57, New York City Public Schools, New York, NY

Susie Legg, Elementary Curriculum Coordinator, Kansas City Public Schools, Kansas City, KS

Sarah Levine, Classroom Teacher, Springhurst Elementary School, Dobbs Ferry School District, Dobbs Ferry, NY

Nicole Peirce, Classroom Teacher, Eleanor Roosevelt Elementary, Pennsbury School District, Morrisville, PA

Donna Phillips, Classroom Teacher, Farmington R-7 School District, Farmington, MO

Maria Rosati, Classroom Teacher, Harwood Elementary School, Warren Consolidated Schools, Warren, MI

Kari Ross, Reading Specialist, MN

Sunita Sangari, Math Coach, PS/MS 29, New York City Public Schools, New York, NY

Eileen Seybuck, Classroom Teacher, PS 57, New York City Public Schools, New York, NY

Mark Hoover Thames, Research Scientist, University of Michigan, Ann Arbor, MI

Shannon Tsuruda, Classroom Teacher, Mt. Diablo Unified School District, Concord, CA

Acknowledgments

Associate Vice President: Renee Gardner
Editorial Director: Cynthia Tripp
Associate Editorial Director: Thomas Super
Editors: Danielle Curran, Pam Halloran, Kathy Kellman, Theresa MacVicar, Dawn Nuttall, Lauren Van Wart

Project Manager: Jillian McCarthy
Cover Design: Matt Pollock
Cover Illustrator: O'Lamar Gibson
Book Design: Jeremy Spiegel, Timothy Theriault

Table of Contents

Table of Contents

M = Lessons that have a major emphasis in the Common Core Standards
S/A = Lessons that have supporting/additional emphasis in the Common Core Standards
Standards in boldface are the focus standards that address major lesson content.

Mathematics Lessons, *continued*

Mathematics Lessons, *continued*

		Standards	Embedded SMPs	Emphasis

Welcome to *Ready® Mathematics*

Ready Mathematics prepares students for mastery of the Common Core's rigorous standards through a balance of conceptual understanding, procedural skills, fluency, and application.

Ready's clear, thoughtful pedagogy and research-based instructional model support a rich classroom environment in which mathematical reasoning, mathematical discourse, and a range of mathematical practices thrive.

Rigor that is reachable

- Uses real-world problem solving as instruction to develop deep conceptual understanding

- Presents multiple representations to make connections and show the conceptual meaning behind procedural fluency

- Connects new problems to prior knowledge, demonstrates multiple approaches, and provides multiple access points to learning

- Strengthens students' ability to use critical thinking and complex reasoning through questions that focus on higher DOK levels

Support that simplifies

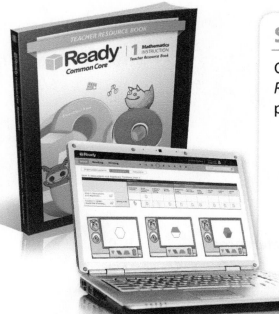

Offering step-by-step guidance and embedded teacher support, *Ready Mathematics'* teacher tools are simple to implement and support powerful, effective teaching.

- A comprehensive Teacher Resource Book provides point-of-use strategies, tips, and mathematical discourse for teaching every step of every lesson

- A K–8 Online Teacher Toolbox offers a virtual filing cabinet of instructional resources to support teaching throughout the year

- A rich array of assessment tools helps monitor student progress and guide responsive instruction

Meet Our *Ready*® Mathematics Authors

Ready Mathematics was built to reflect the connection between the latest research and practical classroom application. Guidance from our program's authors continues to shape *Ready* to ensure that it is rigorous for students yet easy to implement for teachers.

Mark Ellis, Ph.D.

 Awards & Key Positions

- Board of Directors, Executive Committee, NCTM
- Department Chair and Professor, Education, CSU Fullerton
- National Board Certified Teacher

 Known for Research On

- Middle grades mathematics teaching and learning
- Equity, discourse, and technology in mathematics education
- Preparation of teachers of mathematics

Gladis Kersaint, Ph.D.

 Awards & Key Positions

- Board of Directors, Executive Committee, NCTM
- Board of Directors, Association of Mathematics Teacher Educators
- Dean of the Neag School of Education, University of Connecticut

 Known for Research On

- Equity in mathematics education
- Middle grades mathematics teaching and learning
- Preparation of teachers of mathematics

Program Components

Ready® Mathematics

- The **Student Instruction Book** addresses today's rigorous standards with clear, thoughtful instruction, real-world problem solving, and multiple access points to learning.

- The **Teacher Resource Book** provides the point-of-use guidance and embedded teacher support needed for teaching every step of every lesson.

Ready® Practice and Problem Solving

- The **Practice and Problem Solving Book** offers a wealth of resources to extend learning. Lesson-level support includes family letters and rigorous practice for each section in *Ready* Instruction. Unit-level and additional support includes games, practice, and fluency practice worksheets.

Ready® Mathematics Instruction and *Practice and Problem Solving* are available on the Online Teacher Toolbox.

Ready® Online Teacher Toolbox
(Teacher-Toolbox.com)

The easy-to-use **Online Teacher Toolbox** is a virtual filing cabinet of instructional resources designed to address the needs of all learners and differentiate instruction.

Complete access to all K–8 content:

- Interactive Tutorials,
- Lesson Quiz PDFs,
- Center Activities PDFs,
- *Ready* Instruction Prerequisite Lesson PDFs, and
- Tools for Instruction PDFs.

i-Ready®
(i-Ready.com)

i-Ready combines an adaptive diagnostic and growth measure, targeted assessment of grade-level standards, and individualized online instruction in a single program.

- *i-Ready* **Diagnostic** delivers a comprehensive understanding of each student's unique needs across a K-12 continuum and is proven to predict performance on state assessments.
- *i-Ready* **data** shape each student's personalized instruction plan, prescribing a tailored combination of online instruction and downloadable, teacher-led lessons for each student.

Door 24® *Plus*
(Fluency App)

Door 24 Plus is a free iPad® game app that provides personalized fact and computational fluency practice.

iPad® is a trademark of Apple. Inc. registered in the U.S. and other countries.

Using *Ready*® with *i-Ready*®: Program Overview

Whether using the *i-Ready*®/*Ready*® blended program or *Ready* as a stand-alone program, you have the flexibility to meet all your instruction and assessment needs.

Diagnose and Monitor

Adaptive Diagnostic and Growth Monitoring

i-Ready® Diagnostic

45-60 minutes, 3 times a year

An adaptive Diagnostic designed to collect a broad spectrum of information on students' ability that identifies areas where students are struggling, measures growth across a student's career, and plans an instructional path with a single measurement tool

Instruct

Whole Class Instruction

Ready® Books and
Online Teacher Toolbox

Small Group Differentiation

Ready® Online Teacher Toolbox

Personalized Learning and Intervention

i-Ready® Instruction

Instruct
Ready® Instruction

45–60 min per day, 1 lesson per week

Teacher-led whole and small group math instruction following a gradual release model

Practice
Ready® Practice and Problem Solving

20–30 min per day

Practice that can be assigned after every section of the *Ready* lesson for use in class, after school, or at home

Assess
Lesson Quiz PDFs

15–20 min per quiz, 1 quiz per week

Lesson quizzes at the end of each *Ready* lesson to assess students on the lesson content and identify the need for reteaching

Reteach
Ready® Instruction Prerequisite Lesson PDFs

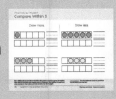

45–90 min per lesson

Teacher-led, in-depth instruction using *Ready* lessons from earlier grades to review prerequisite concepts or fill in gaps in student knowledge

Student-Led Activity
Math Center Activity PDFs

20–30 min per activity

Student-led games and activities available for each standard in three different versions for use with on-level, below-level, and above-level groups

Teacher-Led Activity
Tools for Instruction PDFs

20–30 min per activity

Teacher-led activities for use with small groups of students requiring additional instruction on a prerequisite or on-level skill

Also available with i-Ready instruction

Online Instruction
i-Ready® Instruction

At least 45 min per week

Animated, interactive lessons that allow students to work independently on their personalized online instruction plan

Fluency Practice
Door 24® Plus iPad® App

Optional 30–45 min per week

Fact and computational fluency games that provide personalized practice based on an adaptive assessment

iPad® is a trademark of Apple. Inc. registered in the U.S. and other countries.

Answering the Demands of the Common Core with *Ready*®

The Common Core State Standards have raised the rigor for mathematics instruction in several important ways. *Ready Mathematics* has been written to specifically address those shifts.

Demand: Focus

Ready Mathematics lessons reflect the same focus as the Common Core standards.

- The majority of the lessons in each grade directly address the major focus of the year.

- Each lesson was newly written specifically to address the Common Core standards.

- There is at least one lesson for each standard and only lessons that address the Common Core standards are included.

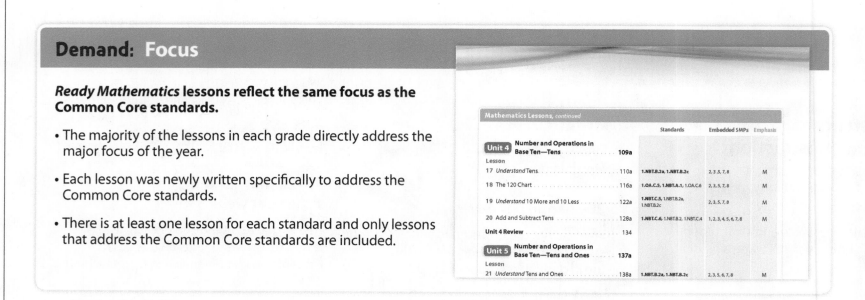

Mathematics Lessons, *continued*

			Standards	Embedded SMPs	Emphasis
Unit 4 Number and Operations in Base Ten—Tens		109a			
Lesson					
17	*Understand* Tens	110a	1.NBT.B.2a, 1.NBT.B.2c	2, 3, 5, 7, 8	M
18	The 120 Chart	116a	1.OA.C.5, 1.NBT.A.1, 1.OA.C.6	2, 3, 5, 7, 8	M
19	*Understand* 10 More and 10 Less	122a	1.NBT.C.5, 1.NBT.B.2a, 1.NBT.B.2c	2, 3, 5, 7, 8	M
20	Add and Subtract Tens	128a	1.NBT.C.6, 1.NBT.B.2, 1.NBT.C.4	1, 2, 3, 4, 5, 6, 7, 8	M
Unit 4 Review		134			
Unit 5 Number and Operations in Base Ten—Tens and Ones		137a			
Lesson					
21	*Understand* Tens and Ones	138a	1.NBT.B.2a, 1.NBT.B.2c	2, 3, 5, 6, 7, 8	M

Demand: Rigor and Higher-Order Thinking

Ready Mathematics lessons balance conceptual understanding, skill and procedural fluency, and application.

- Students are required to use various cognitive strategies as they respond to different types of problem situations.

- Students are asked higher-order thinking questions throughout the lessons as they discuss and interpret concepts, multiple representations, applications, and skills and strategies.

- Students must be able to explain their thinking, critique the reasoning of others, and generalize their results.

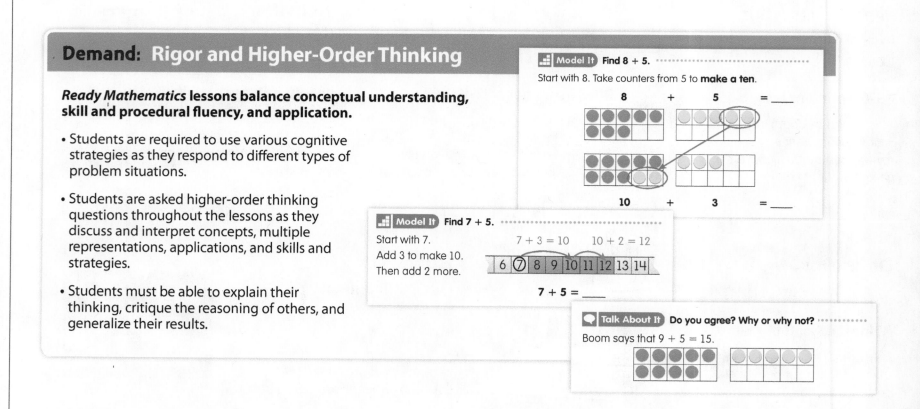

Demand: Mathematical Reasoning

Ready Mathematics **lessons build on problem solving as a main component of instruction.**

- Students analyze problems, determine effective strategies to solve them, and evaluate the reasonableness of their solutions.

- Students work through problems, discuss them, draw conclusions, and make generalizations.

- Guided Practice problems ask students to critique arguments presented by fictional characters and justify their own solutions.

 Explain There are 5 beads. 4 are on the table. The rest are in a cup.

▸ Buzz says there are 9 beads in the cup.

▸ Do you agree? Why? Why not?

Demand: Coherence

Ready Mathematics **lessons build on prior knowledge, making connections within and across clusters and domains, and within and across grade levels.**

- Each lesson starts with an opening activity that builds on prior knowledge and connects to what students already know.

- These connections allow students to see math as more than just a set of rules and isolated procedures to develop a deeper knowledge of mathematics.

- Connections are highlighted in the Learning Progressions of the Teacher Resource Book so teachers can see at a glance how each lesson connects to previous and future learning.

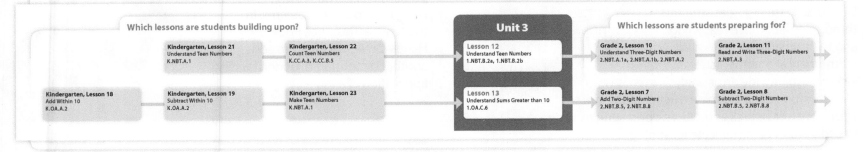

Which lessons are students building upon?

Kindergarten, Lesson 21
Understand Teen Numbers
K.NBT.A.1

Kindergarten, Lesson 22
Count Teen Numbers
K.CC.A.3, K.CC.B.5

Kindergarten, Lesson 18
Add Within 10
K.OA.A.2

Kindergarten, Lesson 19
Subtract Within 10
K.OA.A.2

Kindergarten, Lesson 23
Make Teen Numbers
K.NBT.A.1

Unit 3

Lesson 12
Understand Teen Numbers
1.NBT.B.2a, 1.NBT.B.2b

Lesson 13
Understand Sums Greater than 10
1.OA.C.6

Which lessons are students preparing for?

Grade 2, Lesson 10
Understand Three-Digit Numbers
2.NBT.A.1a, 2.NBT.A.1b, 2.NBT.A.2

Grade 2, Lesson 11
Read and Write Three-Digit Numbers
2.NBT.A.3

Grade 2, Lesson 7
Add Two-Digit Numbers
2.NBT.B.5, 2.NBT.B.8

Grade 2, Lesson 8
Subtract Two-Digit Numbers
2.NBT.B.5, 2.NBT.B.8

The Standards for Mathematical Practice

The Standards for Mathematical Practice (SMP), which support the teaching of the content standards through intentional, appropriate use, are fully integrated throughout each lesson in the *Ready* Student Book. The Teacher Resource Book includes SMP Tips that provide more in-depth information for select practice standards addressed in the lessons.

1 Make sense of problems and persevere in solving them.

Try more than one approach, think strategically, and succeed in solving problems that seem very difficult.

Ready lessons lead students through new problems by using what they already know, demonstrate multiple approaches and access points, and opportunities for cooperative dialogue.

2 Reason abstractly and quantitatively.

Represent a word problem with an equation, or other symbols, solve the math, and then interpret the solution to answer the question posed.

Ready lessons lead students to see mathematical relationships connecting equations, visual representations, and problem situations. Each lesson challenges students to analyze the connection between an abstract representation and pictorial or real-world situations.

3 Construct viable arguments and critique the reasoning of others.

Discuss, communicate reasoning, create explanations, and critique the reasoning of others.

In *Ready* lessons, the teacher-led Mathematical Discourse feature guides students through collaborative reasoning and the exchange of ideas and mathematical arguments. *Ready* lessons also provide error-analysis exercises that ask students to examine a fictional student's wrong answer, as well as multiple opportunities to explain and communicate reasoning.

4 Model with mathematics.

Use math to solve actual problems.

In *Ready* lessons, students create a mathematical model using pictures, diagrams, tables, or equations to solve problems. In the Teacher Resource Book, the Hands-On Activity feature adds another dimension to understanding application of a skill.

Meeting New Expectations &
Best Practices

What Ready™ Mathematics
Instruction Looks Like

How to Implement
Ready™ Mathematics

5 Use appropriate tools strategically.

Make choices about which tools, if any, to use to solve a problem.

Ready lessons model the use of a variety of tools, including diagrams, tables, or number paths. Guided Practice problems may be solved with a variety of strategies that involve the use of tools.

6 Attend to precision.

Explain and argue, draw, label, and compute carefully and accurately.

Ready lessons guide students to focus on precision in both procedures and communication, including special error-analysis tasks and group discussion questions that motivate students to employ precise, convincing arguments.

7 Look for and make use of structure.

Build mathematical understanding by recognizing structures such as place value, decomposition of numbers, and the processes of measurement.

Ready lessons build understanding of new concepts by explicitly reviewing prior knowledge of mathematical structure.

8 Look for and express regularity in repeated reasoning.

Recognize regularity in repeated reasoning and make generalizations or conjectures about other situations.

Ready lessons lead students to focus attention on patterns that reflect regularity. Where appropriate, students draw a conclusion or make a generalization and explain their reasoning by referencing the observed pattern.

Supporting Research

Ready® Mathematics is founded on research from a variety of federal initiatives, national mathematics organizations, and experts in mathematics. As a result, this program may be used in support of several instructional models.

Ready® Uses ...	Examples	Research Says ...
Scaffolded Instruction		
Scaffolded instruction is the gradual withdrawal of support through modeled, guided, and independent instruction and practice.	*Ready* lessons follow the pattern of modeled and guided instruction, guided practice, and independent practice.	"*Successful teachers help to create independent learners ... Contingent scaffolded instruction ... is a powerful tool for achieving this goal.*" —Beed et al., 1991
Applying Prior Knowledge		
These are experiences and knowledge that a student brings with himself or herself to learn about a topic.	Each *Ready* lesson begins with an **Activity** that introduces a new skill by guiding students to solve a problem using prior knowledge.	"*What and how students are taught should reflect not only the topics that fall within a certain academic discipline, but also the key ideas that determine how knowledge is organized and generated within that discipline.*" —Schmidt, Houang, & Cogan, 2002
Collaborative Learning		
Students work together in pairs or small groups to attain their individual goals.	*Ready* lessons provide multiple opportunities for collaborative learning. **Talk About It** leads students through discussions of key ideas and prompts them to compare answers and reasoning to identify misconceptions.	"*Collaborative learning improves computational skills. Use of cooperative or collaborative learning has been advocated in various mathematics education reports and in state curricular frameworks, policies, and instructional guidelines.*" —National Mathematics Advisory Panel, 2008
Visual Representation		
Visual representation is using an image to help describe or define a mathematical problem or relationship, or to depict a real-life problem situation.	*Ready* routinely uses visual representations as part of instruction. • **Model It** and other visual models such as number paths illustrate mathematical concepts. • **Visual Models** in the Teacher Resource Books suggests additional visual representations.	"*Graphic representations of mathematical concepts and problems ... are crucial components of programs used in nations that perform well on international comparisons, such as Singapore, Korea, or the Netherlands.*" —NCTM, 2007

Ready® Uses ...	Examples	Research Says ...
Mathematical Discourse		
Mathematical Discourse in instruction uses questioning, listening, writing, and reflection to encourage conversation about mathematics.	*Ready* lessons include regular verbal exchange of ideas and sharing of understanding in whole group, small group, and pair settings. • **Talk About It** leads students through discussions of key ideas and prompts them to compare answers and reasoning to identify misconceptions. • **Mathematical Discourse** in the Teacher Resource Book suggests thoughtful question prompts.	"*The process of encouraging students to verbalize their thinking—by talking, writing, or drawing the steps they used in solving a problem—was consistently effective.*" —NCTM, 2007
Multiple Representations		
Multiple representations are the ways in which a teacher or student represents a math idea, including spoken, written, symbolic, and concrete formats.	*Ready* lessons routinely use multiple representations to illustrate mathematical concepts. **Hands-On Activities** and **Visual Models** in the Teacher Resource Book offer suggestions for additional representations.	"*The usefulness of numerical ideas is enhanced when students encounter and use multiple representations for the same concept.*" —National Research Council, 2001
Formative Assessment		
Formative assessment (or Progress Monitoring) is a strategy that involves frequent, in-classroom progress checks of students' understanding and mastery of math concepts and skills.	*Ready* lessons are structured so teachers can monitor understanding throughout. • **Talk About It** and **Error Alerts** in the Teacher Resource Books create ongoing formative assessment opportunities, with support for correcting misconceptions. • **Assessment and Remediation** charts at the end of the lesson help the teacher assess mastery of the skill, identify specific misconceptions, and remediate on the spot as necessary.	"*Teachers' regular use of formative assessment improves their students' learning, especially if teachers have additional guidance on using the assessment to design and to individualize instruction.*" —National Mathematics Advisory Panel, 2008
Hands-On Activities		
Hands-On Activities are any activities in which the student uses manipulatives to explore mathematical quantities, relationships, or operations.	**Hands-On Activities** are found throughout the Teacher Resource Book, both at point-of-use during instruction and at the end of the lesson.	"*The benefit of this [hands-on, manipulative] approach may be that its intensity and concreteness help students maintain a framework in their working memory for solving problems of this type.*" —NCTM, 2007

Supporting Research, *continued*

Ready® Uses ...	Examples	Research Says ...
Differentiated Instruction		
Differentiated instruction is an approach to teaching that gives students multiple ways to access and make sense of mathematical ideas.	*Ready* lessons provide a full range of support for differentiating instruction. • *Ready* Student Books provide verbal, visual, and symbolic representations of each new skill and concept. • **Hands-On Activities, Visual Models, Concept Extensions,** and **Challenge Activities** in the Teacher Resource Books provide additional differentiation options.	"*Many teachers and teacher educators have recently identified differentiated instruction as a method of helping more students in diverse classroom settings experience success.*" —Hall et al., 2003
Conceptual Understanding		
Conceptual understanding is the knowledge of why math processes and rules work.	All *Ready* lessons begin by laying a foundation of conceptual understanding of the mathematical principles underlying the skill being addressed. • **Understand** lessons put a special emphasis on these principles. • **Concept Extension** features in the Teacher Resource Book further support conceptual understanding.	"*To prepare students for Algebra, the curriculum must simultaneously develop conceptual understanding, computational fluency, and problem-solving skills.*" —National Mathematics Advisory Panel, 2008
Computational Fluency		
Computational fluency is having quick recall of number facts and knowledge and ability to apply multiple computational methods involving whole numbers, decimals, fractions, and other numbers as appropriate to the grade level.	*Ready* lessons all directly address computation skills, develop the conceptual understanding to support computation, or provide application of computation skills.	"*Basic skills with numbers continue to be vitally important for a variety of everyday uses. They also provide a crucial foundation for the higher-level mathematics essential for success in the workplace, which must now also be part of a basic education.*" —Ball et al., 2005
Problem Solving (or Application)		
Problem solving (or application) is the process of formulating a real-life problem as a mathematical problem, then performing the necessary calculations, and interpreting the result to find the solution to the problem.	Problem solving is at the heart of *Ready*. • *Ready* lessons present new math problems in real-world contexts and model finding the solution in multiple ways. Students then practice with similar problems. • **Independent Practice** problems include real-world problems.	"*. . . An important part of our conception of mathematical proficiency involves the ability to formulate and solve problems coming from daily life or other domains, including mathematics itself.*" —National Research Council, 2001

Ready® Uses ...	Examples	Research Says ...
Standards for Mathematical Practice		
Standards for Mathematical Practice identify habits of mind and everyday ways of approaching math that are hallmarks of successful math students.	The Standards for Mathematical Practice (SMP) are an integral part of *Ready* instruction. • Throughout the *Ready* Student Book, SMP are built into the instruction and problems. • Teacher Resource Books feature SMP Tips in every lesson to alert teachers to particular instances of each SMP.	"*These practices rest on important 'processes and proficiencies' with longstanding importance in mathematics education.*" —CCSS, 2010
ELL Support		
ELL support provides teachers with the content knowledge and pedagogy to minimize obstacles to learning math due to language or cultural issues.	*Ready* lessons use many approaches to help teachers support ELL students. • The *Ready* Student Book uses pictorial and visual representations combined with direct simple text to clearly present concepts. • Point-of-use **ELL Support** tips for teachers are found throughout the Teacher Resource Book. • Language Objectives are included in the Teacher Resource Book for all lessons.	"*Expanded opportunities should be available to English language learners (ELL students) who need them to develop mathematical understanding and proficiency.*" —NCTM, 2008
Answer Explanations for Students		
As a part of scaffolded instruction, students receive immediate feedback on their answers and the reasoning behind correct and incorrect answers.	In the **Guided Instruction, Guided Practice, Independent Practice,** and **Unit Review** sections of the Teacher Resource Book, answers and explanations are given for problems.	"*When students receive direct instruction about the reasons why an answer choice is correct or incorrect, they demonstrate long-term retention and understanding of newly learned content.*" —Pashler et al., 2007

Built for Rigor and Engagement

The Common Core State Standards demand instruction that balances conceptual understanding, procedural skills and fluency, and application. **Ready Mathematics** achieves this balance with lessons that develop understanding and procedural fluency in tandem so students can easily apply what they have learned to new situations.

Skills and strategy lessons focus on helping students acquire and apply efficient procedures for calculation and symbolic representation. They teach a skill, procedure, or algorithm using models and multiple representations to connect to understanding.

Lessons that begin with **Understand** in the title focus on developing conceptual understanding. Occurring at critical points in the instruction sequence, these lessons help students connect new concepts to familiar ones as they learn new skills and strategies.

Table of Contents

Standards in boldface are the focus standards that address major lesson content.

Table of Contents   **iii**

Student Instruction Book

Ready lessons follow a gradual release model that fully transfers responsibility for the learning process from the teacher to the student over the course of a lesson. Carefully scaffolded support is withdrawn as students gain mastery. By the end of a lesson, students have the ability and confidence to reason about and solve problems independently.

Ready® Mathematics Gradual-Release Model
Students are actively engaged in their learning

Teacher Role

Introduction Activates prior knowledge, connecting what students already know with the new skills and concepts they will be learning.	Facilitate		Make Connections
Modeled and Guided Instruction Explores ways to solve problems using multiple representations and prompts students to reason and explain their thinking.	Facilitate		Engage in productive struggles and discussion
Guided Practice Models self-questioning and mathematical habits of mind as students solve problems and discuss their solution methods.	Observe and guide		Collaborate in problem solving
Independent Practice Provides problems in a variety of formats that integrate concepts and skills.	Observe and guide		Apply learning

Student Role

Teacher Resource Book: Lesson Overview

Use the information on these pages to plan whole class instruction, ongoing monitoring, and small group differentiation.

Standards Focus sets expectations for what students should understand and be able to do.

Prerequisite Skills can be used to monitor the understanding of students at different levels and to scaffold instruction for small group discussions.

Content Objectives identify the mathematical goals for the lesson, while **Language Objectives** identify how students demonstrate their understanding of those goals.

The **Learning Progressions** set a context for the standards of the lessons based on how the standard builds on prior knowledge, particularly from the previous grades, and how it leads to expectations for the next year.

LESSON OVERVIEW

Lesson 14
Make a Ten to Add

CCSS Focus

Domain
Operations and Algebraic Thinking

Cluster
C. Add and subtract within 20.

Standards
1.OA.C.6 Add and subtract within 20, demonstrating fluency for addition and subtraction within 10. Use strategies such as counting on; making ten (e.g., $8 + 6 = 8 + 2 + 4 = 10 + 4 = 14$); decomposing a number leading to a ten (e.g., $13 - 4 = 13 - 3 - 1 = 10 - 1 = 9$); using the relationship between addition and subtraction (e.g., knowing that $8 + 4 = 12$, one knows $12 - 8 = 4$); and creating equivalent but easier or known sums (e.g., adding $6 + 7$ by creating the known equivalent $6 + 6 + 1 = 12 + 1 = 13$).

Additional Standards
1.OA.B.3 (See page B3 for full text.)

Standards for Mathematical Practice (SMP)
1 Make sense of problems and persevere in solving them.
2 Reason abstractly and quantitatively.
3 Construct viable arguments and critique the reasoning of others.
4 Model with mathematics.
6 Attend to precision.
7 Look for and make use of structure.
8 Look for and express regularity in repeated reasoning.

Lesson Objectives

Content Objectives
• When adding 2 one-digit numbers, understand the rationale for decomposing one addend to make ten.
• Use the strategy of making ten to add numbers within 20.
• Use and articulate mental math strategies to add.

Language Objectives
• Explain how to use the strategy of making ten to add two numbers.
• Draw jumps on a number path to show making a ten and finding a sum.
• Describe a 10-frame.

Prerequisite Skills

• Know the partner that makes 10 for any number.
• Know all decompositions for numbers within 10.
• Understand that teen numbers can be decomposed as 10 + some number.

Lesson Vocabulary

• **make a ten** a strategy that uses combinations of numbers that add to ten when finding totals greater than 10.

Learning Progression

In Kindergarten children learn to count the number of objects and later to subitize, or recognize the number of objects in a group. They gain understanding of basic addition and subtraction situations and begin learning to compose and decompose numbers 10 or less.

In Grade 1 children learn strategies for adding and subtracting numbers within 20 and develop understanding of the properties of addition.

In this lesson children learn the strategy of making ten to add within 20. This involves breaking apart an addend and associating one part of it with another addend to make 10, and then applying the understanding that teen numbers can be thought of as "10 + some number."

In Grade 2 children become fluent at adding and subtracting within 20. They use strategies to add and subtract within 100.

Teacher Resource Book

Lesson Pacing Guide

Whole Class Instruction

Day 1 *45–60 minutes*	**Introduction** **Use What You Know** • Explore It *25 min* • Try It *20 min*	
Day 2 *45–60 minutes*	**Modeled Instruction** **Explore Together** • Example Problem *5 min* • Model It *20 min* • Hands-On Activity *20 min*	**Practice and Problem Solving** Assign pages 123–124.
Day 3 *45–60 minutes*	**Guided Instruction** **Explore Together** • Example Problem *5 min* • Model It *15 min* • Talk About It *15 min* • Fluency Practice *10 min*	**Practice and Problem Solving** Assign pages 125–126.
Day 4 *45–60 minutes*	**Guided Practice** **Practice Together** • Example Problem *5 min* • Problems 1–2 *25 min* • Visual Model *15 min*	**Practice and Problem Solving** Assign pages 127–128.
Day 5 *45–60 minutes*	**Independent Practice** **Practice by Myself** • Problems 3–5 *10 min* • Concept Extension *10 min* • Quick Check and Remediation *15 min* • Hands-On or Challenge Activity *10 min* **Teacher-Toolbox: Lesson Quiz** Lesson 14 Quiz	

Materials for Lesson Activities

Per child:	20 two-color counters Activity Sheet 11, Activity Sheet 20
Per pair:	20 connecting cubes (10 each in two different colors), 20 counters
For display:	10 chairs

Small Group Differentiation

Teacher-Toolbox.com

Reteach
Ready Prerequisite Lessons *45–90 min*

Grade K
• Lesson 18 Add Within 10
• Lesson 23 Make Teen Numbers

Teacher-led Activities
Tools for Instruction *15–20 min*

Grade 1 *(Lesson 14)*
• Make a Ten to Add Within 20
• Sums of Ten

Student-led Activities
Math Center Activities *30–40 min*

Grade K *(Lessons 18 and 23)*
• K.24 Tell Addition Stories
• K.29 Roll and Make Teen Numbers

Grade 1 *(Lesson 14)*
• 1.08 Make a Ten to Add

Personalized Learning

i-Ready.com

Independent
i-Ready Lessons* *10–20 min*

Grade 1 *(Lesson 14)*
• Addition Facts for 10

* i-Ready lessons may be updated during the 2016–2017 school year. Updated references will be on the Teacher-Toolbox.

Lesson Pacing Guide

The day-by-day pacing guide can be used to plan whole class and small group instruction, for ongoing monitoring, and for individualized learning with *Ready* and *i-Ready* blended learning options.

Plan teacher-led **whole and small group instruction** following *Ready's* gradual release model. Practice can be assigned after every section of the lesson in class, after school, or at home with *Practice and Problem Solving*. Assess students' mastery of lesson content and identify the need for reteaching with lesson quizzes.

Plan **small group differentiation** using *Ready Instruction* prerequisite lessons for in-depth instruction from earlier grades to review prerequisite concepts or fill in gaps in student knowledge, student-led Math Center Activities for standards practice in three different levels, and teacher-led Tools for Instruction activities for small groups of students requiring additional instruction on a prerequisite or on-level skill.

Plan students' **personalized learning** using *i-Ready's* adaptive instruction to remediate and fill gaps.

Use the **Materials for Lesson Activities** to organize and plan support for student learning.

Student Book: Introduction

The Introduction presents a problem or poses a "big idea" question that connects what students already know to what they are about to learn.

Explore It *(whole class)*

Teacher's Role As students engage in hands-on explorations to solve the problem on the page, ask them to explain their reasoning and help them see how they can use what they already know to solve the problem.

Use the question prompts in the Teacher Resource Book (TRB) for active learning to help students connect the math of the lesson to their own experiences. Encourage students from other cultures to share their experiences.

Student's Role Students who come to understand that they can apply what they have already learned to new problem situations develop a deeper understanding of mathematical relationships. This understanding allows them to see mathematics as interconnected concepts and skills rather than as separate, unrelated ideas.

Use What You Know
Make a Ten to Add

Explore It

7 children get on the bus. 5 more children get on the bus. How many children are on the bus?

Meeting New Expectations &
Best Practices

What Ready® Mathematics
Instruction Looks Like

How to Implement
Ready® Mathematics

Student Instruction Book

Use What You Know
Make a Ten to Add

>> **Try It**

9 children get on the bus. 5 more children get
on the bus. How many children are on the bus?

9 and 5 is the same as 10 and _____ more.
_____ children are on the bus.

Introduction **Lesson 14**   **89**

Try It *(whole class)*

Teacher's Role Discuss as a class, guiding
students to see how the problem they just
solved and the new problem are related.
Use the suggestions in the Step By Step to
facilitate the discussion.

As students work through these open-ended
activities and share their reasoning, they
build on prerequisite skills that connect to
the visual representations of the lesson.

Use this as an opportunity to observe
students' understanding and plan for
individualized support as needed before or
during the lesson.

Student's Role As they engage
intellectually with the content, students
build foundational understanding of what
they will be learning in the lesson.

Student Book: Modeled and Guided Instruction

The Modeled and Guided Instruction supports students as they explore different ways of solving a real-world or mathematical problem.

Model It (whole class)

Teacher's Role Read the problem at the top of the page, then work through the *Model It* as a class. Pose the questions in the Teacher Resource Book (TRB) to guide students' understanding of the strategy shown on the page.

Use *Mathematical Discourse* questions in the TRB to promote thoughtful dialogue about the model and strategy. Encourage the exchange of ideas among students by having them explain how the given information connects to the visual representation.

Use the *Hands-On Activities* in the TRB to demonstrate concrete ways to represent problems. This encourages students to look for and use structure as a way to understand concepts and strategies.

Student's Role As they discuss using a visual model to represent a given problem, students begin to understand there are multiple access points from which they can approach a solution.

Explore Together
Make a Ten to Add

8 children are on the bus. 5 more get on the bus. How many are on the bus now?

$8 + 5 = ?$

Model It Find $8 + 5$.

Start with 8. Take counters from 5 to **make a ten**.

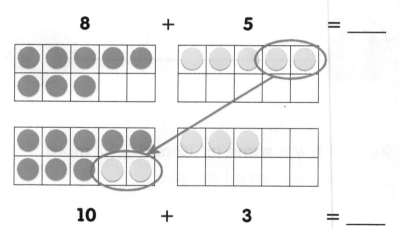

$$8 \qquad + \qquad 5 \qquad = \underline{\quad}$$

$$10 \qquad + \qquad 3 \qquad = \underline{\quad}$$

90 **Lesson 14** Modeled Instruction   ©Curriculum Associates, LLC   Copying is not permitted.

 **Ready** Mathematics
PRACTICE AND PROBLEM SOLVING

Teacher's Role Assign *Practice and Problem Solving* as independent work in class or at home for additional practice with the skills of the lesson.

Learn Together
Make a Ten to Add

7 blocks are small. 5 blocks are big.
How many blocks are there in all?
How do you know?

$7 + 5 = ?$

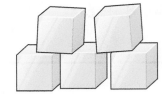

 Model It Find $7 + 5$.

Start with 7.
Add 3 to make 10.
Then add 2 more.

$7 + 3 = 10 \qquad 10 + 2 = 12$

$$7 + 5 = \underline{\quad}$$

 **Talk About It** Do you agree? Why or why not?

Boom says that $9 + 5 = 15$.

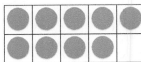 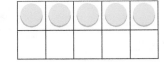

Guided Instruction **Lesson 14**   **91**

Model It (whole class)

Teacher's Role Discuss *Model It* as a class, guiding students to make the connection between the representations on the previous page and a more general symbolic representation of the problem and solution.

Use *SMP Tips* in the TRB to help students advance through the content, critically analyze information, and use complex cognitive thinking. This reflects the expectation that students are actively engaged in doing mathematics rather than passively receiving mathematics instruction.

Student's Role Students who engage with the symbolic representations by making and defending conjectures are able to apply what they have learned to solve similar problems. This helps them understand their own progress as they look for approaches that work best for them and find what they still need feedback on.

Talk About It (small group)

Student's Role Discussing responses to *Talk About It* adds to students' understanding as they apply the newly learned skill to a new situation.

Teacher's Role Have students read and discuss *Talk About It*, then answer the question and explain their thinking.

Student Book: Guided Practice

The Guided Practice provides feedback to students as they share their thinking and find solutions to problems.

Example (whole class)

Teacher's Role Read the example problem aloud and have children describe the model used to solve it. Use this example to connect what students have learned on the previous pages to the new problems they will be solving below. Encourage students to suggest other approaches and explain their reasoning.

Use the *Visual Models* in the TRB to show different ways to represent a given problem. This encourages students to think flexibly.

Student's Role As students explain their thinking they develop the understanding that there are many ways to formulate solutions to mathematical problems. Hearing other approaches guides them to look at each problem from multiple perspectives, enriching their understanding of the mathematics and helping them make connections.

Problems (small group)

Student's Role Students work with a partner to represent their mathematical solutions in concrete, symbolic, or written form as they solve problems.

As students explain their solution pathways to others and respond to clarifying questions, they examine their premises and build logical arguments.

Teacher's Role Circulate and ask guiding questions that require students to elaborate on important information and summarize their thinking.

Practice Together
Make a Ten to Add

$8 + 6 = ?$

$8 + 2 = \underline{10}$

$10 + 4 = \underline{14}$

So, $8 + 6 = \underline{14}$

$8 \quad + \quad 6$

$10 \quad + \quad 4$

1 $8 + 7 = ?$

$8 + \underline{} = 10$

$10 + \underline{} = \underline{}$

$8 + 7 = \underline{}$

2 $7 + 7 = ?$ | 6 | 7 | 8 | 9 | 10 | 11 | 12 | 13 | 14 | 15 |

$7 + \underline{} = 10$

$10 + \underline{} = \underline{}$

$7 + 7 = \underline{}$

92 **Lesson 14** Guided Practice

Ready **Mathematics** PRACTICE AND PROBLEM SOLVING

Teacher's Role Assign *Practice and Problem Solving* as independent work in class or at home for additional practice with all the skills of the lesson.

Student Book: Independent Practice

The Independent Practice provides students with problems that integrate and extend concepts and skills.

Student Instruction Book

Make a Ten to Add

3 $7 + 6 = ?$

$7 + \underline{\quad} = \underline{\quad}$

$10 + \underline{\quad} = \underline{\quad}$

$7 + 6 = \underline{\quad}$

4 $9 + 4 = ?$

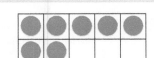

| 6 | 7 | 8 | ⑨ | 10 | 11 | 12 | 13 | 14 | 15 |

$9 + 4 = \underline{\quad}$

5 $8 + 6 = ?$

$8 + 6 = \underline{\quad}$

©Curriculum Associates, LLC   Copying is not permitted.   Independent Practice **Lesson 14**   **93**

Problem *(independent)*

Student's Role As students work independently on each problem, they think about possible approaches, create a plan, and make decisions about how to represent the problem.

Teacher's Role As students work on their own, walk around the room to engage students and to monitor their understanding. Asking open-ended questions provides students with an opportunity to share their reasoning.

Assess and Remediate *(small group)*

Teacher's Role Have students respond to the "exit" question in the *Quick Check and Remediation* in the TRB. For those students who respond incorrectly, identify common errors and provide the additional suggested instruction.

Student's Role Explaining their thinking engages students in learning that requires them to link what they have learned in the lesson to new situations.

Teacher Resource Book

Point-of-use professional development and step-by-step instructional ideas help teachers address even the most challenging standards effectively.

The **Step By Step** organizes content into appropriate chunks for student learning, and provides guiding questions about the key points within each chunk.

The **Mathematical Discourse** questions engage students and advance them through the content. They include answers as well as key ideas to listen for in student responses to facilitate further rich discussion.

SMP Tips highlight a particular Standard for Mathematical Practice within the lesson.

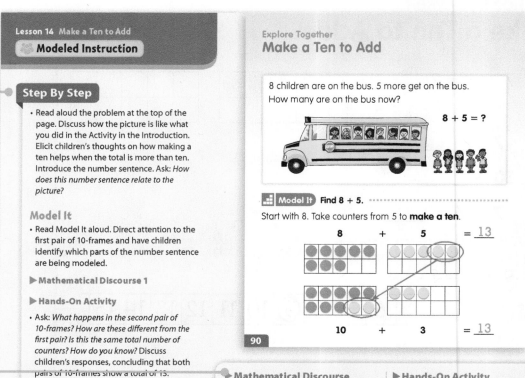

Lesson 14 Make a Ten to Add
Modeled Instruction

Step By Step

- Read aloud the problem at the top of the page. Discuss how the picture is like what you did in the Activity in the Introduction. Elicit children's thoughts on how making a ten helps when the total is more than ten. Introduce the number sentence. Ask: *How does this number sentence relate to the picture?*

Model It

- Read Model It aloud. Direct attention to the first pair of 10-frames and have children identify which parts of the number sentence are being modeled.

▶ **Mathematical Discourse 1**

▶ **Hands-On Activity**

- Ask: *What happens in the second pair of 10-frames? How are these different from the first pair? Is this the same total number of counters? How do you know?* Discuss children's responses, concluding that both pairs of 10-frames show a total of 13.

- Have children fill in the totals. Discuss with them how making ten helps them find the total.

SMP TIP Look for Structure
The structure of 10-frames helps children understand the make a ten strategy. Encourage children to think and talk about how the 10-frames help them go from "8 and some more" to the known structure of "10 and some more." *(SMP 7)*

Ready· Mathematics
PRACTICE AND PROBLEM SOLVING

Assign *Practice and Problem Solving* **pages 123–124** after students have completed this section.

Explore Together
Make a Ten to Add

8 children are on the bus. 5 more get on the bus. How many are on the bus now?

$8 + 5 = ?$

Model It Find 8 + 5.

Start with 8. Take counters from 5 to **make a ten**.

$$8 \quad + \quad 5 \quad = \underline{13}$$

$$10 \quad + \quad 3 \quad = \underline{13}$$

90

▶ **Mathematical Discourse**

1 *How does the model help you make a ten?*
Children should see the empty spots in the 10-frame as a signal to what is needed to make a ten. With more practice, this visual clue will eventually translate to recognizing the number that makes ten.

▶ **Hands-On Activity**
Model adding numbers on 10-frames.

Materials For each child: 10-Frame (Activity Sheet 11), 20 two-color counters

- Write the problem $8 + 5 = ?$ on the board.

- Have children put 8 counters of one color in one 10-frame and 5 of another color in the second frame. Ask how they can use the 5 counters to fill the first 10-frame. [Remove 2 from the frame with 5 and use those to fill the frame with 8.]

- Have them actually move counters and describe what they did. Help them to conclude that the total number of counters didn't change. They just moved the counters around in the 10-frames to show a ten and some ones.

Teacher Resource Book

Learn Together
Make a Ten to Add

7 blocks are small. 5 blocks are big.
How many blocks are there in all?
How do you know?

7 + 5 = ?

 **Model It** Find 7 + 5.

Start with 7. $7 + 3 = 10$ $10 + 2 = 12$
Add 3 to make 10.
Then add 2 more.

 6 ⑦ 8 9 10 11 12 13 14

$7 + 5 = \underline{12}$

Talk About It Do you agree? Why or why not?

Boom says that $9 + 5 = 15$.

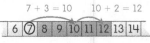

91

▶ Fluency Practice
Practice facts within 10.

Materials For each child: Facts Practice 4 (Activity Sheet 20)

- Have children complete Activity Sheet 20 (Facts Practice 4). Then have pairs work together to review the facts. One partner reads two addends and the other partner gives the sum.
- Children should go "out of order" for this, skipping around the worksheet and choosing addition sentences with different sums.

▶ Mathematical Discourse

2 *How can you tell how big to make the jump from 10 to the sum?*
Children need to understand how many more are left after making the ten. They might respond that after a jump of 3, there is a jump of 2 left since the partner of 3 that makes 5 (the other addend) is 2.

Lesson 14
👥 Guided Instruction

Step By Step

- Read aloud the problem at the top of the page. Ask children how they would approach the problem. Elicit the idea of making a ten and then seeing what's left to add.

Model It

- In Model It, direct attention to the number path. Ask children to describe what it shows. Guide children to see that 7 is circled because it is the addend you start with. Ask: *Why start with 7?* [It's easier if you start with the addend that is closer to 10. But the strategy will work either way.]
- Ask: *How many numbers is the blue jump? Why do you jump this many first?* [The blue jump is 3 because you want to make a ten. $7 + 3 = 10$]
- Explain that now they have used 3 of the big blocks to make 10. Ask: *How many more do you have to add?* [2] Elicit that the total is 10 and 2 more, which is 12. Ask Mathematical Discourse question 2 to check understanding of this idea.

▶ Mathematical Discourse 2

- You may want to have children verify the sum by laying green blocks or counters along the number path: 3 for the blue jump and 2 for the red jump.

Talk About It

- Present the Talk About It question. Have children describe the diagram and number sentence. Then have them answer the question and explain their thinking. [Boom is incorrect. It looks like Boom forgot to fill the 10-frame that has 9 counters but assumed that it had 10 in it. Actually, $9 + 5 = 14$.]

▶ Fluency Practice

Ready Mathematics
PRACTICE AND PROBLEM SOLVING

Assign *Practice and Problem Solving* **pages 125–126** after students have completed this section.

TRB activities such as Concept Extensions, ELL Support, and Visual Models (not shown here) engage students and allow them to participate in activities that support varied abilities. A range of techniques encourages all students to contribute.

Talk About It questions encourage students to analyze and explain a student error based on common misconceptoins.

Teacher Resource Book

Multiple opportunities for informal assessment help teachers monitor understanding to inform ongoing instruction and to identify the need for reteaching.

In the **Quick Check and Remediation,** an "exit" question is given to monitor understanding of the lesson content. A chart provides a list of incorrect answers based on common errors and gives specific remediation suggestions for each error.

A **Hands-On Activity** extends the concepts and skills of the lesson using common classroom manipulatives and small group collaboration.

A **Challenge Activity** gives students who have mastered the skills and concepts of the lesson an opportunity to apply their understanding to more sophisticated problem solving.

Lesson 14
Make a Ten to Add

Differentiated Instruction

▶ Quick Check and Remediation

Materials For each child: 16 counters

- Ask children to solve $8 + 7 = ?$ by making a ten. [Add $8 + 2$ to make a 10. Then $10 + 5 = 15$, so $8 + 7 = 15$.]
- For children who are still struggling, use the chart below to guide remediation.
- After providing remediation, check children's understanding using the following problem: *Solve $9 + 4 = ?$ by making a ten.* [Add $9 + 1$ to make a 10. Then $10 + 3 = 13$, so $9 + 4 = 13$.]

If the error is . . .	Children may . . .	To remediate . . .
$8 + 2$ is 10, so $8 + 7 = 17$	not understand the need to decompose the second addend.	Ask: *Where did you get the 2?* Use counters to model the problem with children. Elicit that the 2 comes from the 7, leaving 5 more to add.
14 or 16	be counting on instead of making a ten, and making a mistake in counting.	Have children demonstrate how they added. If they are counting on from 8, explain that it's easy to lose track when counting on more than 2 or 3. Guide children to use a make a ten approach.
any other teen number, or one of the addends	not have decomposed the addend correctly to make a ten, or may have simply used an addend as the sum.	Have children model "10 and some more," using counters, for 12, 13, 15, and 16. Then have them model $8 + 7$ using counters. Ask: *How can you change this model to show "10 and some more"?*

▶ Hands-On Activity
Use connecting cubes to model making a 10.

Materials For each pair: 20 connecting cubes (10 each in two different colors)

- Provide pairs of children with 10 connecting cubes in each of 2 different colors. Give them an addition problem with a teen number sum, such as $8 + 6$.
- Children write the problem and model it with two trains of different color connecting cubes, one for each addend.
- Children take cubes from one train and connect them to the other train to make a ten. Then they say how many are still left on the first train and solve the problem as "10 and 4 more," or 14. They write $10 + 4 = 14$ and $8 + 6 = 14$.
- Have pairs explain their work. You may wish to repeat the activity with other numbers.

▶ Challenge Activity
Write and solve addition word problems.

Materials For each pair: 20 counters (optional)

- Have children work in pairs to write word problems involving teen numbers. They may wish to use counters to act out their ideas while they write.
- Circulate and offer support and feedback. When the pairs are finished, put the problems in a pile.
- Pairs take turns picking a problem, reading it, and solving by making a ten. The rest of the group listens to see if they are correct. Children may ask questions or recommend strategies as appropriate.
- For extra challenge, see if children can solve the problems without using manipulatives or even paper and pencil.

Teacher Resource Book

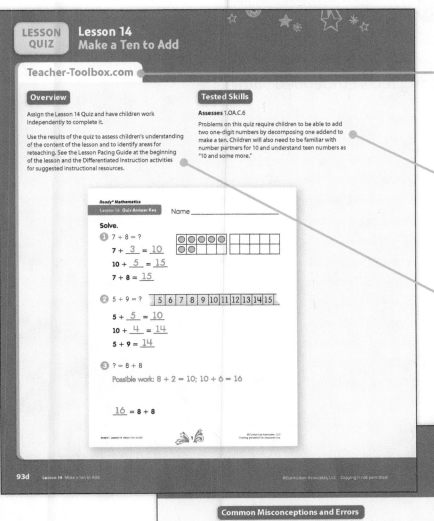

Use the Lesson Quiz at the end of each *Ready* Lesson to assess students' mastery of lesson content. Go to Teacher-Toolbox.com to access and print out the Lesson Quizzes.

Use the summary of **Tested Skills** to gain insight into what students need to be able to do to answer quiz items correctly, how the content is tested, and if there is a prerequisite skill that students must be familiar with to be successful.

The **Overview** provides information on where to find instructional resources to support reteaching needs.

Use the **Common Misconceptions and Errors** to identify thinking that may interfere with students' understanding of the lesson content.

Monitor Understanding in *Ready®* Mathematics

Ready Mathematics provides a comprehensive assessment system, as shown on the following pages. This includes practical, easy-to-use progress monitoring tools embedded within instruction, as well as tools for formal assessment.

Diagnose

Use *i-Ready Diagnostic* to **diagnose individual student skill levels** and identify instructional needs.

Monitor Understanding

Use the informal assessment opportunities in the *Ready* Student Book, Teacher Resource Book, and Teacher Toolbox to **inform ongoing instruction.**

Assess Mastery

Use *Ready Unit Reviews* to **evaluate student mastery of content** at the unit level.

Measure Growth

Use *i-Ready Diagnostic* to **track student progress towards end-of-year goals.**

Meeting New Expectations &
Best Practices

What Ready® Mathematics
Instruction Looks Like

How to Implement
Ready® Mathematics

Tool	What it does	How to use it
Student Book		
Talk About It	Prompts students to explain their thinking	Observe student understanding and respond with specific strategies for additional instruction and to support individual needs
Independent Practice	Provides opportunities for students to demonstrate understanding as they apply lesson skills and concepts to solve problems	
Teacher Resource Book		
Mathematical Discourse and SMP Tips	Encourages classroom discussion so students share their thinking	Use the key topics provided to listen for student responses, provide immediate feedback to address misunderstandings, and support students with targeted remediation strategies and activities
Error Alerts	Explains a common computational error, the wrong answer it might produce, and explanations to help students avoid the error in the future	
Quick Check and Remediation	Poses an "exit" question to check student understanding	
Online Teacher Toolbox		
Lesson Quizzes	Assesses lesson concepts and skills in a variety of item types	Evaluate mastery of lesson content

Pacing for *Ready*® Mathematics

Ready Mathematics provides a full year of instruction. The Year-Long Pacing Guide below shows a recommended schedule for teaching when using *Ready* as a core program.

Year-Long Pacing — Grade 1

Ready Instruction Lesson	Days	Minutes/day
i-Ready Diagnostic	3	60
Lesson 1 Count on to Add	5	30–45
Lesson 2 Count on to Subtract	5	30–45
Lesson 3 Add and Subtract in Word Problems	5	30–45
Lesson 4 *Understand* Missing Addends	4	30–45
Lesson 5 Subtract to Compare in Word Problems	5	30–45
Unit 1 Review	1	30–45
Lesson 6 Doubles and Doubles Plus 1	5	30–45
Lesson 7 Number Partners for 6 and 7	5	30–45
Lesson 8 Number Partners for 8 and 9	5	30–45
Lesson 9 Number Partners for 10	5	30–45
Lesson 10 *Understand* the Equal Sign	4	30–45
Lesson 11 Facts I Know	5	30–45
Unit 2 Review	1	30–45
Lesson 12 *Understand* Teen Numbers	4	30–45
Lesson 13 *Understand* Sums Greater than 10	4	30–45
Lesson 14 Make a Ten to Add	5	30–45
Lesson 15 Add Three Numbers	5	30–45
Lesson 16 Make a Ten to Subtract	5	30–45
Unit 3 Review	1	30–45
i-Ready Diagnostic	3	60
Lesson 17 *Understand* Tens	4	30–45
Lesson 18 The 120 Chart	5	30–45
Lesson 19 *Understand* 10 More and 10 Less	4	30–45
Lesson 20 Add and Subtract Tens	5	30–45

Ready Instruction Lesson	Days	Minutes/day
Unit 4 Review	1	30–45
Lesson 21 *Understand* Tens and Ones	4	30–45
Lesson 22 Compare Numbers	5	30–45
Lesson 23 Add Tens to Any Number	5	30–45
Lesson 24 Add Tens and Add Ones	5	30–45
Lesson 25 Add and Regroup	5	30–45
Unit 5 Review	1	30–45
Lesson 26 *Understand* Shapes	4	30–45
Lesson 27 *Understand* Putting Shapes Together	4	30–45
Lesson 28 *Understand* Breaking Shapes into Parts	4	30–45
Unit 6 Review	1	30–45
Lesson 29 Sort and Count	5	30–45
Lesson 30 Compare Data	5	30–45
Lesson 31 Order Objects by Length	5	30–45
Lesson 32 Compare Lengths	5	30–45
Lesson 33 *Understand* Measurement	4	30–45
Lesson 34 Tell Time	5	30–45
Unit 7 Review	1	30–45
i-Ready Diagnostic	3	60

Ready Mathematics
PRACTICE AND PROBLEM SOLVING

Use the lesson practice and unit resources in *Practice and Problem Solving* throughout the year to extend classroom learning.

- Before each lesson, send **Family Letters** home separately or as part of a family communication package.
- After completing each lesson section, assign two pages of **rigorous lesson practice** as independent work in class or at home.
- After completing each unit, use Unit Games and Unit Practice to **integrate skills and consolidate learning.**
- Throughout instruction, use **Fluency Skills Practice** and **Fluency Repeated Reasoning Practice** worksheets to reinforce procedural fluency.

Pacing for *Ready* Mathematics

Pacing for Ready® Mathematics, continued

Each *Ready Mathematics* lesson provides approximately one week of instruction.
A day of instruction assumes 45–60 minutes of mathematics instruction.

Monthly Pacing Guide

September	Lessons 1–3
October	Lessons 4–7
	Unit 1 Review
November	Lessons 8–11
	Unit 2 Review
December	Lessons 12–15
	Unit 3 Review
January	Lessons 16–19
	Unit 4 Review
February	Lessons 20–23
March	Lessons 24–27
	Unit 5 Review
April	Lessons 28–31
	Unit 6 Review
May	Lessons 32–34
	Unit 7 Review

Weekly Pacing Guide — Whole Class Instruction

Day 1
45–60 minutes

Introduction
Use What You Know
- Explore It *25 min*
- Try It *20 min*

Day 2
45–60 minutes

Modeled Instruction
Explore Together
- Example Problem *5 min*
- Model It *20 min*
- Hands-On Activity *20 min*

Practice and Problem Solving
Assign pages 123–124.

Day 3
45–60 minutes

Guided Instruction
Explore Together
- Example Problem *5 min*
- Model It *15 min*
- Talk About It *15 min*
- Fluency Practice *10 min*

Practice and Problem Solving
Assign pages 125–126.

Day 4
45–60 minutes

Guided Practice
Practice Together
- Example *5 min*
- Problems 1-2 *25 min*
- Visual Model *15 min*

Practice and Problem Solving
Assign pages 127–128.

Day 5
45–60 minutes

Independent Practice
Practice by Myself
- Problems 3–5 *10 min*
- Concept Extension *10 min*
- Quick Check and Remediation *15 min*
- Hands-On or Challenge Activity *10 min*

Toolbox: Lesson Quiz
Lesson 14 Quiz

Instruction for each section of the lesson in the Student
Book follows a similar routine. The chart below shows the
structure and goals for one part of the lesson.

Daily Pacing ~45 minutes

Day 2 **Modeled Instruction** **Explore Together**

Problem/Model It *25 minutes*	Teacher guides via Student Instruction Book, promoting rich classroom discussion (Mathematical Discourse question)
	Goal: To engage in mathematical discourse and deepen instruction in the Student Instruction Book
Hands-On Activity *20 minutes*	Teacher facilitates via Teacher Resource Book, focusing on a specific Standard for Mathematical Practice (SMP Tip) and using concrete representations to clarify learning (Hands-On Activity)
	Goal: To help students actively engage with the lesson content
Practice and Problem Solving	Students work independently at home extending learning
	Goal: To get additional practice with skills and concept of the lesson

Meeting New Expectations &
Best Practices

What Ready® Mathematics
Instruction Looks Like

How to Implement
Ready® Mathematics

Unit 1 Add and Subtract

Which lessons are students building upon?

Kindergarten, Lesson 11
Count 10
K.CC.A.3, K.CC.B.4a, K.CC.B.4b, K.CC.B.5

Kindergarten, Lesson 14
Understand Addition
K.OA.A.1

Kindergarten, Lesson 18
Add Within 10
K.OA.A.2

Kindergarten, Lesson 11
Count 10
K.CC.A.3, K.CC.B.4a, K.CC.B.4b, K.CC.B.5

Kindergarten, Lesson 16
Understand Subtraction
K.OA.A.1

Kindergarten, Lesson 19
Subtract Within 10
K.OA.A.2

Kindergarten, Lesson 18
Add Within 10
K.OA.A.2

Kindergarten, Lesson 19
Subtract Within 10
K.OA.A.2

Kindergarten, Lesson 18
Add Within 10
K.OA.A.2

Kindergarten, Lesson 19
Subtract Within 10
K.OA.A.2

Kindergarten, Lesson 20
Practice Facts to 5
K.OA.A.5

Kindergarten, Lesson 18
Add Within 10
K.OA.A.2

Kindergarten, Lesson 19
Subtract Within 10
K.OA.A.2

Kindergarten, Lesson 20
Practice Facts to 5
K.OA.A.5

Unit 1

Which lessons are students preparing for?

Unit 1		
Lesson 1 Count On to Add 1.OA.C.5	**Grade 2, Lesson 1** Understand Mental Math Strategies (Fact Families) 2.OA.B.2	**Grade 2, Lesson 3** Understand Mental Math Strategies (Make a Ten) 2.OA.B.2
Lesson 2 Count On to Subtract 1.OA.C.6	**Grade 2, Lesson 1** Understand Mental Math Strategies (Fact Families) 2.OA.B.2	**Grade 2, Lesson 3** Understand Mental Math Strategies (Make a Ten) 2.OA.B.2
Lesson 3 Add and Subtract in Word Problems 1.OA.A.1	**Grade 2, Lesson 2** Solve One-Step Word Problems 2.OA.A.1	**Grade 2, Lesson 6** Solve Two-Step Word Problems 2.OA.A.1
Lesson 4 Understand Missing Addends 1.OA.B.4	**Grade 2, Lesson 1** Understand Mental Math Strategies (Fact Families) 2.OA.B.2	**Grade 2, Lesson 3** Understand Mental Math Strategies (Make a Ten) 2.OA.B.2
Lesson 5 Subtract to Compare in Word Problems 1.OA.A.1	**Grade 2, Lesson 2** Solve One-Step Word Problems 2.OA.A.1	**Grade 2, Lesson 6** Solve Two-Step Word Problems 2.OA.A.1

Unit 1
Add and Subtract

Unit 1 – Operations and Algebraic Thinking
Add and Subtract

  6 balloon stickers and 3 star stickers. Lee wants to share some stickers. He wants some stickers for his notebook. What math questions could Lee ask about the stickers?

In this unit you will learn ways to add and subtract. Then you will be able to solve problems like Lee's!

✓ Self Check

Check off the skills you know now. Then see how many more you can check off after each lesson!

I can:	Before this unit	After this unit
count on to add.	☐	☐
count on to subtract.	☐	☐
solve addition and subtraction word problems.	☐	☐
use addition sentences to write subtraction sentences.	☐	☐
find missing addends.	☐	☐
subtract to compare.	☐	☐

Ready Mathematics
PRACTICE AND PROBLEM SOLVING

Practice and Problem Solving Resources

Use the following resources from *Practice and Problem Solving* to engage students and their families and to extend student learning.

- **Family Letters** Send Family Letters home separately before each lesson or as part of a family communication package.

- **Unit Games** Use partner Unit Games at classroom centers and/or send them home for play with family members.

- **Unit Practice** Assign Unit Practice as homework, as independent or small group practice, or for whole class discussion.

- **Fluency Practice** Assign Fluency Skills Practice and Fluency Repeated Reasoning Practice worksheets throughout the unit.

At A Glance

- This page introduces children to the general ideas behind adding and subtracting.

- The checklist allows them to see what skills they will be learning and take ownership of their progress.

Step By Step

- Explain to children that they are going to begin a new unit of lessons. Tell them that in all the lessons in this unit they will be learning to add and subtract.

- Read the introduction to the unit together as a class. Invite children to suggest questions that could be asked about the problem situation. Discuss the questions children pose without the expectation that they are to solve them.

- Then take a few minutes to have each child independently read through the list of skills.

- Ask children to consider each skill and check the box in the *Before* column if it is a skill they think they already have. Remind children that these skills are likely to all be new to them, but it's still possible some children have some of the skills.

- Engage children in a brief discussion about the skills. Invite children to comment on which ones they would most like to learn, or which ones seem similar or related to something they already know. Remind them that the goal is to be able to check off all the skills they have learned by the end of the unit.

- At the end of the unit, have children complete the *After* column. As time allows, pose questions about the problem situation at the top of the page and solve as a class.

Lesson 1
Count On to Add

CCSS Focus

Domain
Operations and Algebraic Thinking

Cluster
C. Add and subtract within 20.

Standard
1.OA.C.5 Relate counting to addition and subtraction (e.g., by counting on 2 to add 2).

Additional Standards
1.OA.A.1, 1.OA.C.6 (See page B3 for full text.)

Standards for Mathematical Practice (SMP)

2 Reason abstractly and quantitatively.
3 Construct viable arguments and critique the reasoning of others.
5 Use appropriate tools strategically.
6 Attend to precision.
7 Look for and make use of structure.

Lesson Objectives

Content Objectives
• Add within ten.
• Apply the counting on strategy.
• Analyze counting strategies.

Language Objectives
• Use fingers, counters, and connecting cubes to model the counting on strategy.
• Explain how to use the counting on strategy to add two numbers.
• Listen to the ideas of others discussing a counting error and decide together how to correct the error.

Prerequisite Skills

• Count up to 10 objects.
• Interpret a number sentence.
• Understand addition as putting things together.

Lesson Vocabulary

• **add** to put together two or more quantities. To find the total of two or more numbers. To find how many in all.
• **addition sentence** one number is added to another in a sentence with numbers and symbols.
• **commutative property of addition** changing the order of addends does not change the total.
• **count on** start with one addend and count to find a total.
• **number path** a diagram that shows numbers in sequential order.
• **tape diagram** a diagram used to represent part-whole number relationships. Also known as a bar model.
• **total** a number found as the result of adding.

Learning Progression

In Kindergarten children count objects using one-to-one correspondence, apply counting strategies to addition within 10, and represent addition with physical models, pictures, and number sentences.

In Grade 1 children use strategies to add within 20 with the unknown in all three positions.

In this lesson children relate counting to addition by applying the counting on strategy to find an unknown sum.

Children develop reasoning skills as they see a group of objects as a single quantity from which they can count on. They also see the number that they start with as a part of the total and keep track of how many they count on.

In Grade 2 children continue to use addition strategies mentally, with the goal of attaining fluency with sums to 20. They also extend addition skills to two-digit numbers.

Lesson Pacing Guide

Whole Class Instruction

Day 1
45–60 minutes

Introduction
Use What You Know
- Explore It *25 min*
- Try It *20 min*

Day 2
45–60 minutes

Modeled Instruction
Explore Together
- Example Problem *5 min*
- Model It *30 min*
- Hands-On Activity *10 min*

Practice and Problem Solving
Assign pages 3–4.

Day 3
45–60 minutes

Guided Instruction
Learn Together
- Example Problem *5 min*
- Model It *10 min*
- Talk About It *15 min*
- Fluency Practice *15 min*

Practice and Problem Solving
Assign pages 5–6.

Day 4
45–60 minutes

Guided Practice
Practice Together
- Example Problem *5 min*
- Problems 1–2 *25 min*
- Concept Extension *15 min*

Practice and Problem Solving
Assign pages 7–8.

Day 5
45–60 minutes

Independent Practice
Practice by Myself
- Problems 3–5 *15 min*
- Quick Check and Remediation *15 min*
- Hands-On or Challenge Activity *15 min*

Teacher-Toolbox: Lesson Quiz
Lesson 1 Quiz

Materials for Lesson Activities

Per student: 10 two-color counters, 12 connecting cubes (6 red, 6 yellow)
Activity Sheet 1

Per pair: 10 two-color counters, number sentence cards

For display: Small box, 8 pencils or other classroom objects, 2 red blocks, 6 yellow blocks

Small Group Differentiation

Teacher-Toolbox.com

Reteach
Ready Prerequisite Lessons *45–90 min*

Grade K
- Lesson 14 *Understand* Addition
- Lesson 18 Add Within 10

Teacher-led Activities
Tools for Instruction *15–20 min*

Grade 1 *(Lesson 1)*
- Count Forward by 1s
- Count On to Add

Student-led Activities
Math Center Activities *30–40 min*

Grade K *(Lessons 14 and 18)*
- K.22 Addition Vocabulary
- K.24 Tell Addition Stories

Grade 1 *(Lesson 1)*
- 1.01 Counting On Cube Trains
- 1.02 Counting On Match

Personalized Learning

i-Ready.com

Independent
i-Ready Lessons* *10–20 min*

Grade 1 *(Lesson 1)*
- Counting On to Solve Addition Problems
- Joining Sets to Add
- Counting On
- Counting On to Add

* i-Ready lessons may be updated during the 2016–2017 school year. Updated references will be on the Teacher-Toolbox.

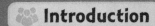

👥 Introduction

Activity Act Out Counting On to Add

Objective

Explore addition as combining two groups whose sum can be found through models and strategies.

Materials for each child

• none

Overview

Children explore the concept of addition, connecting a physical model to a problem situation. Children share ideas for strategies to find a sum and record a solution using pictures or drawings.

Step By Step

Explore It

Introduce the problem.

• Select 3 boys and 2 girls to come to the front of the class. Separate the boys from the girls, leaving a little distance between them.

• Say: *I want 3 boys and 2 girls to work together in a group. How can I find out how many children are in the group in all?* Clarify, as necessary, that both boys and girls belong to the more general group known as "children."

Explore strategies.

• Children should see this as a "put together" situation and suggest combining the two groups.

• Have children find the total number of children and encourage them to share the strategies they used. Some children may count all the children at the front of the class, others may say they just know 3 and 2 is 5, and some may start with the 3 boys and count on 4, 5 (girls) to find the total.

Solve similar problems.

• Tell the children that you want a different number of children in the group. Read the problem on the Student Book page aloud: *There are 4 boys and 2 girls in the group. How many children are in the group?*

⬡ Explore It

There are 4 boys and 2 girls in the group.
How many children are in the group?

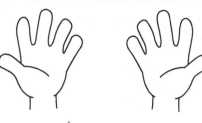

> Pictures will vary. Children should circle 6 fingers in total.

___6___ **children**

There are 4 boys and 3 girls in the group.
How many children are in the group?

> Pictures will vary. Children should circle 7 fingers in total.

___7___ **children**

2

• Tell children to hold up one hand and show the number of boys with their fingers. Then have them hold up the other hand to show the number of girls. Ask: *How can you tell the number of fingers you are holding up altogether?*

• Listen for strategies such as counting by 2s, counting all fingers, saying 4 on one hand then counting 5, 6 on the other hand. Some children may recognize that there is one more boy in this group than there was in the first group discussed, so the sum is 1 more than 5.

• Have children circle the number of fingers they held up and then fill in the total number of children in the group on the Student Book page. [6]

• Repeat the process. Read the second problem on the Student Book page aloud: *There are 4 boys and 3 girls in the group. How many children are in the group?* [7]

• After solving, ask children to try a strategy someone else suggested and talk with a partner about the strategies they liked best and why. Note: It is important for children to try various strategies but recognize that they each have preferences and one strategy is not necessarily better than another.

>> **Try It**

There are 5 girls and 3 boys on a team.
How many children are on the team?

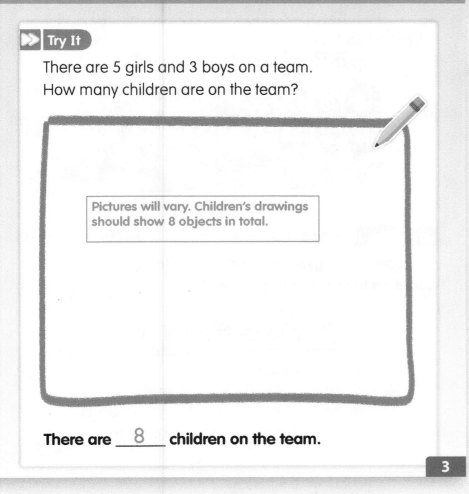

Pictures will vary. Children's drawings
should show 8 objects in total.

There are __8__ children on the team.

3

Step By Step

Try It

Pose the problem.

- Provide the children with the following
  problem: *There are 5 girls and 3 boys on a
  team. How many children are on the team?*

Solve the problem.

- Tell children to pick the strategy they prefer
  and draw a picture to show how they solved
  the problem. Have them use their drawing
  to complete the sentence below.

- Observe children as they work. Some
  children may not be able to represent this
  problem before completing the Student
  Book lesson, but give them a chance to
  struggle with it before going on.

Lead the class in discussion.

- After children have completed their
  drawings, ask them to describe their work.
  Look for children who were able to explain
  that they started with 5 and counted 1, 2, 3
  to find 8.

- Use the Hands-On Activity in the lesson as
  extra support for children who were unable
  to represent the problem or complete the
  sentence correctly.

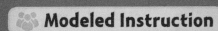

Modeled Instruction

Step By Step

- Read the problem at the top of the page.

Model It

- Read aloud the text in Model It.

▶ **Mathematical Discourse 1**

- Ask children how they know there are 5 girls and 5 smiley faces. Some may need to count, while others may suggest that the problem tells them that there are 5.

- Discuss that when counting on, you start with one of the given numbers and then count on by the other number. Refer children to the model and show them how to use their fingers to count on to find the total.

> **SMP TIP Attend to Precision**
> Connect the physical activity to the model by having children first place counters on the smiley faces representing the girls and eliciting that these show a group of 5. Have children count on as they add counters to represent boys. As they do so, children refine the concept of counting on as a strategy for finding the number of objects in a group without having to count every member of the group. *(SMP 6)*

- Stress the importance of keeping track of the number of times they count on.

▶ **Mathematical Discourse 2**

- Ask children how the number sentence relates to the model, the picture, and the problem.

▶ **Hands-On Activity**

Ready· Mathematics
PRACTICE AND PROBLEM SOLVING

Assign *Practice and Problem Solving* **pages 3–4** after students have completed this section.

Explore Together
Count On to Add

A team has 5 girls and 3 boys.
How many children are on the team in all?

Model It Find 5 + 3.

One part shows girls. One part shows boys.
Count on from 5 to **add** girls and boys.

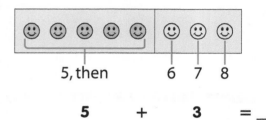

5, then   6 7 8

5   **+**   **3**   = __8__

4

▶ **Mathematical Discourse**

1 *How is the model like the picture of the boys and girls? How is it different?*
The model has 5 girls and 3 boys like the picture. In the model, the girls are all together and the boys are all together. In the picture, they are mixed up. The picture shows boys and girls; the model just shows smiley faces.

2 *Why does it make sense to start with the girls rather than the boys to count on?*
Children may give a variety of responses. Look for suggestions that indicate it is easier to count on 3 than to count on 5 and may reduce the chance of errors.

▶ **Hands-On Activity**
Model addition with counters.

Materials For each child: 8 counters

Model the problem using counters. Have children place 5 counters on the left side of their desk and count on as they add each of the 3 counters to the right side of the desk.

Learn Together
Count On to Add

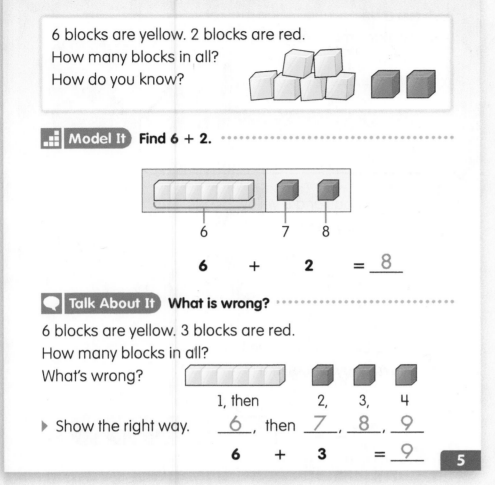

6 blocks are yellow. 2 blocks are red.
How many blocks in all?
How do you know?

⊞ Model It Find 6 + 2. ···

6   7   8

6   +   2   = _8_

💬 Talk About It What is wrong? ·····························

6 blocks are yellow. 3 blocks are red.
How many blocks in all?
What's wrong?

1, then   2,   3,   4

▶ Show the right way.   _6_ , then _7_ , _8_ , _9_

6   +   3   = _9_   `5`

- Read the problem at the top of the page aloud. Allow children to share strategies for solving the problem and then ask how they might use the counting on strategy.

- Ask: *Why does it make sense to start with the yellow blocks?* Children should realize that it is easier to count on by the fewer numbers of objects.

Model It

- Have children count on by swiping their finger across the bar of 6, saying "6," and then pointing to each red block as they count "7, 8." Ask them to complete and read the number sentence. Have children explain how the 2 in the number sentence and the number they counted on are related.

Talk About It

- Read the Talk About It aloud. Demonstrate the incorrect counting and ask: *What's wrong with the way I counted?* Encourage children to describe the error to a partner.

- As a class, discuss why the bar of blocks cannot be counted as 1. Have a volunteer demonstrate the correct way to count and ask children to record it. Help them connect the number sentence to the counting.

▶ **Mathematical Discourse 3**

> **SMP TIP Look for Structure**
> **Mathematical Discourse 3** is a concrete example of the commutative property. Asking children to describe the sets using two different number sentences helps them to make a symbolic connection. Emphasize that the sum has not changed even though the order of the addends has. *(SMP 7)*

▶ **Fluency Practice**

▶ **Fluency Practice**

Practice with the number path model.

Materials For each child: Number Paths (Activity Sheet 1)

- Distribute Activity Sheet 1 (Number Paths). Tell children they are going to model the problem from the top of the Student Book page.

- Have children shade the squares 1–6. Then have them circle the 6 and draw a curved arrow from 6 to 7 and from 7 to 8. Make sure children notice that the two jumps represent counting on two.

- Write 4 other addition number sentences on the board with a blank for the sum. Ask children to model the addition on the number paths and tell the sum.

▶ **Mathematical Discourse**

3 Display 2 red blocks to the left of 6 yellow blocks. Ask: *How can we use the counting on strategy to count these blocks?*

Some children may suggest reversing the order to count the yellow blocks first. Some may recognize that they can start with the yellow blocks and count on from right to left.

Ready· Mathematics
PRACTICE AND PROBLEM SOLVING

Assign *Practice and Problem Solving* **pages 5–6** after students have completed this section.

Guided Practice

Step By Step

- Read the example problem aloud. Encourage children to use their fingers to model the addends and find the sum. Ask: *Why do you think there are only 3 markers shown?*

- Guide children to recognize that the number 5 displayed represents 5 red markers. Help them see that this is like counting on with their fingers, saying 5 without counting all the fingers first and then holding up each of the 3 fingers as they are counted.

- Make connecting cubes available for children who need them as they solve Problems 1 and 2. For example, for Problem 1, they can put together 6 connecting cubes, say 6, then count on the additional 3 cubes.

- Direct attention to Problem 2. Ask children why it might be helpful to have the 6 written on the red blocks. They may want to write the start number like this for other counting on problems.

- Continue to emphasize the importance of tracking how many are counted on.

▶ **Mathematical Discourse 1 and 2**

▶ **Concept Extension**

SMP TIP Reason Abstractly and Quantitatively

As they practice counting on to add, children can use physical objects and drawings to help them reason quantitatively. Recording the process in a number sentence allows them to connect the concrete model to the symbolic model. (*SMP 2*)

Ready Mathematics
PRACTICE AND PROBLEM SOLVING

Assign *Practice and Problem Solving* **pages 7–8** after students have completed this section.

Practice Together
Count On to Add

5 red markers and 3 blue markers. How many markers in all?

$5 + 3 = \underline{8}$

5 red

6 7 8

1 6 red beads and 3 yellow beads. How many beads in all?

$6 + 3 = \underline{9}$

2 6 red blocks and 2 blue blocks. How many blocks in all?

$6 + 2 = \underline{8}$

6

6

▶ **Mathematical Discourse**

1 *How can you check to be sure you counted on correctly?*

Children may suggest counting on again, counting all the objects, or using a physical model or fingers to make sure.

2 *How does knowing the total of 6 + 3 help you find the answer to 6 + 2?*

Some children may notice that both number sentences start with 6 but the other addends are different. Since 2 is 1 less than 3, the sum of 6 + 2 is 1 less than the sum of 6 + 3.

▶ **Concept Extension**

Build the concept of a variable.

Materials For display: small box, 8 pencils or other classroom objects

- Display the box and tell children there are 5 pencils inside the box.

- Set 3 single pencils next to the box and ask: *How many pencils do I have altogether? How can you count on to find out?* Listen for counts of "5, 6, 7, 8" and ask how they knew to start with 5.

- Children should recognize that since they know there are 5 pencils in the box, they do not need to be counted or drawn separately.

- Have children record the process in a number sentence to make a symbolic connection to the problem.

Practice by Myself
Count On to Add

3 5 big balls and 3 small balls.
How many balls in all?

$5 + 3 = \underline{8}$ ⚫⚫⚫

4 1 bee and 7 ants.
How many bugs in all?

$1 + 7 = \underline{8}$ 7

5 6 triangles and 2 squares.
How many shapes in all?

$\underline{8} = 6 + 2$

7

Step By Step

- Before children work on this page, review the models used in this lesson. Emphasize that children are free to use whatever way helps them solve the problem.
- Read each problem aloud, then have children work independently to solve.
- For Problem 4, observe to see if children are still struggling with the idea of the commutative property or starting with the greater number.

▶ **English Language Learners**

- You may wish to draw attention to the number sentence in Problem 5 and ask how this number sentence is different from the others in the lesson. Use the Mathematical Discourse question to begin talking about the concept of equality.
- Ask children who solve Problem 5 without drawing the shapes to explain which strategy they used.

▶ **Mathematical Discourse 3**

SMP TIP Attend to Precision
Seeing number sentences with the totals on both the left and right helps reinforce the idea of a number sentence as a representation of two equal quantities. (*SMP 6*)

▶ **English Language Learners**

Present visual and language support to help children see the relationships presented in the problems. For example: *Ants and bees are both kinds of bugs.*

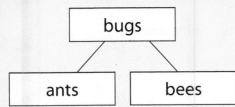

▶ **Mathematical Discourse**

3 *Why is it okay to sometimes write the total at the beginning of the number sentence and sometimes at the end?*

Children may realize that the total is always the same whether it is to the left or right of the equal sign. They may also recognize that the equal sign means the two sides are the same.

Differentiated Instruction

▶ Quick Check and Remediation

Materials For each child: 10 two-color counters, strip of paper divided into ten sections

- Ask children to count on to find the answer to the following problem: 7 children and 2 adults are at the park. How many people are at the park? [9 people at the park]

- For children who are still struggling, use the chart below to guide remediation.

- After providing remediation, check children's understanding using the following problem: There are 6 blue hats and 2 red hats. How many hats in all? [8 hats]

If the error is . . .	Children may . . .	To remediate . . .
8	have counted on using 7 as the first count.	Have children model the addends with counters, each in a different color. Ask what group of counters shows the 7 children. Move one of the 2 counters next to the group of 7 and ask: *How many are there now?* Repeat for the remaining counter. Separate the counters and have children demonstrate the counting on action. Repeat again using other models such as fingers and a number path.
any other number	have miscounted.	Give children counters and a strip of paper divided into ten sections. Help them model the problem using two-color counters. First have them place 7 counters of one color on the strip, counting each one. Then ask them to count on from 7 as they add 2 counters of a different color.

▶ Hands-On Activity

Model number sentences.

Materials For each pair: 10 two-color counters, number sentence cards

- Make number sentence cards for sums to 10. Each includes one addend that is a 1, 2, or 3. Distribute the cards and counters to pairs.

- Have children place the cards facedown. One partner picks a card. The other models the addends with two groups of counters. The child who picked the card counts on to find the total. If they both agree it is correct, they write the total on the card.

- Partners alternate roles and repeat until all cards are completed.

▶ Challenge Activity

Find counting patterns.

Materials Optional: counters

- Write these number sentences on the board:

    $6 + 3 = 9$
    $6 + 2 = 8$
    $6 + 1 = ?$

- Ask children if they can think of an easy way to find the missing total. Listen for responses that indicate that as one addend goes down by 1, the total goes down by 1.

- Challenge children to write similar groups of number sentences. Suggest that they draw pictures or use counters to help. Lead them to also explore what happens when the second addend stays the same and the first addend changes.

Teacher Notes

Teacher-Toolbox.com

Overview

Assign the Lesson 1 Quiz and have children work independently to complete it.

Use the results of the quiz to assess children's understanding of the content of the lesson and to identify areas for reteaching. See the Lesson Pacing Guide at the beginning of the lesson and the Differentiated Instruction activities for suggested instructional resources.

Tested Skills

Assesses 1.OA.C.5

Problems on this quiz require children to be able to add within 10 using the counting on strategy to find a sum. Children will also need to be familiar with counting up to 10 objects, interpreting a number sentence, and understand addition as putting things together.

Ready® **Mathematics**

Lesson 1 Quiz Answer Key

Name _____

Solve.

1. 5 small cups and 2 big cups.
   How many cups in all?

   $5 + 2 = \underline{7}$

2. 6 cats and 3 dogs.
   How many animals in all?

   $\underline{9} = 6 + 3$

3. 2 car stickers and 7 animal stickers.
   How many stickers in all?

   $2 + 7 = \underline{9}$

Grade 1 **Lesson 1** Count On to Add

©Curriculum Associates, LLC
Copying permitted for classroom use.

1

Common Misconceptions and Errors

Errors may result if children:

• count a group as 1 instead of the quantity it represents.

• count on from an addend using the addend as the first count.

• do not keep track of the number of times counted on.

Name _____

Solve.

④ 6 squares and 1 circle.
How many shapes in all?

___7___ = 6 + 1

⑤ Pablo has 8 red balls and 1 green ball.
How many balls does he have in all?

8 + 1 = ___9___

  2

CCSS Focus

Domain
Operations and Algebraic Thinking

Cluster
C. Add and subtract within 20.

Standard
1.OA.C.6 Add and subtract within 20, demonstrating fluency for addition and subtraction within 10. Use strategies such as counting on; making ten (e.g., $8 + 6 = 8 + 2 + 4 = 10 + 4 = 14$); decomposing a number leading to a ten (e.g., $13 - 4 = 13 - 3 - 1 = 10 - 1 = 9$); using the relationship between addition and subtraction (e.g., knowing that $8 + 4 = 12$, one knows $12 - 8 = 4$); and creating equivalent but easier or known sums (e.g., adding $6 + 7$ by creating the known equivalent $6 + 6 + 1 = 12 + 1 = 13$).

Additional Standards
1.OA.A.1, 1.OA.C.5 (See page B3 for full text.)

Standards for Mathematical Practice (SMP)
2 Reason abstractly and quantitatively.

3 Construct viable arguments and critique the reasoning of others.

6 Attend to precision.

7 Look for and make use of structure.

Lesson Objectives

Content Objectives
• Apply the counting on strategy to subtract within 10.

• Model the counting on strategy using physical and visual models.

• Connect the counting on strategy to a number sentence.

Language Objectives
• Use diagrams and number paths to show the counting on strategy to subtract.

• Record answers to related addition and subtraction number sentences.

• Tell how counting on to subtract is like and how it is different from counting on to add.

Prerequisite Skills

• Add/subtract within 5.

• Represent addition and subtraction situations using physical models and number sentences.

• Count on to add.

Lesson Vocabulary

• **subtract** to take objects away from a group or to compare groups.

• **subtraction sentence** one number is subtracted from another in a sentence with symbols and numbers.

Review the following key term.

• **count on** start with one addend and count to find a total.

Learning Progression

In Kindergarten children explore addition and subtraction within 10, using physical models and by acting out situations. Fluency within 5 is expected and is represented in drawings and with number sentences.

In Grade 1 children gain fluency for addition and subtraction within 10 by developing the use of strategies.

In this lesson the familiar strategy of counting on is extended to subtraction in the context of "take from" and "take apart" situations. Children analyze the

situations to identify the number being subtracted and then count on from that number to find the difference. The strategy of counting on to subtract is a building block for understanding the relationship between addition and subtraction.

In Grade 2 children fluently add and subtract within 20 using mental strategies, articulating why the strategy works and recognizing the relationship between addition and subtraction.

Lesson Pacing Guide

Whole Class Instruction

Day 1
45–60 minutes

Introduction
Use What You Know
- Explore It *25 min*
- Try It *20 min*

Day 2
45–60 minutes

Modeled Instruction
Explore Together
- Example Problem *10 min*
- Model It *15 min*
- Fluency Practice *20 min*

Practice and Problem Solving
Assign pages 11–12.

Day 3
45–60 minutes

Guided Instruction
Learn Together
- Example Problem *10 min*
- Model It *10 min*
- Talk About It *15 min*
- Visual Model *10 min*

Practice and Problem Solving
Assign pages 13–14.

Day 4
45–60 minutes

Guided Practice
Practice Together
- Example Problem *15 min*
- Problems 1–2 *30 min*

Practice and Problem Solving
Assign pages 15–16.

Day 5
45–60 minutes

Independent Practice
Practice by Myself
- Problems 3–5 *15 min*
- Quick Check and Remediation *15 min*
- Hands-On or Challenge Activity *15 min*

Teacher-Toolbox: Lesson Quiz
Lesson 2 Quiz

Materials for Lesson Activities

Per child: 25 connecting cubes, 9 counters, 9 blocks, 3 picture books
Activity Sheet 1

Per pair: 1 bowl, 10 counters, whiteboard

For display: none

Small Group Differentiation

Teacher-Toolbox.com

Reteach
Ready Prerequisite Lessons *45–90 min*

Grade K
- Lesson 16 *Understand* Subtraction
- Lesson 19 Subtract Within 10

Teacher-led Activities
Tools for Instruction *15–20 min*

Grade 1 *(Lesson 2)*
- Count On to Add
- Subtraction Number Sentences

Student-led Activities
Math Center Activities *30–40 min*

Grade K *(Lessons 16 and 19)*
- K.23 Subtraction Vocabulary
- K.25 Subtract and Match

Grade 1 *(Lesson 2)*
- 1.03 Count On to Subtract

Personalized Learning

i-Ready.com

Independent
i-Ready Lessons* *10–20 min*

Grade 1 *(Lesson 2)*
- Counting On to Add
- Acting Out Addition and Subtraction

* i-Ready lessons may be updated during the 2016–2017 school year. Updated references will be on the Teacher-Toolbox.

👥 **Introduction**

Activity Relate Subtraction, Addition, and Counting On

Objective
Explore the relationship between addition and subtraction.

Materials for each child
• 25 connecting cubes

Overview
Children act out a subtraction situation and use results to reinforce the concept of embedded numbers. They then apply the concept to counting on to subtract.

Step By Step

Explore It

Pose the problem.
• Read the problem from the Student Book page: *5 children are playing ball. 3 children leave. How many children are still playing ball?*

Act it out.
• Select 5 children to come to the front of the class and stand in a line. As you repeat the problem, have 3 of the children turn and take a couple of steps away from the others.

• Ask: *How many children are still playing ball? How do you know?* Children will likely count the remaining players to find that 2 are still playing ball.

• Provide children with connecting cubes. Have children place the connecting cubes on the workmat on the Student Book page and use them to solve the problem.

• Ask: *How can this problem be represented as a subtraction sentence?* Listen to a few responses, then write on the board $5 - 3 = 2$. Have children record the number sentence.

Introduce counting on to subtract.
• Have 5 different children stand in a line, and then again ask 3 children to turn and take a couple of steps away. Point out that the 3 children who leave are part of the original group of 5 playing ball.

G Explore It

5 children are playing ball. 3 children leave. How many children are still playing ball?

$\underline{5} - \underline{3} = \underline{2}$ $\underline{3} + \underline{2} = \underline{5}$

6 children are playing ball. 4 children leave. How many children are still playing ball?

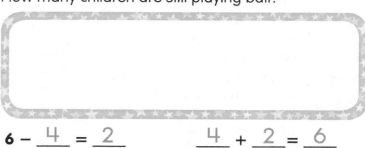

$6 - \underline{4} = \underline{2}$ $\underline{4} + \underline{2} = \underline{6}$

• Tell children that you are going to start with the 3 children who leave and count on to 5. Say "3" and then hold up 2 fingers one at a time as you count "4, 5."

• Ask: *How many did I count on?* [2] Elicit that this action can be represented by the addition sentence $3 + 2 = 5$. Write this on the board next to the related subtraction problem.

• Encourage children to describe how the addition and subtraction sentences are alike.

Apply counting on to another subtraction problem.

• Pose a similar problem. Read aloud the problem on the Student Book page: *6 children are playing ball. 4 children leave. How many children are still playing ball?* Invite children to suggest ways to determine how many children are still playing ball. Discuss their ideas.

• Make sure that counting on is one of the strategies you discuss and demonstrate. Continue to make the connection between the subtraction sentence and the related addition sentence.

• Have children use connecting cubes to show how they solved the problem.

• Guide children to complete the number sentences on the Student Book page.

>> **Try It**

8 children are playing ball. 5 children leave.
How many children are still playing ball?

$8 - \underline{\ 5\ } = \underline{\ 3\ }$ $\underline{\ 5\ } + \underline{\ 3\ } = \underline{\ 8\ }$

6 children are playing ball. 3 children leave.
How many children are still playing ball?

$6 - \underline{\ 3\ } = \underline{\ 3\ }$ $\underline{\ 3\ } + \underline{\ 3\ } = \underline{\ 6\ }$

9

Step By Step

Try It

Pose additional problems.

- Read the problems on the Student Book page aloud:

  8 children are playing ball. 5 children leave. How many children are still playing ball?

  6 children are playing ball. 3 children leave. How many children are still playing ball?

Allow time for children to work.

- Have children solve each of the problems on the Student Book page. Ask them to continue to use connecting cubes as they work.

- Tell children to complete the subtraction sentence and write an addition sentence for each problem.

- Observe and note the children who are able to make the connection between subtraction and counting on.

Share strategies.

- Invite children to share the ways they solved the problems. Listen to all strategies, and make sure that counting on is one of the strategies children share and demonstrate.

- Invite children to share the subtraction and addition sentences that they wrote for these problems.

- Continue to make the connection between the subtraction sentence and the related addition sentence.

- Use the Visual Model in the lesson to help reinforce the idea of starting at a number other than 1 and counting on.

👥 Modeled Instruction

Step By Step

- Read aloud the problem at the top of the page.

- Ask children to discuss what is happening in the problem—what they know and what they need to find out. Remind them that there are many ways to find the answer.

▶ **Mathematical Discourse 1**

Model It

- Read aloud the text in Model It. Ask children to describe how this model is similar to counting on using their fingers.

▶ **Mathematical Discourse 2**

▶ **Fluency Practice**

SMP TIP Reason Abstractly and Quantitatively

Ask children to describe how the number sentence tells what is happening in the problem. In order to contextualize and decontextualize the information in this problem, children need to make a clear connection between the problem situation, the illustration, and the number sentence. (SMP 2)

 **Ready** Mathematics
PRACTICE AND PROBLEM SOLVING

Assign *Practice and Problem Solving* **pages 11–12** after students have completed this section.

Explore Together
Count On to Subtract

6 children play ball. 4 go home early.
How many children are left?

🔲 **Model It** Find 6 − 4.

Start with the number of children who leave.

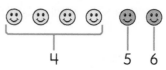

| 4 | 5 | 6 |

Start at 4.   Count on to 6.
                     Count on 2 .

6 − 4 = 2

10

▶ **Mathematical Discourse**

1 Say: *Close your eyes and think about the problem.* (Read the problem.) Ask: *How can you tell in your head how many children are left after 4 go home?*
Children may respond that they can use fingers to count on. Some may say they can see the 2 children that are left. Be sure children can justify their responses. Encourage children to share mental strategies and compare them to the strategies they used in the Activity in the Introduction.

2 *How can you make sure you found the right answer to this problem?*
Some children may return to the original problem and act it out to check. Others may add 4 and 2 to get 6, recognizing that 4 and 2 are parts of the 6 children who are playing.

▶ **Fluency Practice**

Subtract with a number path model.

Materials For each child: 1 counter, Number Paths (Activity Sheet 1)

- Write on the board 6 − 4 = ___ and 4 + ___ = 6.

- Have children put a counter on 4 on the number path. Ask them to count on to 6 and tell how many they counted. Complete the number sentences as they respond.

- Write several different subtraction sentences on the board. Ask children to write the corresponding addition sentence, use the number path to model the problem, then complete the number sentences.

Learn Together
Count On to Subtract

There are 7 bikes. 4 are red.
The rest are black.

How many are black?
How can you find out?

⬛ **Model It** Find 7 − 4. ┈┈┈┈┈┈┈┈┈┈┈

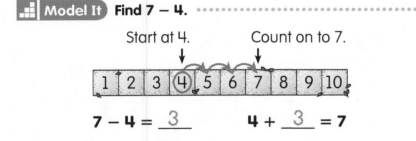

Start at 4.   Count on to 7.

| 1 | 2 | 3 | ④ | 5 | 6 | 7 | 8 | 9 | 10 |

$7 - 4 = \underline{3}$ $4 + \underline{3} = 7$

💬 **Talk About It** **Who is right? How do you know?** ┈┈┈┈┈

There are 8 children. 5 are boys. How many are girls?

Buzz: Boom:

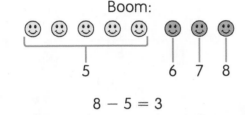

$8 - 5 = 4$ $8 - 5 = 3$

11

▶ Visual Model
Count on with tally marks.

Write 4 + ☐ = 7 on the board and ask
children what they think the box means.
Since the box represents how many more
are needed to get to 7, show children
how they can make tally marks or dots in
the box as they count on:

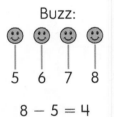

$4 + \boxed{\bullet\ \bullet\ \bullet} = 7$ so 4 + 3 = 7
        5 6 7

▶ Mathematical Discourse

3 *What did Buzz do wrong?*
Children should respond that Buzz
counted the 5 as one of the girls. They
should recognize that 5 is the number
of boys, so 5 is not included in the
count for the number of girls.

Step By Step

- Read the problem aloud. Ask: *How is this like
  the problem about the children playing ball?
  How is it different?* Help children see that this
  is a subtraction problem, but it is not a "take
  away" situation. It is a "take apart" situation.

- Some children may not understand how this
  problem can be modeled with subtraction
  since nothing is being "taken away." Use the
  illustration to help them recognize that
  there are 7 bikes in all; some are red and
  some are black. They can subtract the
  number of red bikes from all the bikes to
  find the number of black bikes.

Model It

- Discuss the number path with children.
  Point out that the first 4 boxes represent the
  red bikes, and that is why you start at 4. Ask:
  *Why do you stop at 7 when counting on in this
  problem?* [There are 7 bikes in all.]

▶ Visual Model

- Help children see that the addition sentence
  for this problem models the counting on
  process they used.

> **SMP TIP Look for Structure**
> Pairs of related number sentences
> throughout the lesson help reinforce the
> idea of inverse operations and prepare
> children for work with number bonds and
> fact families. *(SMP 7)*

Talk About It

- Read Talk About It aloud. Tell children to
  think about the ways that Buzz and Boom
  counted on. Encourage children to share
  ideas and justify using blocks or drawings.

▶ Mathematical Discourse 3

📦 **Ready** Mathematics
PRACTICE AND PROBLEM SOLVING

Assign *Practice and Problem Solving*
pages 13–14 after students have
completed this section.

👥 Guided Practice

Step By Step

- Read the example problem aloud. Ask children to explain why the subtraction sentence $7 - 5 = ?$ can be used to model this problem. Then guide children to make the connection between this subtraction sentence and the addition sentence $5 + 2 = 7$.

▶ **Mathematical Discourse 1**

- Read Problem 1. Give children time to think about the problem and then invite volunteers to demonstrate strategies for solving it. Have children describe how the number sentences given with the problem model the situation and/or strategy used.

> **SMP TIP Look for Structure**
> Draw attention to the addition sentence $8 = \_\_\_ + 5$ and ask why it can also be written $5 + \_\_\_ = 8$. Help children recognize that in addition, the order of the addends doesn't affect the total because of the commutative property of addition. Also emphasize that either the addends or the total can be placed to the left or right of the equal sign. *(SMP 7)*

- Tell children to look at Problem 2. Ask why the 6 is circled. Make sure children understand that the 6 represents the number of balloons that popped. Support children who need help by encouraging them to model the problem with blocks and/or by coloring or outlining the block of squares 1–6 on the page.

▶ **English Language Learners**

🔲 **Ready** **Mathematics**
PRACTICE AND PROBLEM SOLVING

Assign *Practice and Problem Solving* **pages 15–16** after students have completed this section.

Count On to Subtract

> Ali has 7 markers. Some are blue.
> 5 are red.
> How many are blue?
> $7 - 5 = ?$
>
> $5 + \underline{2} = 7$

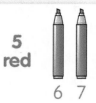

1 There are 8 cups. 5 are big. The rest are small. How many are small?

$8 - 5 = \underline{3}$ $8 = \underline{3} + 5$

2 There are 9 balloons. 6 balloons pop. How many balloons are left?

| 1 | 2 | 3 | 4 | 5 | ⑥ | 7 | 8 | 9 | 10 |

$9 - 6 = \underline{3}$ $6 + 3 = \underline{9}$

12

▶ **Mathematical Discourse**

1 *How does adding help you make sense of a subtraction problem?*
Children should see that addition models the process of counting on, and some may say it is easier to think of counting on than counting back.

▶ **English Language Learners**

In Problem 2, some children may interpret the word *left* as a directional term. Tell them that in problems like Problem 2, the word *left* means *left over* and refers to the balloons that did not pop.

Practice by Myself
Count On to Subtract

3 Jen has 8 buttons. 6 are square.
The rest are round. How many buttons are round?

$8 - 6 = \underline{2}$ $6 + \underline{2} = 8$

4 6 fish are in the weeds. 3 swim away.
How many are left?

| 1 | 2 | 3 | 4 | 5 | 6 | 7 | 8 | 9 | 10 |

$6 - 3 = \underline{3}$ $6 = 3 + \underline{3}$

5 6 flowers are in a vase.
5 flowers are short.
The rest are tall.
How many flowers are tall?

$6 - 5 = \underline{1}$ $5 + \underline{1} = 6$

13

Step By Step

- Before children work on this page, review the models used in this lesson. Children may complete the models given with the problem and then write the answers in the number sentences. Emphasize that children are free to use whatever way helps them solve the problem.

- Read each problem aloud, then have children work independently to solve.

- You may wish to point out that each problem is modeled by a subtraction sentence and that the related addition sentence gives them a clue about how to count on to solve the subtraction sentence.

- For those who struggle to start Problem 5, ask questions such as: *What do you know about the flowers? How many might you draw first? Why? How many more do you need to draw?* Mathematical Discourse question 2 promotes algebraic thinking—any shape or symbol can be used to represent the flowers.

▶ **Mathematical Discourse 2**

- Mathematical Discourse question 3 can be used to check understanding of the counting on strategy.

▶ **Mathematical Discourse 3**

▶ **Mathematical Discourse**

2 *If you don't want to draw flowers, how might you show tall flowers and short flowers?*

Children may suggest drawing long lines to show tall flowers and short lines to show short flowers. Some may suggest using a tape diagram or other shapes.

3 *How is counting on to subtract like counting on to add? How are they different?*

Children should recognize that the process and the numbers used to start are the same, but counting on to subtract involves finding one addend and not the total.

Differentiated Instruction

▶ Quick Check and Remediation

Materials For each child: 9 counters

- Ask children to find the answer to the following problem: *9 leaves are on a tree. 7 leaves fall off. How many leaves are still on the tree?* [2]

- For children who are still struggling, use the chart below to guide remediation.

- After providing remediation, check children's understanding using the following problem: *There are 8 apples in a bowl. Some apples are red and some are yellow. 5 are red. How many apples are yellow?* [3]

If the error is . . .	Children may . . .	To remediate . . .
3	have counted on 7, 8, 9 including 7 in the counts.	Ask children to show with counters how many leaves fell off the tree and then set these aside. Have them count on more counters to get to 9. Encourage children to compare the result with their original answer. Check answers by putting 2 counters and then 3 counters with the group of 7 and counting to find the total.
16	have counted on 7 from 9.	Have children draw a picture of the problem to see that when 7 leaves are taken from 9, only a portion of the original 9 remain.
any other answer	have miscounted.	Repeat the first remediation to check for accuracy.

▶ Hands-On Activity
Find the number of hidden counters.

Materials For each pair: 10 counters, 1 bowl, whiteboard

- Distribute the materials to pairs of children.

- Use a partner to model the activity. Place a number of counters (5–10) on the desk, count them, and then cover them with the bowl. Have your partner record the number of counters under the bowl.

- Lift one side of the bowl and remove some of the counters so your partner doesn't see how many are left under the bowl. The partner writes a missing addend number sentence, uses the counting on strategy to determine the number of counters under the bowl, and then completes the number sentence.

- After children complete several rounds, talk about what numbers were easy to count on (1, 2, 3), what numbers were not so easy, and why.

▶ Challenge Activity
Write subtraction word problems.

Materials For each child: picture books

- Give each child two or three picture books. Tell them to read or look at the books, thinking about subtraction problems they could write using the pictures or context of the story.

- Ask children to write/dictate two subtraction word problems. You may want to suggest that one be a "take away" problem and the other be a "take apart" problem.

- After writing the two word problems, have children write an addition number sentence and a subtraction number sentence to go with each word problem. Have children find and justify the solution to each one using pictures, visuals, or physical models.

Teacher Notes

Teacher-Toolbox.com

Overview

Assign the Lesson 2 Quiz and have children work independently to complete it.

Use the results of the quiz to assess children's understanding of the content of the lesson and to identify areas for reteaching. See the Lesson Pacing Guide at the beginning of the lesson and the Differentiated Instruction activities for suggested instructional resources.

Tested Skills

Assesses 1.OA.C.6

Problems on this quiz require children to be able to use models and apply the counting on strategy to subtract within 10, and to connect the counting on strategy to the related addition and subtraction number sentences. Children will also need to be familiar with counting on to add and representing addition and subtraction with models and number sentences.

Ready **Mathematics**

Lesson 2 Quiz Answer Key

Name _____

Solve.

1. Luna has 7 balls. 5 are big.
The rest are small. How many balls are small?

$7 - 5 = \underline{2}$ $5 + \underline{2} = 7$

2. There are 7 kites. 4 kites are bird kites.
The rest are butterfly kites. How many are butterfly kites?

| 1 | 2 | 3 | 4 | 5 | 6 | 7 | 8 | 9 | 10 |

$7 - 4 = \underline{3}$ $4 + \underline{3} = 7$

3. 8 children are playing.
6 children leave. How many children are left?

$8 - 6 = \underline{2}$ $6 + \underline{2} = 8$

Grade 1 **Lesson 2** Count On to Subtract

1

©Curriculum Associates, LLC
Copying permitted for classroom use.

Common Misconceptions and Errors

Errors may result if children:

• add the two quantities given in the problem.

• count on from the lesser number using the lesser number as the first count.

• count a group as 1 instead of the quantity it represents.

Name _____

Solve.

④ Arun has 8 crayons. He gives away 7 crayons. How many crayons does he have left?

$8 - 7 = \underline{1}$ $7 + \underline{1} = 8$

⑤ There are 9 birds in a tree. 6 birds fly away. How many birds are left in the tree?

$9 - 6 = \underline{3}$ $9 = 6 + \underline{3}$

2

Lesson 3
Add and Subtract in Word Problems

CCSS Focus

Domain
Operations and Algebraic Thinking

Cluster
A. Represent and solve problems involving addition and subtraction.

Standard
1.OA.A.1 Use addition and subtraction within 20 to solve word problems involving situations of adding to, taking from, putting together, taking apart, and comparing, with unknowns in all positions, e.g., by using objects, drawings, and number sentences with a symbol for the unknown number to represent the problem.

Additional Standards
1.OA.B.4, 1.OA.C.5, 1.OA.C.6 (See page B3 for full text.)

Standards for Mathematical Practice (SMP)
1 Make sense of problems and persevere in solving them.

2 Reason abstractly and quantitatively.

4 Model with mathematics.

7 Look for and make use of structure.

Lesson Objectives

Content Objectives
- Use strategies, including counting on, to solve addition and subtraction word problems.
- Complete number sentences to solve addition and subtraction word problems.

Language Objectives
- Identify counting strategies that can be used to solve addition and subtraction word problems.
- Draw jumps on a number path and circles on a tape diagram to show how to complete a number sentence.
- Tell the meaning of the unknown quantity in a word problem and use this to explain where the blank goes in the related number sentence.
- Discuss with a partner strategies used to solve a word problem.

Prerequisite Skills
- Count on to add.
- Count on to subtract.

Lesson Vocabulary
- **addend** a number being added.
- **number bond** a diagram with a total and two addends.

Review the following key term.
- **count on** start with one addend and count to find a total.

Learning Progression

In Kindergarten children count objects and count forward from a given number. They use objects or drawings to solve word problems and they count all to find the total.

In Grade 1 children move from counting all to counting on to add and subtract.

In this lesson children solve "add to," "take from," and "put together/take apart" word problems. Seeing that the unknown appears in different positions helps children begin to develop an algebraic perspective.

In Grade 2 children continue to solve one-step word problems involving all types of situations. They extend this work to solve two-step word problems and add and subtract within 100.

Lesson Pacing Guide

Whole Class Instruction

Day 1
45–60 minutes

Introduction
Use What You Know
- Explore It *25 min*
- Try It *20 min*

Day 2
45–60 minutes

Modeled Instruction
Explore Together
- Example Problem *5 min*
- Model It *20 min*
- Fluency Practice *20 min*

Practice and Problem Solving
Assign pages 19–20.

Day 3
45–60 minutes

Guided Instruction
Learn Together
- Example Problem *5 min*
- Model It *15 min*
- Talk About It *15 min*
- Hands-On Activity *10 min*

Practice and Problem Solving
Assign pages 21–22.

Day 4
45–60 minutes

Guided Practice
Practice Together
- Example Problem *5 min*
- Problems 1–2 *25 min*
- Concept Extension *15 min*

Practice and Problem Solving
Assign pages 23–24.

Day 5
45–60 minutes

Independent Practice
Practice by Myself
- Problems 3–5 *15 min*
- Quick Check and Remediation *15 min*
- Hands-On or Challenge Activity *15 min*

Teacher-Toolbox: Lesson Quiz
Lesson 3 Quiz

Materials for Lesson Activities

Per child: 10 two-color counters, 1 marker, 2 small toy animals or 2 pictures of animals, index cards with subtraction stories
Activity Sheet 2

Per pair: 6 two-color counters

Per group: Activity Sheet 41

For display: 10 cubes, 1 bag

Small Group Differentiation

Teacher-Toolbox.com

Reteach
Ready Prerequisite Lessons *45–90 min*

Grade K
- Lesson 18 Add Within 10
- Lesson 19 Subtract Within 10

Teacher-led Activities
Tools for Instruction *15–20 min*

Grade 1 *(Lesson 3)*
- Count On to Add
- Subtraction Number Sentences

Student-led Activities
Math Center Activities *30–40 min*

Grade K *(Lessons 18 and 19)*
- K.24 Tell Addition Stories
- K.25 Subtract and Match

Grade 1 *(Lesson 3)*
- 1.10 Solve Addition and Subtraction

Personalized Learning

i-Ready.com

Independent
i-Ready Lessons* *10–20 min*

Grade 1 *(Lesson 3)*
- Counting On to Solve Addition Problems
- Acting Out Addition and Subtraction
- Taking Away to Subtract

* i-Ready lessons may be updated during the 2016–2017 school year. Updated references will be on the Teacher-Toolbox.

👥 Introduction

Activity Act Out an "Add To" Word Problem

Objective

Act out an "add to" word problem and draw the associated number bond.

Materials for each child

- 2 small toy animals or 2 pictures of an animal

Overview

Children act out "add to" word problems that are very similar to the Explore Together problem. They count on to reach the total. Then they use a visual model and number sentence to model each problem.

Step By Step

Explore It

Pose the problem.

- Tell children to imagine that they are at a picnic. Say: *There is room for 5 children at a picnic table and 3 children are already sitting down. Some more children sit down and now the table is full.* Explain that they need to figure out how many children joined those sitting by acting it out.

Model the problem.

- Invite 5 children to act out the problem. Explain that 3 of them will sit down, and then the rest will come and join them.

- Read the problem from the Student Book page and have the children act it out. Tell the 2 children who are joining the original 3 to come in one at a time, while the class counts on from 3.

Draw a number bond.

- Draw a number bond on the board. Fill in 5 as the total. Ask children to explain what the 5 means. [The total number of children sitting at the table at the end of the problem.]

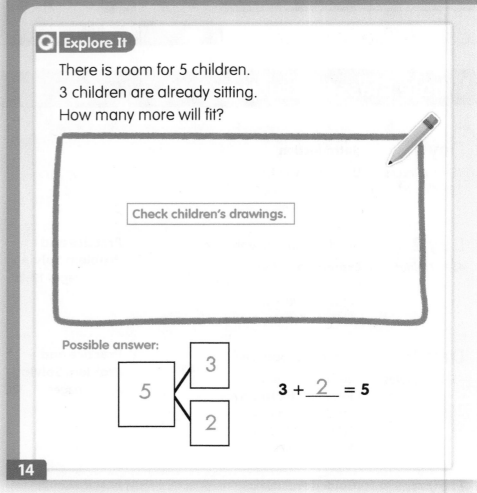

Ⓖ Explore It

There is room for 5 children.
3 children are already sitting.
How many more will fit?

Check children's drawings.

Possible answer:

$$3 + \underline{2} = 5$$

14

- Ask children to describe what else the problem tells. Challenge them to identify what other two numbers are needed to complete the number bond. Finish the number bond with their correct suggestions.

- Have children explain what the 3 means [those who were already seated] and then what the 2 means [those who came after]. Point out that the problem tells how many children in all (point to 5) and how many were already seated (point to 3). But it doesn't say how many came after.

Write the number sentence and talk about the meaning of the unknown.

- Write "3 + ___ = 5" on the board.

- Have children relate the number sentence to the number bond. Ask them which number is missing and why. [The 2 is missing because the problem says "some more children"; it doesn't say how many "some" is.] Review the meaning of the other numbers.

Draw to represent the problem.

- Have children record this activity on the Student Book page. Ask them to first represent the problem by drawing a picture, and then complete a number bond and number sentence.

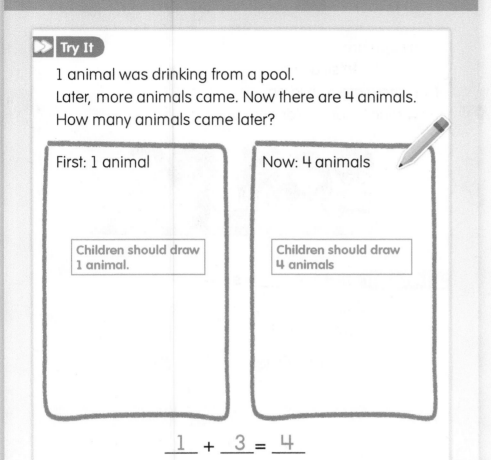

>> Try It

1 animal was drinking from a pool.
Later, more animals came. Now there are 4 animals.
How many animals came later?

First: 1 animal

Children should draw
1 animal.

Now: 4 animals

Children should draw
4 animals

__1__ + __3__ = __4__

15

Step By Step

Try It

Pose the problem.

• Read aloud the problem from the Student
Book page: *1 animal was drinking from a
pool. Later, more animals came. Now there
are 4 animals. How many animals came later?*

Model the problem.

• Have children act out the story in pairs,
using their toy animals or pictures. Ask them
to draw a picture on the Student Book page
and write an associated number sentence.

• Children who are able to solve the problem
by modeling it are able to make sense of the
problem situation.

Lead the class in discussion

• Ask children to explain how they decided
where to put the numbers in the number
sentences.

• It is likely that some children will not be able
to write a number sentence. Activities and
suggestions within the lesson will help them
with the next step—representing the
situation symbolically.

Modeled Instruction

Step By Step

- Begin by asking children what they learned or what they remember from the Activity in the Introduction. Elicit that the problems told "how many in all" and asked for the number of children or animals who joined those who were already there. Explain that this page includes a similar problem.

- Read aloud the problem at the top of the page. Have a volunteer describe the situation. Discuss and elicit that in this problem, we don't know how many children came to sit down.

▶ **English Language Learners**

Model It

- Discuss Model It. Have children set up three counters to represent the seated children. Help them see the connection between the counters and the three yellow faces. Invite a volunteer to demonstrate counting on using counters of a different color. Relate this to the green faces and the numbers beneath. Use Mathematical Discourse question 1 to reinforce the counting on strategy.

▶ **Mathematical Discourse 1**

- Tell children to count the new counters to find the missing addend and then complete the number sentence. Discuss how the number sentence relates to the visual model.

▶ **Fluency Practice**

 **Ready** Mathematics
PRACTICE AND PROBLEM SOLVING

Assign *Practice and Problem Solving* **pages 19–20** after students have completed this section.

Add and Subtract in Word Problems

3 children are sitting.
More children sit down.
Now there are 5 children.
How many more children sit down?

Model It Find 3 + ____ = 5.

Start with 3. Count on.
How many more make 5?

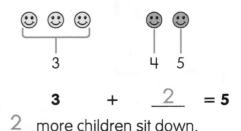

$$3 \quad + \quad \underline{2} \quad = 5$$

$\underline{2}$ more children sit down.

16

▶ **Mathematical Discourse**

1 *How can you use two-color counters to count on and solve this problem?*

Children might describe counting from the initial amount (3) until reaching the total (5). Another approach would be to count out 5 red counters and replace 3 of them with yellow counters. Children may come up with other approaches, but the key is to differentiate between the total, the children who are already sitting, and the children who arrive later.

▶ **English Language Learners**

Discuss the difference between "are sitting" and "sit down." "3 children are sitting" means the children are already there and they continue to sit. "More children sit down" means that these children join the ones that are already sitting. Children may be familiar with "sit up," meaning "do not slouch." But "sit down" is not the opposite of "sit up." You may want to provide a demonstration of these terms.

▶ **Fluency Practice**

Make 5 and 6 with number bonds.

Materials For each child: Number Bond Recording Sheet (Activity Sheet 2)

On the board, display a number bond with the numbers 3, 2, and 5. Have children record as many number bonds as they can that have totals of 5 and 6. Remind them that the parts can include different numbers and appear in different orders.

Learn Together
Add and Subtract in Word Problems

Jan has 6 pencils.
She gives some away.
Now she has 5 pencils.
How many does she give away?

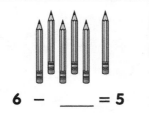

6 − ____ = 5

🔲 **Model It** Find 6 − ____ = 5.

Start with 5. How many more makes 6?

5 + <u>1</u> = 6

6 − <u>1</u> = 5

Jan gives away <u>1</u> pencil(s).

💬 **Talk About It** Who is right? How do you know?

There are 8 pencils.
4 are yellow. The rest are blue.
How many are blue?

Buzz: **4 + 8 = ?** Boom: **4 + ? = 8**

17

▶ **Hands-On Activity**

Model number sentences with counters.

Materials For each pair: 6 two-color counters

• Have children work in pairs to recreate Model It with counters. Ask pairs to share and explain what they did.

• Guide children to consider how their models relate to the number path model and to the number sentence. Ask: *How do counters help you answer the question "How many more to make 6?"*

• Ask children whether they prefer the number path model or the counters and explain why.

▶ **Mathematical Discourse**

2 *How could you check your answer to this problem?*

Children might suggest using pencils to act it out as an addition problem. Some children may act out the subtraction to verify that the counting on process worked. Encourage children to describe their strategies and tell why their approach makes sense.

Step By Step

• Read aloud the problem at the top of the page and discuss. Have children relate the illustration and the number sentence to the numbers in the problem.

Model It

• Read aloud Model it. Ask: *How can the addition sentence and the number path help you count on to solve the problem?* Have them draw an arrow on the number path to model the addition and fill in the blanks.

• To check understanding, ask children how they know that "1" answers the question. Guide them to see that if Jan starts with 6 pencils and gives away 1, she has 5 left. Connect this to the original problem.

▶ **Mathematical Discourse 2**

Talk About It

• Read Talk About It aloud. Have children tell what the numbers in the problem mean and how the picture supports the meaning.

• Point out the two number sentences. Ask: *Who is correct? How do you know?* Listen to responses to ensure children understand that 8 is the total number of pencils and that 4 is one of the addends. Discuss why Boom's number sentence shows this and Buzz's does not.

▶ **Hands-On Activity**

SMP TIP Reason Abstractly
Reinforcing the connection between the numbers, the model, and what these represent in the problem helps children contextualize and decontextualize the problem situation. Ask questions to support a focus on how the different representations are related. *(SMP 2)*

 Ready· Mathematics
PRACTICE AND PROBLEM SOLVING

Assign *Practice and Problem Solving* **pages 21–22** after students have completed this section.

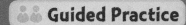
👥👥 Guided Practice

Step By Step

- Read the example problem aloud. Ask: *Why is this a subtraction problem?* [The total is given and you need to find the number in one group.] Invite volunteers to describe what the number path model shows, including how many to count on.

- Problem 1 is a "take from" subtraction problem. Have children explain what is happening and tell what the unknown represents. [the toys Greg put away]

- Ask: *How can you use the circles and tape diagram to model this problem?* One way is to put a bracket under 6 circles to represent the toys that are left. Then count on from 6 to 8, making circles to record the counts.

- The number sentence in Problem 2 starts with an unknown quantity. Ask children what strategy they might use to solve this problem. Guide children to discover that they can use a counting on strategy, using the known addend (5), even if it is not the first addend in the number sentence.

▶ **Mathematical Discourse 1**

SMP TIP Look for Structure
Counting on makes intuitive sense to many children. It also helps them grasp the structure of numbers, such as 6 and 2 within the number 8. You can use number bonds to further reinforce the "hidden" numbers within the numbers in a problem. *(SMP 7)*

▶ **Concept Extension**

 **Ready** Mathematics
PRACTICE AND PROBLEM SOLVING

Assign *Practice and Problem Solving* **pages 23–24** after students have completed this section.

Add and Subtract in Word Problems

There are 8 frogs. Some are big.
5 are small.
How many are big?
Count on __3__.

| 4 | 5 | 6 | 7 | 8 | 9 |

8 − __3__ = 5

__3__ frogs are big.

---

1 Greg has 8 toys. He puts some away.
Now there are 6 toys.
How many toys are put away?

8 − __2__ = 6

🔵🔵🔵🔵🔵🔵

__2__ toys are put away.

---

2 There are 7 balls. 5 are soccer balls.
The rest are kickballs.
How many kickballs are there?

__2__ + 5 = 7

There are __2__ kickballs.

18

▶ **Mathematical Discourse**

1 *When you read a new problem, how would you decide where to put the blank in a number sentence?*

Children need to understand that the unknown quantity in a number sentence can be in any position and that the location of the "missing number" in a number sentence depends on the meaning of the unknown quantity in the problem context. Discuss the meaning of each quantity, how to construct the associated number sentence, including where the blank goes and why.

▶ **Concept Extension**

Use the commutative property of addition.

Materials For each group: Expression Cards (Activity Sheet 41)

- After Problem 2, write the completed number sentence 2 + 5 = 7, and draw a model of 2 balls and 5 balls.

- Write 5 + 2 = 7 under the first number sentence, and draw a model of 5 balls and 2 balls.

- Ask: *Does it matter which number I start with when I add?* [No.] *Why not?* [The total is the same either way.]

- Give each child 1 expression card. Then have children find the child who has the other part of the pair. (There are 16 pairs in Activity Sheet 41, so take care that pairs are handed out.)

- Repeat as time allows.

Practice by Myself
Add and Subtract in Word Problems

3 Emma has 3 beads. She gets more beads.
Now she has 6.
How many new beads does she get?

3 + _3_ = 6

Emma gets _3_ new beads.

4 9 kites are flying. Some fall.
Now there are 7 kites.
How many kites fall?

9 − _2_ = 7

_2_ kites fall.

5 Jimmy picks 7 peppers. 5 are green.
The rest are red.
How many peppers are red?

5 + _2_ = 7

_2_ peppers are red.

`19`

▶ **Mathematical Discourse**

2 *Think about what Problem 3 says. What does the addition sentence mean for this problem? What subtraction sentence could be used to solve the problem?*

The addition sentence is 3 + 3 = 6. Emma has 3 beads and she gets 3 more beads. Now she has 6 beads. The subtraction sentence that can be used is 6 − 3 = 3. Emma has 6 beads now. She started with 3 beads, and she got 3 new ones. There are many ways to describe these situations, so allow several children to present their interpretations. Encourage children to discuss each other's ideas.

Step By Step

- Before children work on this page, review the models used in this lesson. Explain that the models are started for them, and that children can complete them or use some other method they prefer to solve the problem.
- Read each problem aloud, then have children work independently to solve.
- If children have difficulty with the subtraction sentence in Problem 4, guide them to write a related addition sentence.
- Ask volunteers to describe how they solved Problem 5. To check understanding, ask: *What model did you use? Why? How did you know what numbers to write?*
- You may want to take advantage of the opportunity to explore the relationship between addition and subtraction, which is an emphasis of the next lesson. Have children write a related number sentence for each problem (if the given number sentence is addition, they write a subtraction sentence, and vice versa). Use Mathematical Discourse question 2 to relate addition and subtraction contextually.

▶ **Mathematical Discourse 2**

Differentiated Instruction

▶ Quick Check and Remediation

Materials For each child: 9 counters

• Ask children to draw a model and complete the number sentence to solve the following problem: *There are 9 dogs. Some are big. 6 are small. How many are big? 9 − ___ = 6* [9 − 3 = 6]

• For children who are still struggling, use the chart below to guide remediation.

• After providing remediation, check children's understanding using the following problem: *There are 7 crackers. Danny eats some. There are 5 left. 7 − ___ = 5. Danny says he ate 3. Is this correct?* [No.] *Can you correct his mistake?* [He ate 2. 7 − 2 = 5]

If the error is . . .	Children may . . .	To remediate . . .
15	not understand the relationship of the numbers to the meaning of the problem, or the part and whole relationship.	Give children 9 counters to represent the 9 dogs. Emphasize that this is the total. Ask them what else they know from the problem. Then guide children to make a group of 6 counters to show the 6 small dogs. Relate the counters to the number sentence. Have children use the counters to count on from 6, then say how many big dogs there are.
9 or 6	not understand the relationship of the numbers to the meaning of the problem.	Ask what each number in the problem and what each number in the number sentence represents. Then have children tell what's missing or what they need to find. Guide children to answer these questions and have them count on to find the missing number.
a number that is not 9, 6, or 3	not have counted on correctly.	Review the meaning of the numbers in the problem. Ask: *How do you know what number to start with to count on? How do you know when to stop? How do you find how many dogs are big?* Then ask children to try the problem again.

▶ Hands-On Activity

Count on to solve subtraction problems.

Materials For display: bag, cubes

• Put some number of cubes in the bag. Invite one child to help you with the activity.

• Tell a story: *This bag has [number] cubes in it. [Child's name] takes some out.* (Child removes and conceals some cubes. Then you dump the bag.) *There are [number] cubes left. How many did [child's name] take?*

• To answer the question, children count on from the visible cubes to reach the total.

• Reveal the hidden cubes. Repeat the story with different numbers.

▶ Challenge Activity

Retell a subtraction story as addition, then solve.

Materials For each child: index cards, counters (counters are optional)

• Write subtraction stories on cards, with the missing number being subtracted (e.g., 7 puppets: some are people, 5 are animals).

• Have children retell the story as an addition story, write a number sentence, and solve (e.g., 5 puppets are animals, some are people and there are 7 in all. 5 + ___ = 7, so 2 puppets are people). Children may use counters.

• Discuss how the stories and the number sentences are related and generalize how addition and subtraction are related.

Teacher Notes

Teacher-Toolbox.com

Overview

Assign the Lesson 3 Quiz and have children work independently to complete it.

Use the results of the quiz to assess children's understanding of the content of the lesson and to identify areas for reteaching. See the Lesson Pacing Guide at the beginning of the lesson and the Differentiated Instruction activities for suggested instructional resources.

Tested Skills

Assesses 1.OA.A.1

Problems on this quiz require children to be able to solve addition and subtraction word problems with the unknown in different positions. Children will also need to be familiar with using the counting on strategy to add and subtract.

Ready® **Mathematics**

Lesson 3 Quiz Answer Key

Name _____

Solve.

1. 7 children are on the swings. More get on.
   Now there are 9 children on the swings.
   How many more children got on the swings?

   $7 + \underline{2} = 9$

5	6	7	8	9	10

   $\underline{2}$ more children got on the swings.

2. Carl has 9 hats. He gives away some hats.
   Now he has 6 hats.
   How many hats does he give away?

   $9 - \underline{3} = 6$

   Carl gives away $\underline{3}$ hats.

3. There are 7 apples. 4 are red.
   The rest are green.
   How many apples are green?

   $7 = \underline{3} + 4$

   $\underline{3}$ apples are green.

Grade 1 **Lesson 3** Add and Subtract in Word Problems   1

Common Misconceptions and Errors

Errors may result if students:

• confuse an addend with the sum or a part with the whole.

• always add the two quantities given in the problem.

• assume the unknown is always either the sum or the difference.

• do not count on correctly.

Name _____

Solve.

4 There are 7 dogs. Some are brown.
5 are black.
How many dogs are brown?

$7 - \underline{2} = 5$

There are _2_ brown dogs.

5 Emma has 6 shirts. She buys more shirts.
Now she has 8 shirts.
How many shirts does she buy?

$8 = 6 + \underline{2}$

Emma buys _2_ shirts.

Grade 1 Lesson 3 Add and Subtract in Word Problems   2 ©Curriculum Associates, LLC
Copying permitted for classroom use.

Lesson 4
Understand Missing Addends

CCSS Focus

Domain
Operations and Algebraic Thinking

Cluster
B. Understand and apply properties of operations and the relationship between addition and subtraction.

Standard
1.OA.B.4 Understand subtraction as an unknown-addend problem. *For example, subtract 10 – 8 by finding the number that makes 10 when added to 8.*

Additional Standards
1.OA.C.6, 1.OA.D.8 (See page B3 for full text.)

Standards for Mathematical Practice (SMP)
1 Make sense of problems and persevere in solving them.
2 Reason abstractly and quantitatively.
3 Construct viable arguments and critique the reasoning of others.
4 Model with mathematics.
7 Look for and make use of structure.
8 Look for and express regularity in repeated reasoning.

Lesson Objectives

Content Objectives
• Understand the relationship between addition and subtraction.
• Write a missing addend sentence for a corresponding subtraction sentence.
• Connect addition and subtraction sentences to a number bond.
• Relate subtraction sentences and missing addend sentences to a problem situation.

Language Objectives
• Draw dots and write numbers in number bonds to represent addition and subtraction sentences.
• Use counters to model addition and subtraction sentences.
• Listen to the ideas of others discussing how addition and subtraction are alike and how they are different and ask questions to clarify.

Prerequisite Skills

• Add and subtract within 10.
• Model addition and subtraction problems with number sentences.

Lesson Vocabulary

There is no new vocabulary. Review the following key terms.

• **addend** a number being added.
• **total** a number found as the result of adding.

Learning Progression

In Kindergarten children solve addition and subtraction problems within 10. They also decompose numbers to 10 using objects or drawings.

In Grade 1 children fluently add and subtract within 10 by applying strategies and by recognizing the relationship between addition and subtraction.

In this lesson children explore the concept of missing addends through the visual model of a number bond and by utilizing addition to solve a subtraction

problem. Connecting a number bond to its corresponding number sentences is achieved through hands-on exploration and visual models, and by engaging children in open-ended problem solving.

In Grade 2 children continue to use the relationship between addition and subtraction as one strategy for developing fluency with addition and subtraction within 20. They also learn to apply mental strategies and solve problems with the unknown in all positions.

Lesson Pacing Guide

Whole Class Instruction

Day 1
45–60 minutes

Introduction
Use What You Know
- Explore It *25 min*
- Try It *20 min*

Day 2
45–60 minutes

Modeled Instruction
Explore Together
- Opening Question *5 min*
- Think *10 min*
- Talk About It *15 min*
- Hands-On Activity *15 min*

Practice and Problem Solving
Assign pages 27–28.

Day 3
45–60 minutes

Guided Instruction
Explore Together
- Hands-On Problem *5 min*
- Problems 1–2 *20 min*
- Talk About It *10 min*
- Concept Extension *10 min*

Practice and Problem Solving
Assign pages 29–30.

Day 4
45–60 minutes

Guided Practice
Connect It
- Problems 3–5 *15 min*

Independent Practice
Show What I Know
- Problem 6 *15 min*
- Intervention, On-Level, or Challenge Activity *15 min*

Practice and Problem Solving
Assign pages 31–32.

Teacher-Toolbox: Lesson Quiz
Lesson 4 Quiz

Materials for Lesson Activities

Per child: 8 small objects such as dried beans, 10 counters, 1 cup, red and blue crayons, 1 sheet of colored paper
Activity Sheet 2, Activity Sheet 3*

Per pair: None

For display: None

*Used for more than one activity.

Small Group Differentiation

Teacher-Toolbox.com

Reteach
Ready Prerequisite Lessons *45–90 min*

Grade K
- Lesson 18 Add Within 10
- Lesson 19 Subtract Within 10

Teacher-led Activities
Tools for Instruction *15–20 min*

Grade 1 *(Lesson 4)*
- Find Missing Addends for Sums to 10

Student-led Activities
Math Center Activities *30–40 min*

Grade K *(Lessons 18 and 19)*
- K.24 Tell Addition Stories
- K.25 Subtract and Match

Grade 1 *(Lesson 4)*
- 1.12 Missing Addend Number Bonds
- 1.13 Missing Addend Trains

Personalized Learning

i-Ready.com

Independent
i-Ready Lessons* *10–20 min*

Grade 1 *(Lesson 4)*
- Part 1: Addition and Subtraction Fact Families
- Part 2: Addition and Subtraction Fact Families

* *i-Ready lessons may be updated during the 2016–2017 school year. Updated references will be on the Teacher-Toolbox.*

Introduction

Activity Show Missing Addends in Number Bonds

Objective

Explore missing addends and number bonds

Materials for each child

• 8 small objects such as dried beans

Overview

Children explore the concept of missing addends by modeling a problem with dried beans on a number bond mat.

Step By Step

Explore It

Pose the problem.

• Say: *8 rabbits are eating lunch. Some rabbits eat carrots and some eat lettuce. 5 rabbits eat carrots. How many rabbits eat lettuce?*

Use familiar strategies to model the problem.

• Encourage children to think of what they would do to solve the problem. Remind them that there are many ways to solve.

• Invite volunteers to share their solution strategies with the class. Expect children to suggest counting on and subtracting to determine the missing addend. Listen to all strategies and validate correct reasoning.

Use a number bond to model the problem.

• Ask children to place 8 beans in the top section of their number bond mats. On the board, display a number bond with 8 circles in the top box and the bottom sections labeled "Carrots" and "Lettuce."

• Ask children to tell how they might show that 5 of the 8 rabbits eat carrots. Guide them to move 5 of the beans from the top portion of the mat to the section labeled "Carrots." Mimic this action on the board by erasing 5 circles in the top box and drawing 5 circles in the "Carrots" section.

Explore It

8 rabbits are eating lunch.
Some rabbits eat carrots and some eat lettuce.
5 rabbits eat carrots. How many rabbits eat lettuce?

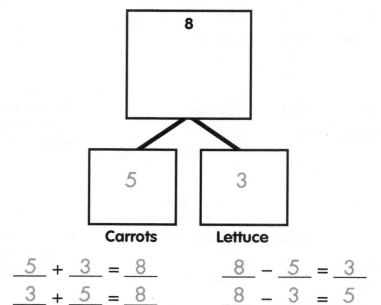

$$\underline{5} + \underline{3} = \underline{8} \qquad \underline{8} - \underline{5} = \underline{3}$$
$$\underline{3} + \underline{5} = \underline{8} \qquad \underline{8} - \underline{3} = \underline{5}$$

20

• Discuss how the number bond can help them find the number of rabbits that eat lettuce. Have children move the 3 remaining beans from the top box to the "Lettuce" section. Do the same with the number bond on the board.

• Have children count the number of beans in each box and complete the number bond by recording the numbers.

• Help children analyze the structure of the number bond by asking questions such as: *Why is the number 8 in the top box? What can you tell me about the numbers in the bottom boxes?*

• Then ask children to identify number sentences that model the problem. Record them on the board. Discuss how each sentence does or does not model the problem. Guide children to identify two addition and two subtraction sentences using the numbers 5, 3, and 8. Erase all but these four number sentences and have children record them on the Student Book page.

• Have children compare the numbers in the number bond to those in the number sentences on the board. Lead them to see that all sentences have the same three numbers but in different orders and involve addition or subtraction.

Use What You Know
Understand Missing Addends

 Try It

7 mice are eating lunch.
Some mice eat nuts and some eat seeds.
3 mice eat nuts. How many mice eat seeds?

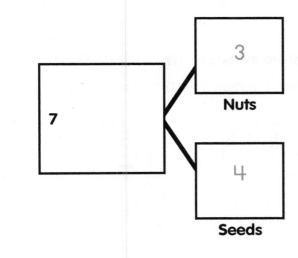

$\underline{7} = \underline{3} + \underline{4}$ $\underline{3} = \underline{7} - \underline{4}$
$\underline{7} = \underline{4} + \underline{3}$ $\underline{4} = \underline{7} - \underline{3}$

21

Step By Step

Try It

Pose the problem.

- Say: *7 mice are eating lunch. Some mice eat nuts and some eat seeds. 3 mice eat nuts. How many mice eat seeds?*

Use a number bond and equations to model the problem.

- Have children use beans and the number bond workmat on the Student Book page to find the number of mice that eat seeds.

- Then have children write two addition and two subtraction sentences using the numbers in their number bond.

- Look for children who write only one addition and one subtraction sentence and help them see how the parts of the number bond can be arranged in different ways to form four number sentences.

Share strategies.

- Invite children to share and demonstrate the strategies they used to solve the problem.

- Ask: *How is the number bond for this problem similar to the number bond in the first problem? How is it different?*

- Ask children to identify number sentences that model the problem. Record them on the board. Discuss how each number sentence does or does not model the problem and ensure that children identify two addition and two subtraction sentences that do model the problem.

- Ask: *How are these number sentences similar to the number sentences we wrote for the first problem? How are they different?*

- Make sure children recognize that all 4 number sentences have the same three numbers in different orders and involve addition or subtraction.

👥 Modeled Instruction

Step By Step

• Read the question at the top of the page. Remind children they used counting on to subtract before. Ask: *Do you think it is easier to add or subtract? Why?* Engage children in a discussion of the similarities and differences between addition and subtraction. Encourage them to suggest answers to the question: *How can adding help me subtract?*

Think

• Read through the Think question. Allow children time to examine the number bonds. It may be helpful for some children to circle two groups of dots in the top portion of the number bond that correspond to the dots in the two lower portions.

• Ask children to identify the number bond that would help them find 5 − 4. Discuss why each number bond can or cannot be used.

▶ **Hands-On Activity**

Talk About It

• Ask the Talk About It question. Have children talk to a partner and decide what addition sentence they could write and explain why. Guide them to think "4 plus what numbers equals 5?" as they discuss and answer the Talk About It question. Lead children to recognize that combining the parts at the bottom of the number bond results in the number at the top.

▶ **Mathematical Discourse 1**

SMP TIP Critique Reasoning
Asking children to evaluate the ideas of others builds an understanding of reasonableness of strategies and solutions and helps them avoid misconceptions and common errors. (*SMP 3*)

📦 Ready· Mathematics
PRACTICE AND PROBLEM SOLVING

Assign *Practice and Problem Solving* **pages 27–28** after students have completed this section.

Understand Missing Addends

(How can adding help you subtract?)

$$5 - 4 = \;?$$

💭 Think **What are the two parts?** ··········
Which number bond shows 5 − 4? Circle.

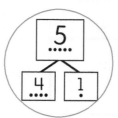

💬 Talk About It ··················
What addition sentence helps you find 5 − 4?

22

▶ **Mathematical Discourse**

1 *Shawn says that 5 + 1 is an addition expression for the number bond that includes 5, 4, and 1. What do you think? Why might he think that?*
Children should notice that this does not fit with the number bond. Although a 5 and a 1 are both present, 5 represents the whole and 1 represents a part.

▶ **Hands-On Activity**
Model number bonds with counters.

Materials For each child: counters, Number Bond Mat (Activity Sheet 3)

• Have children use counters and number bond mats to model each of the number bonds on the page by placing 5 counters in the top and moving the correct number of counters into each section.

• Make sure children recognize that each of the number bonds represents a different way to show 5.

Explore Together
Understand Missing Addends

 Find 7 − 3.

Use 7 counters. → Put the rest in → Write the
Keep 3.   a cup.   answer.

$3 + \underline{4} = 7$

$7 - 3 = \underline{4}$

---

① **Find 7 − 5.**

Draw and write.

$5 + \underline{2} = 7$

$7 - 5 = \underline{2}$

② **Find 7 − 4.**

Draw and write.

$4 + \underline{3} = 7$

$7 - 4 = \underline{3}$

💬 **Talk About It** ··

How can you add to find 6 − 4?

`23`

▶ **Concept Extension**

Analyze structure in number bonds.

- Show a number bond using the numbers 3, 4, 7. Point out that there are four sentences that can be written for this number bond.

- Ask: *Do you think there will **always** be four number sentences for a number bond? Can you think of a number bond that has only two number sentences?* Allow children to think about this briefly. If no one suggests an answer, demonstrate how a number bond with 6, 3, 3 includes only two sentences.

- You may want to challenge children to find other number bonds where only two sentences can be written and explain why.

▶ **Mathematical Discourse**

2 *I see that [child's name] wrote 5 + 2 for his number sentence and [child's name] wrote 2 + 5 for her number sentence. How can they both be right?*

Children should recognize that the order of addends does not affect the sum.

Step By Step

- Provide each child with 7 counters and a cup. Read aloud the directions for the Hands-On Problem and have children model this situation with counters.

- Read Problem 1. Ask: *How many counters do you keep? How many do you put in the cup?* [Keep 5 and put 2 in the cup.]

- Connect this problem to a number bond. Allow children to work with counters on Number Bond Mats (Activity Sheet 3) and then write a number sentence.

▶ **Mathematical Discourse 2**

- Have children work with a partner to complete Problem 2. Compare the results with the example problem. Ask: *How many counters are in and how many are out of the cup in the example problem? What about Problem 2?* Lead children to recognize that in both situations, 7 is broken into groups of 3 and 4 and that when combined, the result is always 7.

SMP TIP Look for Structure

To reinforce the structure of operations, demonstrate that the commutative property applies to addition but not to subtraction. Show a complete fact family. Guide children to see that in the two addition facts, the numbers on each side of the equal sign are the same, but this is not true with subtraction. (*SMP 7*)

Talk About It

- Have children work with a partner to discuss and solve the Talk About It question. Share results and connect to a number bond.

▶ **Concept Extension**

📦 **Ready** **Mathematics**
PRACTICE AND PROBLEM SOLVING

Assign *Practice and Problem Solving* **pages 29–30** after students have completed this section.

Step By Step

- Discuss each **Connect It** problem as a class.

Show

- The number bond in this problem includes only numbers. Some children may still need the visual support of dots and may find it helpful to draw them.

- Have children share the number sentences they wrote. Discuss why there are two possible sentences for each operation.

- If time permits, you may want to draw several number bonds on the board and ask children to think of other numbers that have a total of 8. Record their suggestions.

Reason

- Read the problem aloud. Encourage children to use a strategy that makes sense to them to solve the problem. You might suggest drawing a picture or diagram and writing a number sentence.

- Have children share their strategies and solutions with the class, emphasizing that there are many ways to approach problems like this.

- If children provide a number sentence solution to the problem, ask: *Why does the number sentence you wrote make sense?* Listen for children to relate the number sentence to the situation. Some may think in terms of subtraction and some in terms of addition. They should be able to justify the sentence they wrote and be confident that it is an accurate representation of the problem.

Explain

- Read the problem aloud and ask children how this problem is like the counters and cup activity they did on the previous page.

Understand Missing Addends

3 **Show** Write a subtraction sentence. Then write an addition sentence.

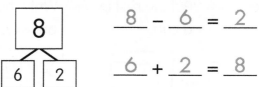

$$\underline{8} - \underline{6} = \underline{2}$$

$$\underline{6} + \underline{2} = \underline{8}$$

4 **Reason** There are 8 cats. 5 are black. The rest are gray. How many are gray?

Show how you solve.

Possible work: $5 + \underline{\quad} = 8$

$5 + 3 = 8$

3 are gray.

5 **Explain** There are 5 beads. 4 are on the table. The rest are in a cup.

▸ Buzz says there are 9 beads in the cup.
▸ Do you agree? Why? Why not?

Possible explanation: I don't agree. There are 5 beads in all. So the cup has fewer than 5 beads.

- Allow children time to think about the problem and talk about it with a partner. Tell them to make a plan for "proving" their decision by using drawings or counters.

- Invite volunteer pairs to share their ideas about the error Buzz made. Encourage articulation of mathematical reasoning using questions such as: *Why did you put 5 in the top section of the number bond? How do you think Buzz got 9 as the answer? Why doesn't it make sense to add 5 and 4?*

- Ask children to correct Buzz's answer.

Ready · **Mathematics**
PRACTICE AND PROBLEM SOLVING

Assign *Practice and Problem Solving* **pages 31–32** after students have completed this section.

Show What I Know
Understand Missing Addends

6 **Think about missing addends.**

A: Color some triangles red and some blue.
Complete the number bond. Write a subtraction
and an addition sentence.

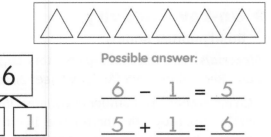

Possible answer:

$6 - 1 = 5$

$5 + 1 = 6$

B: Color a different number of triangles red and blue.
Complete the number bond. Write a subtraction
and an addition sentence.

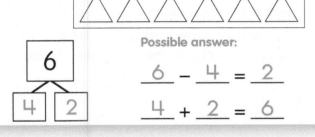

Possible answer:

$6 - 4 = 2$

$4 + 2 = 6$

25

Step By Step

- Tell children that they will complete this page independently.

- Read the directions aloud, making sure children understand what they are expected to do.

- For Part A, provide children with a red and blue crayon or marker. Make sure they understand that there is not just one correct way to color the triangles, so their number bonds and number sentences may be different from others in the class.

- In Part B, children color the triangles using a different combination of blue and red.

- Watch to make sure children complete all parts of the problems, including coloring the triangles, completing the number bonds, and writing the number sentences.

Scoring Rubrics

Expectations for 4–3 Points

Points	Expectations
4	The child: • colors triangles appropriately to show two different partners of 6. • correctly completes the number bonds and writes an addition and subtraction number sentence that corresponds to each number bond.
3	The child: • colors triangles appropriately to show two different partners of 6. • correctly completes the number bonds but may have one or two minor errors in the number sentences.

Expectations for 2–0 Points

Points	Expectations
2	The child: • colors triangles to show partners of 6 but may not have shown two different partners. • completes the number bonds and number sentences with some errors.
1	The child: • colors the triangles but the number bonds and number sentences are inaccurate and/or incomplete.
0	The child: • colors the triangles but does not attempt to complete the number bonds and number sentences.

Differentiated Instruction

▶ Intervention Activity

Connect number bonds to number sentences.

Materials For each child: Number Bond Mat (Activity Sheet 3), 10 counters

- Distribute materials to children.
- Provide children with related open number sentences, such as:

  $6 - 2 = $ ___ and $2 + $ ___ $= 6$,
  $8 - 5 = $ ___ and $5 + $ ___ $= 8$,
  $7 + $ ___ $= 9$ and $9 - 7 = $ ___ .

- Have children model the related number sentences using the counters and Number Bond Mat (Activity Sheet 3). They then complete the number sentences.

▶ On-Level Activity

Build number bonds.

Materials For each child: 10 counters, cup, Number Bond Recording Sheet (Activity Sheet 2), colored paper

- Children choose a number of counters (5–10) to place in the cup. They write this number in the top of a number bond on the recording sheet.
- Children empty the cup so some counters land on the paper and some land off of the paper.
- In the number bond, they record the numbers of counters on and off the paper.
- Children then write number sentences that correspond with the number bond.
- Repeat until the recording sheet is full. If the result of a "toss" is a duplicate, the child makes the toss again.

▶ Challenge Activity

Make number bonds to find number partners.

Challenge children to find all the ways to create a number bond for the numbers 2–5.

- Have children make a simple table as shown to record their work.
- Ask children to find all the ways to create a number bond for the number 2, then fill in the table as shown.

Note: For this activity, children should count partners with the same addends in a different order as two different ways. They should also include partners where 0 is an addend. So, for the number 2, there are 3 ways: $0 + 2$, $1 + 1$, $2 + 0$.

- Provide children with scratch paper or whiteboards and demonstrate how they can make a quick draw of number bonds to help them keep track of the different ways to make each number.

Number	How many ways?
2	3

- When completed, ask children to find a pattern. They should notice that for each consecutive number, one more number bond can be made. Some may notice that the number of ways is one more (if zeros are included) than the number of counters used. Ask children to predict whether this pattern continues with numbers greater than 5. Make sure children justify their conjecture.

Teacher Notes

Teacher-Toolbox.com

Overview

Assign the Lesson 4 Quiz and have children work independently to complete it.

Use the results of the quiz to assess children's understanding of the content of the lesson and to identify areas for reteaching. See the Lesson Pacing Guide at the beginning of the lesson and the Differentiated Instruction activities for suggested instructional resources.

Tested Skills

Assesses 1.OA.B.4

Problems on this quiz require children to be able to write a subtraction sentence and its related missing addend sentence based on a problem situation and/or a number bond. Children will also need to be familiar with adding and subtracting within 10 and representing addition and subtraction problems with number sentences.

Ready® Mathematics

Lesson 4 Quiz Answer Key

Name _____

Solve.

1 Color some triangles red and some blue.
Complete the number bond.
Write a subtraction and an addition sentence.

Possible answer:

$$\underline{7} - \underline{3} = \underline{4}$$
$$\underline{4} + \underline{3} = \underline{7}$$

2 Write a subtraction sentence.
Then write an addition sentence.

Possible answer:

$$\underline{9} - \underline{6} = \underline{3}$$
$$\underline{6} + \underline{3} = \underline{9}$$

Grade 1 Lesson 4 *Understand Missing Addends*

1

©Curriculum Associates, LLC
Copying permitted for classroom use.

Common Misconceptions and Errors

Errors may result if children:

• incorrectly read or complete a number bond.

• always add the two quantities given in a problem.

• confuse an addend with the sum or a part with the whole.

• do not understand the relationship between addition and subtraction.

Name _____

Solve.

3 Write a subtraction sentence.
Then write an addition sentence.

Possible answer:

$$\underline{1} = \underline{8} - \underline{7}$$

$$\underline{8} = \underline{7} + \underline{1}$$

4 There are 5 stickers. 3 are blue.
The rest are yellow.
How many stickers are yellow?

__2__ stickers are yellow.

5 There are 9 balloons. Some are big.
7 are small.
How many balloons are big?

__2__ balloons are big.

  2

Lesson 5
Subtract to Compare in Word Problems

CCSS Focus

Domain
Operations and Algebraic Thinking

Cluster
A. Represent and solve problems involving addition and subtraction.

Standard
1.OA.A.1 Use addition and subtraction within 20 to solve word problems involving situations of adding to, taking from, putting together, taking apart, and comparing, with unknowns in all positions, e.g., by using objects, drawings, and equations with a symbol for the unknown number to represent the problem.

Additional Standards
1.OA.C.6, 1.OA.D.8 (See page B3 for full text.)

Standards for Mathematical Practice (SMP)
2 Reason abstractly and quantitatively.

4 Model with mathematics.

Lesson Objectives

Content Objectives
- Understand a comparison problem situation as subtraction and/or related addition.
- Compare two amounts, determining which is more or less and identifying how many more or less.
- Write and solve subtraction and addition sentences to solve comparison word problems.

Language Objectives
- Orally define and use the key mathematical terms *compare*, *more*, and *fewer* when communicating with a partner.
- Complete a tape diagram to show how a comparison word problem relates to a subtraction sentence.
- Draw lines to align objects and identify how many more or fewer objects are in one group.

Prerequisite Skills
- Count on to subtract.
- Add and subtract in word problems.
- Find the missing addend.

Lesson Vocabulary
- **compare** to decide if amounts or sizes are greater than, less than, or equal to each other.
- **fewer** indicating a lesser quantity or amount.
- **more** indicating a greater quantity or amount.

Review the following key terms.
- **subtract** to take objects away from a group or to compare groups.
- **subtraction sentence** one number is subtracted from another in a sentence with symbols and numbers.

Learning Progression

In Kindergarten children compare groups of objects and identify which has more or less, without finding the difference between the numbers. They also compare written numerals from 1 to 10. Children understand subtraction as taking away and taking apart.

In Grade 1 children understand subtraction as taking away, taking apart, or comparing.

In this lesson children solve comparison word problems. They use models that show one-to-one correspondence to find the difference between two quantities.

In Grade 2 children solve subtraction word problems that involve take away, take apart, or compare situations. They extend subtraction to quantities within 100 and they solve two-step problems.

Lesson Pacing Guide

Whole Class Instruction

Day 1
45–60 minutes

Introduction

Use What You Know
- Explore It *25 min*
- Try It *20 min*

Day 2
45–60 minutes

Modeled Instruction

Explore Together
- Example Problem *10 min*
- Model It *15 min*
- Fluency Practice *20 min*

Practice and Problem Solving
Assign pages 35–36.

Day 3
45–60 minutes

Guided Instruction

Learn Together
- Example Problem *10 min*
- Model It *15 min*
- Talk About It *20 min*

Practice and Problem Solving
Assign pages 37–38.

Day 4
45–60 minutes

Guided Practice

Practice Together
- Example Problem *10 min*
- Problems 1–2 *20 min*
- Hands-On Activity *15 min*

Practice and Problem Solving
Assign pages 39–40.

Day 5
45–60 minutes

Independent Practice

Practice by Myself
- Problems 3–5 *15 min*
- Visual Model *10 min*
- Quick Check and Remediation *10 min*
- Hands-On or Challenge Activity *10 min*

Teacher-Toolbox: Lesson Quiz
Lesson 5 Quiz

Materials for Lesson Activities

Per child: 20 connecting cubes, 8 two-color counters, 3 groups of up to 7 objects each (such as books, crayons, and play money) Activity Sheet 4, Activity Sheet 35

Per pair: none

For display: 4 umbrellas, masking tape

Small Group Differentiation

Teacher-Toolbox.com

Reteach
Ready Prerequisite Lessons *45–90 min*

Grade K
- Lesson 19 Subtract Within 10
- Lesson 20 Practice Facts to 5

Teacher-led Activities
Tools for Instruction *15–20 min*

Grade 1 *(Lesson 5)*
- Subtraction Number Sentences

Student-led Activities
Math Center Activities *30–40 min*

Grade K *(Lessons 19 and 20)*
- K.25 Subtract and Match
- K.26 Add and Move
- K.27 Solve and Color

Grade 1 *(Lesson 5)*
- 1.11 Subtract to Compare

Personalized Learning

i-Ready.com

Independent
i-Ready Lessons* *10–20 min*

Grade 1 *(Lesson 5)*
- Subtraction Concepts: Comparison
- Counting with One-to-One Correspondence
- Comparing Sets

* i-Ready lessons may be updated during the 2016–2017 school year. Updated references will be on the Teacher-Toolbox.

Activity Act Out a Comparison Word Problem

Objective

Act out a "subtract to compare" word problem and find the difference.

Materials for each child

• 8 two-color counters (optional)

Materials for display

• 4 umbrellas

Overview

Children act out a "subtract to compare" word problem. They discuss the meaning of the comparison and use a matching strategy to find the difference. Then they apply the strategy to another problem.

Step By Step

Explore It

Pose a problem.

• Say: *Suppose it's raining outside. Imagine that 6 animals are getting ready to go outside in the rain. But they have only 4 umbrellas! We can figure out how many animals will not have an umbrella.*

Match the quantities.

• Remind children that they know how to compare two quantities to find out which is more and which is less. Explain that you can also find out how many more or how many less one number is than the other.

• Elicit that they can compare the umbrellas and animals by matching up 1 umbrella for each animal.

• Ask: *Are there more animals or umbrellas?* [more animals]

• Have children circle the row with more items.

• Direct children's attention to the next problem on the Student Book page. Ask them to circle the row that shows fewer.

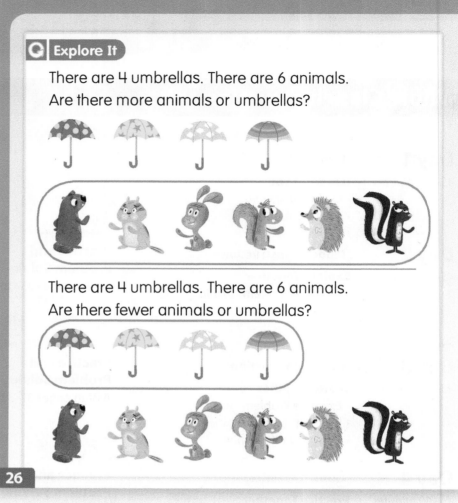

Act out the problem.

• Invite 6 children to act out the problem. Set out 4 umbrellas (or pieces of paper that can be used to represent umbrellas).

• Restate the problem: *There are 6 of you. There are 4 umbrellas. Are there more umbrellas or more of you? How many of you will not get an umbrella?* Have the children acting out the problem raise their hands one at a time while the class counts to 6. Ask a volunteer to count the 4 umbrellas.

• Have the 6 children each extend a hand. Give an umbrella to each of the first 4 children.

Find the difference.

• Ask: *Are there more umbrellas or more children?* [more children] Ask: *How many children get an umbrella?* [4]

• Ask the class how they can determine the number of children who do not get an umbrella. Discuss ways of finding the solution, such as counting on, counting the children without umbrellas, adding (4 and how many more make 6), and subtracting (6 children minus the 4 who have umbrellas). Invite volunteers to demonstrate finding the solution. Ask: *How many children did not get an umbrella?* [2] *How many animals will not have an umbrella?* [2]

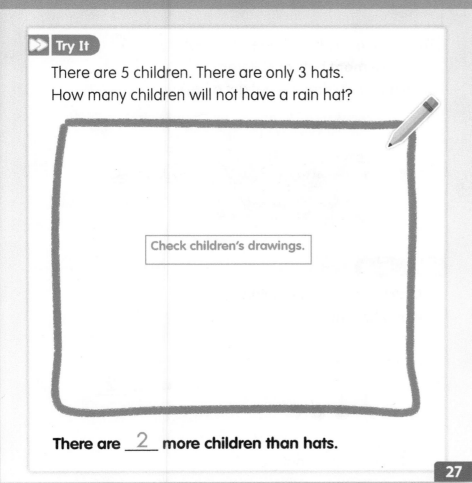

▶▶ Try It

There are 5 children. There are only 3 hats. How many children will not have a rain hat?

Check children's drawings.

There are __2__ more children than hats.

27

Step By Step

Try It

Repeat the problem.

- Read aloud the problem from the Student Book page: *There are 5 children. There are only 3 hats. How many children will not have a rain hat?*

Match the quantities.

- Have children draw a picture to represent the problem. Encourage them to use shapes such as triangles and circles to show the number of hats and the number of children.

- Remind children of the strategies they can use to compare the number of hats and the number of children

- Ask: *Are there more hats or children?* [more children]

Find the difference.

- Allow children to choose a strategy and work on their own to determine how many more children there are than hats. Have them write their answer on the Student Book page.

Lead the class in discussion.

- Ask them how this problem was alike and how it was different from the problem they acted out. Have children share their strategies.

- As children talk about and demonstrate solution strategies, you may find that some can simply add or subtract to find the solution. Allow others to count as necessary to solve the problem. Those children who have difficulty making the connection between comparing and one-to-one correspondence may need the support of concrete materials, such as two-color counters.

Modeled Instruction

Step By Step

- Begin by asking children what they learned or remember from the Activity in the Introduction. Elicit that the problems asked children to compare the number of animals and the number of umbrellas, and the number of children and number of rain hats.

- Read aloud the problem at the top of the page. Ask a volunteer to describe the situation. Have the class count the children and then count the hats.

- Discuss what it means to compare: to see how quantities are alike or different, or in math terms, to see which set has more or which has less. Have children discuss whether there are more hats or more children.

- Read aloud the last question. Ask: *What do we need to find out to answer how many children do not get a hat?* [How many more children there are than hats.] Ask: *How can we find out?* Allow children to suggest a variety of strategies.

Model It

- Read Model It aloud. Discuss how this model is like the action of matching the hats and the children. Have children describe what the model shows.

- Use Mathematical Discourse question 1 to introduce and discuss the subtraction number sentence.

▶ **Mathematical Discourse 1**

- Then ask: *How will you solve this subtraction problem?* Children may count on or may use other methods. Have them explain or demonstrate their approaches.

▶ **Fluency Practice**

 Mathematics
PRACTICE AND PROBLEM SOLVING

Assign *Practice and Problem Solving* **pages 35–36** after students have completed this section.

Subtract to Compare in Word Problems

There are 6 children. There are 4 hats.
Are there **more** hats or children?
How many children do not get a hat?

▦ Model It   Find 6 − 4. ••••••••••••••••••••••

Match 4 hats with 4 children.
4 and how many more make 6?

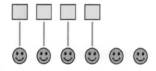

6 − 4 = __2__

28   __2__ children do not get a hat.

▶ **Mathematical Discourse**

1 *What number sentence would you use to solve this problem? Why?*

Children might suggest either subtraction (6 − 4 = ?) or missing-addend addition (4 + ? = 6) to represent the comparison.

Children who use addition may think of this as: "4 children with hats, plus how many children who don't get hats, equals 6 children." Children who use subtraction may think of this as: "6 children, minus 4 who get hats, equals the number who don't get hats." Have children explain their reasoning for preferring one approach or the other.

▶ **Fluency Practice**
What's missing?

Materials For each child: Number Bond Practice to 5 (Activity Sheet 4)

Have children fill in the missing numbers. You may want to review the completed activity sheets and ask children to say or write corresponding number sentences.

Learn Together
Subtract to Compare in Word Problems

There are 5 pieces of cheese and 8 mice.
Are there **fewer** mice or pieces of cheese?
How many mice do not get cheese?

⊞ Model It Find 8 − 5.

Start with 5.
5 and how many more make 8?

8 − 5 = _3_

💬 Talk About It Who is right? How do you know?

How many fewer sticks than skates
are there?

Buzz says there are 3 fewer sticks.
Boom says there is 1 fewer stick.

29

Step By Step

- Read the problem. Discuss how the illustration represents the problem.

- Introduce the word *fewer* and discuss its meaning. Ask: *Which is less, the number of mice or the number of pieces of cheese?* Guide children to understand that *how many fewer* and *how many less* are other ways to compare two quantities.

▶ **English Language Learners**

- Ask how this problem is like the previous problem and how it is different. Help children recognize that whether the question involves *fewer* or *more*, the same solution process can be used.

Model It

- Read aloud Model It. Ask how the model is like the one on the first page. Then ask what the numbers in the number sentence mean and how they relate to the problem. Have children work in pairs to solve and then share their solutions with the class.

▶ **Mathematical Discourse 2**

Talk About It

- Read Talk About It. Encourage children to discuss with a partner what the illustration shows. Ask: *Who is right, Buzz or Boom? How do you know?* Discuss responses.

▶ **Mathematical Discourse 3**

> **SMP TIP Model with Mathematics**
> Encourage children to model comparisons by aligning numbers of objects to visually show *how many more* and *how many fewer*. Have children explain what the modeled objects mean in the context of the problem. *(SMP 4)*

 Ready Mathematics
PRACTICE AND PROBLEM SOLVING

Assign *Practice and Problem Solving* **pages 37–38** after students have completed this section.

▶ **English Language Learners**

Some children may think that *less* and *more* have the same meaning. Explain that *less* and *fewer* mean *not as many as*. They are the opposite of *more*. Use pictures or objects to provide practice with *less* and *fewer*.

▶ **Mathematical Discourse**

2 *What does the model in Model It show?*
There are more mice than pieces of cheese. There are 3 more mice than there are pieces of cheese. 3 mice don't get a piece of cheese.

3 *What is Buzz's mistake in this problem?*
Children might suggest that Buzz does not understand what *fewer* means. 3 is the number of sticks, not how many fewer sticks there are. The number of sticks is 1 fewer than the number of skates, because 3 is 1 less than 4.

👥 Guided Practice

Step By Step

- Read the example problem aloud. Explain that the problem tells us which child sees fewer birds [Nan] and asks us to find *how many* fewer. Ask how the number sentence represents the problem situation.

- Direct attention to the tape diagram. Discuss how this is like the previous visual models and how it is different. Ask the class which part shows the birds Nan sees, which shows the birds Cam sees, and how they can tell. Ask what the "?" represents. [How many fewer birds Nan sees.]

- Explain that in Problem 1, children need to complete the diagram. Allow children time to work, then have some children demonstrate how they completed the diagram and answered the question.

- Read Problem 2 aloud. Have children work in pairs to fill in the tape diagram. Then have them explain how they got their results.

- Discuss the fact that children must find how many more in both problems. Challenge children to tell how many fewer red markers and bananas there are. Guide them to understand that the "more number" and "fewer number" are the same.

▶ **Mathematical Discourse 1**

▶ **Hands-On Activity**

> **SMP TIP Model with Mathematics**
> Help children understand that they can use a variety of models to show a single situation. Describe a comparison situation and assign different groups a type of model to make to represent the problem. Discuss what is the same and different about each model, and how the models relate to the subtraction sentence. *(SMP 4)*

 **Ready** Mathematics
PRACTICE AND PROBLEM SOLVING

Assign *Practice and Problem Solving* **pages 39–40** after students have completed this section.

Subtract to Compare in Word Problems

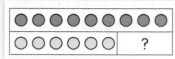

> Nan sees 6 birds. Cam sees 9 birds. How many fewer birds does Nan see?
>
> **9 − 6 =** __3__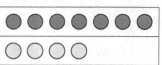
>
> Nan sees __3__ fewer birds.

1 4 red markers and 7 blue markers. How many more blue markers are there?

7 − 4 = __3__

__3__ more blue markers

2 8 apples and 6 bananas. How many more apples are there?

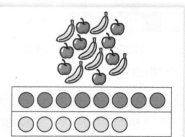

__2__ more apples

30

▶ **Mathematical Discourse**

1 *How can you check your answer in a comparison problem?*
One way to check the answer is to add the lesser quantity and the result of the "how many less comparison" or "how many more comparison" and see if this is equal to the greater quantity. Another way would be to use the tape diagram or a visual matching model to see if the quantities match. Children should be able to explain their approach and justify their reasoning.

▶ **Hands-On Activity**

Use length to model comparison.

Materials For each child: 20 connecting cubes

- Have children use connecting cubes to model a comparison problem, such as: *May has 4 books. Rick has 8 books. How many fewer books does May have?* Children model each quantity by making a train of connecting cubes.

- Then have them line up their models so that the left ends are aligned. Children can compare the lengths to see which quantity is greater or less and by how much.

- Discuss how this model relates to the tape diagrams shown on the page.

Practice by Myself
Subtract to Compare in Word Problems

3 Jo has 7 fish. Pat has 6 fish.
How many more fish does Jo have?

$7 - \underline{1} = 6$

Jo has _1_ more fish.

4 7 big shells and 9 small shells.
How many more small shells are there?
Possible number sentence:

$9 - \underline{7} = \underline{2}$

_2_ more small shells

5 5 chairs and 6 desks.
How many fewer chairs are there?
Possible number sentence:

$6 - \underline{1} = \underline{5}$

_1_ fewer chair(s)

31

Step By Step

- Before children work on this page, review the models used in this lesson. Emphasize that children are free to use whatever way helps them solve the problems.

- Read each problem aloud, then have children work independently to solve.

- In Problem 3, challenge children to solve without counting. Ask them why this is easy to do with the numbers in the problem.

▶ **Visual Model**

- In Problem 4, help children distinguish between comparing size (small vs. big) and comparing number (more vs. fewer). Point out that a model is started. They can complete it to solve the problem. Children may write the number sentence $9 - 7 = 2$ or the number sentence $9 - 2 = 7$. You may want to take advantage of the opportunity to discuss how each number sentence represents the problem, and how they are similar and different.

- For those who struggle to start Problem 5, ask questions such as: *What do you know?* [how many chairs and desks there are; there are fewer chairs] *What do you need to find out?* [how many fewer chairs there are] Encourage children to draw a picture or use a model to solve the problem. You may want to take advantage of the opportunity to explore the idea that there are 2 subtraction sentences that children could write to represent this problem [$6 - 1 = 5$ and $6 - 5 = 1$]. Ask children which number sentence makes it easier to find the answer.

- Invite volunteers to share the models and solution strategies they used for the problems on this page. Use Mathematical Discourse question 2 to check children's understanding of comparing quantities.

▶ **Mathematical Discourse 2**

▶ **Visual Model**

Make a tape diagram with numbers.

- On the board, draw the tape diagram from Problem 3. Copy the size and shape of the diagram, but leave the sections empty.

- Ask: *What's another way to represent the 7 fish that Jo has?* Guide children to recognize that the 7 circles can be replaced with "7." Do likewise with the 6 circles that represent Pat's fish.

- Have children discuss the differences between the two visual models and think of advantages for each one. Some children may be ready to use numbers in their tape diagrams.

▶ **Mathematical Discourse**

2 *How do you compare two quantities?*
When comparing two quantities, children must find a way to represent the *how many more* or *how many less* (the difference) conceptually and through representation. They need to understand that there are two parts to a comparison question:

1. Which quantity is more (or less)?
2. How much more (or less)?

Children should also be able to act out the problem, create a visual model, and write an appropriate subtraction sentence to answer both questions.

Differentiated Instruction

▶ Quick Check and Remediation

Materials For each child: 8 two-color counters

- Ask children to use counters to model and answer the following problem: *6 cats and 2 dogs. How many more cats than dogs?* [4 more cats than dogs]

- For children who are still struggling, use the chart below to guide remediation.

- After providing remediation, check children's understanding using the following problem: *9 cars and 4 trucks. How many more cars than trucks?* [5 more cars than trucks]

If the error is . . .	Children may . . .	To remediate . . .
6 or 2	have only identified the greater (or lesser) number.	Ask children to explain the meaning of the problem. Guide them to consider the question: *Which is more, cats or dogs?* Then repeat the words "How many more." Help children use a model to answer.
8	added the quantities rather than comparing them.	Ask children to explain the meaning of the problem. Have them put their answer in the sentence "There are __ more cats than dogs." Guide children to match the cats and dogs to see that this is a comparison situation and then answer the question.
a number that is not 6, 2, or 8	not understand the comparison relationship.	Reread the problem. Have children use counters to model 6 cats and 2 dogs. Guide them to match the quantities and then answer the question.

▶ Hands-On Activity

Act out a comparison using a tape diagram.

Materials For display: masking tape

- Make a tape diagram on the classroom floor, large enough for children to stand in.

- Give children a problem from the book or one that you make up, using numbers within 10. Write the problem using simple words.

- Have children act out the problem in the tape diagram, using themselves as counters. Children may count off to check that the right number is in each part of the diagram. To compare quantities, children may count on from the lesser number to the greater number.

▶ Challenge Activity

Use a graph to compare quantities.

Materials For each child: Chart Template (Activity Sheet 35), 3 groups of up to 7 objects each (such as books, crayons, and play money), 20 connecting cubes

- Give children Activity Sheet 35 (Chart Template) and different numbers of objects for each of three categories. Help children write the names of the objects in the headings of the chart.

- Have children count the objects in each category and represent them on the chart with connecting cubes.

- Children use the chart to ask and answer "how many more" and "how many fewer" questions about the objects they classified. Consider having children write subtraction sentences to represent each question and answer.

Teacher Notes

Teacher-Toolbox.com

Overview

Assign the Lesson 5 Quiz and have children work independently to complete it.

Use the results of the quiz to assess children's understanding of the content of the lesson and to identify areas for reteaching. See the Lesson Pacing Guide at the beginning of the lesson and the Differentiated Instruction activities for suggested instructional resources.

Tested Skills

Assesses 1.OA.A.1

Problems on this quiz require children to compare two amounts and identify how much more or less there is of one amount than the other, and write and solve addition and subtraction sentences to solve comparison word problems. Children will also need to be familiar with counting on to subtract, finding the missing addend, and adding and subtracting in word problems.

Ready® **Mathematics**

Lesson 5 Quiz Answer Key

Name _____

Solve.

1 5 ducks and 3 chicks.
How many more ducks than chicks?

5 − 3 = _2_

_2_ more ducks

2 8 apples and 4 oranges.
How many fewer oranges than apples?

8 − 4 = _4_

_4_ fewer oranges

3 Linda has 2 rocks and 6 shells.
How many more shells than rocks?

_4_ = 6 − 2

_4_ more shells

Common Misconceptions and Errors

Errors may result if children:

- identify the greater (or lesser) number rather than how many more (or less).
- add the quantities instead of compare them.
- do not understand a comparison relationship.

Name _____

Solve.

④ There are 9 yellow birds and 5 blue birds. How many fewer blue birds?

$9 - 5 =$ __4__

__4__ fewer blue birds

⑤ Dan has 5 balloons. Paco has 7 balloons. How many more balloons does Paco have?

__2__ $= 7 - 5$

Paco has __2__ more balloons.

Grade 1 **Lesson 5** Subtract to Compare in Word Problems   2

©Curriculum Associates, LLC
Copying permitted for classroom use.

Assessment

Step By Step

- Have children solve the problems independently. Encourage them to show their work. Emphasize that children are free to use whatever way helps them solve the problems.

  Student Misconception Alert
  Look for children who seem confused by Problem 2 and Problem 5 where the total is to the left of the equal sign. Some children may think that the equal sign always means *makes* or *results in* rather than always meaning *is the same number as*.

Solve the problems.

1 8 blocks in all. 6 are red.
Some are blue.
How many are blue?

$8 - \underline{\ 2\ } = 6$

---

2 5 children play. 3 more children come.
How many children in all?

| 1 | 2 | 3 | 4 | 5 | 6 | 7 | 8 | 9 | 10 |

$\underline{\ 8\ } = 5 + 3$

---

3 $7 - 2 = \underline{\ 5\ }$ **4** $6 + 3 = \underline{\ 9\ }$

5 $\underline{\ 7\ } = 9 - 2$ **6** $6 + 1 = \underline{\ 7\ }$

32

Teacher Notes

7 6 birds and 3 ants. How many more
birds are there than ants?

Draw a picture that shows the problem.
Then write a number sentence.

Possible answer: Children may draw a row of 3 squares
above a row of 6 circles to show the comparison of 6 − 3.

__6__ − __3__ = __3__

There are __3__ more birds than ants.

---

8 9 buttons in all.
7 are square. Some are round.
How many are round?

Complete the number bond.
Write an addition sentence.
Then write a subtraction sentence.

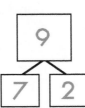

__7__ + __2__ = __9__   __9__ − __7__ = __2__

There are __2__ round buttons.

33

• Observe as children work. For Problem 7,
children draw to represent a comparison
problem, then write a number sentence. You
may wish to prompt children who are
having difficulty getting started by asking
questions such as: *Which will you draw first,
birds or ants?* or *How many birds will you draw?
How many ants? How do you know?*

Teacher Notes

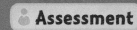
Assessment

Step By Step

Put It Together

- On this page, children are given three numbers—7, 5, and 2—and use those numbers to draw and write or tell an addition story. They then record the addition as a number sentence.

- Read the directions and task aloud. Make sure children understand what they need to do to complete the task.

- Direct children to complete problem 9 on their own.

- As children work on their own, observe their progress and understanding. Respond to their questions and provide additional support as needed.

- If time permits, have children share their addition stories and number sentences with the class.

- Ask children how this question is different from the other questions in this review. Point out that there are lots of ways they can show what they have learned.

- Have children return to the Unit Opener page and complete the *After* column of the progress chart.

Put It Together

9 **Draw a picture to show an addition story problem.**

Use the numbers 7, 5, and 2.
Tell or write your addition problem.
Write the addition sentence.

Possible answer: Children may show 5 pencils of one color and 2 pencils of another color. Their addition problem may be written as: 5 pencils and 2 pencils. How many pencils in all?

$$\underline{\quad 5 \quad} + \underline{\quad 2 \quad} = \underline{\quad 7 \quad}$$

34

Teacher Notes

Scoring Rubric

Points	Expectations
4	The child: • represents the given numbers accurately and completely in his or her drawing. • correctly states the total and addends when writing or telling the addition story. • correctly writes the addition sentence.
3	The child: • may represent the given numbers accurately and completely in his or her drawing. • may correctly state the total and addends when writing or telling the addition story. • may incorrectly write the total or one of the addends in the addition sentence.
2	The child: • may inaccurately represent the given numbers in his or her drawing. • may incorrectly state the total or one of the addends when writing or telling the addition story. • may incorrectly write the total of one of the addends in the addition sentence.
1	The child: • may inaccurately represent the given numbers in his or her drawing. • may incorrectly state the total and addends when writing or telling the addition story. • may incorrectly write the total and addends in the addition sentence.
0	The child: • does not attempt to do the task.

Which lessons are students building upon?

Kindergarten, Lesson 18 Add Within 10 K.OA.A.2	**Kindergarten, Lesson 19** Subtract Within 10 K.OA.A.2	**Kindergarten, Lesson 20** Practice Facts to 5 K.OA.A.5
Kindergarten, Lesson 18 Add Within 10 K.OA.A.2	**Kindergarten, Lesson 19** Subtract Within 10 K.OA.A.2	**Kindergarten, Lesson 20** Practice Facts to 5 K.OA.A.5
Kindergarten, Lesson 18 Add Within 10 K.OA.A.2	**Kindergarten, Lesson 19** Subtract Within 10 K.OA.A.2	**Kindergarten, Lesson 20** Practice Facts to 5 K.OA.A.5
Kindergarten, Lesson 18 Add Within 10 K.OA.A.2	**Kindergarten, Lesson 19** Subtract Within 10 K.OA.A.2	**Kindergarten, Lesson 20** Practice Facts to 5 K.OA.A.5
Kindergarten, Lesson 18 Add Within 10 K.OA.A.2	**Kindergarten, Lesson 19** Subtract Within 10 K.OA.A.2	**Kindergarten, Lesson 20** Practice Facts to 5 K.OA.A.5
Kindergarten, Lesson 18 Add Within 10 K.OA.A.2	**Kindergarten, Lesson 19** Subtract Within 10 K.OA.A.2	**Kindergarten, Lesson 20** Practice Facts to 5 K.OA.A.5

Unit 2

Lesson 6
Doubles and Doubles Plus 1
1.OA.C.6

Lesson 7
Number Partners for 6 and 7
1.OA.D.8

Lesson 8
Number Partners for 8 and 9
1.OA.B.3

Lesson 9
Number Partners for 10
1.OA.C.6

Lesson 10
Understand the Equal Sign
1.OA.D.7

Lesson 11
Facts I Know
1.OA.C.6

Which lessons are students preparing for?

Grade 2, Lesson 1
Understand Mental Math Strategies
(Fact Families)
2.OA.B.2

Grade 2, Lesson 5
Add Using Arrays
2.OA.C.4, 2.NBT.A.2

Grade 2, Lesson 1
Understand Mental Math Strategies
(Fact Families)
2.OA.B.2

Grade 2, Lesson 3
Understand Mental Math Strategies
(Make a Ten)
2.OA.B.2

Grade 2, Lesson 1
Understand Mental Math Strategies
(Fact Families)
2.OA.B.2

Grade 2, Lesson 3
Understand Mental Math Strategies
(Make a Ten)
2.OA.B.2

Grade 2, Lesson 3
Understand Mental Math Strategies
(Make a Ten)
2.OA.B.2

Grade 2, Lesson 5
Add Using Arrays
2.OA.C.4, 2.NBT.A.2

Grade 2, Lesson 4
Understand Even and Odd Numbers
2.OA.C.3

Grade 2, Lesson 5
Add Using Arrays
2.OA.C.4, 2.NBT.A.2

Grade 2, Lesson 1
Understand Mental Math Strategies
(Fact Families)
2.OA.B.2

Grade 2, Lesson 3
Understand Mental Math Strategies
(Make a Ten)
2.OA.B.2

Unit 2
Learn Facts to 10

Unit 2 – Operations and Algebraic Thinking
Learn Facts to 10

 3 red flowers and 3 blue flowers. 5 yellow flowers and 4 pink flowers. Beth wants to draw pictures of the some of the flowers. What math questions could Beth ask about the flowers?

In this unit, you will learn different ways to make and add numbers to 10. Then you will be able to solve problems like Beth's.

✓ Self Check

Check off the skills you know now. Then see how many more you can check off after each lesson!

I can:	Before this unit	After this unit
use doubles and doubles plus 1 to add.	☐	☐
find number partners for 6 and 7.	☐	☐
find number partners for 8 and 9.	☐	☐
find number partners for 10.	☐	☐
tell the meaning of the equal sign (=).	☐	☐
tell if a number sentence is true or untrue.	☐	☐
add numbers with totals to 10.	☐	☐

Ready Mathematics
PRACTICE AND PROBLEM SOLVING

Practice and Problem Solving Resources

Use the following resources from *Practice and Problem Solving* to engage students and their families and to extend student learning.

- **Family Letters** Send Family Letters home separately before each lesson or as part of a family communication package.

- **Unit Games** Use partner Unit Games at classroom centers and/or send them home for play with family members.

- **Unit Practice** Assign Unit Practice as homework, as independent or small group practice, or for whole class discussion.

- **Fluency Practice** Assign Fluency Skills Practice and Fluency Repeated Reasoning Practice worksheets throughout the unit.

At A Glance

- This page introduces children to the general ideas behind number partners and adding.

- The checklist allows them to see what skills they will be learning and take ownership of their progress.

Step By Step

- Explain to children that they are going to begin a new unit of lessons. Tell them that in all the lessons in this unit they will be learning different ways to make and add numbers to 10.

- Read the introduction to the unit together as a class. Invite children to suggest questions that could be asked about the problem situation. Discuss the questions children pose without the expectation that they are to solve them.

- Then take a few minutes to have each child independently read through the list of skills.

- Ask children to consider each skill and check the box in the *Before* column if it is a skill they think they already have. Remind children that these skills are likely to all be new to them, but it's still possible some children have some of the skills.

- Engage children in a brief discussion about the skills. Invite children to comment on which ones they would most like to learn, or which ones seem similar or related to something they already know. Remind them that the goal is to be able to check off all the skills they have learned by the end of the unit.

- At the end of the unit, have children complete the *After* column. As time allows, pose questions about the problem situation at the top of the page and solve as a class.

CCSS Focus

Domain
Operations and Algebraic Thinking

Cluster
C. Add and subtract within 20.

Standard
1.OA.C.6 Add and subtract within 20, demonstrating fluency for addition and subtraction within 10. Use strategies such as counting on; making ten (e.g., $8 + 6 = 8 + 2 + 4 = 10 + 4 = 14$); decomposing a number leading to a ten (e.g., $13 - 4 = 13 - 3 - 1 = 10 - 1 = 9$); using the relationship between addition and subtraction (e.g., knowing that $8 + 4 = 12$, one knows $12 - 8 = 4$); and creating equivalent but easier or known sums (e.g., adding $6 + 7$ by creating the known equivalent $6 + 6 + 1 = 12 + 1 = 13$).

Standards for Mathematical Practice (SMP)

7 Look for and make use of structure.

8 Look for and express regularity in repeated reasoning.

Lesson Objectives

Content Objectives

• Relate an image of two equal groups to doubles.

• Relate an image of two equal groups with one left over as doubles plus one.

• Write addition sentences for doubles and doubles plus one.

• Use properties to write a doubles plus one expression (3 addends) as an expression with 2 addends.

Language Objectives

• Draw picture cards to create visual examples of several doubles and doubles plus one facts.

• Use visual models or counters to create addition sentences and solve a doubles or a doubles plus one problem.

• Tell how a doubles plus one expression with 3 addends and a related doubles plus one expression with 2 addends are alike.

• Justify conclusions and communicate the conclusions to others.

Prerequisite Skills

• Count on to add.

• Add and subtract in word problems.

• Find the missing addend.

Lesson Vocabulary

• **doubles** an addition fact that has two addends that are the same, such as $4 + 4$.

• **doubles plus 1** an addition fact that has a double as one addend and the double and one more as the other addend, such as $4 + 5$.

Learning Progression

In Kindergarten children solve addition and subtraction word problems, and add and subtract within 10 by using objects or drawings to represent the problem.

In Grade 1 children are expected to fluently add and subtract numbers to 10 and have experience adding and subtracting within 20. Adding and subtracting fluently refers to knowledge of procedures, knowledge of when and how to use them, and skill in performing them flexibly by using different strategies.

In this lesson children are introduced to the strategy of doubles and doubles plus one. Children use models to first find sums of doubles, then to find sums of doubles plus one. As they continue to work with doubles and doubles plus one addition sentences, children come to recognize that they can double the smaller number and add 1 more.

In Grade 2 children fluently add and subtract within 20 using mental strategies.

Lesson Pacing Guide

Whole Class Instruction

Day 1
45–60 minutes

Introduction
Use What You Know
- Explore It *25 min*
- Try It *20 min*

Day 2
45–60 minutes

Modeled Instruction
Explore Together
- Example Problem *5 min*
- Model It *20 min*
- Hands-On Activity *20 min*

Practice and Problem Solving
Assign pages 51–52.

Day 3
45–60 minutes

Guided Instruction
Learn Together
- Example Problem *5 min*
- Model It *10 min*
- Talk About It *10 min*
- Hands-On Activity *10 min*
- Concept Extension *10 min*

Practice and Problem Solving
Assign pages 53–54.

Day 4
45–60 minutes

Guided Practice
Practice Together
- Example Problem *5 min*
- Problems 1–2 *25 min*
- Fluency Practice *15 min*

Practice and Problem Solving
Assign pages 55–56.

Day 5
45–60 minutes

Independent Practice
Practice by Myself
- Problems 3–5 *15 min*
- Visual Model *5 min*
- Quick Check and Remediation *10 min*
- Hands-On or Challenge Activity *15 min*

Teacher-Toolbox: Lesson Quiz
Lesson 6 Quiz

Materials for Lesson Activities

Per child: 9 counters, 5 index cards
Activity Sheet 5

Per pair: 10 connecting cubes (5 each of two different colors)

For display: none

Small Group Differentiation

Teacher-Toolbox.com

Reteach
Ready Prerequisite Lessons *45–90 min*

Grade K
- Lesson 18 Add Within 10
- Lesson 20 Practice Facts to 5

Teacher-led Activities
Tools for Instruction *15–20 min*

Grade 1 *(Lesson 6)*
- Doubles Addition Facts
- One More
- Add and Subtract 1 and 2

Student-led Activities
Math Center Activities *30–40 min*

Grade K *(Lessons 18 and 20)*
- K.24 Tell Addition Stories
- K.26 Add and Move
- K.27 Solve and Color

Grade 1 *(Lesson 6)*
- 1.04 Doubles and Doubles Plus 1

Personalized Learning

i-Ready.com

Independent
i-Ready Lessons* *10–20 min*

Grade 1 *(Lesson 6)*
- Addition Facts: Doubles
- Acting Out Addition and Subtraction
- One More

* i-Ready lessons may be updated during the 2016–2017 school year. Updated references will be on the Teacher-Toolbox.

👥 Introduction

Activity Doubles and Doubles Plus 1

Objective

Model a doubles and doubles plus 1 addition problem and identify corresponding addition number sentences.

Materials for each child

- 9 counters

Overview

Children act out a doubles and a doubles plus 1 addition problem. They identify the addends in the doubles problem as the same and relate adding one more to a double to find another sum. Then they solve a similar problem.

Step By Step

Explore It

Pose the problem.

- Tell children to imagine they are at soccer practice. Read the problem on the Student Book page aloud: *Children line up on both sides of the field. There are 4 children on each side. How many children are there?*

Act out the problem.

- Have 4 children line up on each side of the classroom.

- Ask: *How many children are on the left side of the classroom?* [4] *How many children are on the right side?* [4]

- Point out that there are 4 pairs of children. You may want to have the lines face each other and move closer together to help children see the pairs. Together count the children aloud by 2s.

- Have children use counters on the workmat on the Student Book page to model the problem. Then have children point to the pairs of counters on their workmats. Count the pairs of counters aloud by 2s.

- Write 4 + 4 on the board. Ask: *What is the total?* [8] Complete the doubles addition sentence 4 + 4 = 8 on the board. Then have

Ⓖ Explore It

Children line up on both sides of the field.
There are 4 children on each side.
How many children are there?

$$\underline{4} + \underline{4} = \underline{8}$$

One more child joins the group on the left.
Now how many children are there?

$$\underline{4} + \underline{4} + \underline{1} = \underline{9}$$

36

children record the number sentence on the Student Book page.

- Have one more child join the group on the left side of the classroom.

- Ask: *Does she (or he) have a partner?* [No.]

- Have children add one counter to the group of counters on the left side of the workmat.

- Write 4 + 4 + 1 on the board. Ask: *What is the total?* [9] Complete the doubles plus 1 addition sentence 4 + 4 + 1 = 9 on the board. Then have children record the number sentence on the Student Book page.

Talk about the doubles and doubles plus 1 addition sentences.

- Point to the addends in the doubles addition sentence 4 + 4 = 8. Ask: *What do you notice about these numbers?* [They are the same.] Identify the addends as doubles. Ask children why they think the term *doubles* is used. Children might say that the 4 appears twice or that there are two 4s.

- Ask children how they know the total is 8. Children may respond that they counted on from 4 or that they counted by 2s.

- Identify the addition sentence 4 + 4 + 1 = 9 as doubles plus 1. Ask: *How do you know 4 + 4 + 1 = 9?* Children may say that they know 4 + 4 = 8 and 8 + 1 = 9.

Use What You Know
Doubles and Doubles Plus 1

 Try It

Max has 3 red beads and 3 blue beads.
How many beads does Max have?
Then Max finds 1 more red bead.
Now how many beads does Max have in all?

$\underline{3} + \underline{3} = \underline{6}$

Max has $\underline{6}$ beads.

$\underline{3} + \underline{3} + \underline{1} = \underline{7}$

Now Max has $\underline{7}$ beads in all.

37

Step By Step

Try It

Pose the problem.

• Read aloud the problem from the Student Book page: *Max has 3 red beads and 3 blue beads. How many beads does Max have? Then Max finds 1 more red bead. Now how many beads does Max have in all?*

Solve the problem.

• Allow time for children to solve the problem. Encourage them to use counters to show each part of the problem.

• Observe and note children who notice that the addends in the first part of the problem match exactly. Look for an understanding that 7 is one more than 6 in the second part of the problem.

• Have children write a number sentence for each part of the problem and record their solution for each.

Lead a classroom discussion.

• Have children look at the addends they wrote in the doubles addition sentence $3 + 3 = 6$. Ask: *What do you notice about these numbers?* [They are the same.] Encourage children to identify the addends as doubles and explain why they think the term *doubles* can be used to describe this part of the number sentence. Children might say that the 3 appears twice or that there are two 3s.

• Ask children how they know the total is 6. Children may respond that they counted on from 3 or that they counted by 2s.

• Have children identify the addition sentence they wrote, $3 + 3 + 1 = 7$, as doubles plus 1. Ask: *How do you know $3 + 3 + 1 = 7$?* Children may say that they know $3 + 3 = 6$ and $6 + 1 = 7$.

👥 Modeled Instruction

Step By Step

- Explain that this page is about doubles, just like the Activity in the Introduction. Read aloud the problem at the top of the page. Tell children they can use counters to model the problem.

▶ **English Language Learners**

- Use Hands-On Activity 1 to connect adding doubles to the problem on this page.

▶ **Hands-On Activity 1**

Model It

- Direct children's attention to the Model It. Read aloud the addition fact. Have children discuss what they notice about the addends. [They are the same.] Tell children this addition is a doubles.

▶ **Mathematical Discourse 1**

- Read aloud the directive to use doubles to find the total. Have children explain how the counters and 3 + 3 are related. Then have children complete the doubles number sentence.

> **SMP TIP Repeated Reasoning**
> Ask children to name some other doubles facts that they know, for example 1 + 1 and 2 + 2. Children use repeated reasoning to conclude that in these doubles facts, the same addend is added twice. (SMP 8)

 **Mathematics**
PRACTICE AND PROBLEM SOLVING

Assign *Practice and Problem Solving* **pages 51–52** after students have completed this section.

Doubles and Doubles Plus 1

3 players pass a ball.
3 players trap a ball.
How many players in all?

🔳 **Model It** Find 3 + 3. ···

Each addend is 3.
Use **doubles** to find the total.

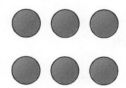

$$3 + 3 = \underline{6}$$

38

▶ **Mathematical Discourse**

1 *How would you explain in your own words what is a double and what is not a double?*

Some children may say that addition where the two numbers being added are the same are doubles and addition with two different numbers being added are not doubles. Other children may say that two groups in which each item in one group matches with an item in the other group are doubles and groups in which there is a leftover item are not doubles.

▶ **English Language Learners**

Some children may not understand the meaning of the term *doubles*. Relate doubles to pairs of body parts, such as two eyes, two hands, and two feet. Point out words of similar meaning such as *pairs* and *partners*. Provide images that show examples of greater doubles, such as four wheels on a car and four legs on a table.

▶ **Hands-On Activity 1**
Use models to add doubles.

Materials For each child: 6 counters

- Have children make two rows of counters using the number partners 3 and 3.

- Ask: *Are there the same number of counters in each row?* [Yes] *How do you know?* [Each counter has a partner.]

- Ask children how they can find the total number of counters. Children may count on from 3 or add 3 + 3 to find the total of 6.

Learn Together
Doubles and Doubles Plus 1

3 players on the blue team. 4 players on the red team.
How many players in all?

Model It Use doubles. Add 1 more.

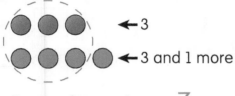

← 3

← 3 and 1 more

$$3 + 3 + 1 = 7$$
$$3 + 4 = 7$$

Talk About It Who is right? How do you know?

Boom wrote: $4 + 4 + 1$.

Buzz wrote: $5 + 5 - 1$.

39

▶ Hands-On Activity 2
Use models to add doubles plus 1.

Materials For each child: 7 counters

- Have children make two rows of counters using the number partners 3 and 4.

- Ask: *Are there the same number of counters in each row?* [No.] *How do you know?* [Pairing the counters in each row leaves one counter left over.]

- Ask children how they can find the total number of counters. Some children may say that they can count on from 3 or 4; others may notice that there are 3 pairs of counters and one left over so they add 3 + 3, then add 1 more for the leftover counter.

- Ask children how many counters there are in all. [7]

▶ Mathematical Discourse

2 *How is 3 + 4 related to 3 + 3?*
Some children may suggest that since they know that 3 + 3 = 6, 3 + 4 is the same as adding a double (3) and a double plus one (4).

3 *How is 3 + 3 + 1 like 3 + 4?*
Some children may say that they are alike because both are a way to show doubles plus 1. Other children may suggest they are alike because when added, they have the same total (7).

▶ Concept Extension
Use grouping to add 3 numbers.

Materials For each child: 7 counters

Help children apply the associative property of addition to see how the two number sentences are related. Have children group counters to represent the three addends in 3 + 3 + 1. Then have them group the counters to represent the addends in 3 + 4. Discuss whether the total number of counters remains the same.

Step By Step

- Read aloud the problem at the top of the page. Ask children to explain whether they would use addition or subtraction to find the answer.

- Use Hands-On Activity 2 to connect adding doubles plus 1 to the problem on this page.

▶ **Hands-On Activity 2**

Model It

- Direct children's attention to Model It. Read aloud the directive. Have children look at the model and tell what they think the dashed circle shows. Discuss the labels "3" and "3 and 1 more" with children.

- Ask: *What doubles are in the first number sentence?* [3 + 3] *Why is + 1 in the number sentence?* [After making doubles, there is one more counter.] In using the doubles plus 1 strategy, children are grouping numbers differently, that is, using three addends, for the first time.

▶ **Mathematical Discourse 2 and 3**

Talk About It

- As children discuss the problem posed in Talk About It, encourage them to describe how the solutions are alike and how they are different. Listen for children who say that only Boom is correct and ask them to explain their reasoning. Discuss why both strategies are correct and how either strategy can be used to find the total, 9.

▶ **Concept Extension**

📦 Ready· Mathematics
PRACTICE AND PROBLEM SOLVING

Assign *Practice and Problem Solving* **pages 53–54** after students have completed this section.

👥👥 Guided Practice

Step By Step

- Read the problem at the top of the page. Ask: *What do you notice about the number of blue blocks compared to the number of red blocks?* Children may say that there is one more blue block than red blocks.
- Ask children how they can solve the problem. Children may say that they can use the doubles 2 + 2, then add 1 more.
- Ask: *How do you know to add one more?* [Because there are 3 blue blocks and 3 is one more than 2.]
- Connect the first addition sentence, 2 + 2 + 1, to the term *doubles plus 1*. Then relate the two addition sentences to each other. Ask: *How does finding the total of 2 + 2 + 1 help you find the total of 2 + 3?* Children may say that breaking apart 3 into 2 + 1 helps them use doubles plus 1 (2 + 2 + 1) to find the total (5).
- Read aloud the first problem. Relate the picture to the number bond.

▶ **Mathematical Discourse 1**

- Read aloud the second problem. Have children circle the pencils that show the doubles fact and explain how they knew which pencils to circle. [The number of pencils in each group are the same, 3.] Ask: *How many pencils are left over?* [1] Guide children to see how the one leftover pencil relates to the missing addend 1.

▶ **Fluency Practice**

> **SMP TIP Look for and Use Structure**
> Children may observe patterns and structure as they discover that some numbers make equal groups, but others have one left over. Continue to reinforce these concepts as children use the doubles and doubles plus 1 strategies. *(SMP 7)*

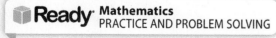**Ready** Mathematics
PRACTICE AND PROBLEM SOLVING

Assign *Practice and Problem Solving* **pages 55–56** after students have completed this section.

Practice Together
Doubles and Doubles Plus 1

> 2 red blocks and 3 blue blocks.
> How many blocks in all?
>
> $2 + 2 + 1 = \underline{5}$
> $2 + \quad 3 \quad = \underline{5}$

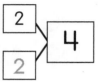

① There are 4 balls. 2 are big. The rest are small. How many balls are small?

$2 + \underline{2} = 4$

② Jo has 4 pencils. She finds 3 more pencils. How many pencils does Jo have in all?

$3 + 3 + \underline{1} = \underline{7}$

$3 + 4 = \underline{7}$

40

▶ **Mathematical Discourse**

1 *How can you find the missing addend in 2 + ___ = 4?*
Children may respond with a variety of suggestions. Look for responses that indicate children see the missing number as a double (2). Since 2 + 2 = 4, the missing number is 2.

▶ **Fluency Practice**

Stand and sit on even numbers.

Have children sit in a circle and count aloud by ones. Each child says the next consecutive number. Children who say even numbers stand up and do not continue counting: 1, 2 [child stands], 3, 4 [child stands], etc. Continue until all children are standing. Then have children count backward from the last number spoken, continuing in the same direction around the circle. This time children who say even numbers sit and do not continue counting. Continue until all children are sitting.

Practice by Myself
Doubles and Doubles Plus 1

③ 2 books and 3 books.
How many books in all?

$\underline{2} + \underline{2} + \underline{1} = \underline{5}$

2 + 3 = $\underline{5}$

④ There are 4 birds. More birds join them.
Now there are 8 birds.
How many birds join?

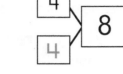

4 + $\underline{4}$ **= 8**

⑤ Nick has 5 sun stickers.
He has 5 moon stickers.
How many stickers does Nick have in all?

5 + 5 = $\underline{10}$

41

Step By Step

- Before children work on this page, review the models used in the lesson. Emphasize that children can use whatever way helps them solve the problems.

- Read each problem aloud, then have children work independently to solve.

- For Problem 4, observe to see if children recognize that the problem requires them to find an unknown change. Look for children who connect the phrase "how many more" with subtraction and use what they know about doubles and the relationship between addition and subtraction to find the missing addend: $8 - 4 = 4$ and $4 + 4 = 8$.

- Ask children who solve Problem 5 without showing their work to explain which strategy helped them find their solution.

▶ **Mathematical Discourse 2**

▶ **Visual Model**

▶ **Visual Model**

Use fingers to model doubles facts.

Have children use their fingers to show and name doubles facts.

- Partner A shows two pinkies. Partner B says the number sentence: $1 + 1 = 2$.

- Partner A shows pinkies and ring fingers. Partner B says the number sentence: $2 + 2 = 4$.

- Partners continue showing fingers and naming doubles facts : $3 + 3 = 6$, $4 + 4 = 8$, and $5 + 5 = 10$.

- Have partners switch roles and repeat the activity.

- Then have children use their hands to show doubles facts using 5, 3, 1, 4, and 2.

▶ **Mathematical Discourse**

2 *2 + 3 is a doubles plus 1. Is 3 + 2 also a doubles plus 1? How do you know?*

Children are not expected to name the commutative property, but some may be familiar enough with the concept to use it with precision in their explanation. For example, you can draw pictures that show $2 + 3$ and $3 + 2$. The pictures are the same because they each show two equal groups with one left over, so $2 + 3$ and $3 + 2$ are the same. Both are doubles plus 1.

Differentiated Instruction

▶ Quick Check and Remediation

Materials For each child: 4 counters, 5 index cards

- Ask children to tell how many apples Rob has in all if Rob had 2 apples and Tom gave him 2 more. [4]

- For children who are still struggling, use the chart below to guide remediation.

- After providing remediation, check children's understanding using the following problem: *Kara puts 3 pencils in a cup. Her teacher puts in 3 more pencils. How many pencils are in the cup?* [6]

If the error is . . .	Children may . . .	To remediate . . .
2	have failed to recognize that they need to use addition.	Have children draw a picture showing Rob's 2 apples and Tom's 2 apples. Have children count to find the total number of apples.
0	have used subtraction instead of addition.	Have children record "2 more" as "+ 2." Then have them use counters to show one group of 2 and another group of 2 and record the doubles fact 2 + 2 = 4.
3	have failed to recognize 2 + 2 as a doubles fact.	Have children make picture cards for each of the doubles and write the doubles fact on the card. (For example, two eyes for 1 + 1 = 2, two hands for 5 + 5 = 10.)

▶ Hands-On Activity

Use connecting cubes to model adding doubles and doubles plus 1.

Materials For each pair: 10 connecting cubes (5 each of two different colors)

- One partner uses two different-colored connecting cubes to show 1 + 1.

- The other partner records the doubles fact on a sheet of paper. [1 + 1 = 2]

- The first partner uses cubes of two different colors to continue modeling the doubles 2 + 2, 3 + 3, 4 + 4, and 5 + 5 as the second partner records each doubles fact.

- Partners switch roles and use the cubes to show and record doubles plus 1 facts: 1 + 2 and 2 + 1, 2 + 3 and 3 + 2, 3 + 4 and 4 + 3, and 4 + 5 and 5 + 4.

▶ Challenge Activity

Find doubles, doubles plus 1, and doubles minus one patterns on an addition chart.

Materials For each child: Addition Table 1 (Activity Sheet 5)

- Provide children with Activity Sheet 5 (Addition Table 1).

- Have children write the totals below each addition. Then have them color the doubles facts.

- Ask children to make observations about the doubles facts on the table. [Doubles facts fall on a diagonal line in the chart.]

- Have children look above and below each doubles fact. Ask them what facts they see. [doubles plus 1, doubles minus 1]

Teacher Notes

Lesson 6
Doubles and Doubles Plus 1

Teacher-Toolbox.com

Overview

Assign the Lesson 6 Quiz and have children work independently to complete it.

Use the results of the quiz to assess children's understanding of the content of the lesson and to identify areas for reteaching. See the Lesson Pacing Guide at the beginning of the lesson and the Differentiated Instruction activities for suggested instructional resources.

Tested Skills

Assesses 1.OA.C.6

Problems on this quiz require children to recognize two equal groups as doubles and two equal groups with one left over as doubles plus one, write addition sentences for doubles and doubles plus one, and write a doubles plus one expression (three addends) as a two addends expression. Children will also need to be familiar with counting on to add, finding the missing addend, and adding and subtracting in word problems.

Ready® **Mathematics**

Lesson 6 Quiz Answer Key

Name _____

Solve.

1 Jamal has 3 yellow balls and 4 blue balls.
How many balls does Jamal have in all?

$3 + 3 + \underline{1} = \underline{7}$

$3 + 4 = \underline{7}$

Jamal has $\underline{7}$ balls in all.

2 Ana has 6 toy cars. 3 are small. The rest are big.
How many cars are big?

$3 + \underline{3} = 6$

$\underline{3}$ cars are big.

1

Common Misconceptions and Errors

Errors may result if children:

• do not understand that they need to use addition.

• use subtraction instead of addition.

• fail to recognize a doubles fact.

Name _____

Solve.

3 Tom has 5 books. He buys 5 more books.
How many books does Tom have now?

__10__ = 5 + 5

__10__ books

4 Cho has 4 shells. She finds 4 more shells.
How many shells does she have now?

4 + __4__ = __8__

__8__ shells

5 There are 2 large dogs and 3 small dogs at the park.
How many dogs are at the park?

__5__ = 2 + __2__ + 1

__5__ dogs are in the park.

Grade 1 **Lesson 6** Doubles and Doubles Plus 1

2

©Curriculum Associates, LLC
Copying permitted for classroom use.

Lesson 7
Number Partners for 6 and 7

CCSS Focus

Domain
Operations and Algebraic Thinking

Cluster
D. Work with addition and subtraction equations.

Standard
1.OA.D.8 Determine the unknown whole number in an addition or subtraction equation relating three whole numbers. *For example, determine the unknown number that makes the equation true in each of the equations* $8 + ? = 11, 5 = \square - 3, 6 + 6 = \square$.

Additional Standards
1.OA.B.3, 1.OA.C.6 (See page B3 for full text.)

Standards for Mathematical Practice (SMP)
2 Reason abstractly and quantitatively.

3 Construct viable arguments and critique the reasoning of others.

5 Use appropriate tools strategically.

6 Attend to precision.

7 Look for and make use of structure.

8 Look for and express regularity in repeated reasoning.

Lesson Objectives

Content Objectives
- Develop fluency in addition and subtraction for sums 6 and 7.
- Model facts for 6 and 7 in a number bond.
- Complete number sentences.

Language Objectives
- Orally define and use the key mathematical term *number partners* when communicating with a partner.
- Use visual models and number bonds to find missing number partners for 6 and 7.
- Record number partners for 6 or 7 in a number bond and use to complete up to four related addition and subtraction sentences.
- Listen to the ideas of others about related number sentences and ask questions to clarify.

Prerequisite Skills
- Organize facts in a number bond.
- Read and write number sentences.

Lesson Vocabulary
- **compose** to combine lesser numbers to make greater numbers.
- **decompose** to break a number into two or more parts.
- **number** tells how much or how many.
- **number partners** two addends that make up a given total.

Learning Progression

In Kindergarten children fluently add and subtract within 5. They explore operations on numbers within 10 by decomposing numbers less than 10 through pictures, drawings, and number sentences.

In Grade 1 children gain fluency in addition and subtraction within 10 through physical and visual models, utilization of strategies, and through number sentences.

In this lesson children examine the partners for 6 and 7 by first modeling physical and pictorial representations of the partners, and then by completing number bonds and number sentences. Throughout the lesson children pair visual models with the symbolic representation to help them analyze the structure and reasoning inherent in number partners.

In Grade 2 children extend their knowledge of facts by applying them to fact families and using them to add and subtract two-digit numbers.

Lesson Pacing Guide

Whole Class Instruction

Day 1
45–60 minutes

Introduction
Use What You Know
- Explore It *25 min*
- Try It *20 min*

Day 2
45–60 minutes

Modeled Instruction
Explore Together
- Example Problem *10 min*
- Model It *20 min*
- Hands-On Activity *15 min*

Practice and Problem Solving
Assign pages 59–60.

Day 3
45–60 minutes

Guided Instruction
Learn Together
- Example Problem *15 min*
- Model It *10 min*
- Talk About It *10 min*
- Concept Extension *10 min*

Practice and Problem Solving
Assign pages 61–62.

Day 4
45–60 minutes

Guided Practice
Practice Together
- Example Problem *5 min*
- Problems 1–2 *25 min*
- Concept Extension *15 min*

Practice and Problem Solving
Assign pages 63–64.

Day 5
45–60 minutes

Independent Practice
Practice by Myself
- Problems 3–5 *10 min*
- Visual Model *5 min*
- Fluency Practice *10 min*
- Quick Check and Remediation *10 min*
- Hands-On or Challenge Activity *10 min*

Teacher-Toolbox: Lesson Quiz
Lesson 7 Quiz

Materials for Lesson Activities

Per child: 12 connecting cubes (6 blue, 6 green), 7 two-color counters, dominoes, 2 colors of crayons
Activity Sheet 6, Activity Sheet 7, Activity Sheet 8

Per pair: 14 connecting cubes (7 orange, 7 purple), 7 counters, paper bag
Activity Sheet 3, Activity Sheet 25

For display: 2 sets of large paper squares containing 1-6 dots in domino patterns, 6 connecting cubes (3 blue, 3 yellow), domino showing 2 and 4 as partners

Small Group Differentiation

Teacher-Toolbox.com

Reteach
Ready Prerequisite Lessons *45–90 min*

Grade K
- Lesson 8 Make 6 and 7
- Lesson 18 Add Within 10

Teacher-led Activities
Tools for Instruction *15–20 min*

Grade 1 *(Lesson 7)*
- Number Pairs for Sums to 10
- Missing Numbers
- Find Missing Addends for Sums to 10

Student-led Activities
Math Center Activities *30–40 min*

Grade K *(Lessons 8 and 18)*
- K.18 Fish to Make Numbers
- K.24 Tell Addition Stories

Grade 1 *(Lesson 7)*
- 1.14 Partners for 6 and 7
- 1.15 Addition to 7

Personalized Learning

i-Ready.com

Independent
i-Ready Lessons* *10–20 min*

Grade 1 *(Lesson 7)*
- Part 1: Addition Facts
- Part 2: Addition Facts
- Addition Number Sentences
- Composing and Decomposing with 5 as a Benchmark

* i-Ready lessons may be updated during the 2016–2017 school year. Updated references will be on the Teacher-Toolbox.

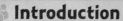

Introduction

Activity Domino Partners

Objective

Explore partners of 6 and 7.

Materials for each child

• 7 counters

Materials for display

• 2 sets of large paper squares containing 1-6 dots in domino patterns

Overview

Children explore the concept of number partners by finding the other half of a domino with totals of either 6 or 7.

Step By Step

Explore It

Pose the problem.

• Show children a domino piece and direct their attention to the picture of a domino on the Student Book page. Tell children to pretend that they have been given the job of building dominos. Say: *Your first job is to make dominoes that show a total of 6 dots.*

Act it out.

• Display the paper squares containing 1, 2, 4, and 5 dots. Distribute 6 counters to each child.

• Invite a child to come to the front of the class and choose a square. Ask the child to face the class holding the square so all can see it.

• Ask all children to place counters on their workmats to match this square, and then to use their remaining counters to model the other side of a domino that shows a total of 6 dots.

• Ask a volunteer to find the square that would finish the 6-dot domino. Have the children hold the two squares next to each other to form a domino and engage the class in determining whether the domino was built correctly and how they know. Listen for children to use previously learned strategies such as counting on.

Number Partners for 6 and 7

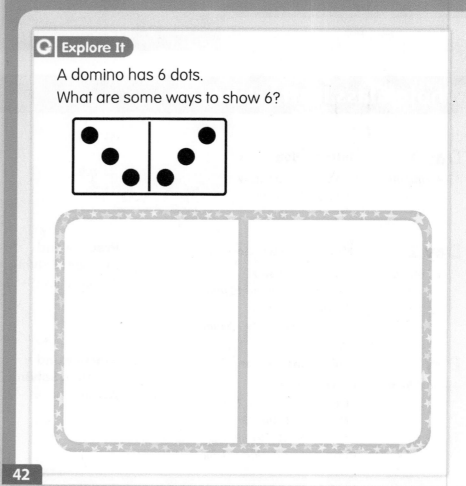

Explore It

A domino has 6 dots.
What are some ways to show 6?

42

• Repeat until all the possible domino combinations of 6 have been formed.

Explore the concept.

• Build a domino using the dot card showing 4 and the dot card showing 2, and show it to the class. Ask children to confirm that it was built correctly. Then remove the card showing 4 dots and ask: *Can anyone find a different partner for 2?*

• Allow children to wrestle with this question briefly before asking why there are no other partners.

• Repeat for another partner pair before asking children to generalize to all the partner pairs.

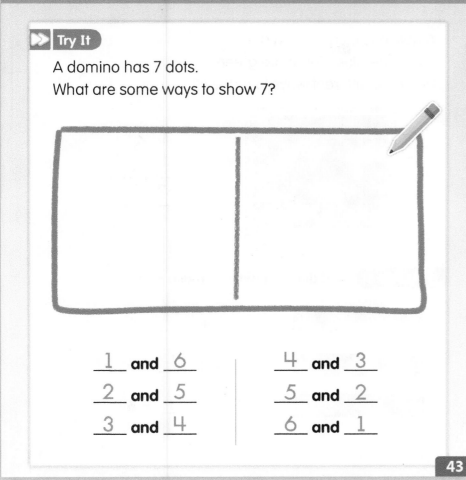

▶▶ **Try It**

A domino has 7 dots.
What are some ways to show 7?

___1___ and ___6___   ___4___ and ___3___

___2___ and ___5___   ___5___ and ___2___

___3___ and ___4___   ___6___ and ___1___

43

Step By Step

Try It

Apply to partners of 7.

- Distribute additional counters so that each child has 7 counters in total. Display the paper squares containing 1–6 dots.

- Hold up the square containing 4 dots and ask: *If we were making dominoes that show 7 dots, how many partners do you think there are for this square? Why?*

- Have children use their counters to find the partner to make 7. Then have one child select the dot card showing the partner [3] and set the squares next to each other to check.

- Have children use the counters on the workmat on the Student Book page to find all of the dominos that show a total of 7. As children complete making the "dominoes" with their counters, have them record the partners below the workmat.

- Have children draw the dots from one of the squares on one side of their "domino" workmat and draw the partner to make that 7-dot domino on the other side. Then have children circle the partner pair that matches the domino they drew.

- Look for children who are having difficulty determining how many dots to draw for each pair of partners. The Hands-On Activity in the lesson provides additional support.

Modeled Instruction

Step By Step

- Direct children's attention to the quilt shown and explain that a quilt is made of pieces of cloth sewn together. Tell them that this quilt is made up of small blue and green squares. Ask children how the rows are like the dominoes from the Activity in the Introduction.

- Display the number bond from the problem at the top of the page. Ask children to tell what numbers belong in the bottom boxes to model the first row of squares. Guide children to recognize that 5 and 1 model the number of blue and green squares in the first row.

> **SMP TIP Repeated Reasoning**
> Explore each row of squares in the same way as above, writing number sentences for each one. Help children recognize that the reasoning techniques they use to find the number sentences are used repeatedly. *(SMP 8)*

Model It

- Discuss Model It. Explain that the first addend represents the number of blue squares in the row. Have children fill in the blanks to show the number of green squares in each row.

- Invite volunteers to share their answers. Have children identify 2 addition facts and 2 subtraction facts for the first 2 rows of squares. Then discuss why there is only 1 addition fact and 1 subtraction fact for the last row of squares. Record the number sentences.

▶ **Mathematical Discourse 1 and 2**

▶ **Hands-On Activity**

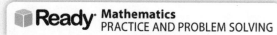 **Mathematics**
PRACTICE AND PROBLEM SOLVING

Assign *Practice and Problem Solving* **pages 59–60** after students have completed this section.

Explore Together
Number Partners for 6 and 7

A quilt has 6 squares in a row.
Some are blue. Some are green.
What are different ways to make 6?

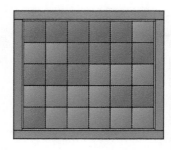

■ **Model It** **Find different ways to make 6.**

 $1 + \underline{5} = 6$

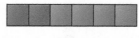 $2 + \underline{4} = 6$

 $3 + \underline{3} = 6$

▶ **Mathematical Discourse**

1 *Are all the ways to make 6 shown? How do you know?*
   Some children may say these are all the ways because that they used the pattern $1 + 5, 2 + 4, 3 + 3, 4 + 2, 5 + 1$. Other children may notice that $0 + 6$ and $6 + 0$ are not shown as number partners and that means these are not all the ways to make 6. Accept both responses, encouraging children who suggested 0 as a potential partner to explain their thinking. Children will explore using 0 as a number partner in later lessons.

2 *How does knowing number partners help you find the missing number in a number sentence?*
   Children should recognize that by knowing the partners, they can think about the one that is missing in the number sentence.

▶ **Hands-On Activity**
   Make a cube quilt.

Materials For each child: 12 connecting cubes (6 blue, 6 green)

Have children replicate the quilt pattern by connecting sets of 6 blue and green cubes together as shown and then lay each row of cubes together to form the quilt.

Learn Together
Number Partners for 6 and 7

A painting has 7 circles in a row.
Some are purple. Some are orange.
What are different ways to make 7?

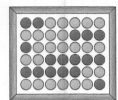

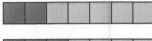 **Model It** Find different ways to make 7. •••••••••••••••••

 $1 + \underline{6} = 7$

 $2 + \underline{5} = 7$

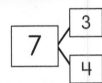 $3 + \underline{4} = 7$

💬 **Talk About It** Who is right? How do you know? ••••••••••

$$\begin{array}{c} 7 \end{array} \begin{array}{c} 3 \\ 4 \end{array}$$

Boom writes: $3 + 4 = 7$.

Buzz writes: $4 = 7 - 3$.

45

▶ Concept Extension

Use zero as a number partner.

Materials For each pair: 14 connecting cubes (7 orange, 7 purple)

- Some children may question whether $7 + 0$ and $0 + 7$ could be used in a number bond. If so, engage them in modeling a bar of cubes that would show the number bond and discuss that 0 implies that there are no purple cubes or no orange cubes in that bar. Have children work in pairs to model.

- You may extend the concept to subtraction by asking children to model $7 - 0$ and $7 - 7$.

- Note: 0 is introduced as a potential partner in a later lesson, so explore the concept without expectation of complete understanding.

▶ Mathematical Discourse

3 *Does it matter where you put the 5 and the 2 in the number bond? Explain.*

Children may suggest that 5 and 2 are partners for the number 7 so they can go in either of the small boxes. It doesn't matter which box they are in as long as they are not in the big box. That's for the 7.

Step By Step

- Draw attention to the painting and engage children in discussing similarities and differences between the painting and the quilt from the previous page.

- Provide pairs of children with 7 orange and 7 purple connecting cubes. Have children use the two colors of cubes to model each row of circles in the picture. Then have children write corresponding number sentences.

Model It

- Draw children's attention to Model It and ask: *What can you do to find the missing number in the number sentence?* Allow children to discuss strategies they may use before examining the number bond.

- Guide children to see how the number bond shown relates to the rows of circles.

▶ **Mathematical Discourse 3**

Talk About It

- As children discuss the Talk About It questions, ask what other number sentences Boom and Buzz could have written.

- Display a number bond with the 3 and 4 reversed. Ask if Boom and Buzz would still be correct if this was the number bond they used to write their number sentences. Reinforce that the order of the addends in the bond does not affect the corresponding number sentences.

> **SMP TIP Attend to Precision**
> Engage children in describing their number sentences, justifying them with words and/or models. Encourage children to articulate clearly using accurate mathematical language and to use their justification to check for accuracy. *(SMP 6)*

▶ **Concept Extension**

Ready· **Mathematics** PRACTICE AND PROBLEM SOLVING

Assign *Practice and Problem Solving* **pages 61–62** after students have completed this section.

Guided Practice

Step By Step

- Read the example problem aloud. Revisit how children found the missing addends to number sentences on the previous pages.

▶ **Mathematical Discourse 1**

> **SMP TIP Look for Structure**
> Help children notice the structure of the addends in the example problem. Emphasize the commutative property by having children model the partners with cubes, and then invert them to show each addition. *(SMP 7)*

- Ask children to compare the addition sentences in Problem 1 to the sentences in the sample problem. Have physical cubes available for modeling.

▶ **Mathematical Discourse 2**

- Direct children's attention to Problem 2. Ask if they can think of another subtraction sentence for the number bond. Show children a bar of 3 blue and 3 yellow connecting cubes. Ask: *If there are 3 left after taking some away, how many do I need to take away?* [3] *Does it matter if I take away the blue cubes or the yellow cubes? Why not?*

- Model why there is only one subtraction sentence as well as only one addition sentence for this number bond.

▶ **Concept Extension**

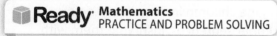 **Ready** Mathematics
PRACTICE AND PROBLEM SOLVING

Assign *Practice and Problem Solving* **pages 63–64** after students have completed this section.

Practice Together
Number Partners for 6 and 7

Write four number sentences.

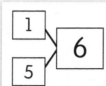

$6 = \underline{1} + \underline{5}$
$6 = \underline{5} + \underline{1}$
$6 - \underline{1} = \underline{5}$
$6 - \underline{5} = \underline{1}$

1 Complete the number bond.
Write two addition sentences.

$7 = \underline{3} + \underline{4}$

$7 = \underline{4} + \underline{3}$

2 Complete the number bond.
Write a subtraction sentence.

3 3

6

$3 = 6 - \underline{3}$

46

▶ **Mathematical Discourse**

1 *How do you know that you have found all the number sentences?*
Children may reply that modeling with cubes tells them; others may recognize that each number partner is used in every possible position in the number sentences.

2 *Can the number partners for ANY number bond be switched around to make two addition sentences? Explain.*
Most children will respond that yes they can. Some may justify by inverting bars of cubes; others may explain that since there are only two numbers to add, you can start with one or start with the other. Some children may respond that when 3 + 3 are switched around it is the same number sentence so there is only one addition sentence for it.

▶ **Concept Extension**
Recognize twin partners.

Materials For each child: 7 connecting cubes, dominoes

- Ask children if they can find number partners for 7 that only make two number sentences. Allow children to use cubes, dominoes, number bonds, or any strategies they want to explore this idea.

- Compare the partners of 7 to the partners of 6 and ask: *Why do you think 6 has two identical partners and 7 does not?* The focus should be on recognizing "twin" partners.

- Challenge children to find other numbers that have identical partners. Then discuss how twin partners are related to doubles facts.

Practice by Myself
Number Partners for 6 and 7

3 Complete the number bond.
Write two subtraction sentences.

$6 - \underline{1} = \underline{5}$

$\underline{1} = 6 - \underline{5}$

4 Complete the number bond.
Write two addition sentences.

$7 = \underline{2} + \underline{5}$

$\underline{5} + \underline{2} = 7$

5 Complete the number bond.
Write four number sentences.

$\underline{6} + \underline{1} = 7$ $7 - \underline{6} = \underline{1}$

$7 = \underline{1} + \underline{6}$ $\underline{6} = 7 - \underline{1}$

47

Step By Step

- Before children work on this page, review the models used in this lesson. Emphasize that children are free to use whatever way helps them solve the problem.

- Read each problem aloud. Draw attention to the varied positions of the equal sign in the problems on this page as you read. Then have children work independently to solve.

    Error Alert Watch for children who randomly place numbers in the blanks without connecting them to the number bond or model shown. Encourage those children to physically model the problem by acting out the additions and subtractions before recording the results.

▶ **Visual Model**

- You may wish to draw attention to the four number sentences in Problem 5, and use Mathematical Discourse question 3 to discuss.

▶ **Mathematical Discourse 3**

▶ **Fluency Practice**

▶ **Visual Model**
   Show number partners with fingers.

- Reinforce number partners by having children model them with their fingers. Demonstrate the partners 1 and 5 for the number 6 by holding up 1 finger on one hand and 5 fingers on the other.

- Have children imitate your representation. Then have them show another set of partners for 6, making sure each partner is shown on separate hands.

▶ **Mathematical Discourse**

3 *Can you find more than four number sentences for each number bond? Explain.*
No. There are only two numbers to add, so there are only two ways to write addition sentences. There are only two numbers to take away, so there are only two ways to write subtraction sentences.

▶ **Fluency Practice**
   Model number partners with connecting cubes.

Materials For each child: 7 connecting cubes, Partners for 6 Practice (Activity Sheet 6), Partners for 7 Practice (Activity Sheet 7)

Distribute Activity Sheets 6 and 7 for practice modeling number partners for 6 and 7 in a number bond. Allow children to model the partners with cubes to help them complete each number bond.

Differentiated Instruction

▶ Quick Check and Remediation

Materials For each child: 7 counters; for display: domino showing 2 and 4 as partners

- Ask children to complete the following number sentences: 2 + ___ = 7, 7 − ___ = 2. [5, 5]
- For children who are still struggling, use the chart below to guide remediation.
- After providing remediation, check children's understanding by asking them to find the missing numbers in the following number sentences: 6 = 1 + ___, 1 = 6 − ___. [5, 5]

If the error is . . .	Children may . . .	To remediate . . .
9	have added the 7 and 2.	Model the addition with counters. Help them see that 7 is the sum of 2 and another number. Encourage children to check reasonableness of answers by modeling 2 + 9. They should notice that it does not equal 7. Then model the subtractions in the same way.
4	have recorded the fact for 6.	Show children a domino with 2 and 4 as partners. Ask children what number they are partners for. Ask if it is possible for them to be partners for 7 also. Ask them to find the partner that results in 7 and record it.
any other number	have miscounted.	Provide children with physical and/or visual models representing the number sentence. Have them check the reasonableness of their answer. Encourage children to use strategies such as counting on to help them count accurately.

▶ Hands-On Activity

Find the number of counters left in the bag.

Materials For each pair: 7 counters, 1 paper bag, Number Bond Mat (Activity Sheet 3), Number Cards 0 to 11 (Activity Sheet 25), whiteboards or paper

- Provide pairs with the number cards 1–7. Have them place 6 counters in a paper bag and the number card 6 on the Number Bond Mat. One partner removes some, but not all, of the counters from the bag and places the corresponding number card in the number bond.
- The other partner determines the number of counters left in the bag and places the missing number card in the number bond. They check by counting the counters left in the bag. Children then take turns writing a number sentence for the bond until all are written.
- Repeat until all combinations of 6 are recorded and then complete for partners of 7.

▶ Challenge Activity

Build number patterns for 6 and 7.

Materials For each child: Grid Paper (Activity Sheet 8), two colors of crayons

- Have children build number patterns for the numbers 6 and 7 by coloring squares in two colors on grid paper to represent the partners of each number.
- Challenge children to find as many ways to organize the combinations as possible. The only restriction is that each square must be touching another square on a side and each color must be grouped together.
- You may want to give each child a different set of partners to explore, one for 6 and one for 7, to make it more manageable for them.
- Have children display their patterns and share how many different ways they found to arrange the partners.

Teacher Notes

Teacher-Toolbox.com

Overview

Assign the Lesson 7 Quiz and have children work independently to complete it.

Use the results of the quiz to assess children's understanding of the content of the lesson and to identify areas for reteaching. See the Lesson Pacing Guide at the beginning of the lesson and the Differentiated Instruction activities for suggested instructional resources.·

Tested Skills

Assesses 1.OA.D.8

Problems on this quiz require children to be able to fluently add and subtract within 6 and 7 and write facts for 6 and 7 in number bonds and number sentences. Children will also need to be familiar with decomposing numbers 6 and 7 and organizing facts in number bonds.

Ready® Mathematics

Lesson 7 Quiz Answer Key

Name _____

Solve.

1 Complete the number bond.
Write two subtraction sentences.

Possible answer:

$6 - \underline{5} = \underline{1}$

$\underline{5} = 6 - \underline{1}$

2 Complete the number bond.
Write two addition sentences.

Possible answer:

$7 = \underline{4} + \underline{3}$

$\underline{3} + \underline{4} = 7$

3 Complete the number bond.
Write four number sentences.

Possible answer:

$6 = \underline{2} + \underline{4}$ $6 - \underline{2} = \underline{4}$

$\underline{4} + \underline{2} = 6$. $\underline{2} = 6 - \underline{4}$

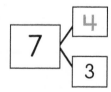

Grade 1 Lesson 7 Number Partners for 6 and 7   1

©Curriculum Associates, LLC
Copying permitted for classroom use.

Common Misconceptions and Errors

Errors may result if children:

• confuse the number partners for 6 and 7.

• incorrectly read or complete a number bond.

• incorrectly write a number sentence from a related number bond.

• do not understand the relationship between addition and subtraction.

Name _____

Solve.

④ Complete the number bond.
Write four number sentences.

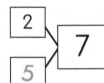

Possible answer:

$\underline{2} + \underline{5} = 7$ $\underline{2} = 7 - \underline{5}$

$7 = \underline{5} + \underline{2}$ $7 - \underline{2} = \underline{5}$

⑤ Two children are making a picture with stickers.
Each child uses flower and duck stickers to make a row of 6.
Complete the number sentence to show how each child made 6.

 $4 + \underline{2} = 6$

 $3 + \underline{3} = 6$

Grade 1 **Lesson 7** Number Partners for 6 and 7   ©Curriculum Associates, LLC
Copying permitted for classroom use.

Lesson 8
Number Partners for 8 and 9

CCSS Focus

Domain
Operations and Algebraic Thinking

Cluster
B. Understand and apply properties of operations and the relationship between addition and subtraction.

Standard
1.OA.B.3 Apply properties of operations as strategies to add and subtract. *Examples: If 8 + 3 = 11 is known, then 3 + 8 = 11 is also known. (Commutative property of addition.) To add 2 + 6 + 4, the second two numbers can be added to make a ten, so 2 + 6 + 4 = 2 + 10 = 12. (Associative property of addition.)*

Additional Standards
1.OA.C.6, 1.OA.D.8 (See page B3 for full text.)

Standards for Mathematical Practice (SMP)
2 Reason abstractly and quantitatively.

3 Construct viable arguments and critique the reasoning of others.

4 Model with mathematics.

5 Use appropriate tools strategically.

6 Attend to precision.

7 Look for and make use of structure.

8 Look for and express regularity in repeated reasoning.

Lesson Objectives

Content Objectives
- Demonstrate fluency in addition and subtraction for sums 8 and 9.
- Relate the operations of addition and subtraction through number bonds.
- Recognize 0 as a number partner.

Language Objectives
- Use visual models and number bonds to find missing number partners for 8 and 9.
- Record number partners for 8 or 9 in a number bond and use to complete up to four related addition and subtraction sentences.
- Tell why 0 can be a number partner for any number.

Prerequisite Skills

- Interpret a number bond.
- Write number sentences.
- Add and subtract within 5.

Lesson Vocabulary

- **zero** a whole number that tells when a set has no objects in it.

Review the following key terms.

- **number bond** a diagram with a total and two addends.
- **total** a number found as the result of adding.

Learning Progression

In Kindergarten children develop fluency for addition and subtraction within 5 and explore addition involving 0.

In Grade 1 children develop fluency within 10 through visual, tactile, and abstract models as well as through the use of strategies.

In this lesson children focus on the partners for 8 and 9, building on previous work with number bonds and the commutative property. They develop strategies for finding partners and extend the concept of partners to include zero, analyzing and defending it as a valid addend.

In Grade 2 children use fact families as a tool to explore sums within 20 and expand their use of strategies to gain fluency in them.

Lesson Pacing Guide

Whole Class Instruction

Day 1
45–60 minutes

Introduction
Use What You Know
• Explore It *25 min*
• Try It *20 min*

Day 2
45–60 minutes

Modeled Instruction
Explore Together
• Example Problem *5 min*
• Model It *15 min*
• Hands-On Activity *15 min*
• Fluency Practice *10 min*

Practice and Problem Solving
Assign pages 67–68.

Day 3
45–60 minutes

Guided Instruction
Learn Together
• Example Problem *10 min*
• Model It *5 min*
• Talk About It *10 min*
• Concept Extension *10 min*
• Fluency Practice *10 min*

Practice and Problem Solving
Assign pages 69–70.

Day 4
45–60 minutes

Guided Practice
Practice Together
• Example Problem *20 min*
• Problems 1–2 *25 min*

Practice and Problem Solving
Assign pages 71–72.

Day 5
45–60 minutes

Independent Practice
Practice by Myself
• Problems 3–5 *10 min*
• Concept Extension *5 min*
• Quick Check and Remediation *15 min*
• Hands-On or Challenge Activity *15 min*

Teacher-Toolbox: Lesson Quiz
Lesson 8 Quiz

Materials for Lesson Activities

Per child: 10 connecting cubes (7 of one color and 3 of another color), 9 small objects such as dried beans, 9 counters
Activity Sheet 3, Activity Sheet 9, Activity Sheet 10

Per pair: 9 connecting cubes
Activity Sheet 3*, Activity Sheet 25

For display: number bonds for 8 and 9 that include a 0, 9 red connecting cubes

* Used for more than one activity

Small Group Differentiation

Teacher-Toolbox.com

Reteach
Ready Prerequisite Lessons *45–90 min*

Grade K
• Lesson 10 Make 8 and 9
• Lesson 18 Add Within 10

Teacher-led Activities
Tools for Instruction *15–20 min*

Grade 1 *(Lesson 8)*
• Number Pairs for Sums to 10
• Missing Numbers
• Doubles Addition Facts
• Find Missing Addends for Sums to 10

Student-led Activities
Math Center Activities *30–40 min*

Grade K *(Lessons 10 and 18)*
• K.19 Show the Number
• K.24 Tell Addition Stories

Grade 1 *(Lesson 8)*
• 1.16 Number Bonds for 8 and 9
• 1.17 Cube Trains for 8 and 9

Personalized Learning

i-Ready.com

Independent
i-Ready Lessons* *10–20 min*

Grade 1 *(Lesson 8)*
• Part 1: Addition Facts
• Part 2: Addition Facts
• Addition Number Sentences
• Composing and Decomposing with 5 as a Benchmark

* i-Ready lessons may be updated during the 2016–2017 school year. Updated references will be on the Teacher-Toolbox.

👥 Introduction

Activity Explore Partners of 8 and 9

Objective

Explore combinations for the numbers 8 and 9.

Materials for each child

• 9 dried beans or other small objects

Overview

Children use counters and/or pictures to solve open-ended problems exploring possible partners for 8 and 9.

Step By Step

Explore It

Pose the problem.

• Ask children to imagine there is a field trip to a park. Then read the problem on the Student Book page aloud: *There are 2 vans to carry 8 people. How many people are in each van?*

Solve the problem.

• Have children solve the problem using the workmats on the Student Book page and dried beans, then share how they found their solution.

• Support children by asking questions such as: *How could dried beans help you find an answer? What do the beans represent?*

• Watch as children solve the problem, making sure they understand the problem and have devised a workable strategy. As they work, guide them with questions such as: *Is it possible for only 1 person to be in a van?* [Yes.] *Why?* [If 1 person is in one van, the rest can be in the other van.] *If there were 3 people in this van, how many would be in the other van?* [5] *How do you know?* [3 + 5 = 8]

• Some children will notice that there is more than one right answer. Encourage them to find additional answers.

◯ Explore It

There are 2 vans to carry 8 people.
How many people are in each van?

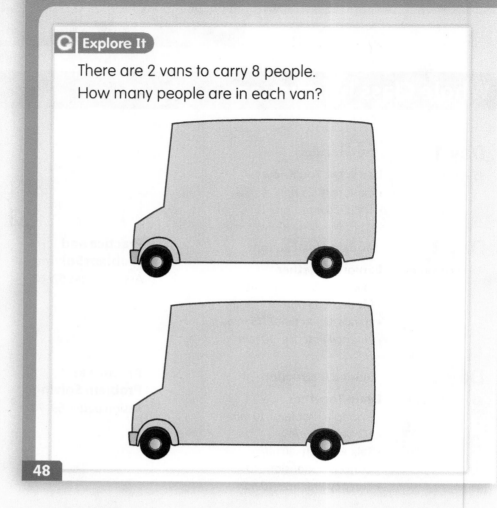

48

Share solutions.

• Invite volunteers to share their solutions and strategies in front of the class. Ask questions such as: *How can you be sure there are only 8 people in the vans? Why did you put 6 people in this van?*

• As children share solutions, write a number sentence corresponding to each solution on the board. Ask children if they think there are any other solutions to this problem and how they can be sure.

• Ask children why they think there is more than one correct solution to this problem.

Use What You Know
Number Partners for 8 and 9

 Try It

There are 9 apples. There are 2 apple trees.
Show all the ways the apples could be on the 2 trees.

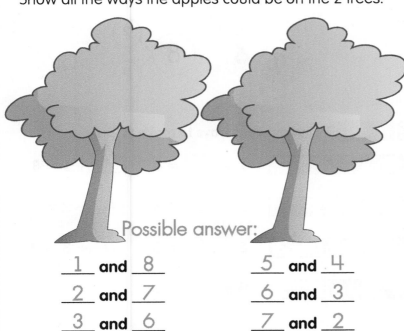

Possible answer:

___1___ and ___8___   ___5___ and ___4___

___2___ and ___7___   ___6___ and ___3___

___3___ and ___6___   ___7___ and ___2___

___4___ and ___5___   ___8___ and ___1___

49

Step By Step

Try It

Pose the problem.

• Read the problem from the Student Book page aloud: *There are 9 apples. There are 2 apple trees. Show all the ways the apples could be on the 2 trees.*

Solve the problem.

• Have children solve the problem using dried beans on the workmat on the Student Book page, then write partners of 9.

• Watch as children solve the problem, making sure they understand the problem and have devised a workable strategy. As they work, guide them with questions such as: *Is it possible for only 1 apple to be on a tree?* [Yes.] *Why?* [If 1 apple is on one tree, the rest can be on the other tree.] *If there were 3 apples on this tree, how many would be on the other tree?* [6] *How do you know?* [3 + 6 = 9]

• Have children write as many partners for 9 as they can.

• Children may not be able to show all the partners for 9 before completing the lesson, but encourage them to try to find as many combinations as they can. Then explain that the lesson will help them see all the possible ways to solve problems like this one.

• Accept, but don't expect, the use of 0 as one partner for 9. This will be explored in more detail later in this lesson.

Modeled Instruction

Step By Step

- Read aloud the problem at the top of the page. Then ask: *If there is a 3 in the top circle, what number would be in the bottom circle?* [5] *How do you know?* [3 + 5 = 8]

Model It

- Discuss how the organization of the colored squares in Model It relates to the number bond and the number sentences. Guide children to see that the number of colored squares in each strip represent the addends in both number sentences on the right.

- Have children describe how the paired number sentences are alike and how they are different. Then ask children to explain which number sentence the strip of squares shows and how they could show the other sentence using the same squares. Encourage children to make use of structure as they find the ways to make 8.

- Guide children to notice the pattern shown by the number sentences. [As the first addend increases by 1, the second addend decreases by 1.] Use the Hands-On Activity to reinforce this concept.

▶ **Hands-On Activity**

▶ **Mathematical Discourse 1 and 2**

▶ **Fluency Practice 1**

> **SMP TIP Look for Structure**
> To help children discern the structure within number partners, draw attention to the application of the commutative property by asking questions such as: *Does it matter if the blue square is the first square or the last square? Does it matter if 1 is shown first or last in the number sentence? Explain.* (SMP 7)

 **Ready** Mathematics
PRACTICE AND PROBLEM SOLVING

Assign *Practice and Problem Solving* **pages 67–68** after students have completed this section.

Number Partners for 8 and 9

> Ed rolls two number cubes.
> He adds to get 8.
> What are different ways to make 8?

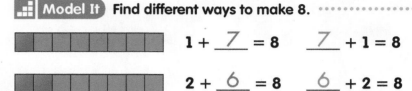

Model It Find different ways to make 8.

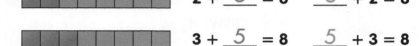

$1 + \underline{7} = 8$ $\quad$ $\underline{7} + 1 = 8$

$2 + \underline{6} = 8$ $\quad$ $\underline{6} + 2 = 8$

$3 + \underline{5} = 8$ $\quad$ $\underline{5} + 3 = 8$

$4 + \underline{4} = 8$

50

▶ **Mathematical Discourse**

1 *Why is there only 1 addition sentence for the bottom row of cubes?*

Children should notice that since both addends are the same, flipping them results in the same addition sentence. Some children may recall from the Hands-On Activity that 4 and 4 was listed only once. There is only one way to model it with an addition sentence.

Can Ed use the number cubes to show all the ways to make 8?

Children should notice that 0, 7, and 8 are not on Ed's number cubes, so he cannot show the partners 1 and 7 or 0 and 8. Some children may also notice that Ed could roll two numbers that do not add to 8.

▶ **Fluency Practice 1**

Find number partners for 8.

Materials For each child: Partners for 8 Practice (Activity Sheet 9)

Use Activity Sheet 9 (Partners for 8 Practice) to help children find and record partners for 8 in a number bond and in number sentences.

▶ **Hands-On Activity**

Model number bonds with counters.

Materials For each child: 8 counters, Number Bond Mat (Activity Sheet 3)

- Have children write an "8" in the large square of the number bond. Have them place 1 counter in one small square and the remaining counters in the second small square. Record the number in each square on the board.

- Ask: *What do you need to do so that there are 2 counters in the square that has 1 in it?* Children should see that by taking 1 counter from the square with 7 and placing it in the other square, they have the partners 2 and 6. Record these groups under the first group on the board. Continue until there are 7 counters in the first square.

- Children should see that taking a counter from one square decreases the number of counters there by one, and adding the counter to the other square, increases the number of counters there by one.

Learn Together
Number Partners for 8 and 9

A teacher makes a group of 9 children.
Some are girls. Some are boys.
What are all the ways to make 9?

📊 Model It Find different ways to make 9.

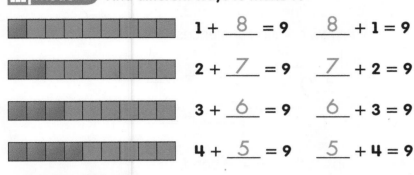

$1 + \underline{8} = 9$ $\underline{8} + 1 = 9$

$2 + \underline{7} = 9$ $\underline{7} + 2 = 9$

$3 + \underline{6} = 9$ $\underline{6} + 3 = 9$

$4 + \underline{5} = 9$ $\underline{5} + 4 = 9$

💬 Talk About It Do you agree? Why or why not?

Buzz says that 0 and 9
are partners of 9.

51

▶ Concept Extension
Use addition patterns to add with 0.

- Use addition patterns to help children make sense of addition with 0. Display the words "red" and "blue" on one side of a paper.

- Add a large circle with a 9 above it and display red and blue cubes. Ask: *If I put 0 red cubes in the circle, how many blue cubes should I put in to have 9?* Record 0 and 9 below the labels.

- Continue adding 1 red and 8 blue, etc. until there are 9 red and 0 blue in the circle. Make the numbers in the columns into number sentences, pointing out the partner of 9 and the partner of 0.

▶ Mathematical Discourse

3 *Boom says that 0 means nothing and you cannot have 'nothing' for a partner. What can you tell Boom?*

Children may respond that 0 means nothing more was added to a group or that it means there are no blue cubes.

4 *Can 0 be a partner for any number? Why?*

Yes. Children may use examples, such as, if there are 8 girls and no boys, there are still 8 people. Some children may also demonstrate their understanding by using greater numbers.

▶ Fluency Practice 2
Find number partners for 9.

Materials For each child: Partners for 9 Practice (Activity Sheet 10)

Use Activity Sheet 10 (Partners for 9 Practice) to help children find and record partners for 9 in a number bond and in number sentences.

Step By Step

- Read the problem at the top of the page aloud. Allow children to work in pairs to find all the ways to make 9 using Activity Sheet 3 (Number Bond Mat).

- Have children share the strategies they used, demonstrating them for the class, if appropriate. Discuss how they knew they found all of the combinations.

Model It

- Guide children to see the similarities among the addition sentences in Model It for both 8 and 9. Ask: *If you know one addition sentence, how does that help you know another one?* Reinforce that the commutative property allows them to "flip" the addends to make another sentence.

Talk About It

- Read Talk About It aloud. Allow children to "think out loud" about this question with a partner.

- Listen to children's ideas, helping those who think Buzz is wrong to articulate and clarify their reasoning by asking: *If there 9 children in a group, is it possible that 9 of them are girls?* [Yes.] *How many boys would be in the group?* [0]

▶ Mathematical Discourse 3 and 4

- Model addition with zero using connecting cubes. Show a bar of red cubes and write the number sentence $9 + \underline{} = 9$. Ask: *How many blue cubes can I add so that I have 9 cubes?*

▶ Concept Extension

▶ Fluency Practice 2

Ready Mathematics
PRACTICE AND PROBLEM SOLVING

Assign *Practice and Problem Solving* **pages 69–70** after students have completed this section.

👥👥 Guided Practice

Step By Step

- Have children build a bar of 3 connecting cubes of one color and 5 connecting cubes of another color. Demonstrate how to use the cubes to model each of the number sentences shown.

- Once children have modeled each number sentence in the example, ask: *Would 6 + 2 = 8 be a number sentence for this number bond?* [No.] *Why?* Guide children to understand that, although there are many ways to make 8, only the numbers in the number bond can be used in the number sentences.

- Direct children's attention to Problem 1. Ask children to share what they know about the number of addition sentences [2] that can be written for the given number bond.

- As children complete the number sentences, point out the addends they have written and ask them to describe what they notice about them. Reinforce the commutative property in the "switched around" arrangement of addends in the number sentence.

- Direct attention to Problem 2. Help children recognize that in this problem, both number sentences begin with 9, but the number that is subtracted is different.

- Have children model the subtraction sentences with connecting cubes.

▶ **Mathematical Discourse 1 and 2**

SMP TIP Repeated Reasoning

As children explore the four number sentences for a given number bond, they will begin to recognize this as a consistency (regularity in mathematics) that allows them to flexibly add and subtract within any number group. *(SMP 8)*

 **Mathematics**
PRACTICE AND PROBLEM SOLVING

Assign *Practice and Problem Solving* **pages 71–72** after students have completed this section.

Practice Together
Number Partners for 8 and 9

Write four number sentences.

$$8 = \underline{3} + \underline{5}$$
$$8 = \underline{5} + \underline{3}$$
$$8 - \underline{3} = \underline{5}$$
$$8 - \underline{5} = \underline{3}$$

1 Complete the number bond.
Write two addition sentences.

$$\underline{2} + \underline{7} = 9$$
$$\underline{7} + \underline{2} = 9$$

2 Complete the number bond.
Write two subtraction sentences.

$$9 - \underline{2} = \underline{7}$$
$$9 - \underline{7} = \underline{2}$$

52

▶ **Mathematical Discourse**

1 *Would it make sense to write the subtraction sentence 2 − 9 = 7? Why?*

Children may use examples such as: If you had 2 apples you couldn't give 9 away. Others may notice that since 9 is the total in the number bond, it must be the number from which another is subtracted.

2 *How does knowing that 2 + 7 is 9 help you know what 9 − 7 equals?*

Children should relate addition to subtraction by responding that if 2 and 7 are put together to make 9, when you take them apart again and take 7 away, 2 is left.

Practice by Myself
Number Partners for 8 and 9

3 Complete the number bond.
Write two subtraction sentences.

$\underline{3} = 9 - \underline{6}$

$9 - \underline{3} = \underline{6}$

4 Complete the number bond.
Write two addition sentences.

$9 = \underline{5} + \underline{4}$

$\underline{4} + \underline{5} = 9$

5 Complete the number bond.
Write four number sentences.

$\underline{6} + \underline{2} = 8$ $\underline{8} - \underline{6} = 2$

$8 = \underline{2} + \underline{6}$ $\underline{6} = 8 - \underline{2}$

53

▶ Concept Extension
Model subtracting 0 from 8 and 9.

Materials For display: Number bonds for 8 and 9 that include a 0

• Display the number bonds and write addition sentences for each one.

• Model and explain each sentence. Draw 9 balloons and color them blue. Relate each number sentence to the balloons.

• Invite children to write two subtraction sentences from this number bond. To help children understand, write the word "blue" under the box in the number bond containing the number 9 and "red" under the box containing the number 0 and model the sentences.

• For children who still see subtraction as "take away" say: *If I have 9 balloons and 0 balloons pop, how many balloons do I have?* [9] *If I have 9 balloons and 9 of them pop, how many do I have?* [0] In this way children are using modeling to make sense of an abstract idea.

• Repeat for the number bond for 8.

▶ Mathematical Discourse

3 *Buzz says he remembers that 5 + 4 is 9 because he knows 5 + 5 is 10 and 4 is 1 less than 5 so the answer must be 1 less than 10, or 9. What do you think of his strategy?*

Children may respond that this strategy makes sense because it uses doubles plus 1 . Some may compare it to an addition: Because 5 + 3 = 8, 5 + 4 is one more (9). They may suggest that it works backward also.

Step By Step

• Before children work on this page, review the models used in this lesson. Emphasize that children are free to use whatever way helps them solve the problems.

• Read each problem aloud. Then have children work independently to solve.

   Error Alert Observe as children work. Look for those who are struggling with the placement of the totals in the number sentences. Use the phrase *is the same as* and the word *equals* interchangeably as you discuss the placement of the equal sign.

• As children complete Problem 3, ask: *How can you be sure you have put the numbers in the correct places?* Discuss how they can check to see that the addends in the addition sentences are "flipped" and that each partner is subtracted in the subtraction sentences.

SMP TIP Repeated Reasoning
Model the situation above to emphasize the regularity within the base-ten number system. This will lead to increased curiosity and application of strategies that make use of this type of reasoning. *(SMP 8)*

▶ **Mathematical Discourse 3**

▶ **Concept Extension**

Differentiated Instruction

▶ Quick Check and Remediation

Materials For each child: 9 counters

- Ask children to write four number sentences for the number bond that includes the numbers 9, 1, and 8. [$8 + 1 = 9, 1 + 8 = 9, 9 - 1 = 8, 9 - 8 = 1$]

- For children who are still struggling, use the chart below to guide remediation.

- After providing remediation, check children's understanding using the following problem: *Write four number sentences for the number bond that includes the numbers 8, 3, and 5.* [$3 + 5 = 8, 5 + 3 = 8, 8 - 3 = 5, 8 - 5 = 3$]

If the error is . . .	Children may . . .	To remediate . . .
$1 - 9 = 8$ or $8 - 9 = 1$	be applying the commutative property to subtraction of whole numbers.	Have children read the subtraction sentence and attempt to model it with counters. Invite them to draw 1 counter and attempt to cross out 9. Lead them to recognize the only possible subtraction sentences by modeling with counters or fingers.
$9 + 1 = 8$	have written an addition sentence using the numbers in the order they were given, without regard to whether the number sentence is true.	Watch children as they model the addition with counters or fingers and ask if it makes sense that 9 and 1 more is 8. Help them model and record accurately.

▶ Hands-On Activity

Play "Break Apart" game with a partner.

Materials For each pair: 9 connecting cubes, Number Bond Mat (Activity Sheet 3), Number Cards 0 to 11 (Activity Sheet 25)

- Provide pairs with the 8 and 9 number cards. One child connects either 8 or 9 cubes and places the corresponding number card on the Number Bond Mat.

- The child hides the cubes behind his or her back and breaks the bar into two sections. One section of the cubes is placed on the number bond while the other section remains hidden.

- The partner attempts to figure out how many cubes are hidden. If correct, the child hiding the cubes reveals them. If not correct, the partner tries again until a correct answer is given.

- The partner tells either an addition or subtraction sentence that describes the number bond.

- Roles are reversed and play continues. Pairs continue reversing roles after each play until allotted time has expired.

▶ Challenge Activity

Write word problems.

Tell children to choose a number bond for 8 or a number bond for 9.

Each child should:

- Write as many different number sentences as possible for the number bond. Then write a word problem for each number sentence that uses items of interest to their classmates.

- Exchange the set of word problems with a partner.

- Solve each problem, write a number sentence for it, and make the number bond that was used for that set of problems.

- Check to see if the number bond matches the one that was used to write the problems.

- If a problem cannot be solved or the number bonds do not match, return them to the partner to be revised. If the number bonds match, post the word problems for classmates to solve.

- Repeat for another number bond, if time permits.

Teacher Notes

Teacher-Toolbox.com

Overview

Assign the Lesson 8 Quiz and have children work independently to complete it.

Use the results of the quiz to assess children's understanding of the content of the lesson and to identify areas for reteaching. See the Lesson Pacing Guide at the beginning of the lesson and the Differentiated Instruction activities for suggested instructional resources.

Tested Skills

Assesses 1.OA.B.3

Problems on this quiz require children to be able to fluently add and subtract within 8 and 9 and write facts for 8 and 9 in number bonds and number sentences. Children will also need to be familiar with decomposing numbers 8 and 9 and organizing facts in number bonds.

Ready® Mathematics

Lesson 8 Quiz Answer Key

Name _____

Solve.

1 Complete the number bond.
Write two subtraction sentences.

Possible answer:

$8 - \underline{1} = \underline{7}$

$\underline{1} = 8 - \underline{7}$

2 Complete the number bond.
Write two addition sentences.

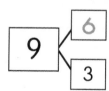

Possible answer:

$9 = \underline{6} + \underline{3}$

$\underline{3} + \underline{6} = 9$

3 Complete the number bond.
Write four number sentences.

Possible answer:

$8 = \underline{5} + \underline{3}$ $8 - \underline{5} = \underline{3}$

$\underline{3} + \underline{5} = 8$ $\underline{5} = 8 - \underline{3}$

Grade 1 Lesson 8 Number Partners for 8 and 9

1

Common Misconceptions and Errors

Errors may result if children:

- confuse the number partners for 8 and 9.
- incorrectly read or complete a number bond.
- incorrectly write a number sentence from a related number bond.
- do not understand the relationship between addition and subtraction.

Name _____

Solve.

4 Complete the number bond.
Write four number sentences.

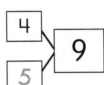

Possible answer:

__4__ + __5__ = 9   __4__ = 9 − __5__

9 = __5__ + __4__   9 − __4__ = __5__

5 Two children are making a quilt.
Each child uses pieces with ducks and bears
on them to make a row of 8.
Complete the number sentence to show how
each child made 8.

   4 + __4__ = 8

   __2__ + 6 = 8

Grade 1 Lesson 8 Number Partners for 8 and 9   2   ©Curriculum Associates, LLC
Copying permitted for classroom use.

CCSS Focus

Domain
Operations and Algebraic Thinking

Cluster
C. Add and subtract within 20.

Standard
1.OA.C.6 Add and subtract within 20, demonstrating fluency for addition and subtraction within 10. Use strategies such as counting on; making ten (e.g., $8 + 6 = 8 + 2 + 4 = 10 + 4 = 14$); decomposing a number leading to a ten (e.g., $13 - 4 = 13 - 3 - 1 = 10 - 1 = 9$); using the relationship between addition and subtraction (e.g., knowing that $8 + 4 = 12$, one knows $12 - 8 = 4$); and creating equivalent but easier or known sums (e.g., adding $6 + 7$ by creating the known equivalent $6 + 6 + 1 = 12 + 1 = 13$).

Additional Standards
1.OA.B.3, 1.OA.D.8 (See page B3 for full text.)

Standards for Mathematical Practice (SMP)

2 Reason abstractly and quantitatively.

3 Construct viable arguments and critique the reasoning of others.

4 Model with mathematics.

5 Use appropriate tools strategically.

6 Attend to precision.

7 Look for and make use of structure.

8 Look for and express regularity in repeated reasoning.

Lesson Objectives

Content Objectives

• Fluently add and subtract within 10.

• Apply strategies to addition and subtraction of sums within 10.

• Understand inverse operations as a tool for adding and subtracting.

Language Objectives

• Use visual models, 10-frames, and number bonds to find missing number partners for 10.

• Record number partners for 10 in a number bond and use to complete up to four related addition and subtraction sentences.

• Listen to the ideas of others about how finding number partners for 10 is like finding number partners for numbers less than 10 and decide if they make sense.

Prerequisite Skills

• Add and subtract within 9.

• Interpret a number bond.

• Apply the commutative property of addition.

Lesson Vocabulary

There is no new vocabulary. Review the following key terms.

• **doubles** an addition fact that has two addends that are the same, such as $4 + 4$.

• **number bond** a diagram with a total and two addends.

• **total** a number found as the result of adding.

Learning Progression

In Kindergarten children explore combinations of numbers whose sum is 10 by decomposing them with physical objects and writing corresponding number sentences.

In Grade 1 children fluently add and subtract within 10, moving beyond the physical representation by developing strategies and utilizing inverse operations.

In this lesson children gain fluency in partners for 10 by relating visual models

to number sentences and applying properties of addition and inverse operations. They analyze the structure of addends and use the structure as a strategy for developing fluency.

In Grade 2 children utilize facts of 10 as they develop strategies for finding sums within 20. These strategies provide the basis for adding numbers beyond 20 and facts of ten are applied to additions involving multiples of 10.

Lesson Pacing Guide

Whole Class Instruction

Day 1
45–60 minutes

Introduction
Use What You Know
- Explore It *25 min*
- Try It *20 min*

Day 2
45–60 minutes

Modeled Instruction
Explore Together
- Example Problem *10 min*
- Model It *20 min*
- Visual Model *15 min*

Practice and Problem Solving
Assign pages 75–76.

Day 3
45–60 minutes

Guided Instruction
Learn Together
- Example Problem *5 min*
- Model It *15 min*
- Talk About It *15 min*
- Hands-On Activity *10 min*

Practice and Problem Solving
Assign pages 77–78.

Day 4
45–60 minutes

Guided Practice
Practice Together
- Example Problem *5 min*
- Problems 1–2 *25 min*
- Fluency Practice *15 min*

Practice and Problem Solving
Assign pages 79–80.

Day 5
45–60 minutes

Independent Practice
Practice by Myself
- Problems 3–5 *15 min*
- Quick Check and Remediation *15 min*
- Hands-On or Challenge Activity *15 min*

Teacher-Toolbox: Lesson Quiz
Lesson 9 Quiz

Materials for Lesson Activities

Per child: 10 two-color counters, 10 connecting cubes
Activity Sheet 11, Activity Sheet 12, Activity Sheet 25

Per pair: Activity Sheet 25 (on colored paper), Activity Sheet 42 (on a different color paper)

For display: none

*Used for more than one activity.

Small Group Differentiation

Teacher-Toolbox.com

Reteach
Ready Prerequisite Lessons *45–90 min*

Grade K
- Lesson 13 Make 10
- Lesson 18 Add Within 10

Teacher-led Activities
Tools for Instruction *15–20 min*

Grade 1 *(Lesson 9)*
- Doubles Addition Facts
- Number Pairs for Sums to 10
- Missing Numbers
- Sums of Ten

Student-led Activities
Math Center Activities *30–40 min*

Grade K *(Lessons 13 and 18)*
- K.20 Make 10
- K.21 Draw to Make 10
- K.24 Tell Addition Stories

Grade 1 *(Lesson 9)*
- 1.05 Match to Make 10

Personalized Learning

i-Ready.com

Independent
i-Ready Lessons* *10–20 min*

Grade 1 *(Lesson 9)*
- Part 1: Addition and Subtraction Fact Families
- Part 2: Addition and Subtraction Fact Families
- Addition Facts for 10

* i-Ready lessons may be updated during the 2016–2017 school year. Updated references will be on the Teacher-Toolbox.

 **Introduction**

Activity Ways to Make 10

Objective
Explore combinations of ten.

Materials for each child
- 10 connecting cubes
- Number Cards 0 to 11 (Activity Sheet 25)

Overview
Children model a situation presented in a story and find different ways to make 10.

Step By Step

Explore It

Pose the problem.

- Ask children to imagine that they work at a space airport on a distant planet. Then read the problem on the Student Book page aloud: *10 spaceships return home from Earth. Some land on the left and some land on the right. How could the spaceships land?*

Solve the problem.

- Have children use the workmat on the Student Book page and 10 connecting cubes to solve the problem.

- Support children by asking questions such as: *How can you use the cubes to show how the 10 spaceships land? What does each cube represent?*

- Watch as children solve the problem, making sure they understand the problem and have devised a workable strategy. As they work, guide them with questions such as: *Could 9 spaceships land on the left side?* [Yes.] *If so, how many spaceships would land on the right?* [1] *How do you know?* [If 9 landed on the left side, that would leave only 1 of 10 spaceships to land on the right.]

- Encourage children to think about all the different ways the 10 spaceships could land on the left and right. Ask them to think about a quick way to find different ways to make 10.

Use What You Know
Number Partners for 10

Explore It

10 spaceships return home from Earth.
Some land on the left and some land on the right.
How could the spaceships land?

__1__ and __9__ make 10.
__2__ and __8__ make 10.
__3__ and __7__ make 10.
__4__ and __6__ make 10.

54

Share strategies.

- Ask different children to share one way the 10 spaceships could land. Discuss how there is more than one answer to the problem.

- Ask children to share if they found different ways to make 10 on their own. Listen to all strategies and discuss if any strategies seem easier than others for finding different ways to make 10.

Extend a strategy.

- Ask children to hold up both hands showing all their fingers and ask: *How many fingers do you have?* Write 10 on the board and circle it.

- Tell children to fold down a thumb and ask how many fingers are folded down and how many are held up. Write 1 and 9 under the 10. Continue folding down one finger at a time. Have children record each corresponding number pair on the Student Book page.

Relate the strategy.

- Discuss how the finger activity was like the cube activity and how it was different. Relate this activity to one the children completed in the previous lesson using cubes and a number bond. As one group was made larger by 1, the other group became smaller by 1.

55

▶▶ Try It

Mia needs to show two cards that make 10.
What are five ways she could show 10?
Possible answer:

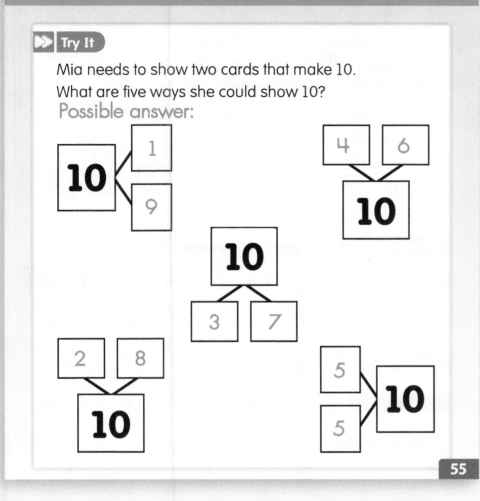

Step By Step

Try It

Pose the problem.

- Say: *Mia is playing a math game. Her friend has a card with the number 10. Mia needs to show two cards that make 10. What are five ways she could show a set of cards showing the numbers 1–9?*

Solve the problem.

- Distribute a set of cards showing the numbers 1–9 to each child.

- Guide children to solve the problem by using the number cards to find pairs of numbers that make 10. Have them record the number partners in the number bonds on the Student Book page. Children may not be able to find all the ways to make 10, but allow time for them to find as many as possible.

- Some children may benefit from continuing to use the connecting cubes. Make sure they are available for children who choose to use them. Encourage children who are struggling to model the situation with cubes.

Share strategies.

- Invite volunteers to share the strategies they used to find number pairs for 10. Listen to all strategies, but focus on the strategies that incorporate the idea that as one group is made larger by 1, the other group becomes smaller by 1.

- Look for children who name a limited number of combinations. Additional support is provided in the Visual Model and the Hands-On Activity in the lesson.

👥 **Modeled Instruction**

Step By Step

- Begin by having children share their understandings from the Activity in the Introduction. Encourage them to clearly articulate the structure they noticed. Rephrase or question statements that may not be easily understood.

- Read the example problem aloud. Have children draw lines to connect each partner pair for 10 shown by the number cards. Discuss why 5 does not have a partner shown.

▶ **Visual Model**

Model It

- Remind children of how they used fingers in the Activity in the Introduction to model ways to make 10 and compare that model to the colored cube illustration shown in Model It. Then have children complete the addition sentences.

▶ **Mathematical Discourse 1 and 2**

- Engage children in finding a subtraction for each of the additions shown. Display an open addition sentence and an open subtraction sentence. Place cards with numbers on them in the addition sentence to show $1 + 9 = 10$.

- Invite a volunteer to rearrange the cards to make a subtraction sentence. Repeat for each of the addition sentences.

SMP TIP Repeated Reasoning

To emphasize the relationship between addition and subtraction, alter the above activity by creating either an addition or subtraction sentence and allowing children to find a related number sentence. Their work with related number sentences helps children recognize regularity and lays the groundwork for advanced addition and subtraction strategies. (SMP 8)

 **Ready**® **Mathematics**
PRACTICE AND PROBLEM SOLVING

Assign *Practice and Problem Solving* **pages 75–76** after students have completed this section.

Explore Together
Number Partners for 10

Jen has cards with numbers 1 to 9.
She adds two of the cards to get 10.
What are different ways to make 10?

▦ **Model It** **Find different ways to make 10.** ·················

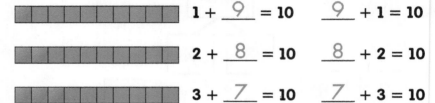

$1 + \underline{9} = 10$ $\underline{9} + 1 = 10$

$2 + \underline{8} = 10$ $\underline{8} + 2 = 10$

$3 + \underline{7} = 10$ $\underline{7} + 3 = 10$

$4 + \underline{6} = 10$ $\underline{6} + 4 = 10$

$5 + \underline{5} = 10$

56

▶ **Mathematical Discourse**

1 *How are finding the addition sentences for 10 like finding addition sentences for 8 and 9?*
Some children may refer to the pattern, noting that as one addend increases, the other decreases. Others may suggest that when you know the addition for one set of numbers, you can "flip" it to find another addition.

2 *Boom says 0 and 10 are also a number pair for 10. Do you agree? What cards would you need to find all the number pairs for 10?* Yes, because $0 + 10 = 10$ and $10 + 0 = 10$. You would need all of the cards showing the numbers 0–10.

▶ **Visual Model**
See partner pairs.

- Provide children with another visual representation of partners. Write the numbers 0–10 on the board horizontally.

- Ask children why you included 0 at the beginning of the model. Children should notice that 0 and the number you are finding partners for will always be a number pair, so it should be included when finding all the partner pairs.

- Ask children to find the partners for 10 and connect each partner pair.

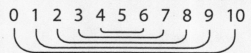

Learn Together
Number Partners for 10

10 beads. 6 are red. The rest are yellow.
How many are yellow? How do you know?

 Model It Find 6 + ____ = 10. ·····················

Start with 6.
Add counters to make 10.
How many did you add?

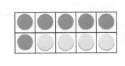

6 + _4_ = 10

 Talk About It Who is right? How do you know? ············

Buzz writes:	Boom writes:
10 + 8 = 2	8 + 2 = 10
2 + 10 = 12	2 + 8 = 10
8 = 10 − 2	8 = 10 − 2
6 = 8 − 2	2 = 10 − 8

57

▶ Hands-On Activity
Use a 10-frame to make 10.

Materials For each child: 20 counters (10 red and 10 yellow), 10-Frame (Activity Sheet 11)

- Provide each child with a 10-frame. Point out that each frame is divided into two groups of 5 just as their hands are divided into two groups of 5 fingers.

- Have children place 6 red counters on the frame and ask how many more they need to add to fill the frame. Instruct them to fill the remaining squares with yellow counters.

▶ Mathematical Discourse

3 *How is the 10-frame like the other models you have used? How is it different?*

Children may notice similarities such as it is like holding up and folding down fingers. Children may say that a difference is that it is a rectangle divided into 10 squares.

Step By Step

- Read the problem at the top of the page aloud. Discuss several ways children could know there are 4 yellow beads. Encourage children to recall strategies or visual models they used earlier in the lesson.

Model It

- Direct children's attention to Model It. Ask: *How does the 10-frame show the partner for 6?* Have children share addition and subtraction sentences for number bond.

▶ **Hands-On Activity**

▶ **Mathematical Discourse 3**

Talk About It

- Have children discuss Talk About It with a partner. Direct attention to the number bond. Guide children to model each number sentence on a 10-frame, then compare that to the sentences Buzz and Boom wrote. Ask children to discuss why the first sentence Buzz wrote does not make sense.

- Ask: *If Buzz wrote the first number sentence correctly, would he then be correct, too?* Help children recognize that not all the numbers he used are included in the number bond so he would not be correct.

- Ask: *Why do you think Buzz wrote these number sentences?* Discuss how the numbers from the number bond were added or subtracted, but not in a way that resulted in another number from the number bond.

> **SMP TIP Repeated Reasoning**
> Pointing out the relationships among the models and strategies children have used emphasizes the regularity in reasoning used in mathematics and leads children to realize that they can apply what they have learned to new situations. *(SMP 8)*

 Mathematics PRACTICE AND PROBLEM SOLVING

Assign *Practice and Problem Solving* **pages 77–78** after students have completed this section.

👥👥 Guided Practice

Step By Step

- Read the example problem aloud. Ask: *Why are there only two number sentences for these partners?* Encourage children to think about activities from previous lessons that explored the concept of "twin" partners.

- Revisit the partners from the Activity in the Introduction and the Visual Model from earlier in the lesson to see that 5 stands alone. Model with cubes how "flipping" the addition results in an identical number sentence.

- Direct children to Problem 1. Ask: *What strategy might you use to find the missing number in the number bond?* Listen for strategies such as counting on, using fingers, etc. Model any strategies not already discussed.

- Have children model the number sentences by drawing counters in 10-frames.

▶ **Mathematical Discourse 1 and 2**

- Have children model the addends with connecting cubes and discuss how this model compares to their drawings in the 10-frames. Compare these models to the other models children have seen and discuss which model(s) each child prefers and why.

- As children discuss, make sure they understand that no one model is better than another and that their choices are individual. What works for one child may or may not work for another child.

- Encourage children to model the subtraction sentences in Problem 2 with 10-frames. Ask: *Why doesn't it make sense to write 9 − 1 as a subtraction sentence for this number bond?* Revisit the problem on the previous page and the misconception Buzz had in combining the numbers in the bond inappropriately.

▶ **Fluency Practice**

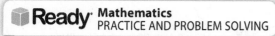

PRACTICE AND PROBLEM SOLVING

Assign *Practice and Problem Solving* **pages 79–80** after students have completed this section.

Practice Together
Number Partners for 10

Write two number sentences.

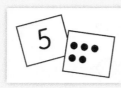

$$10 = \underline{5} + \underline{5}$$

$$10 - \underline{5} = 5$$

❶ Complete the number bond.
Write two addition sentences.

$$10 = \underline{9} + \underline{1}$$

$$\underline{1} + \underline{9} = 10$$

❷ Complete the number bond.
Write two subtraction sentences.

$$10 - 9 = \underline{1}$$

$$9 = 10 - \underline{1}$$

▶ **Mathematical Discourse**

1 *How do the 10-frame drawings show both addition sentences?*

Children may respond that in the first 10-frame, 1 yellow is shown and then 9 red. In the second 10-frame, 9 red are shown and then 1 yellow. Children may also notice that the frames are "flipped" versions of each other.

2 *How can thinking about a 10-frame or other model help you make sure you write the correct number sentences for a number bond?*

Children may respond that when they "see" the problem they can tell what numbers go together and how to take one away to get the other number.

▶ **Fluency Practice**

Identify number partners for 10.

Materials For each child: Partners for 10 Practice (Activity Sheet 12)

Use the activity sheet to help children practice identifying partners with totals of 10 in a number bond.

Practice by Myself
Number Partners for 10

3 Complete the number bond.
Write two subtraction sentences.

$10 - \underline{3} = \underline{7}$

$10 - \underline{7} = \underline{3}$

4 Complete the number bond.
Write two addition sentences.

$10 = \underline{2} + \underline{8}$

$\underline{8} + \underline{2} = 10$

5 Complete the number bond.
Write four number sentences.

| 4 | 6 |

10

$\underline{4} + \underline{6} = 10$ $10 - \underline{4} = \underline{6}$

$10 = \underline{6} + \underline{4}$ $\underline{4} = 10 - \underline{6}$

59

Step By Step

- Before children work on this page, review the models used in the lesson. Emphasize that children are free to use whatever way helps them solve the problem.

- Read each problem aloud. Encourage children to notice what some of the differences among the three problems are.

- Some children may see that the totals in the number bonds and/or number sentences are displayed differently, that there are both addition and subtraction sentences to complete, or that Problem 3 is the only Problem that shows a number card and a dot card.

▶ **English Language Learners**

- Have children work independently to solve the problems.

- You may wish to encourage children to use a different representation to model the number bond in Problem 5. Have children explain why they chose the model they did to show the number bond.

▶ **Mathematical Discourse 3**

SMP TIP Look for Structure/Repeated Reasoning
Have children model all the ways to decompose 10 in a 10-frame. As children organize counters on a 10-frame, they are repeatedly finding combinations whose sum is 10. Lead them to recognize that one color decreases in number each time the other color increases in number. Relate this to the modeling done with partners for 8 and 9 in the previous lesson. (SMP 7 and 8)

▶ **English Language Learners**

Some children may find it difficult to express themselves in sharing what they notice about the differences among the problems, so may not offer ideas. To get a window on their thinking, encourage them to share ideas with a partner they trust, or speak with you later when there is no peer pressure.

▶ **Mathematical Discourse**

3 *How can you always know what number to start with when writing a subtraction sentence?*

Some children may notice that the number in the number bond from which both lines extend is the one to begin with. Others may say to start with the greatest number. Encourage students to focus on the meaning of the numbers based on their locations in the number bond. Avoid emphasizing that the greatest number comes first, as this could cause misconceptions in later math courses.

Differentiated Instruction

▶ Quick Check and Remediation

Materials For each child: 10 connecting cubes, 10 counters

- Ask children to write the four number sentences for the number bond including 10, 3, and 7. [3 + 7 = 10, 7 + 3 = 10, 10 − 3 = 7, 10 − 7 = 3]

- For children who are still struggling, use the chart below to guide remediation.

- After providing remediation, check children's understanding using the following problem: *Write the four number sentences for the number bond including 10, 4, and 6.* [4 + 6 = 10, 6 + 4 = 10, 10 − 4 = 6, 10 − 6 = 4]

If the error is . . .	Children may . . .	To remediate . . .
10 + 3 = 13 3 + 7 = 10 10 − 7 = 3 7 − 3 = 4	be using any numbers in the number bond to create number sentences.	Write the number 10 in an open number bond. Have children model the two addends in the other sections of the number bond with bars of 3 and 7 cubes. Model combining and separating the two bars as children complete the number sentences.
7 − 10 = 3	applying the commutative property to subtraction.	Have children read the subtraction sentence and attempt to model it with a picture. Invite them to draw 7 circles and attempt to cross out 10. Lead them to recognize the corresponding subtraction sentences by modeling with counters or fingers.

▶ Hands-On Activity

Play "Sums of Ten" memory game.

Materials For each pair: Number Cards 0 to 11 (Activity Sheet 25), Dot Cards—Small (Activity Sheet 42)

- Print number cards 1–9 on colored paper and dot cards 1–9 on different color paper and provide for each pair.

- Mix up the cards and place them facedown. Children take turns turning up two cards, one of each color. If the sum of the two cards is 10, the child keeps the cards. If not, the cards are turned facedown again. Play continues until all combinations have been found.

- Optional: add cards with the numbers 10 and 0 and cards containing ten and 0 dots.

▶ Challenge Activity

Make a book.

- Tell children they will work together in pairs to create a book. Each page will include a different combination of two colors of dots that make 10.

- Challenge pairs to put the dots into contexts so that the pages of their book tell a story.

- When the pages are complete, help children think of a title and have them design a cover and then make a book for their classmates to read.

Teacher Notes

Teacher-Toolbox.com

Overview

Assign the Lesson 9 Quiz and have children work independently to complete it.

Use the results of the quiz to assess children's understanding of the content of the lesson and to identify areas for reteaching. See the Lesson Pacing Guide at the beginning of the lesson and the Differentiated Instruction activities for suggested instructional resources.

Tested Skills

Assesses 1.OA.C.6

Problems on this quiz require children to be able to fluently add and subtract within 10 and write facts for 10 in number bonds and number sentences. Children will also need to be familiar with decomposing the number 10 and organizing facts in number bonds.

Ready® **Mathematics**

Lesson 9 **Quiz Answer Key**

Name _____

Solve.

1 Complete the number bond.
Write two addition sentences.

10 ⟨ 8 / 2 ⟩

Possible answer:

10 = __8__ + __2__

__2__ + __8__ = 10

2 Complete the number bond.
Write two subtraction sentences.

1   9 / 10

Possible answer:

10 − __1__ = __9__

__1__ = 10 − __9__

3 Complete the number bond.
Write four number sentences.

10 / 6   4

Possible answer:

10 = __6__ + __4__   10 − __6__ = __4__

__4__ + __6__ = 10   __6__ = 10 − __4__

Grade 1 **Lesson 9** Number Partners for 10   **1**

Common Misconceptions and Errors

Errors may result if children:

• incorrectly read or complete a number bond.

• incorrectly write a number sentence from a related number bond.

• do not understand the relationship between addition and subtraction.

Name _____

Solve.

4 Complete the number bond.
Write four number sentences.

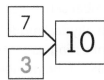

Possible answer:

__7__ + __3__ = 10   __3__ = 10 − __7__

10 = __3__ + __7__   10 − __3__ = __7__

5 Tina and Lata each make a bracelet with 10 gray and white beads.
Complete the number sentence to show how each girl used 10 beads.

Tina's bracelet

8 + __2__ = 10

Lata's bracelet

__5__ + 5 = 10

2

Lesson 10
Understand the Equal Sign

CCSS Focus

Domain
Operations and Algebraic Thinking

Cluster
D. Work with addition and subtraction equations.

Standard
1.OA.D.7 Understand the meaning of the equal sign, and determine if equations involving addition and subtraction are true or false. *For example, which of the following equations are true and which are false? $6 = 6, 7 = 8 - 1, 5 + 2 = 2 + 5, 4 + 1 = 5 + 2$.*

Additional Standards
1.OA.C.6, 1.OA.D.8 (See page B3 for full text.)

Standards for Mathematical Practice (SMP)

2 Reason abstractly and quantitatively.

6 Attend to precision.

Lesson Objectives

Content Objectives

• Understand that the equal sign is used to indicate that one quantity is the same as another.

• Match equivalent expressions.

• Write and identify true and false number sentences.

• Rewrite a false number sentence so that it is true.

Language Objectives

• Orally define and use the key mathematical term *equal sign (=)* when communicating with a partner.

• Draw diagrams to explain whether a number sentence is true or false.

• Use physical models such as connecting cubes to show how to make a false number sentence true.

Prerequisite Skills

• Add to find totals up to 10.

• Find missing addends.

Lesson Vocabulary

• **equal sign (=)** a symbol that means "is the same as."

• **is the same as** indicates that quantities equal each other.

• **number sentence** a sentence with symbols and numbers that compares two amounts as equal, less than, or greater than.

Learning Progression

In Kindergarten children work with number partners through 10 using mostly objects and drawings. Children solve joining situations that lead to an understanding of "equal" as groups that have the same amount or quantity.

In Grade 1 children connect the concepts of "joining," "separating," and "equal" to the symbols $+$, $-$, and $=$. Children understand that the equal sign signifies an equivalent relationship.

In this lesson children are introduced to the meaning of the equal sign, working with picture models and number bonds that show equal quantities on both sides

of the equal sign. Children also write number sentences to show that equivalent expressions are equal, identify true and false number sentences, and rewrite false number sentences as true.

In Grade 2 children use the equal sign to write number sentences for adding to, taking from, putting together, taking apart, and comparing situations. Children write number sentences to express uneven numbers as totals of two equal addends and represent rectangular arrays with number sentences expressing totals as sums of equal addends.

Lesson Pacing Guide

Whole Class Instruction

Day 1 45–60 minutes	**Introduction** **Use What You Know** • Explore It *25 min* • Try It *20 min*	
Day 2 45–60 minutes	**Modeled Instruction** **Explore Together** • Opening Question *5 min* • Think *15 min* • Talk About It *10 min* • Hands-On Activity *15 min*	**Practice and Problem Solving** Assign pages 83–84.
Day 3 45–60 minutes	**Guided Instruction** **Explore Together** • Hands-On Problem *10 min* • Problem 1 *10 min* • Talk About It *10 min* • Concept Extension *15 min*	**Practice and Problem Solving** Assign pages 85–86.
Day 4 45–60 minutes	**Guided Practice** **Connect It** • Problems 2–4 *15 min* **Independent Practice** **Show What I Know** • Problem 5 *15 min* • Intervention, On-Level, or Challenge Activity *15 min*	**Practice and Problem Solving** Assign pages 87–88.

Teacher-Toolbox: Lesson Quiz
Lesson 10 Quiz

Materials for Lesson Activities

Per child:	20 connecting cubes (10 each in two different colors), 16 two-color counters, 1 pan balance Activity Sheet 13
Per pair:	Activity Sheet 41
For display:	none

Small Group Differentiation

Teacher-Toolbox.com

Reteach
Ready Prerequisite Lessons *45–90 min*

Grade K
• Lesson 18 Add Within 10
• Lesson 20 Practice Facts to 5

Teacher-led Activities
Tools for Instruction *15–20 min*

Grade 1 *(Lesson 10)*
• Sums of Ten

Student-led Activities
Math Center Activities *30–40 min*

Grade K *(Lessons 18 and 20)*
• K.24 Tell Addition Stories
• K.26 Add and Move
• K.27 Solve and Color

Grade 1 *(Lesson 10)*
• 1.18 Use Vocabulary for *Equal*
• 1.19 True Number Sentences

Personalized Learning

i-Ready.com

Independent
i-Ready Lessons* *10–20 min*

Grade 1 *(Lesson 10)*
• Part 1: Addition Facts
• Part 2: Addition Facts
• Addition Facts for 10
• Joining Sets to Add

* i-Ready lessons may be updated during the 2016–2017 school year. Updated references will be on the Teacher-Toolbox.

Introduction

Activity Understand the Equal Sign

Objective

Model that the same total can have different parts and write number sentences to show that the total is equal to the sum of the parts.

Materials for each child

- 16 two-color counters (or 10 counters of one color and 6 of another color)

Overview

Children act out two addition problems that have different parts and the same total. They identify the total as equal to the sum of the parts and write number sentences for each.

Step By Step

Explore It

Pose the problem.

- Tell children to imagine that the playground has new swings for children to use during recess. Then read the problem from the Student Book page aloud: *Yesterday there were 6 girls and 2 boys on the swings. Today there are 4 boys and 4 girls on the swings. How many children played on the swings each day?*

Act out the problem.

- Have 6 girls and 2 boys go to one side of the classroom.

- Have 4 boys and 4 girls go to the opposite side of the classroom.

- Point to the side with 6 girls and 2 boys. Ask: *How many girls are there?* [6] *How many boys?* [2]

- Then point to the side with 4 boys and 4 girls. Ask: *How many boys are there?* [4] *How many girls?* [4]

Write addition number sentences.

- Write 6 + 2 on the board. Ask: *What is the total?* [8] Complete the number sentence by writing the equal sign and the total: 6 + 2 = 8.

Use What You Know

Understand the Equal Sign

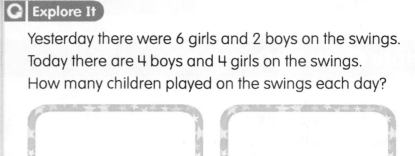

Explore It

Yesterday there were 6 girls and 2 boys on the swings.
Today there are 4 boys and 4 girls on the swings.
How many children played on the swings each day?

Yesterday	Today

$\underline{6} + \underline{2} = \underline{8}$ $\underline{4} + \underline{4} = \underline{8}$

60

- Have children use counters to model this part of the problem on the "Yesterday" workmat on the Student Book page, then write the number sentence below.

- Write 4 + 4 on the board. Ask: *What is the total?* [8] Complete the number sentence by writing the equal sign and the total: 4 + 4 = 8.

- Have children use counters to model this part of the problem on the "Today" workmat on the Student Book page, then write the number sentence below.

Talk about the addition sentences.

- Ask: *What does 6 + 2 show?* [how many girls and how many boys]

- Ask: *What does 4 + 4 show?* [how many boys and how many girls]

- Point to the totals in the two number sentences on the board. Ask: *What do you notice about the totals?* [They are the same, 8.]

- Discuss how different parts can make the same total.

- Discuss how the number sentences show that the same number of children played on the swings each day.

⏩ **Try It**

Tom has 3 red beads and 4 yellow beads.
Dee has 2 blue beads and 5 green beads.
Do Tom and Dee each have the same number
of beads?

Tom's beads:

$$\underline{3} + \underline{4} = \underline{7}$$

Dee's beads:

$$\underline{2} + \underline{5} = \underline{7}$$

61

Step By Step

Try It

Pose the problem.

- Read the problem on the Student Book page aloud: *Tom has 3 red beads and 4 yellow beads. Dee has 2 blue beads and 5 green beads. Do Tom and Dee each have the same number of beads?*

Model and solve the problem.

- Ask children to draw a picture and write an addition number sentence to represent the number of beads each child has.

Lead the class in discussion.

- Invite volunteers to share the number sentences they wrote. Discuss whether the number sentences children wrote accurately represent the information in the problem by asking questions such as: *What does 3 + 4 show?* [how many red beads and how many yellow beads Tom has] and *What does 2 + 5 show?* [how many blue beads and how many green beads Dee has].

- Choose a correct number sentence to represent the number of beads each child has and write it on the board.

- Point to the totals in the two number sentences on the board. Ask: *What do you notice about the totals?* [They are the same, 7.]

- Discuss how this problem shows that different parts can make the same total.

- Discuss how the number sentences show that Tom and Dee each have the same number of beads.

- Encourage children to use the words *"is the same as"* when describing the totals.

- Watch for children who do not see the quantities as equal after completing the additions. Additional support is provided in the Hands-On Activity in the lesson.

Modeled Instruction

Step By Step

- Read aloud the question at the top of the page. Relate "is the same as" to the equal sign (=).

▶ **English Language Learners**

- Use the two picture models on the page to demonstrate the equality of the quantities on either side of the equal sign. The first model, 4 = 4, shows the identity property of addition. The second model shows that a quantity may be an expression or a number.

Think

- Review the Think section with the children. Reinforce the connection between the equal sign and the phrase "is the same as." Read the number sentence under the first number bond aloud and ask: *Is 1 + 3 the same as 4? Why or why not?* Ask a similar question for the second number sentence: *Is 4 the same as 1 + 3? How do you know?*

- Ask children what they notice about the placement of the equal sign. Children may say that it comes before the total in one number sentence and after the total in the other. Discuss how the equal sign still means "is the same as" no matter where it is placed in a number sentence.

Talk About It

- Present the Talk About It questions. Discuss that "true" means "correct" or "right." Children may identify the first number sentence as false and the second number sentence as true.

▶ **Mathematical Discourse 1**

▶ **Hands-On Activity**

 **Ready** **Mathematics**
PRACTICE AND PROBLEM SOLVING

Assign *Practice and Problem Solving* **pages 83–84** after students have completed this section.

Understand the Equal Sign

 What does = mean?

= is the **equal sign**.
= means **is the same as**.

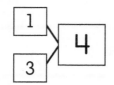 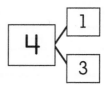

4   =   4   1 + 3 = 4

Think The total can go to the left or right of = .

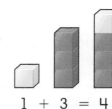

1 + 3 = __4__   __4__ = 1 + 3

Talk About It

4 + 2 = 5   5 = 2 + 3

Are both number sentences true?
How do you know?

62

▶ **Mathematical Discourse**

1 *How do you know that 4 + 2 = 5 is not a true number sentence?*

Children may say that first they find 4 + 2 [6], then compare the total they find to the total that is given [5]. 6 is not equal to 5, so the number sentence is not true.

▶ **English Language Learners**

Provide cards to support the meaning of the mathematical symbols + and =. One card shows the symbol "+" with the word "plus" beneath it; another card shows the symbol "=" with the word "equal" beneath it. Have children use the cards to help them talk about the concept of equality using mathematical language.

▶ **Hands-On Activity**

Use counters to make equal quantities.

Materials For each child: 8 counters

- Have children make two groups of 4 counters.

- Children count and write the number sentence that shows the equality: 4 = 4.

- Have children repeat with groups of 1 and 3 counters and a group of 4 counters for the number sentence 1 + 3 = 4.

Explore Together
Understand the Equal Sign

 Find partners with equal totals.

Look at the → Use cubes. → Complete the
numbers.   Make partners. number sentences.

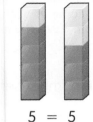

4 $\boxed{?}$ → 5

3 $\boxed{?}$ → 5

5 = 5

$4 + \underline{1} = 5$

$5 = 3 + \underline{2}$

$4 + \underline{1} = 3 + \underline{2}$

① **Find partners with equal totals.**

2 $\boxed{?}$ → 6   6 $\boxed{?}$ → 3

$2 + \underline{4} = 6 \quad 6 = \underline{3} + 3$

$\underline{2} + \underline{4} = \underline{3} + \underline{3}$

💬 **Talk About It** ·······························

Mia joins 2 cubes and 6 cubes.
Dan joins 4 cubes and 3 cubes.
Do they have the same number of cubes? How do you know?

63

▶ Concept Extension
Make a false number sentence true.

- Talk with children about ways to change the number of cubes that Mia and Dan have so that they have an equal number of cubes.

- Ask: *Who has more cubes, Mia or Dan?* [Mia] *How many more cubes?* [1] *What could you do to make the number of cubes that they have equal?* [take 1 cube away from Mia or give Dan 1 more cube]

- Ask: *What number sentences could you write if you take 1 cube away from Mia?* Make sure children see that one of the addends representing Mia's cubes will decrease by 1, but that the other addends will stay the same. You could write the number sentence $1 + 6 = 4 + 3$ or the number sentence $2 + 5 = 4 + 3$. Then ask: *What number sentences could you write if you give Dan 1 more cube?* Children should suggest that one of the addends representing Dan's cubes will increase by 1, but the other addends will stay the same. So you could write $2 + 6 = 5 + 3$ or $2 + 6 = 4 + 4$.

▶ Mathematical Discourse

2 *How can a number sentence that has different addends on each side of the equal sign be a true number sentence?*

The addends make the same total; the totals are equal so the number sentence is true.

Step By Step

- Provide connecting cubes of two different colors to children. Have children look at the first picture on the page and join cubes to model adding $4 + 1$ and $3 + 2$.

- Children may count cubes or compare lengths to find the total. Relate the parts and the total to the number sentences $4 + 1 = 5$ and $5 = 3 + 2$. Ask: *What do you notice about the totals?* [They are the same.] *Does 5 = 5?* [yes]

- Then draw attention to the number sentence showing $4 + 1 = 3 + 2$. Discuss the connection between the number bonds and the number sentences.

- Listen for statements that indicate children's understanding that the totals on each side of the equal sign are the same even though the parts are different.

- Have children complete Problem 1. Relate the number bonds to the number sentences.

▶ **Mathematical Discourse 2**

Talk About It

- Present the Talk About It problem and questions. Children may say that Mia and Dan do not have the same number of cubes. Children may find the total number of cubes each has and compare the totals: $2 + 6 = 8$ and $4 + 3 = 7$; 8 is not equal to 7.

▶ **Concept Extension**

SMP TIP Attend to Precision
In this lesson, children examine the precise meaning of the equal sign. *(SMP 6)*

 **Mathematics**
PRACTICE AND PROBLEM SOLVING

Assign *Practice and Problem Solving* **pages 85–86** after students have completed this section.

👥👥 Guided Practice

Step By Step

- Discuss each Connect It problem as a class using the discussion points outlined below.

Draw

- Guide children to recognize that both expressions have the same addends, but in a different order.
- Encourage children to think of a way to tell whether the number sentence is true without finding the totals on each side of the equal sign. [The addends are the same on both sides of the equal sign, so the number sentence is true.]
- Invite children to share their drawings. Ask questions such as: *Why did you draw the number of objects you did? Does anyone have a question about [child's name]'s drawing?*
- Encourage children to answer questions about their drawings. You may wish to have them modify their drawings or make new ones based on the questions from others.

Evaluate

- As children decide whether the number sentences are true, revisit the earlier discussion about addends that make the same total. Guide children to recall that when any two addends on each side of an equal sign make the same total, the number sentence is true.
- Ask children to explain their reasoning about why each false number sentence is not true.

Create

- Ask children to talk to a partner about the problem. After a few minutes, begin a class discussion about the number sentences children have written.
- Have volunteers share their number sentences. Record their responses on the board. Then have children explain why they think there is more than one correct way to make the number sentences true.

Connect It

Understand the Equal Sign

 Draw Is $3 + 5 = 5 + 3$ a true number sentence? Draw to explain why or why not.

Possible answer: Yes, $3 + 5 = 5 + 3$ is true.

Children's drawings might demonstrate that adding 5 objects to 3 objects is the same as adding 3 objects to 5 objects. In both cases the total is 8.

---

❸ **Evaluate** Circle the true number sentences.

$4 = 6$ $(7 = 4 + 3)$

$(1 + 3 = 2 + 2)$ $4 + 2 = 1 + 6$

$2 + 7 = 5 + 3$ $(8 + 2 = 4 + 6)$

---

❹ **Create** Make true number sentences.

Possible answer:

 $\underline{8} + \underline{2} = 3 + 7$ $4 + 5 = \underline{3} + \underline{6}$

SMP TIP Reason Quantitatively
Finding equivalent and non-equivalent expressions involves making sense of quantities and their relationships. *(SMP 2)*

📘 **Ready** **Mathematics**
PRACTICE AND PROBLEM SOLVING

Assign *Practice and Problem Solving* **pages 87–88** after students have completed this section.

Show What I Know
Understand the Equal Sign

⑤ **Think about the equal sign.**

A: Write the number of shapes below each group.
Write = in the box if it is a true number sentence.
Write X in the box if it is not a true number sentence.

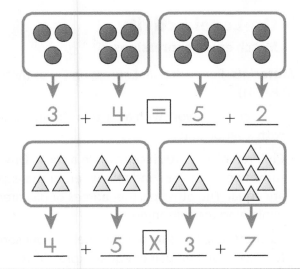

<u>3</u> + <u>4</u> [=] <u>5</u> + <u>2</u>

<u>4</u> + <u>5</u> [X] <u>3</u> + <u>7</u>

B: Use the number sentence that is not true.
Write a true number sentence. Show your work.

Possible answer:

<u>4</u> + <u>5</u> [=] <u>6</u> + <u>3</u>

65

Step By Step

- Tell children they will work on their own to complete the problems on this page.

- Review the directions aloud, making sure children understand what they are expected to do.

- In Part A, children count and write the number of shapes in groups to find addends in number sentences.

- In Part B, children correct the false number sentence from Part A.

- Observe children as they work. Ask questions such as the following to encourage thinking and problem-solving strategies.

Do you write an equal sign in the box for the number sentence in Part B? Why or why not?

What would happen if you remove 1 triangle from the right group in the right box of the second problem? What would happen if you add 1 triangle to the left group in the right box?

Do you think there is more than one way to fix the number sentence that is not true in Part A? Explain why you think so.

Scoring Rubrics

Expectations for 4–3 Points

Points	Expectations
4	The child: • correctly identifies and writes the number of objects in each group as an addend. • writes the equal sign between expressions in a true number sentence and marks an X between expressions in a false number sentence. • shows work in Part B that accurately represents groups that make a false number sentence true and writes a number sentence that is supported by the work shown.
3	The child: • may correctly identify and write the addends, but find incorrect totals for one of the expressions. • may show work in Part B that accurately represents the groups, but may write an incorrect number sentence.

Expectations for 2–0 Points

Points	Expectations
2	The child: • may write incorrect addends. • may show work in Part B that inaccurately represents one side of the number sentence. • may write an incorrect number sentence.
1	The child: • writes addends that have no relationship to the objects in the groups. • may show work in Part B that has no connection to the number sentence. • fails to write a number sentence.
0	The child: • does not attempt to solve the problems.

Differentiated Instruction

▶ Intervention Activity

Use a balance to model equal quantities.

Materials For each child: 20 connecting cubes 1, pan balance

- For children who have difficulty, provide connecting cubes and a pan balance to model making equal and unequal quantities.

- Have children place 1 connecting cube in each pan. Connect the idea of the balanced pans to the equal sign. Explain that the pans balance because the quantities in each pan are the same, or equal. Write 1 = 1 on the board.

- Repeat with different quantities, using the same number of connecting cubes in each pan to balance. Record examples on the board, e.g., 3 = 3, 4 = 4, etc.

- Connect the idea of pans that do not balance to quantities that are not equal: 3 cubes in one pan and 4 cubes in the other. Have children add 1 cube to the pan with 3 cubes and tell whether it balances. Record the number sentence on the board: 3 + 1 = 4.

- Have children determine by experimentation how many cubes on each side make the pans balance. Record the number sentences.

▶ On-Level Activity

Match equal expressions.

Materials For each pair: Expression Cards (Activity Sheet 41)

- Have children work with a partner. Provide partners with a set of cards.

- Children place cards facedown in a stack. One partner turns two cards over and tells whether the expressions are equal. The other partner agrees or disagrees, explaining the reasoning.

- Partners take turns recording true number sentences for each matched pair of equal expressions.

- Once players have gone through all the cards in the stack, shuffle the cards that did not match and continue playing for as long as time allows.

▶ Challenge Activity

Make a false number sentence true.

Materials For each child: True and Untrue Number Sentences (Activity Sheet 13)

- Provide children with Activity Sheet 13 (True and Untrue Number Sentences).

- Have them write the number sentence represented by the drawing and tell whether it is true or false. [4 + 5 = 3 + 7 is a false number sentence because 4 + 5 = 9 and 3 + 7 = 10; 9 is not equal to 10.]

- Challenge children to fix the number sentence to be true and make a new drawing to represent the true number sentence.

- Discuss whether children found different ways to make a true number sentence. [Possible drawings and true number sentences: draw 1 more triangle in the group in the left box: 5 + 5 = 3 + 7; remove 1 star from the group in the right box: 4 + 5 = 3 + 6]

Teacher Notes

Teacher-Toolbox.com

Overview

Assign the Lesson 10 Quiz and have children work independently to complete it.

Use the results of the quiz to assess children's understanding of the content of the lesson and to identify areas for reteaching. See the Lesson Pacing Guide at the beginning of the lesson and the Differentiated Instruction activities for suggested instructional resources.

Tested Skills

Assesses 1.OA.D.7

Problems on this quiz require children to be able to use the equal sign (=) to indicate that one quantity is the same as another and write and identify true and false number sentences. Children will also need to be familiar with adding to find totals up to 10 and finding missing addends.

Ready® **Mathematics**

Lesson 10 Quiz Answer Key

Name _____

Solve.

1. Write the number of shapes below each group.
   Write = in the box if it is a true number sentence.
   Write X in the box if it is not a true number sentence.

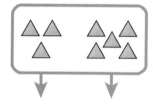 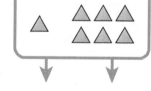

___3___ + ___5___   [X]   ___1___ + ___6___

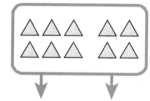

___6___ + ___4___   [=]   ___7___ + ___3___

2. Make true number sentences.

   Possible answer:

   ___4___ + ___6___ = 8 + 2   2 + 4 = ___3___ + ___3___

Grade 1 **Lesson 10** *Understand* the Equal Sign   1   ©Curriculum Associates, LLC
Copying permitted for classroom use.

Common Misconceptions and Errors

Errors may result if children:

- do not understand that the equal sign signifies an equivalent relationship.
- incorrectly count objects in a group and write incorrect addends.
- incorrectly read or complete a number sentence.

Lesson 10 **Quiz Answer Key** continued

Name _____

Solve.

3 Circle the true number sentences.

$\boxed{2 + 3 = 5}$ $6 = 7$

$\boxed{5 + 3 = 4 + 4}$ $5 + 5 = 6 + 3$

$6 + 4 = 7 + 2$ $\boxed{1 + 9 = 7 + 3}$

4 Make true number sentences.
Possible answer:

$\underline{3} + \underline{6} = 4 + 5$ $2 + 6 = \underline{4} + \underline{4}$

5 Find partners with equal totals.
Complete the number sentences.

```
 3                    ?
    → 7        7 ←
 ?                    2
```

$3 + \underline{4} = 7$ $\underline{5} + 2 = 7$

$\underline{3} + \underline{4} = \underline{5} + \underline{2}$

Grade 1 **Lesson 10** *Understand the Equal Sign*

2

©Curriculum Associates, LLC
Copying permitted for classroom use.

Lesson 11
Facts I Know

CCSS Focus

Domain
Operations and Algebraic Thinking

Cluster
C. Add and subtract within 20.

Standard
1.OA.C.6 Add and subtract within 20, demonstrating fluency for addition and subtraction within 10. Use strategies such as counting on; making ten (e.g., $8 + 6 = 8 + 2 + 4 = 10 + 4 = 14$); decomposing a number leading to a ten (e.g., $13 - 4 = 13 - 3 - 1 = 10 - 1 = 9$); using the relationship between addition and subtraction (e.g., knowing that $8 + 4 = 12$, one knows $12 - 8 = 4$); and creating equivalent but easier or known sums (e.g., adding $6 + 7$ by creating the known equivalent $6 + 6 + 1 = 12 + 1 = 13$).

Additional Standard
1.OA.D.8 (See page B3 for full text.)

Standards for Mathematical Practice (SMP)
2 Reason abstractly and quantitatively.

3 Construct viable arguments and critique the reasoning of others.

6 Attend to precision.

7 Look for and make use of structure.

Lesson Objectives

Content Objectives
- Fluently add and subtract within 10.
- Use strategies such as counting on; using the relationship between addition and subtraction; and using a known sum or difference to find an unknown sum or difference to add and subtract.

Language Objectives
- Identify and use more than one strategy to complete addition or subtraction sentences in which the unknown is located in all positions.
- Record addition facts to 10 in an addition table.
- Compare two approaches to addition or subtraction and describe how they are the same or different.

Prerequisite Skills

- Add and subtract within 10.
- Understand the relationship between addition and subtraction.

Lesson Vocabulary

- **addition table** a table showing expressions for sums to 20.

Review the following key term.

- **addend** a number being added.

Learning Progression

In Kindergarten children fluently add and subtract within 5 and record number partners within 10 using a drawing or number sentence.

In Grade 1 children develop fluency in addition and subtraction within 10 through the use of models and strategies.

In this lesson children complete and analyze addition tables, using strategies they have developed to find sums and differences. They demonstrate fluency by completing addition and subtraction number sentences in which the unknown is located in all positions.

In Grade 2 children become fluent in addition and subtraction within 20, applying strategies developed for addition and subtraction within 10.

Lesson Pacing Guide

Whole Class Instruction

Day 1
45–60 minutes

Introduction
Use What You Know
• Explore It *25 min*
• Try It *20 min*

Day 2
45–60 minutes

Modeled Instruction
Explore Together
• Model It *30 min*
• Fluency Practice *15 min*

Practice and Problem Solving
Assign pages 91–92.

Day 3
45–60 minutes

Guided Instruction
Learn Together
• Model It *15 min*
• Talk About It *5 min*
• Concept Extension *10 min*
• Fluency Practice *15 min*

Practice and Problem Solving
Assign pages 93–94.

Day 4
45–60 minutes

Guided Practice
Practice Together
• Problems 1–3 *25 min*
• Visual Model *5 min*
• Concept Extension *15 min*

Practice and Problem Solving
Assign pages 95–96.

Day 5
45–60 minutes

Independent Practice
Practice by Myself
• Problem 4 *15 min*
• Quick Check and Remediation *15 min*
• Hands-On or Challenge Activity *15 min*

Teacher-Toolbox: Lesson Quiz
Lesson 11 Quiz

Materials for Lesson Activities

Per child: 1 red and 1 green colored pencil, 10 connecting cubes, 10 counters, index cards
Activity Sheet 15, Activity Sheet 16, Activity Sheet 17, Activity Sheet 18

Per pair: 20 two-color counters, 1-in. by 11-in. strip of heavy paper divided into a 0-10 game board
Activity Sheet 14, Activity Sheet 25 (printed on two different colors of paper)

For display: none

Small Group Differentiation

Teacher-Toolbox.com

Reteach
Ready Prerequisite Lessons *45–90 min*

Grade K
• Lesson 18 Add Within 10
• Lesson 19 Subtract Within 10

Teacher-led Activities
Tools for Instruction *15–20 min*

Grade 1 *(Lesson 11)*
• Doubles Addition Facts
• Number Pairs for Sums to 10
• Count on to Add

Student-led Activities
Math Center Activities *30–40 min*

Grade K *(Lessons 18 and 19)*
• K.24 Tell Addition Stories
• K.25 Subtract and Match

Grade 1 *(Lesson 11)*
• 1.06 Number Bond Facts

Personalized Learning

i-Ready.com

Independent
i-Ready Lessons* *10–20 min*

Grade 1 *(Lesson 11)*
• Part 1: Addition Facts
• Part 2: Addition Facts
• Addition Facts for 10
• Counting On to Add
• Acting Out Addition and Subtraction

* i-Ready lessons may be updated during the 2016–2017 school year. Updated references will be on the Teacher-Toolbox.

Introduction

Activity Number Detectives

Objective

Build addition/subtraction fluency

Materials for each pair

• 20 two-color counters

Overview

Children apply familiar strategies for addition and subtraction to find a missing number from a set of clues provided by the teacher.

Step By Step

Explore It

Pose the problem.

• Tell children that today they are going to be detectives (remind them that a detective uses clues to solve a mystery). Explain that you will give them clues that they will use to find missing numbers.

Playing the game.

• Place each child with a partner and provide them with counters. Ask them to work together using counters on the workmat on the Student Book page to find the missing number or numbers from each clue given.

• Once the "mystery" is solved, have children write a corresponding addition or subtraction sentence, circling the number or numbers they "found."

Mystery numbers.

• Read the following clue: *I have 6 marbles. Some are red and some are yellow. There is the same number of red marbles as yellow marbles. How many are red and how many are yellow?* [3 are red and 3 are yellow]

• Watch children as they work together towards a solution, repeating the clue as necessary.

• Encourage children to share their number sentences and explain how they solved the mystery. Listen for and rephrase strategies to validate their use.

Explore It

Listen to the clues.
Use counters to find missing numbers.

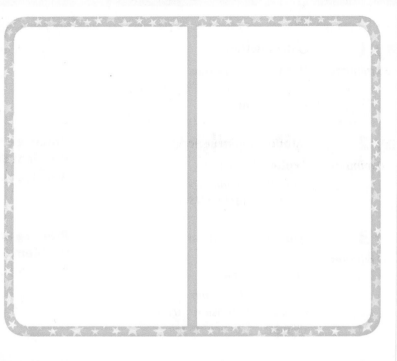

66

• Read the next clue: *I have 7 marbles. Some are red and some are yellow. I have 2 yellow marbles, how many are red?* [5] This clue could result in an addition or subtraction sentence. Discuss why either sentence models the solution.

• Continue giving children clues similar to the first two clues, asking them to share solutions and strategies after each one.

One more or one less.

• Pose the open-ended clue: *I have 9 marbles. Some are red and some are yellow. There are more red marbles than yellow marbles. How many red marbles and how many yellow marbles could I have?* [The number of red marbles plus the number of yellow marbles should sum to 9.]

• Allow children to share results and explain reasoning. Children should notice that there are many correct answers. Then ask: *What if there was 1 more red marble than yellow marbles? How many of each color would I have?* [5 red and 4 yellow] Ask for volunteers to demonstrate their strategy or thinking for the class to observe.

• Read the clue: *I have the same number of red marbles as yellow marbles. If I take a yellow marble away, I will have 7 marbles. How many red and how many yellow marbles will I have?* [3 yellow and 4 red] Have children share solutions and strategies.

• Continue with similar clues as long as interest is sustained.

▶▶ **Try It**

I have 8 marbles.
5 marbles are red, the rest are blue.
How many are blue?

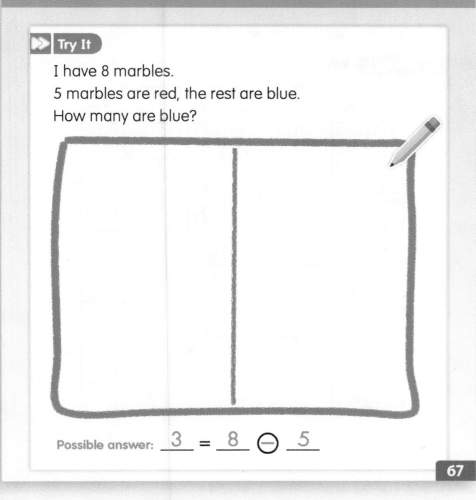

Possible answer: __3__ = __8__ ⊖ __5__

67

Step By Step

Try It

Pose the problem.

- Read the problem from the Student Book page aloud: *I have 8 marbles. 5 marbles are red, the rest are blue. How many are blue?*

Use a model to solve.

- Have children draw a picture to model the problem.

- Then have children write a number sentence for their solution and strategy.

- Observe as children work, asking questions that encourage reasoning.

Lead the class in discussion.

- Encourage children to share their number sentences and explain how they solved the mystery. Listen for and rephrase strategies to validate their use.

- This clue could result in an addition or subtraction sentence. Discuss why either sentence models the solution.

Modeled Instruction

Step By Step

Model It

- Draw attention to the addition table. Have children use green to lightly shade the boxes containing number partners that they already know, such as sums within 5; or that are easy to remember, such as + 1 sums.

- Have children use red to lightly shade addition facts where they need to stop and think. Build confidence by pointing out that there are only a limited number of addition facts such as these.

- Provide children time to complete the table. Encourage them to use strategies to find addition facts they do not know.

- Discuss strategies children used to find more difficult sums. Help children see how the sums on the table resemble number paths. To find 4 + 3 by counting on, find 4 + 1 and say *4 + 1 is 5* as the first count then move to the right saying *4 + 2 is 6, 4 + 3 is 7.*

- Demonstrate how children can use a known fact such as 2 + 3 to find 2 + 4 by adding 1. You may want them to model with their fingers to show that when an addend increases by 1 the sum also increases by 1.

- Reinforce that the structure of the table can help you know more facts. Show only the column beginning with 1 + 4 and cover the 3 in 3 + 4. Ask children how the table could help them know what number you covered. The total and the first addend each increase by 1 as you move down the column, so knowing that 2 + 4 = 6 can help children know that the covered number is 3.

▶ **Mathematical Discourse 1**

- Use the table to practice subtraction facts. Point to several addition facts, and ask for a related subtraction fact.

▶ **Fluency Practice 1**

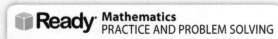

Ready® Mathematics
PRACTICE AND PROBLEM SOLVING

Assign *Practice and Problem Solving* **pages 91–92** after students have completed this section.

Explore Together

Facts I Know

What addition facts do you know?

Model It Write the totals. ·······································

1 + 1 2	1 + 2 3	1 + 3 4	1 + 4 5	1 + 5 6	1 + 6 7	1 + 7 8	1 + 8 9	1 + 9 10
2 + 1 3	2 + 2 4	2 + 3 5	2 + 4 6	2 + 5 7	2 + 6 8	2 + 7 9	2 + 8 10	
3 + 1 4	3 + 2 5	3 + 3 6	3 + 4 7	3 + 5 8	3 + 6 9	3 + 7 10		
4 + 1 5	4 + 2 6	4 + 3 7	4 + 4 8	4 + 5 9	4 + 6 10			
5 + 1 6	5 + 2 7	5 + 3 8	5 + 4 9	5 + 5 10				
6 + 1 7	6 + 2 8	6 + 3 9	6 + 4 10					
7 + 1 8	7 + 2 9	7 + 3 10						
8 + 1 9	8 + 2 10							
9 + 1 10								

68

▶ **Mathematical Discourse**

1 *How can an addition table help you find sums you do not remember?*
Children may respond that they can use the table to count on. Some may notice the "pattern" where the sum is increased by one when an addend is increased by one.

▶ **Fluency Practice 1**

Find the missing number.

Materials For each pair: Addition Table 2 (Activity Sheet 14)

Distribute Activity Sheet 14 (Addition Table 2). Have partners take turns covering an addend or sum in the table while their partner's eyes are closed. The partner must find the missing addend or sum and tell or write an addition and/or subtraction for the number sentence. Once successful, children cross out the fact. Play continues until all facts are crossed out.

Learn Together
Facts I Know

What is the same about the facts in any row? What is different?

Model It Look at the facts in the colored boxes.

1+1 2	1+2 3	1+3 4	1+4 5	1+5 6	1+6 7	1+7 8	1+8 9	1+9 10
2+1 3	2+2 4	2+3 5	2+4 6	2+5 7	2+6 8	2+7 9	2+8 10	
3+1 4	3+2 5	3+3 6	3+4 7	3+5 8	3+6 9	3+7 10		
4+1 5	4+2 6	4+3 7	4+4 8	4+5 9	4+6 10			
5+1 6	5+2 7	5+3 8	5+4 9	5+5 10				
6+1 7	6+2 8	6+3 9	6+4 10					
7+1 8	7+2 9	7+3 10						
8+1 9	8+2 10							
9+1 10								

💬 **Talk About It**

How can the table help you learn addition facts?

69

Step By Step

Model It

- Provide children time to examine the table on this page. Explain that it is the same addition table that they completed, but it is colored to show facts that are alike.

- Direct attention to the yellow boxes. Ask: *What addend is the same in all boxes?* [1] *How are the facts in the yellow row different from the facts in the yellow column?* [The order of addends is different.] Use the same questions to talk about the green boxes.

- Ask children to describe how the facts in the orange boxes are alike. Guide them to recognize that these are all doubles facts.

- Have children examine the purple boxes and tell how these facts are alike. They should notice that these facts are all partners of 10. Use Mathematical Discourse question 2 to extend the discussion about patterns in the addition table.

▶ **Mathematical Discourse 2**

Talk About It

- Read the Talk About It question aloud. Continue to reinforce the idea that children can use patterns in the table to remember addition facts.

> **SMP TIP Look for Structure**
> As children examine the addition table, help them notice the structure inherent in the table—as an addend increases by one, the sum increases by one—leading them to recognize how the structure in our number system can be used to remember addition facts. *(SMP 7)*

▶ **Concept Extension**

▶ **Fluency Practice 2**

📦 **Ready**· **Mathematics**
PRACTICE AND PROBLEM SOLVING

Assign *Practice and Problem Solving* **pages 93–94** after students have completed this section.

▶ **Concept Extension**

Examine doubles plus 1 facts on the addition table.

Have children find the doubles facts on the table (the orange boxes). Explain that they can use these facts to find other facts that they may not know. Direct attention to the doubles fact 4 + 4. Have children circle the facts 4 + 5 and 5 + 4. Guide them to recognize that in these facts one addend is 4 and one is 1 more than 4. Write the three facts on the board as they appear in the table. Ask: *How many more is the total of 4 + 5 than 4 + 4?* [1 more] Explain that these facts are called doubles plus 1 because the total is 1 more than the related doubles fact.

▶ **Mathematical Discourse**

2 *Which other boxes could also be colored yellow? Green? Purple? Why?*

Children should recognize that 1 + 1 can be yellow since one addend is 1 and 2 + 1, 2 + 2, and 2 + 8 can also be green since one addend is 2. The facts 9 + 1 and 5 + 5 can be purple since they are partners of 10. Some children might respond that some facts fit with two different categories.

▶ **Fluency Practice 2**

Practice facts for sums 6, 7, 8, 9 and 10.

Materials For each child: Facts Practice 1 (Activity Sheet 16)

Use Activity Sheet 16 (Facts Practice 1) to provide children practice with facts for sums 6, 7, 8, 9, and 10.

👥👥 Guided Practice

Step By Step

- Draw attention to the problems shown on this page. Point out that each question shows a section of the addition table.
- Remind children of the activity they completed in the Explore Together portion of the lesson. Help them see that this page is similar except that in some boxes more than one number is missing.
- Draw attention to the boxes at the end of each row in Problem 1. Ask: *Both of these boxes show 10 as the sum so how can you decide what numbers go in the empty spaces?* Help children notice that in each row the first addend remains the same while the second addend increases by one.
- Encourage children to use the observation above as they complete the sections of the table in each problem.

▶ **Mathematical Discourse 1**

▶ **Concept Extension**

▶ **Visual Model**

Ready® Mathematics
PRACTICE AND PROBLEM SOLVING

Assign *Practice and Problem Solving* **pages 95–96** after students have completed this section.

Practice Together
Facts I Know

Fill in the blanks.

①

$4 + \underline{3}$	$\underline{4} + 4$	$4 + 5$	$\underline{4} + 6$
7	8	$\underline{9}$	10
$\underline{5} + 3$	$5 + \underline{4}$	$\underline{5} + 5$	
8	9	10	

②

$\underline{7} + 1$	$7 + \underline{2}$	$\underline{7} + 3$
8	9	10
$8 + \underline{1}$	$\underline{8} + 2$	
9	10	

③

$2 + \underline{4}$	$\underline{2} + 5$	$2 + 6$	$\underline{2} + 7$	$2 + \underline{8}$
6	7	$\underline{8}$	$\underline{9}$	10
$\underline{3} + 4$	$3 + \underline{5}$	$\underline{3} + 6$	$3 + \underline{7}$	
7	8	9	$\underline{10}$	

70

▶ **Mathematical Discourse**

1 *How can you use what you know to find a fact you do not know?*

Some children may say that they know doubles so if $4 + 4 = 8$, then $4 + 5 = 9$. Others may apply inverse operations, saying that if $5 + 3$ is 8, then $8 - 5$ is 3.

▶ **Visual Model**

Relate subtraction to addition.

Write on the board.

$$4 + 3$$
$$7$$

Relate subtraction to addition by changing the plus sign to an equal sign and drawing a line from the 7 to each addend, as shown.

$$4 = 3$$
$$\diagdown\diagup$$
$$7$$

Discuss how to visualize subtraction by making a path with your finger from 7 to 3 to 4 saying: *Seven minus 3 equals 4.* Repeat moving from 7 to 4 to 3.

▶ **Concept Extension**

Use structure to extend the addition table.

Materials Optional: Addition Table 3 (Activity Sheet 15)

Draw attention to the empty boxes on the page. Ask the children what addition sentences might go in those boxes. Remind them that although they have not learned those sums yet, they can use the table to find them. Discuss how they can use the structure of the table to find that $8 + 3 = 11$ since $8 + 2 = 10$.

Have children needing an additional challenge complete Activity Sheet 15 (Addition Table 3) by filling in all the missing addition facts. Then have them describe how the original addition facts in the table help them find those that are not shown.

Practice by Myself

Facts I Know

4️⃣ Fill in the table.

Partners of 7	Partners of 8	Partners of 9	Partners of 10
0 + 7 = _7_	0 + 8 = _8_	0 + 9 = 9	0 + 10 = 10
1 + _6_ = 7	1 + 7 = 8	1 + 8 = 9	1 + 9 = 10
_2_ + 5 = 7	2 + 6 = 8	2 + 7 = 9	2 + 8 = 10
3 + _4_ = 7	3 + 5 = 8	3 + 6 = 9	3 + 7 = 10
4 + _3_ = 7	4 + 4 = 8	4 + 5 = 9	4 + 6 = 10
_5_ + 2 = 7	5 + 3 = 8	5 + 4 = 9	5 + 5 = 10
6 + _1_ = 7	6 + 2 = 8	6 + 3 = 9	6 + 4 = 10
_7_ + 0 = 7	7 + 1 = 8	7 + 2 = 9	7 + 3 = 10
	8 + 0 = 8	8 + 1 = 9	8 + 2 = 10
		9 + 0 = 9	9 + 1 = 10
			10 + 0 = 10

71

Step By Step

- Before children work on this page, discuss similarities and differences between the table on this page and the ones on previous pages. Emphasize that children are free to use whatever strategies help them complete the table.

▶ **English Language Learners**

- Have children work independently to fill in the table. Remind children who are having difficulty completing the table that organizing information is a good strategy to use whenever there are many combinations to keep track of.

- Encourage children to relate number sentences where the numbers are written in reverse order. Listen for observations children make about the structure of the addition sentences.

- After children have completed their work, you may wish to ask Mathematical Discourse question 2. If time allows, follow up by having children write subtraction facts for partners of 8, 9, and 10. Some children may notice that there are two subtraction sentences that can be written for each addition sentence. Encourage them to articulate a strategy, such as moving the sum to the other side of the addition fact then writing a subtraction fact.

▶ **Mathematical Discourse 2**

> **SMP TIP Attend to Precision/Critique Reasoning**
> Emphasize the value of accuracy in calculations by displaying the incorrect addition 3 + 4 = 8 and the corresponding subtraction facts. Tell children that the addition you just wrote is Boom's work and ask them to respond to it. Discuss how, by miscalculating the addition, all the other sentences were incorrect as well. *(SMP 3 and 6)*

▶ **English Language Learners**

During whole group discussions or when giving oral directions, assist children by either writing the given numbers on the board or repeating the numbers in the child's native language.

▶ **Mathematical Discourse**

2 *How could you find a subtraction sentence for any addition sentence?*

Children should recognize that for any addition fact, a subtraction fact resulting in one of the addends can be written by subtracting the other addend from the sum.

Differentiated Instruction

▶ Quick Check and Remediation

Materials For each child: Facts Practice 2 (Activity Sheet 17), Facts Practice 3 (Activity Sheet 18), 10 connecting cubes

- Ask children to complete Activity Sheet 17 (Facts Practice 2), containing sums for 6, 7, 8, 9, and 10.

- For children who are still struggling, use the chart below to guide remediation.

- After providing remediation, check children's understanding using Activity Sheet 18 (Facts Practice 3), containing sums for 6, 7, 8, 9, and 10 in a different arrangement.

If the error is . . .	Children may . . .	To remediate . . .
incorrect responses primarily among subtraction facts	not be relating subtraction to addition.	Model an addition fact with cubes, fingers, and number bonds. Write a related subtraction fact. Model and discuss with the children how knowing an addition fact can help find a difference. Write another subtraction fact and have children find a related addition fact.
incorrect responses primarily among missing addends	not recognize the application of partner pairs.	Provide children with additional opportunities to play partner games where the sum is known and one addend must be found.
incorrect responses among a specific fact family	not have developed strategies for that family.	Review possible strategies with the children allowing them to develop and practice strategies that enable them to work with the challenging facts.

▶ Hands-On Activity

Play an addition/subtraction game.

Materials For each pair: 1-in. by 11-in. strip of heavy paper divided into a 0–10 game board, 12 counters, Number Cards 0 to 11 (Activity Sheet 25)

- Print number cards 1–9 on colored paper and number cards 0–5 on a different color paper and provide for each pair.

- Place the two sets of cards facedown. One partner turns up one card from each pile, makes an addition or subtraction sentence, and places a counter on the sum or difference found on the game board. The cards are then placed back under the piles.

- The other partner repeats the activity. If both the sum and difference of the cards drawn are already covered, play goes to the other partner.

- Play continues until all the numbers on the strip are filled.

▶ Challenge Activity

Write clues for number partners.

Materials For each child: counters, index cards

- Remind children of the "Number Detectives" game from the Activity in the Introduction. Challenge them to write their own "clues" for number partners. Tell them they may work in pairs to make up clues that are different from the ones in the Activity in the Introduction.

- Encourage them to try "2 more or 2 less" clues. They should write each clue clearly on a card and then read it to their partner who works it out to make sure it is clear and has a solution.

- These clues can be placed in a container for other children to try to solve.

Teacher Notes

Teacher-Toolbox.com

Overview

Assign the Lesson 11 Quiz and have children work independently to complete it.

Use the results of the quiz to assess children's understanding of the content of the lesson and to identify areas for reteaching. See the Lesson Pacing Guide at the beginning of the lesson and the Differentiated Instruction activities for suggested instructional resources.

Tested Skills

Assesses 1.OA.C.6

Problems on this quiz require children to be able to fluently add and subtract within 10 using counting on and other strategies, analyze and complete addition tables, and complete addition number sentences in which the unknown is located in all positions. Children will also need to be familiar with the relationship between addition and subtraction.

Ready Mathematics
Lesson 11 Quiz Answer Key

Name _____

Solve.

 Color all the partners of 8.

1 + 1	1 + 2	1 + 3	1 + 4	1 + 5	1 + 6	1 + 7	1 + 8	1 + 9
2 + 1	2 + 2	2 + 3	2 + 4	2 + 5	2 + 6	2 + 7	2 + 8	
3 + 1	3 + 2	3 + 3	3 + 4	3 + 5	3 + 6	3 + 7		
4 + 1	4 + 2	4 + 3	4 + 4	4 + 5	4 + 6			
5 + 1	5 + 2	5 + 3	5 + 4	5 + 5				
6 + 1	6 + 2	6 + 3	6 + 4					
7 + 1	7 + 2	7 + 3						
8 + 1	8 + 2							
9 + 1								

Common Misconceptions and Errors

Errors may result if children:

- do not recognize the application of partner pairs to find missing addends.
- have not developed strategies for a specific fact family.
- incorrectly read or complete a number sentence.

Lesson 11 **Quiz Answer Key** continued

Name _____

Solve.

2 Complete the addition sentences to show the partners of 10.

$0 + 10 = \underline{10}$ $6 + \underline{4} = 10$

$1 + \underline{9} = 10$ $\underline{7} + 3 = 10$

$\underline{2} + 8 = 10$ $\underline{8} + 2 = 10$

$3 + \underline{7} = 10$ $9 + \underline{1} = 10$

$4 + \underline{6} = 10$ $10 + \underline{0} = 10$

$\underline{5} + 5 = 10$

3 Fill in the blanks.

3 + 2	3 + 3	3 + 4	3 + 5	3 + 6
5	6	7	8	9
4 + 2	4 + 3	4 + 4	4 + 5	4 + 6
6	7	8	9	10
5 + 2	5 + 3	5 + 4	5 + 5	
7	8	9	10	

Grade 1 **Lesson 11** Facts I Know

2

Assessment

Step By Step

- Have children solve the problems individually and show their work. Emphasize that children are free to use whatever way helps them solve the problems.

- For Problems 1 and 2, children model the given problem using number bonds and number sentences. If some children struggle, suggest that they draw a picture to help them understand what is happening.

- Observe as children work. Be alert to those who may still have difficulty with the meaning of the equal sign, particularly in problems 3, 5, and 6. Elicit that the equal sign means *is the same as*.

Solve the problems.

1. Al has 5 toy trucks. He has 5 toy cars. How many toy trucks and cars does Al have?

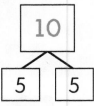

$5 + 5 = \underline{10}$

---

2. There are 3 birds. More birds join them. Now there are 7 birds. How many birds join?

$3 + \underline{4} = 7$

---

3. Make a true number sentence.
   Possible answer:
   $\underline{8} + \underline{1} = 2 + 7$

4. $10 - 8 = \underline{2}$

---

5. $\underline{7} = 5 + 2$

6. Make a true number sentence.

   $5 + \underline{3} = 3 + 5$

72

Teacher Notes

---

7 4 books and 2 books. How many books in all?

4 + 2 = __6__   __6__ = 2 + 4

Is 4 + 2 = 2 + 4 a true number sentence? __Yes__
Draw to explain why or why not.

Possible answer: Drawings might demonstrate that
adding 2 objects to 4 objects is the same as adding
4 objects to 2 objects.

In both cases, the total is 6.

8 10 beads in all.
3 are red. The rest are yellow.
How many are yellow?

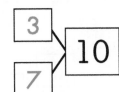

Complete the number bond.
Write four number sentences
for this problem.

__3__ + __7__ = 10   10 − __3__ = __7__

10 = __7__ + __3__   __3__ = 10 − __7__

73

Teacher Notes

Assessment

Step By Step

Put It Together

- On this page, children write the partners of 8 or 9 in number bonds and use these to write a true number sentence equating two sets of the partners.

- Read the directions and task aloud. Make sure children understand what they need to do to complete the task.

- Direct children to complete problem 9 on their own.

- As children work on their own, observe their progress and understanding. Respond to their questions and provide additional support as needed.

- Have children share their number bonds and number sentences with the class.

- Have children explain how they know their number sentence is true. Explanations should state that the quantities are the same.

- Have children return to the Unit Opener page and complete the *After* column of the progress chart.

Put It Together

9 **Use the partners of 8 or 9.**

Write all the partners of 8 or 9 in the number bonds. Then write a true number sentence. Use two different partners. Explain how you know your number sentence is true.

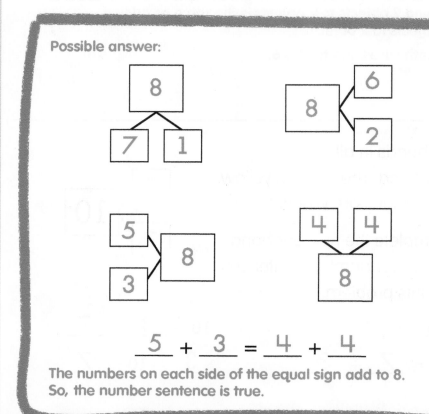

Possible answer:

$$\underline{5} + \underline{3} = \underline{4} + \underline{4}$$

The numbers on each side of the equal sign add to 8. So, the number sentence is true.

74

Teacher Notes

Scoring Rubric

Points	Expectations
4	The child: • correctly completes all number bonds with partners of 8 or 9. • writes a correct addition sentence with two different sets of partners. • explains that the number sentence is true because both sides have the same total.
3	The child: • may complete three or four number bonds correctly. • may write a correct addition sentence with two different sets of partners. • may be able to explain why the number sentence is true, but the explanation may be unclear or incomplete.
2	The child: • may complete two or three of the number bonds correctly. • may write a correct addition sentence with 8 or 9 on one side instead of a partner. • may not be able to clearly explain why the number sentence is true.
1	The child: • may complete fewer than two of the number bonds correctly. • may not write a correct addition sentence with two different sets of partners. • may not be able to explain why a number sentence is true or false.
0	The child: • does not attempt to complete the task.

Which lessons are students building upon?

Kindergarten, Lesson 21
Understand Teen Numbers
K.NBT.A.1

Kindergarten, Lesson 22
Count Teen Numbers
K.CC.A.3, K.CC.B.5

Kindergarten, Lesson 18
Add Within 10
K.OA.A.2

Kindergarten, Lesson 19
Subtract Within 10
K.OA.A.2

Kindergarten, Lesson 23
Make Teen Numbers
K.NBT.A.1

Kindergarten, Lesson 18
Add Within 10
K.OA.A.2

Kindergarten, Lesson 19
Subtract Within 10
K.OA.A.2

Kindergarten, Lesson 23
Make Teen Numbers
K.NBT.A.1

Kindergarten, Lesson 18
Add Within 10
K.OA.A.2

Kindergarten, Lesson 19
Subtract Within 10
K.OA.A.2

Kindergarten, Lesson 23
Make Teen Numbers
K.NBT.A.1

Kindergarten, Lesson 18
Add Within 10
K.OA.A.2

Kindergarten, Lesson 19
Subtract Within 10
K.OA.A.2

Kindergarten, Lesson 23
Make Teen Numbers
K.NBT.A.1

Unit 3

Lesson 12
Understand Teen Numbers
1.NBT.B.2a, 1.NBT.B.2b

Lesson 13
Understand Sums Greater than 10
1.OA.C.6

Lesson 14
Make a Ten to Add
1.OA.C.6

Lesson 15
Add Three Numbers
1.OA.A.2

Lesson 16
Make a Ten to Subtract
1.OA.C.6

Which lessons are students preparing for?

Grade 2, Lesson 10
Understand Three-Digit Numbers
2.NBT.A.1a, 2.NBT.A.1b, 2.NBT.A.2

Grade 2, Lesson 11
Read and Write Three-Digit Numbers
2.NBT.A.3

Grade 2, Lesson 7
Add Two-Digit Numbers
2.NBT.B.5, 2.NBT.B.8

Grade 2, Lesson 8
Subtract Two-Digit Numbers
2.NBT.B.5, 2.NBT.B.8

Grade 2, Lesson 7
Add Two-Digit Numbers
2.NBT.B.5, 2.NBT.B.8

Grade 2, Lesson 8
Subtract Two-Digit Numbers
2.NBT.B.5, 2.NBT.B.8

Grade 2, Lesson 7
Add Two-Digit Numbers
2.NBT.B.5, 2.NBT.B.8

Grade 2, Lesson 8
Subtract Two-Digit Numbers
2.NBT.B.5, 2.NBT.B.8

Grade 2, Lesson 7
Add Two-Digit Numbers
2.NBT.B.5, 2.NBT.B.8

Grade 2, Lesson 8
Subtract Two-Digit Numbers
2.NBT.B.5, 2.NBT.B.8

Unit 3
Add and Subtract to 20

Unit 3 – Operations and Algebraic Thinking
Add and Subtract to 20

13 red apples and 5 green apples. Danna wants to give some apples to her aunt. She wants to keep some apples for herself. What math questions could Danna ask about the apples?

In this unit, you will learn ways to add and subtract within 20. Then you will be able to solve problems like Danna's.

✓ Self Check

Check off the skills you know now. Then see how many more you can check off after each lesson!

I can:	Before this unit	After this unit
name and write teen numbers.	☐	☐
make totals greater than 10.	☐	☐
make a ten to add.	☐	☐
add three numbers.	☐	☐
make a ten to subtract.	☐	☐
solve addition and subtraction word problems.	☐	☐

At A Glance

- This page introduces children to the general ideas behind adding and subtracting teen numbers.
- The checklist allows them to see what skills they will be learning and take ownership of their progress.

Step By Step

- Explain to children that they are going to begin a new unit of lessons. Tell them that in all the lessons in this unit they will be learning ways to add and subtract within 20.
- Read the introduction to the unit together as a class. Invite children to suggest questions that could be asked about the problem situation. Discuss the questions children pose without the expectation that they are to solve them.
- Then take a few minutes to have each child independently read through the list of skills.
- Ask children to consider each skill and check the box in the *Before* column if it is a skill they think they already have. Remind children that these skills are likely to all be new to them, but it's still possible some children have some of the skills.
- Engage children in a brief discussion about the skills. Invite children to comment on which ones they would most like to learn, or which ones seem similar or related to something they already know. Remind them that the goal is to be able to check off all the skills they have learned by the end of the unit.
- At the end of the unit, have children complete the *After* column. As time allows, pose questions about the problem situation at the top of the page and solve as a class.

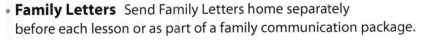

◼ Ready Mathematics
PRACTICE AND PROBLEM SOLVING

Practice and Problem Solving Resources

Use the following resources from *Practice and Problem Solving* to engage students and their families and to extend student learning.

- **Family Letters** Send Family Letters home separately before each lesson or as part of a family communication package.

- **Unit Games** Use partner Unit Games at classroom centers and/or send them home for play with family members.

- **Unit Practice** Assign Unit Practice as homework, as independent or small group practice, or for whole class discussion.

- **Fluency Practice** Assign Fluency Skills Practice and Fluency Repeated Reasoning Practice worksheets throughout the unit.

Lesson 12
Understand Teen Numbers

CCSS Focus

Domain
Number and Operations in Base Ten

Cluster
B. Understand place value.

Standards
1.NBT.B.2 Understand that the two digits of a two-digit number represent amounts of tens and ones. Understand the following special cases:

a. 10 can be thought of as a bundle of ten ones — called a "ten."

b. The numbers from 11 to 19 are composed of a ten and one, two, three, four, five, six, seven, eight, or nine ones.

Standards for Mathematical Practice (SMP)

1 Make sense of problems and persevere in solving them.

2 Reason abstractly and quantitatively.

3 Construct viable arguments and critique the reasoning of others.

4 Model with mathematics.

5 Use appropriate tools strategically.

6 Attend to precision.

7 Look for and make use of structure.

8 Look for and express regularity in repeated reasoning.

Lesson Objectives

Content Objectives

• Recognize that 10 ones and 1 ten represent the same quantity.

• Understand that numbers between 10 and 20 are composed of 1 ten and some ones.

• Model teen numbers.

Language Objectives

• Use connecting cubes to show that one 10-cube bar represents 10 ones or the number 10 and not the number 1.

• Tell the meaning of each digit in a teen number.

• Use 10-frames and number bonds to model teen numbers.

Prerequisite Skills

• Count to 20.

• Interpret a number bond.

Lesson Vocabulary

• **ones** single units or objects.

• **teen number** a ten and some number of ones from 1 to 9; the numbers 11–19.

• **tens** groups of 10 ones.

Learning Progression

In Kindergarten children count to 20, connect the counts to objects and written numerals, and write numerals from 0 to 20. They compose and decompose numbers 11 to 19 into 10 ones and more ones.

In Grade 1 children add and subtract within 20 and develop the concept of two-digit numbers.

In this lesson children explore the structure of numbers between 10 and 20,

often referred to as teen numbers. They develop the concept that teen numbers are composed of a group of ten and a group of ones. This understanding leads to the idea that numbers 20 and greater are composed of multiple tens and from 1 to 9 ones.

In Grade 2 children continue to develop understanding of the structure of two-digit numbers and extend these concepts to three-digit numbers.

Lesson Pacing Guide

Whole Class Instruction

Day 1
45–60 minutes

Introduction
Use What You Know
- Explore It *25 min*
- Try It *20 min*

Day 2
45–60 minutes

Modeled Instruction
Explore Together
- Opening Question *5 min*
- Think *15 min*
- Talk About It *5 min*
- Hands-On Activity *20 min*

Practice and Problem Solving
Assign pages 107–108

Day 3
45–60 minutes

Guided Instruction
Explore Together
- Hands-On Problem *5 min*
- Problems 1–3 *20 min*
- Talk About It *10 min*
- Fluency Practice *10 min*

Practice and Problem Solving
Assign pages 109–110.

Day 4
45–60 minutes

Guided Practice
Connect It
- Problems 4–6 *15 min*

Independent Practice
Show What I Know
- Problem 7 *15 min*
- Intervention, On-Level, or Challenge Activity *15 min*

Practice and Problem Solving
Assign pages 111–112.

Teacher-Toolbox: Lesson Quiz
Lesson 12 Quiz

Materials for Lesson Activities

Per child: 20 connecting cubes (10 each in two different colors), crayons, whiteboard
Activity Sheet 11*, Activity Sheet 19, Activity Sheet 25

Per pair: 40 connecting cubes (20 each in two different colors)
Activity Sheet 11

Per group: Activity Sheet 22

For display: none

*Used for more than one activity.

Small Group Differentiation

Teacher-Toolbox.com

Reteach
Ready Prerequisite Lessons *45–90 min*

Grade K
- Lesson 21 *Understand* Teen Numbers
- Lesson 22 Count Teen Numbers

Teacher-led Activities
Tools for Instruction *15–20 min*

Grade 1 *(Lesson 12)*
- Counting Up to 20 Objects

Student-led Activities
Math Center Activities *30–40 min*

Grade K *(Lessons 21 and 22)*
- K.28 Teen Number Vocabulary
- K.08 Pick and Write

Grade 1 *(Lesson 12)*
- 1.20 Make Teen Numbers
- 1.22 Teen Number Match
- 1.23 Compare Teens

Personalized Learning

i-Ready.com

Independent
i-Ready Lessons* *10–20 min*

Grade 1 *(Lesson 12)*
- Part 1: Counting to 20
- Part 2: Counting to 20
- Numerals & Counting 0–10

* i-Ready lessons may be updated during the 2016–2017 school year. Updated references will be on the Teacher-Toolbox.

👥 Introduction

Activity Ten Fingers

Objective

Children explore numbers between 10 and 20 as a group of ten and some ones.

Overview

Children discover ways to represent numbers greater than 10 with their fingers. They work with a partner to model teen numbers with their fingers.

Step By Step

Explore It

Pose the problem.

- Tell children you are going to say some numbers and you want them to show the numbers with their fingers as quickly as they can. Begin with numbers such as 4, 6, 3, and 8; then ask for 13. When children respond that they can't do it, ask for an explanation. Then ask: *Can you think of a way you could show 13 using fingers?*

Explore strategies.

- Allow children to discuss ways they can show 13 using fingers. Some may suggest thinking of 10 fingers and then using their fingers to count on from 10. Others may suggest working with a partner to use two sets of hands. Listen to all responses.

- Have children model the suggested strategies. Begin with methods such as holding up ten fingers and then "thinking" of three more fingers and counting on. You may want to save the partner strategy until last as an introduction to the next step.

Partner counting.

- Have children work with a partner to show 13 with fingers. One partner shows 10 fingers and the other holds up 3 fingers.

- Ask children how they know which partner is showing 10 fingers. Discuss why they don't need to count all 10 fingers.

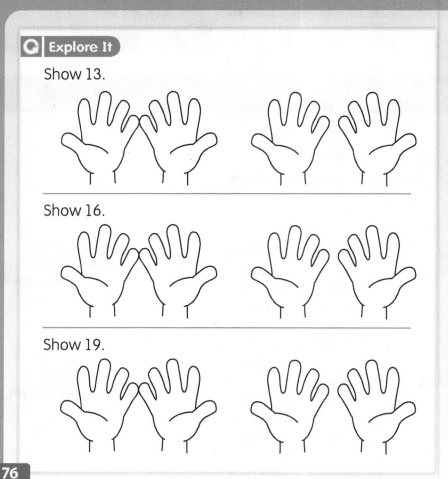

Ⓖ Explore It

Show 13.

Show 16.

Show 19.

76

- Have the children showing 10 fingers move their hands together so that their little fingers touch each other (you may want to model this). Tell children that this shows there is one group of 10 fingers.

- Direct children's attention to the pairs of hands pictured on the Student Book page. Have children color the fingers to show 13.

Model teen numbers.

- Now tell children you are going to say some teen numbers and ask them to work with a partner to show the numbers as quickly as possible. You may want them to take turns showing the ten and the extra fingers. Then say the numbers: *16, 12, 19.*

- As you call out the teen numbers, observe whether children are modeling correctly.

- Have children color the fingers on the Student Book page to show 16 and 19.

Use What You Know
Understand Teen Numbers

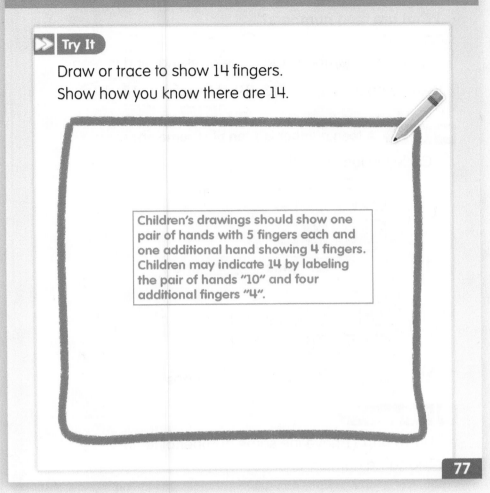

>> Try It

Draw or trace to show 14 fingers.
Show how you know there are 14.

Children's drawings should show one pair of hands with 5 fingers each and one additional hand showing 4 fingers. Children may indicate 14 by labeling the pair of hands "10" and four additional fingers "4".

77

Step By Step

Try It

Pose the problem.

• Say: *Draw or trace on your Student Book page to show 14 fingers. Show how you know there are 14.*

• Some children may benefit from first modeling 14 with a partner before drawing or tracing the fingers.

Lead the class in discussion.

• Have children share their drawings and ask them to explain how they know there are 14 fingers.

• Ask children how their drawing of 14 fingers and the hands showing teen numbers on the first page are alike and how they are different. Listen for children who express teen numbers as a group of ten and some ones.

• Some children may fail to identify 10 fingers as a group of ten. You can utilize the modeling options provided throughout the lesson to support these children.

Modeled Instruction

Step By Step

- Revisit the Activity in the Introduction. Ask: *What was the same about all the teen numbers you and your partner made with your fingers?* Lead children to recognize that, in each case, one partner was showing 10 fingers locked together.

- Read the question and directions at the top of the page. As children say the numbers, have them listen for the word "teen" in the number. Emphasize the connection between "teen" and "ten."

▶ **English Language Learners**

Think

- Read through Think with the class. Ask Mathematical Discourse question 1 to help children connect the models to the Activity in the Introduction.

▶ **Mathematical Discourse 1**

- Use the Hands-On Activity to explore the concept that 10 ones can be described as 1 ten.

▶ **Hands-On Activity**

Talk About It

- As you discuss Talk About It, some children may focus on the digits rather than on the composition of each number as 1 ten and a different number of ones. Ask questions like: *Why do you think both 10 and 11 start with a one?*

Ready Mathematics
PRACTICE AND PROBLEM SOLVING

Assign *Practice and Problem Solving* **pages 107–108** after students have completed this section.

Explore Together
Understand Teen Numbers

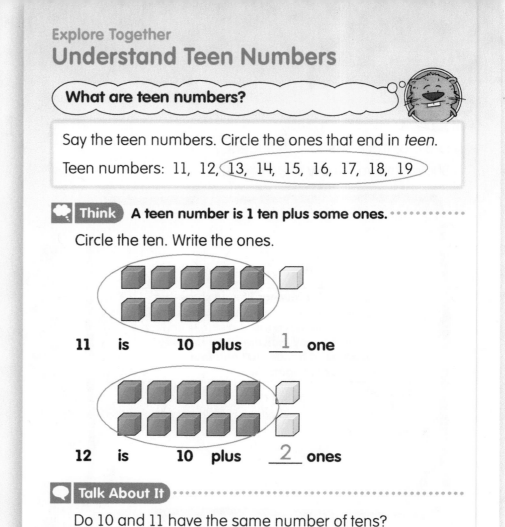

What are teen numbers?

Say the teen numbers. Circle the ones that end in *teen*.

Teen numbers: 11, 12, ⟨13, 14, 15, 16, 17, 18, 19⟩

Think A teen number is 1 ten plus some ones. ⋯⋯

Circle the ten. Write the ones.

11   is   10   plus   __1__ one

12   is   10   plus   __2__ ones

Talk About It ⋯⋯⋯⋯⋯⋯⋯

Do 10 and 11 have the same number of tens?

78 The same number of ones?

▶ **Mathematical Discourse**

1 *How are the cubes like counting with your fingers?*

Children should respond that 10 cubes are grouped together to make a ten just like connecting 10 fingers. You count on the extra cubes like you count on the extra fingers. Some may notice that the blocks are organized into 2 groups of 5 just as fingers are organized into 2 hands of 5 fingers.

▶ **English Language Learners**

Encourage children to tell the class how to count from ten to twenty in their native language. Help them see how teen numbers use *ten* in the number, such as in the Spanish word for 16, "**diez** y seis" (10 and 6), or the French word for 17, "**dix**-sept" (ten-7). Emphasize the similarity to the word "teen" used in English to name a ten.

▶ **Hands-On Activity**

Model teen numbers with 10-frames.

Materials For each pair: 19 connecting cubes, 10-Frame (Activity Sheet 11)

- Have children work in pairs to count out 11 cubes and organize them on 2 10-frames.

- Ask: *How do you know when you have a group of ten?* Have children connect the 10 cubes from the full frame. Say together: *One ten and one cube is eleven.*

- Repeat for 12. Ensure children recognize that the 10 cubes on the full frame and the bar of cubes represent the same number of cubes.

- Ask children what they think 14 would look like on the 10-frames and then with 10 connected cubes. Ask: *What is another way you could say 14?* [1 ten and 4 ones]

Explore Together
Understand Teen Numbers

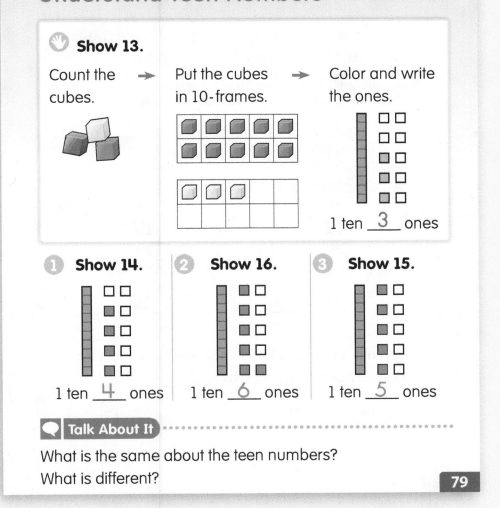

✋ **Show 13.**

Count the cubes. → Put the cubes in 10-frames. → Color and write the ones.

1 ten __3__ ones

1 Show 14.   **2** Show 16.   **3** Show 15.

1 ten __4__ ones   1 ten __6__ ones   1 ten __5__ ones

💬 **Talk About It**

What is the same about the teen numbers?
What is different?

79

Step By Step

- Distribute Activity Sheet 11 (10-Frame) and 20 connecting cubes (10 each in two different colors) to each child.

- Explain the directions at the top of the page. Model placing 13 cubes in the 10-frames and have children do the same.

- Now take the 10 cubes out of the first 10-frame and connect them. Help children make the connection between this train of 10 cubes and the red tens illustrated on the Student Book page.

- Ask Mathematical Discourse question 2 to reinforce the concept that 10 ones is equal to 1 ten. For children who struggle with this concept, refer to the 1 ten as "1 group of ten."

▶ **Mathematical Discourse 2**

- Allow children time to complete Problems 1–3. Circulate to check that they are displaying the cubes correctly and coloring to record their work.

Talk About It

- Discuss Talk About It. Help children recognize that the numbers 13–16 are all composed of 1 ten but of a different number of ones.

▶ **Fluency Practice**

> **SMP TIP   Look for Structure**
> Display the numbers 1, 21, and 16 with distance between them. Ask: *Which of these numbers has 1 ten and some ones? How do you know?* Activities like this can help children focus on the structure of two-digit numbers and prepare them for understanding numbers greater than 19. *(SMP 7)*

📦 **Ready** Mathematics
PRACTICE AND PROBLEM SOLVING

Assign *Practice and Problem Solving* **pages 109–110** after students have completed this section.

▶ **Fluency Practice**

Model teen numbers on a hundreds chart.

Materials For each child: Hundreds Chart (Activity Sheet 19), crayons

- Have children circle the number 15 on the hundreds chart. Lead them to see that 15 represents 15 squares on the chart.

- Have children shade the first row of 10 squares, emphasizing that this is 1 ten. Ask: *How many more squares do you count to get to 15?* [5] *How many ones and tens are in 15?* [5 ones, 1 ten]

- Continue with other teen numbers.

▶ **Mathematical Discourse**

2 Say: *10 cubes and 1 ten are the same amount. I thought 10 was more than 1. How can 10 and 1 ten be equal?*

Children should respond that the 1 tens bar is the 10 cubes grouped together.

👥 Guided Practice

Step By Step

- Discuss each Connect It problem as a class using the discussion points outlined below.

Compare

- If children struggle to get started, give pairs 40 connecting cubes (20 each in two different colors). Have one partner model 10 and 7 more while the other shows 18 as 1 ten and 8 ones.

- Ask children to name each model as a teen number, as ten cubes and some ones, and as 1 ten and some ones. This reinforces the fact that there are multiple ways to describe a number.

- To have children start thinking about tens and ones in a more abstract way, say: *How can you know, just by looking at two numbers like 15 and 19, which one is more?* Some children may respond that they know by counting. Others may realize that both numbers have 1 ten, but 19 has 9 ones and 15 has 5 ones. Since 9 is more than 5, 19 is more than 15.

Apply

- Help children connect the number bond to other models they have explored, noting that each of the teen numbers is composed of 1 ten (shown in one part of the number bond) and some ones.

- Reinforce the concept of equality by asking children why the teen number is always shown alone on one side of the equal sign.

Explain

- To introduce the problem, ask children to describe what the model shows. [1 ten, 3 ones]

- Invite children to present their arguments about whether they agree or disagree with Buzz. Encourage the use of mathematical language and precise explanations, prompting them with questions such as: *How do you know the model shows 13? Why is the bar the only one counted as 10?*

- Encourage children to demonstrate the correct way to count the cubes.

Connect It
Understand Teen Numbers

4 **Compare** Cora has 10 cubes and 7 more cubes. Dan has 18 cubes. Who has more cubes?

Possible answer: Cora has 10 + 7. Dan has 10 + 8. There are more ones in 10 + 8. Dan has more.

5 **Apply** Complete each number bond. Write number sentences.

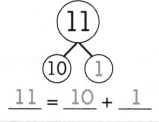

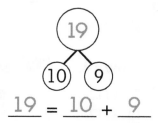

$11 = 10 + 1$ $19 = 10 + 9$

6 **Explain** Buzz says that this shows 4. Do you agree? Why or why not?

Possible answer: This shows 1 ten and 3 ones. It is 13, not 4.

80

SMP TIP Critique Reasoning
Extend children's ability to critique and justify their thinking by asking: *Why do you think Buzz said that the model shows 4? What did he do wrong?* (SMP 3)

🔲 **Ready** **Mathematics**
PRACTICE AND PROBLEM SOLVING

Assign *Practice and Problem Solving* **pages 111–112** after students have completed this section.

Show What I Know
Understand Teen Numbers

7️⃣ **Think about teen numbers.**

A: Draw more stickers.

Make two different teen numbers.

Possible answer: Children draw 4 star stickers.

Possible answer: Children draw 5 moon stickers.

B: Make number bonds for your teen numbers.
Then write your teen numbers.

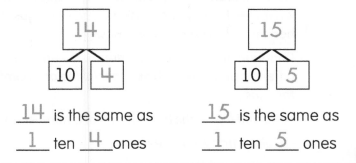

__14__ is the same as

__1__ ten __4__ ones

__15__ is the same as

__1__ ten __5__ ones

81

- Encourage children to complete the problems on this page independently.

- As children work, support them with questions such as the ones below.

What is the fewest number of star stickers you can draw to show a teen number?

What is the greatest number of moon stickers you can draw to show a teen number?

How can the stickers help you find the tens and ones?

What number do you think should go in the top box of the number bonds? What does that number tell you? What does the number in the box next to the ten tell you?

Scoring Rubrics

	Expectations for 4–3 Points		Expectations for 2–0 Points
Points	**Expectations**	**Points**	**Expectations**
4	The child: • draws stickers to represent two different numbers from 11 to 19. • accurately decomposes each teen number in a number bond and represents it as a two-digit number and as a ten and some ones.	2	The child: • draws stickers to represent at least one number from 11 to 19. • may attempt to complete the number bonds; however, all numbers used do not correspond to the teen numbers drawn. This results in inaccuracies with the two-digit numbers and the tens and ones recorded.
3	The child: • draws stickers to represent two different numbers from 11 to 19. • completes the number bonds and writes two-digit numbers; however, there may be minor errors with placement in the number bond or with the number of ones recorded.	1	The child: • may draw some stickers; however, there is no evidence the child relates the number drawn to a number bond, a two-digit number, or a number of tens and ones.
		0	The child: • makes little or no attempt to solve the problem.

Differentiated Instruction

▶ Intervention Activity

Relate cubes in 10-frames to digits in teen numbers.

Materials For each child: 20 connecting cubes, 10-Frame (Activity Sheet 11), Number Cards 0 to 11 (Activity Sheet 25)

- Distribute the materials. Include only the number cards 1–10 from Activity Sheet 25.

- Instruct children to mix up the set of 1–9 cards and set the pile facedown next to the 10 card.

- Have children fill one of the 10-frames with ten cubes. Ask them to turn one of the number cards faceup and place that number of cubes on the other 10-frame. Lead children to read the total as, for example, "10 and 3 more is 13." Have them place the 3 card over the 0 on the 10 card to see the number 13 displayed.

- Repeat until all the cards are used.

▶ On-Level Activity

Play: What's my number?

Materials For each child: whiteboard

This is a teacher-led activity. You may want to display an open number bond and 10-frame on the board for reference.

- Think of a teen number, for example 14, and say: *I'm thinking of a number that has 1 ten and 4 ones. If you think you know my number, write it down.*

- Have children hold up their numbers and compare what they have written. Ask a volunteer to justify his or her answer using tens and ones.

- Continue giving other teen numbers and using different prompts such as: *I'm thinking of a number that has:*

  - *a 10 and a 6 on the bottom part of a number bond.*

  - *a full 10-frame and 5 extra ones.*

  - *one group of 10 cubes and 1 extra cube.*

- Make the prompts as challenging as your group of children allows.

▶ Challenge Activity

Represent teen numbers in multiple ways.

Materials For each group: Teen Number Cards (Activity Sheet 22)

- Provide each child with a different teen number card and challenge them to find as many ways as possible to show the number. Discuss how combining varied groups of numbers (for example, $8 + 7 = 15$) is one way to show the number.

- Encourage them to use more than two addends and to look for patterns that might help them find more ways to represent the number. Don't expect, but accept representations involving subtraction.

- Have children compile their findings on a large sheet of paper for display. Encourage them to show each example clearly and write neatly so that everyone can read their work.

Teacher Notes

Teacher-Toolbox.com

Overview

Assign the Lesson 12 Quiz and have children work independently to complete it.

Use the results of the quiz to assess children's understanding of the content of the lesson and to identify areas for reteaching. See the Lesson Pacing Guide at the beginning of the lesson and the Differentiated Instruction activities for suggested instructional resources.

Tested Skills

Assesses 1.NBT.B.2a, 1.NBT.B.2b

Problems on this quiz require children to be able to use models and number bonds to apply the concept that numbers between 10 and 20 are composed of 1 ten and some ones. Children will also need to be familiar with interpreting and completing number bonds and counting to 20.

Ready® **Mathematics**

Lesson 12 Quiz Answer Key

Name _____

Solve.

1 Complete the number bond to show the number of flowers.

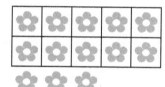

2 Complete the number bond to show the number of shells.

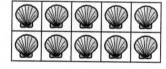

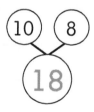

Common Misconceptions and Errors

Errors may result if children:

• incorrectly relate a number of objects to a two-digit number.

• incorrectly decompose a teen number in a number bond.

• incorrectly connect a two-digit number to a number bond, number of tens and ones, or a number sentence.

Name _____

Solve.

3 Complete the number bonds.
Then write the tens and ones.

___1___ ten and ___6___ ones   ___1___ ten and ___9___ ones

4 Complete each number bond. Write number sentences.

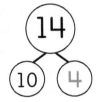

__10__ + __4__ = __14__   __10__ + __2__ = __12__

5 Kim has a bag with 10 apples in it. She has 5 more apples.
How many apples does she have in all?

___1___ ten and ___5___ ones = __15__ apples

CCSS Focus

Domain
Operations and Algebraic Thinking

Cluster
C. Add and subtract within 20.

Standard
1.OA.C.6 Add and subtract within 20, demonstrating fluency for addition and subtraction within 10. Use strategies such as counting on; making ten (e.g., $8 + 6 = 8 + 2 + 4 = 10 + 4 = 14$); decomposing a number leading to a ten (e.g., $13 - 4 = 13 - 3 - 1 = 10 - 1 = 9$); using the relationship between addition and subtraction (e.g., knowing that $8 + 4 = 12$, one knows $12 - 8 = 4$); and creating equivalent but easier or known sums (e.g., adding $6 + 7$ by creating the known equivalent $6 + 6 + 1 = 12 + 1 = 13$).

Additional Standards
1.NBT.B.2a, 1.NBT.B.2b (See page B3 for full text.)

Standards for Mathematical Practice (SMP)
1 Make sense of problems and persevere in solving them.
2 Reason abstractly and quantitatively.
3 Construct viable arguments and critique the reasoning of others.
4 Model with mathematics.
6 Attend to precision.
7 Look for and make use of structure.
8 Look for and express regularity in repeated reasoning.

Lesson Objectives

Content Objectives
- Find the partners of teen numbers.
- Recognize the different ways that numbers can be decomposed and composed.

Language Objectives
- Use 10-frames and number bonds to show how 10 does not always have to be one of the number partners of a teen number.
- Complete number bonds and number sentences for sums greater than 10.
- Compare the different approaches used by others to find sums greater than 10 and identify connections among the approaches.

Prerequisite Skills

- Know the partner that makes 10 for any number.
- Know all decompositions for numbers within 10.
- Understand that teen numbers can be decomposed as $10 +$ some number.

Lesson Vocabulary

There is no new vocabulary. Review the following key terms.

- **addend** a number being added.
- **teen number** a ten and some number of ones from 1 to 9. The numbers 11–19.
- **total** a number found as the result of adding.

Learning Progression

In Kindergarten children learn to subitize, or recognize the number of objects in a group without counting. They begin to add and subtract by acting out situations and using physical models and drawings as they develop mathematical language.

In Grade 1 children develop strategies to extend addition and subtraction beyond 10 to include numbers within 20. They use numbers in diagrams that show the relationships between the quantities.

In this lesson children explore ways to compose and decompose teen numbers, using number bonds and systematic approaches to help build the conceptual foundation for fluency.

In Grade 2 children fluently add and subtract within 20, using a variety of strategies. They build on this fluency to add and subtract within 100.

Lesson Pacing Guide

Whole Class Instruction

Day 1
45–60 minutes

Introduction
Use What You Know
• Explore It 25 min
• Try It 20 min

Day 2
45–60 minutes

Modeled Instruction
Explore Together
• Opening Question 10 min
• Think 15 min
• Talk About It 10 min
• Visual Model 10 min

Practice and Problem Solving
Assign pages 115–116.

Day 3
45–60 minutes

Guided Instruction
Explore Together
• Hands-On Problem 10 min
• Problems 1–3 15 min
• Talk About It 10 min
• Concept Extension 10 min

Practice and Problem Solving
Assign pages 117–118.

Day 4
45–60 minutes

Guided Practice
Connect It
• Problems 4–6 15 min

Independent Practice
Show What I Know
• Problem 7 15 min
• Intervention, On-Level, or Challenge Activity 15 min

Practice and Problem Solving
Assign pages 119–120.

Teacher-Toolbox: Lesson Quiz
Lesson 13 Quiz

Materials for Lesson Activities

Per child: 13 connecting cubes, 2 different colored crayons, 20 two-color counters
Activity Sheet 2, Activity Sheet 11*, Activity Sheet 25

Per pair: 40 two-color counters

For display: none

*Used for more than one activity.

Small Group Differentiation

Teacher-Toolbox.com

Reteach
Ready Prerequisite Lessons 45–90 min

Grade K
• Lesson 18 Add Within 10
• Lesson 23 Make Teen Numbers

Teacher-led Activities
Tools for Instruction 15–20 min

Grade 1 (Lesson 13)
• Doubles Addition Facts
• Sums of Ten
• Subtraction Number Sentences

Student-led Activities
Math Center Activities 30–40 min

Grade K (Lessons 18 and 23)
• K.24 Tell Addition Stories
• K.29 Roll and Make Teen Numbers

Grade 1 (Lesson 13)
• 1.07 Partners for Teen Numbers

Personalized Learning

i-Ready.com

Independent
i-Ready Lessons* 10–20 min

Grade 1 (Lesson 13)
• Addition Number Sentences
• Acting Out Addition and Subtraction

i-Ready lessons may be updated during the 2016–2017 school year. Updated references will be on the Teacher-Toolbox.

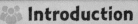

Introduction

Activity Act Out Partners of 11

Objective
Act out the various number partners that make 11 and model the partners with connecting cubes.

Materials for each child
- 11 connecting cubes
- Number Cards 0 to 11 (Activity Sheet 25)
- 2 different colored crayons
- Number Cards.

Overview
Children form two groups, starting with 10 and 1, and shift one child at a time from the larger group to the smaller group, then model partners of 11 with connecting cubes.

Step By Step

Explore It

Pose the problem.
- Say: *11 crates need to be shipped by cargo train. There are two train cars. How many different ways can the crates be loaded on the two cars? Let's act this out.*

Model the problem.
- Distribute cards with numbers 0–11. Tell children that you are going to ask some questions about the situation, and that they can respond by holding up the correct card.
- Have 10 children stand in a group to model filling one car with crates. Ask: *How many crates are in this car?* [Children hold up "10" card.]
- Have 1 child stand alone to model 1 crate in the other car. Ask: *How many crates are in this car?* [Children hold up "1" card.]
- Have children place 1 cube and in the bottom "train car" on the Student Book page.

Explore It
Find ways to make 11.

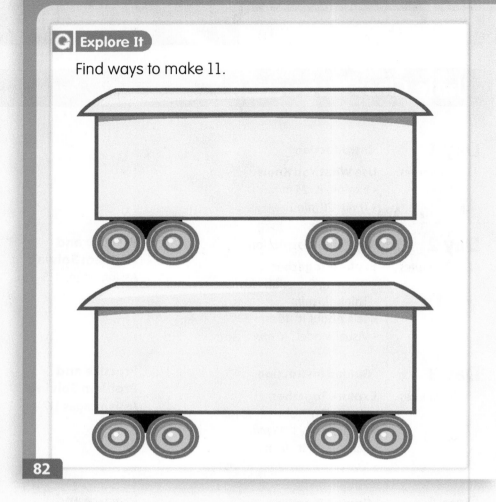

82

- Ask: *How many crates are there in all?* [Children hold up "11" card.] Elicit that 11 is "10 and 1 more." Write $11 = 10 + 1$ on the board.

Find another pair of partners for 11.
- Say: *Let's fill the cars a different way.*
- Have 1 child (crate) from the "10" car move to the "1" car.
- Ask: *How many crates are in this car?* [Children hold up the "9" card.] Ask: *How many are in this car?* [Children hold up the "2" card.] Ask: *How many crates are there in all?* [Children hold up the "11" card.] Write $11 = 9 + 2$ on the board.
- Have children model this by moving one connecting cube from the top "train car" to bottom "train car."
- Continue in this way until all the partners for 11 have been found.

Use What You Know
Understand Sums Greater than 10

>> **Try It**

Show ways to make 11.

> Children's shading should show the number partners for each equation.

11 = 10 + __1__

11 = 9 + __2__

11 = 8 + __3__

11 = 7 + __4__

11 = 6 + __5__

83

Step By Step

Try It

Discuss the findings.

- Ask: *Did we find all the partners? How can you tell?*

- Elicit that, if each child (crate) moves back, one at a time, the partners will be the same as a previous pair of partners, but in reverse order. Show this by reversing a set of connecting cubes, and discuss.

- If children lose track of the process (decreasing one car by 1 and increasing the other by 1) or don't understand that the sum remains the same, ask: *What happens to this car when [name] comes over? What happens to the other car? Is the total still 11, or did it change? How do you know?*

Show ways to make partners for 11.

- Have children complete the number sentences on the Student Book page and shade the squares using 2 different colors to show the number partners for each.

- If children seem stuck, encourage them to model the number sentence using cubes.

- Have children explain how the squares they colored and the cube trains they made show the same thing.

- Discuss why changing the order of the partners does not change the total. Ask: *How are 11 = 10 + 1 and 11 = 1 + 10 alike and how are they different?*

Modeled Instruction

Step By Step

- Read aloud the question at the top of the page and encourage children to suggest answers.

- Remind children that they learned that teen numbers can be written as 1 ten and some ones. Elicit that 12 is 1 ten and 2 ones. Ask children to describe how this relates to the blue and red bar at the top of the page.

- Have children model 12 as 10 and 2, using two different colors of connecting cubes.

- Point out the number bond. Have children explain how the number bond shows the same thing as the visual model. Ask Mathematical Discourse question 1 to check that children can make connections among all the different models on the page.

▶ **Mathematical Discourse 1**

Think

- Read Think aloud. Ask Mathematical Discourse question 2 to relate the visual models and number sentences to a familiar situation.

▶ **Mathematical Discourse 2**

Talk About It

- Present the Talk About It question. Discuss why changing the order of the partners does not change the total.

▶ **Visual Model**

 **Mathematics**
PRACTICE AND PROBLEM SOLVING

Assign *Practice and Problem Solving* **pages 115–116** after students have completed this section.

Understand Sums Greater than 10

How do you find partners of teen numbers?

You know that 12 is 10 + 2.

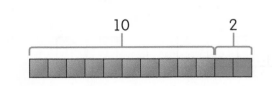

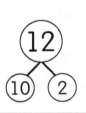

Think Change the first addend. Find the partner.

$12 = 10 + 2$

$12 = 9 + 3$

$12 = 8 + \underline{4}$

$12 = 7 + \underline{5}$

$12 = 6 + \underline{6}$

Talk About It

Change the order of the addends.
What happens when you add?

84

▶ **Mathematical Discourse**

1 *How does the number bond relate to the number sentence 12 = 10 + 2?*
The number bond shows partners of 12. The number sentence is one of the two number sentences you can make using this number bond. You can also reverse the addends.

2 *How are the pictures of the blue and red bars on this page like the Activity in the Introduction?*
Children should be able to describe the process of taking 1 from one addend and increasing the other addend by 1.

▶ **Visual Model**

Recognize patterns in addends.

Materials For each child: Number Bond Recording Sheet (Activity Sheet 2)

- Have children complete number bonds to show all the partners of 12.

- Discuss the patterns they see. Help children recognize that as one addend increases by 1, the other decreases by 1.

Explore Together
Understand Sums Greater than 10

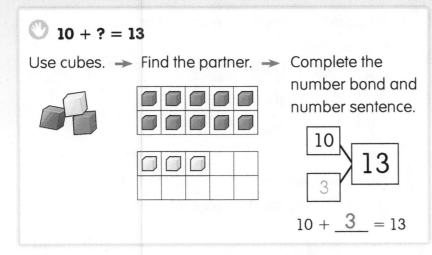

✋ **10 + ? = 13**

Use cubes. → Find the partner. → Complete the number bond and number sentence.

10
3
→ 13

10 + __3__ = 13

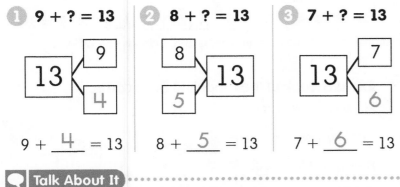

1 9 + ? = 13

13
9
4

9 + __4__ = 13

2 8 + ? = 13

8
5
→ 13

8 + __5__ = 13

3 7 + ? = 13

13
7
6

7 + __6__ = 13

💬 **Talk About It**

How did you find the partners of 13?

85

▶ **Concept Extension**

Relate partners to the concept of equality.

• Write the following on the board:

13 = 10 + 3
    −__ +__
13 = 8 + 5

• Ask: *What number do you subtract from 10 to get 8?* [2] *What number do you add to 3 to get 5?* [2] Fill in the blanks.

• Continue with 9 + 4 and 7 + 6. Discuss that if the same number is subtracted from one addend and added to the other, the total remains the same.

▶ **Mathematical Discourse**

3 *What subtraction sentences could you write for these number bonds?*

Children should give two subtraction sentences for each number bond.

Step By Step

• Distribute Activity Sheet 11 (10-Frame). Read the directions aloud. Have children put 13 connecting cubes in their 10-frames to match the picture on the page.

• Draw a number bond on the board and invite a volunteer to complete it using numbers that correspond to the 10-frames. Ask: *How did you know what numbers to write?*

• Have children work in pairs, using connecting cubes and 10-frames to complete the page. Circulate and monitor their work. If children seem stuck, explain that in each problem they need to fill the 10-frames with 13 cubes using different numbers of each color.

• When children are finished, ask pairs to come up and demonstrate the partners for 13 with connecting cubes. Have them write a number sentence. Ask a volunteer to reverse the order of the connecting cubes and write the number sentence. Use Mathematical Discourse question 3 to extend this idea to subtraction.

▶ **Mathematical Discourse 3**

Talk About It

• Present the Talk About It question. Ask children how their methods are the same or different and to explain why each works.

▶ **Concept Extension**

SMP TIP Use Structure

Encourage children to be aware of and make use of the structure of teen numbers: "10 and some more." When they see a teen number, ask them how many tens are in it [1 ten], and how many more ones. Use number bonds, number sentences, connecting cubes, and 10-frames to reinforce this concept. *(SMP 7)*

Ready Mathematics
PRACTICE AND PROBLEM SOLVING

Assign *Practice and Problem Solving* **pages 117–118** after students have completed this section.

👥👥 Guided Practice

Step By Step

- Discuss each Connect It problem as a class using the discussion points outlined below.

Interpret

- You may want to have children work alone and then compare their responses with a partner.

- Ask: *How does the 8 in the number bond relate to the picture?* [It is the number of blue squares.] *How can you find the missing number in the number bond?* [Count the red squares.]

- Direct attention to the addition sentences. Ask children to explain how the number sentences are alike and how they are different. Make sure they notice that the number sentences have the same total and addends, but that the addends are written in a different order.

Illustrate

- Relate the circles in the 10-frames to the cube activity with the 10-frames on the Explore Together page. Ask children how the 10-frames on the Explore Together page show teen numbers. Guide them to understand that they show 1 ten in one color on the first frame and the ones in a different color on the second frame.

- Ask: *What if the first addend is 9?* Remind children of the work they did on the previous page. Make sure they understand that part of the second addend is in the first frame and the rest is in the second.

- Have children explain how they wrote the addition sentences. You may wish to ask them to write and explain subtraction sentences for this number bond.

Explain

- Read the problem. Have children discuss it in pairs. Then bring the whole group together and have each pair share their conclusions and reasoning.

- Ask children: *Why do you think Buzz wrote that 8 + 6 equals 15? What would you say to help Buzz understand?*

---

④ **Interpret** Complete the number bond and number sentences.

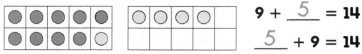

$$14 = 8 + \underline{6}$$
$$14 = \underline{6} + 8$$

⑤ **Illustrate** Use two colors. Color the circles. Then complete the number sentences.

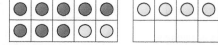

$$9 + \underline{5} = 14$$
$$\underline{5} + 9 = 14$$

Children color 9 circles in one color and 5 circles in a different color.

⑥ **Explain** Look at the model. Is Buzz correct? How do you know?

Buzz writes:

$$8 + 6 = 15$$

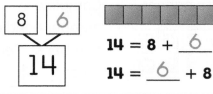

Possible answer: Buzz is not correct. The model shows 8 + 6. One 10-frame is full. The other one has 4 circles. 10 + 4 = 14, not 15.

86

SMP TIP Repeated Reasoning

On this page, children investigate different partners of 14. Support their learning by pointing out the relationship between the parts: for example, because 6 + 8 = 14 and 9 + 5 = 14, you know that 6 + 8 = 9 + 5. To draw attention to the regularity in these relationships, have children apply the reasoning from the Activity in the Introduction (decrease one addend by 1 and increase the other addend by 1) to the three problems on this page. *(SMP 8)*

📖 **Ready· Mathematics**
PRACTICE AND PROBLEM SOLVING

Assign *Practice and Problem Solving* **pages 119–120** after students have completed this section.

Show What I Know
Understand Sums Greater than 10

7 **Think about different ways to make totals greater than 10.**

A: Draw to show partners of 15.
Complete the number bonds.

Possible answer: Children might use two different-colored objects in drawings to show the partners of 15.

B: Show all of the partners of 16.

Possible answer: Children might make drawings, number bonds, or number sentences to show the partners of 16.

87

Step By Step

- Read aloud Problem 7 and the directions for Part A. Explain that children can choose how to draw the partners of 15.
- Read aloud the directions for Part B. Children can use any of the models from this lesson to help find the partners of 16.
- Observe children as they work. Provide support by asking questions, such as the following, to encourage thinking and problem-solving strategies.

How could a 10-frame help you with this page?

How many tens and ones are in 16? How can this help you find the other partners of 16?

Scoring Rubrics

Expectations for 4–3 Points

Points	Expectations
4	The child: • draws accurate models and completes number bonds correctly. • accurately shows all the number partners of 16.
3	The child: • may draw models and complete number bonds for 15; however, there are a few minor errors. • may correctly show most of the partners of 16 or show all of the partners with one or two errors.

Expectations for 2–0 Points

Points	Expectations
2	The child: • may have some incomplete or inaccurate drawings and number bonds. • may be able to show one or two accurate partners of 16, but not all.
1	The child: • attempts to draw partners of 15 and complete the number bonds, but may be unable to complete the task and shows little evidence of a strategy or understanding. • attempts to model the partners of 16, but the work is inaccurate and incomplete.
0	The child: • does not attempt to solve the problem.

Differentiated Instruction

▶ Intervention Activity

Compose teen numbers in 10-frames.

Materials For each child: 10-Frame (Activity Sheet 11), 20 two-color counters

- Have children count out 13 counters. Then have them put 10 of one color in the first frame and 3 of the second color in the second frame. Discuss how this shows 10 + 3. Have children write a number sentence. [10 + 3 = 13]

- Instruct children to turn over the last counter in the first frame so that it is now the same color as the counters in the second frame. Ask children to identify this new partner of 13 and write a number sentence. [9 + 4 = 13]

- Continue until you have found all the partners of 13. You may want to repeat with other teen numbers.

▶ On-Level Activity

Explore partners with equal totals.

Materials For each pair: 40 two-color counters

- Write two pairs of partners of 13 on the board as addition expressions (e.g., 9 + 4 and 10 + 3). Have children work in pairs to model both sums with counters, using one color for each partner.

- Ask: *Are these sums the same or different? Why do you think so?* Children may mention that both sets are partners of 13. Or they may say that by lining up the counters they can see that the total number of counters in each line is the same. Or they may note that 9 is one less than 10 and 4 is one more than 3. If a child thinks the sums are different, gently challenge that child to show and explain why.

- Continue with other partners of teen numbers.

▶ Challenge Activity

Change one partner to 10.

Materials For each child: 10-Frame (Activity Sheet 11), 20 two-color counters

- Write 8 + 7 = 15 on the board.

- Point to the 8 and ask: *What can you do to make this 10?* Children may use counters and 10-frames as supports if needed. Guide children to understand that you need 2 more to make 10, so take 2 from the 7. The new addition sentence is 10 + 5 = 15.

- Repeat with other partners of teen numbers where one addend is 8 or 9, such as 9 + 3 = 12, 8 + 5 = 13, or 9 + 5 = 14.

- Consider having children work in pairs to check each other's work.

Teacher Notes

Teacher-Toolbox.com

Overview

Assign the Lesson 13 Quiz and have children work independently to complete it.

Use the results of the quiz to assess children's understanding of the content of the lesson and to identify areas for reteaching. See the Lesson Pacing Guide at the beginning of the lesson and the Differentiated Instruction activities for suggested instructional resources.

Tested Skills

Assesses 1.OA.C.6

Problems on this quiz require children to be able to find the partners of teen numbers by using number bonds and 10-frames to compose and decompose teen numbers. Children will also need to be familiar with number partners for 10, decompositions for numbers within 10, and understand that teen numbers can be decomposed into 10 + some number.

***Ready*® Mathematics**

Lesson 13 Quiz Answer Key

Name _____

Solve.

1 Find the partner and total.

$12 = 10 + 2$

$12 = 9 + \underline{3}$

$12 = 8 + \underline{4}$

$12 = 7 + \underline{5}$

$12 = 6 + \underline{6}$

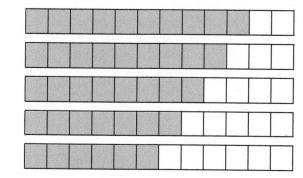

2 Color the 10-frame. Then complete the number bond and number sentences.

14

8   6

$14 = 8 + \underline{6}$

$14 = \underline{6} + 8$

Grade 1 **Lesson 13** *Understand* Sums Greater Than 10   1   ©Curriculum Associates, LLC
Copying permitted for classroom use.

Common Misconceptions and Errors

Errors may result if children:

- do not recognize the application of partner pairs when decomposing numbers.
- incorrectly interpret or complete a number bond or inaccurately connect it to a related number sentence.
- incorrectly interpret a 10-frame or inaccurately connect the number it represents to a related number bond.

Name _____

3　Draw to show partners of 16 and 17. Complete the number bonds and number sentences.

16

7　9

7 + 9 = **16**

16

8　8

8 + 8 = **16**

17　8　9

8 + 9 = **17**

2

©Curriculum Associates, LLC
Copying permitted for classroom use.

Lesson 14
Make a Ten to Add

CCSS Focus

Domain
Operations and Algebraic Thinking

Cluster
C. Add and subtract within 20.

Standard
1.OA.C.6 Add and subtract within 20, demonstrating fluency for addition and subtraction within 10. Use strategies such as counting on; making ten (e.g., $8 + 6 = 8 + 2 + 4 = 10 + 4 = 14$); decomposing a number leading to a ten (e.g., $13 - 4 = 13 - 3 - 1 = 10 - 1 = 9$); using the relationship between addition and subtraction (e.g., knowing that $8 + 4 = 12$, one knows $12 - 8 = 4$); and creating equivalent but easier or known sums (e.g., adding $6 + 7$ by creating the known equivalent $6 + 6 + 1 = 12 + 1 = 13$).

Additional Standard
1.OA.B.3 (See page B3 for full text.)

Standards for Mathematical Practice (SMP)
1 Make sense of problems and persevere in solving them.

2 Reason abstractly and quantitatively.

3 Construct viable arguments and critique the reasoning of others.

4 Model with mathematics.

6 Attend to precision.

7 Look for and make use of structure.

8 Look for and express regularity in repeated reasoning.

Lesson Objectives

Content Objectives
• When adding 2 one-digit numbers, understand the rationale for decomposing one addend to make ten.

• Use the strategy of making ten to add numbers within 20.

• Use and articulate mental math strategies to add.

Language Objectives
• Explain how to use the strategy of making ten to add two numbers.

• Draw jumps on a number path to show making a ten and finding a sum.

• Describe a 10-frame.

Prerequisite Skills
• Know the partner that makes 10 for any number.

• Know all decompositions for numbers within 10.

• Understand that teen numbers can be decomposed as 10 + some number.

Lesson Vocabulary
• **make a ten** a strategy that uses combinations of numbers that add to ten when finding totals greater than 10.

Learning Progression

In Kindergarten children learn to count the number of objects and later to subitize, or recognize the number of objects in a group. They gain understanding of basic addition and subtraction situations and begin learning to compose and decompose numbers 10 or less.

In Grade 1 children learn strategies for adding and subtracting numbers within 20 and develop understanding of the properties of addition.

In this lesson children learn the strategy of making ten to add within 20. This involves breaking apart an addend and associating one part of it with another addend to make 10, and then applying the understanding that teen numbers can be thought of as "10 + some number."

In Grade 2 children become fluent at adding and subtracting within 20. They use strategies to add and subtract within 100.

Lesson Pacing Guide

Whole Class Instruction

Day 1
45–60 minutes

Introduction
Use What You Know
• Explore It *25 min*
• Try It *20 min*

Day 2
45–60 minutes

Modeled Instruction
Explore Together
• Example Problem *5 min*
• Model It *20 min*
• Hands-On Activity *20 min*

Practice and Problem Solving
Assign pages 123–124.

Day 3
45–60 minutes

Guided Instruction
Learn Together
• Example Problem *5 min*
• Model It *15 min*
• Talk About It *15 min*
• Fluency Practice *10 min*

Practice and Problem Solving
Assign pages 125–126.

Day 4
45–60 minutes

Guided Practice
Practice Together
• Example Problem *5 min*
• Problems 1–2 *25 min*
• Visual Model *15 min*

Practice and Problem Solving
Assign pages 127–128.

Day 5
45–60 minutes

Independent Practice
Practice by Myself
• Problems 3–5 *10 min*
• Concept Extension *10 min*
• Quick Check and Remediation *15 min*
• Hands-On or Challenge Activity *10 min*

Teacher-Toolbox: Lesson Quiz
Lesson 14 Quiz

Materials for Lesson Activities

Per child: 20 two-color counters
Activity Sheet 11, Activity Sheet 20

Per pair: 20 connecting cubes (10 each in two different colors), 20 counters

For display: 10 chairs

Small Group Differentiation

Teacher-Toolbox.com

Reteach
Ready Prerequisite Lessons *45–90 min*

Grade K
• Lesson 18 Add Within 10
• Lesson 23 Make Teen Numbers

Teacher-led Activities
Tools for Instruction *15–20 min*

Grade 1 *(Lesson 14)*
• Make a Ten to Add Within 20
• Sums of Ten

Student-led Activities
Math Center Activities *30–40 min*

Grade K *(Lessons 18 and 23)*
• K.24 Tell Addition Stories
• K.29 Roll and Make Teen Numbers

Grade 1 *(Lesson 14)*
• 1.08 Make a Ten to Add

Personalized Learning

i-Ready.com

Independent
i-Ready Lessons* *10–20 min*

Grade 1 *(Lesson 14)*
• Addition Facts for 10

* i-Ready lessons may be updated during the 2016–2017 school year. Updated references will be on the Teacher-Toolbox.

Introduction

Activity Act Out Making a Ten

Objective

Act out a "Make Ten" problem and model with counters.

Materials for each pair

• 15 counters

Materials for display

• 10 chairs

Overview

Children act out a scenario in which they make a ten to add. They model the problem with counters and discuss. Then children solve a new problem.

Step By Step

Explore It

Pose the problem.

• Say: *Let's imagine you are getting on a bus for a fabulous field trip! So far there are 7 children on the bus. 5 more are ready to get on. How can thinking about 10 help us find how many children are on the bus now? Let's see.*

Model the problem.

• Organize 10 chairs in 2 rows to be the "bus." Have 7 children sit down.

• Gather a group of 5 more children. Say: *We're going to let a few children on the bus at a time. How many more children do I need to have 10 on the bus?* [3]

• Have the 5 children separate into a group of 2 and a group of 3. Have the 3 children sit with the "bus" children. Ask a child to count to verify that there are 10 children on the bus.

• Say: *There are 10 children on the bus. How many more children still need to get on the bus?* [2] Have the remaining 2 children join the "bus" children. Then ask: *What's the total number of children on the bus?* [12] Have the class count to verify the total.

G Explore It

7 children get on the bus. 5 more children get on the bus. How many children are on the bus?

Watch for children to start with 7 counters on the bus, move 3 counters onto the bus to make 10, and then move the remaining 2 counters onto the bus to show 12.

88

Use counters.

• Have children work in pairs to model the situation. They put 7 counters in the "bus" in 2 rows to represent 7 children on the bus. They put 5 more counters below the bus.

• Remind children that at first 3 children are added to make 10 on the bus. Tell them to break apart their group of 5 counters and move 3 of them onto the bus.

• Then they put the remaining 2 counters on the bus.

Discuss.

• Ask: *How many children are there in all?* [12] *How do you know?*

• Have pairs explain how they used the counters to model the problem. Ask why they think making a ten is a good strategy for finding totals that are teen numbers.

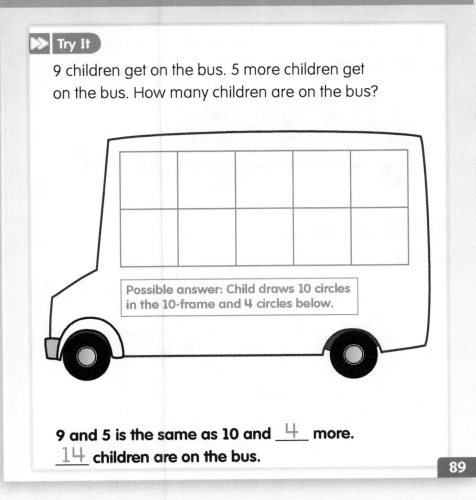

▶▶ **Try It**

9 children get on the bus. 5 more children get on the bus. How many children are on the bus?

Possible answer: Child draws 10 circles in the 10-frame and 4 circles below.

9 and 5 is the same as 10 and ___4___ more.

___14___ children are on the bus.

89

Try It

Pose a different problem.

• Provide the children with the following problem: *What if there were 9 children on the bus and 5 more wanted to get on? How would thinking about 10 help you find how many children are on the bus?*

Model the problem.

• Have children work in pairs, using counters to model the problem. Have them use the 10-frame in the bus and the space below it to draw a picture of the problem. Then have them use their drawing to complete the sentence below. Observe children as they work.

Lead the class in discussion.

• After children have completed their drawings, ask them to describe their work. Look for children who are able to explain that if 1 child boards the bus, that makes 10 on the bus. Then there are 4 more, which makes 14 (10 and 4 more).

• Use the Hands-On Activity on page 90 as extra support for children who were unable to represent the problem or complete the sentence correctly.

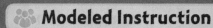

Modeled Instruction

Step By Step

- Read aloud the problem at the top of the page. Discuss how the picture is like what you did in the Activity in the Introduction. Elicit children's thoughts on how making a ten helps when the total is more than ten. Introduce the number sentence. Ask: *How does this number sentence relate to the picture?*

Model It

- Read Model It aloud. Direct attention to the first pair of 10-frames and have children identify which parts of the number sentence are being modeled.

▶ **Mathematical Discourse 1**

▶ **Hands-On Activity**

- Ask: *What happens in the second pair of 10-frames? How are these different from the first pair? Is this the same total number of counters? How do you know?* Discuss children's responses, concluding that both pairs of 10-frames show a total of 13.

- Have children fill in the totals. Discuss with them how making ten helps them find the total.

> **SMP TIP Look for Structure**
> The structure of 10-frames helps children understand the make-a-ten strategy. Encourage children to think and talk about how the 10-frames help them go from "8 and some more" to the known structure of "10 and some more." *(SMP 7)*

Assign *Practice and Problem Solving* **pages 123–124** after students have completed this section.

Make a Ten to Add

8 children are on the bus. 5 more get on the bus. How many are on the bus now?

$$8 + 5 = ?$$

Model It Find 8 + 5.

Start with 8. Take counters from 5 to **make a ten**.

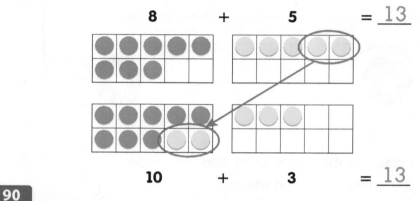

| 8 | + | 5 | = 13 |

| 10 | + | 3 | = 13 |

▶ Mathematical Discourse

1 *How does the model help you make a ten?*

Children should see the empty spots in the 10-frame as a signal to what is needed to make a ten. With more practice, this visual clue will eventually translate to recognizing the number that makes ten.

▶ Hands-On Activity

Model adding numbers on 10-frames.

Materials For each child: 10-Frame (Activity Sheet 11), 20 two-color counters

- Write the problem 8 + 5 = ? on the board.

- Have children put 8 counters of one color in one 10-frame and 5 of another color in the second frame. Ask how they can use the 5 counters to fill the first 10-frame. [Remove 2 from the frame with 5 and use those to fill the frame with 8.]

- Have them actually move counters and describe what they did. Help them to conclude that the total number of counters didn't change. They just moved the counters around in the 10-frames to show a ten and some ones.

Learn Together
Make a Ten to Add

7 blocks are small. 5 blocks are big.
How many blocks are there in all?
How do you know?

7 + 5 = ?

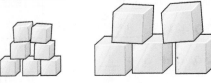

📱 **Model It** Find **7 + 5**.

Start with 7.
Add 3 to make 10.
Then add 2 more.

$7 + 3 = 10$ $10 + 2 = 12$

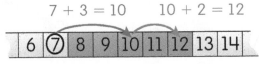

7 + 5 = _12_

💬 **Talk About It** Do you agree? Why or why not?

Boom says that 9 + 5 = 15.

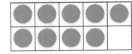 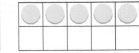

91

Step By Step

- Read aloud the problem at the top of the page. Ask children how they would approach the problem. Elicit the idea of making a ten and then seeing what's left to add.

Model It

- In Model It, direct attention to the number path. Ask children to describe what it shows. Guide children to see that 7 is circled because it is the addend you start with. Ask: *Why start with 7?* [It's easier if you start with the addend that is closer to 10. But the strategy will work either way.]

- Ask: *How many numbers is the blue jump? Why do you jump this many first?* [The blue jump is 3 because you want to make a ten. $7 + 3 = 10$]

- Explain that now they have used 3 of the big blocks to make 10. Ask: *How many more do you have to add?* [2] Elicit that the total is 10 and 2 more, which is 12. Ask Mathematical Discourse question 2 to check understanding of this idea.

▶ **Mathematical Discourse 2**

- You may want to have children verify the sum by laying green blocks or counters along the number path: 3 for the blue jump and 2 for the red jump.

Talk About It

- Present the Talk About It question. Have children describe the diagram and number sentence. Then have them answer the question and explain their thinking. [Boom is incorrect. It looks like Boom forgot to fill the 10-frame that has 9 counters but assumed that it had 10 in it. Actually, $9 + 5 = 14$.]

▶ **Fluency Practice**

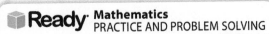

📦 **Ready**· Mathematics
PRACTICE AND PROBLEM SOLVING

Assign *Practice and Problem Solving* **pages 125–126** after students have completed this section.

▶ **Fluency Practice**
Practice facts within 10.

Materials For each child: Facts Practice 4 (Activity Sheet 20)

- Have children complete Activity Sheet 20 (Facts Practice 4). Then have pairs work together to review the facts. One partner reads two addends and the other partner gives the sum.

- Children should go "out of order" for this, skipping around the worksheet and choosing addition sentences with different sums.

▶ **Mathematical Discourse**

2 *How can you tell how big to make the jump from 10 to the sum?*

Children need to understand how many more are left after making the ten. They might respond that after a jump of 3, there is a jump of 2 left since the partner of 3 that makes 5 (the other addend) is 2.

Guided Practice

Step By Step

- Read the example problem aloud and have children describe the two sets of 10-frames. Ask: *What can you do in the first set of 10-frames to get what is shown in the second set of 10-frames?* [Take 2 counters from the 6 and fill the first 10-frame.]

- Read Problem 1 aloud. Point out that the model only shows one set of 10-frames. Make sure children can identify the 8 and the 7 in the model. Have some children demonstrate how to solve this problem.

- In Problem 2, children need to draw jumps to 10 and then to the total. Suggest that they answer these questions: *How many do I need to make 10?* [3] *This number and how many more make the second addend?* [4] You may wish to have children work with a partner. Have some children demonstrate their solution and explain how they solved it.

▶ **Mathematical Discourse 1**

▶ **Visual Model**

SMP TIP Repeated Reasoning

Discuss the equivalent expressions on this page, for example $8 + 6$ and $10 + 4$. Continue to develop the repeated reasoning that as one addend increases, the other decreases by the same amount. (SMP 8)

 **Ready** Mathematics
PRACTICE AND PROBLEM SOLVING

Assign *Practice and Problem Solving* **pages 127–128** after students have completed this section.

Make a Ten to Add

$8 + 6 = ?$

$8 + 2 = \underline{10}$
$10 + 4 = \underline{14}$
So, $8 + 6 = \underline{14}$

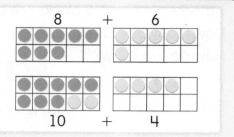

$$8 \qquad + \qquad 6$$

$$10 \qquad + \qquad 4$$

1 $8 + 7 = ?$

$8 + \underline{2} = 10$
$10 + \underline{5} = \underline{15}$
$8 + 7 = \underline{15}$

2 $7 + 7 = ?$ | 6 | 7 | 8 | 9 | 10 | 11 | 12 | 13 | 14 | 15 |

$7 + \underline{3} = 10$
$10 + \underline{4} = \underline{14}$
$7 + 7 = \underline{14}$

92

▶ **Mathematical Discourse**

1 *Can you explain in your own words how to use the make-a-ten strategy to add two numbers?*

Children should describe a two-part process. Start with one addend (preferably the greater addend) and find the partner that makes ten. To find what's left, remove the quantity added to make a ten from the other addend. In other words, the partner that makes ten has a partner that makes the other addend.

▶ **Visual Model**

Use number bonds to make a ten and add within 20.

- Write $7 + 5$ on the board. Then draw a circle around the 5 and connect it to two circles below to form a number bond. Ask: *Starting with 7, how can you make a ten?* [Add 3.]

- Write 3 in the left circle of the number bond. Ask children what needs to go in the right circle and why. [2, because 2 and 3 are the partners that make 5.]

- Below the number bond, write: $10 + \underline{\quad} = \underline{\quad}$. Ask children what numbers go in the blanks. [2, 12]

- Consider trying this approach with different numbers for those who find it helpful.

Practice by Myself
Make a Ten to Add

3 7 + 6 = ?

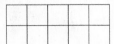

7 + __3__ = __10__

10 + __3__ = __13__

7 + 6 = __13__

4 9 + 4 = ?

| 6 | 7 | 8 | ⑨ | 10 | 11 | 12 | 13 | 14 | 15 |

Possible work: 9 + 1 = 10; 10 + 3 = 13

9 + 4 = __13__

5 8 + 9 = ?

Possible work: 8 + 9 = 17; 10 + 7 = 17

8 + 9 = __17__

93

Step By Step

- Read each problem aloud, then have children work independently to solve.

- If children struggle with Problem 3, ask what the red counters show. [The addend 7.] Point out that they will make ten when the first frame is filled, and that they need to add more to add a total of 6.

- After children complete Problem 4, you may wish to present the following reasoning: *Nine is 1 less than 10, so 9 + 4 is 1 less than 10 + 4.*

▶ **Mathematical Discourse 2**

- For Problem 5, children can use any model or strategy that they choose. Invite several children to demonstrate their solutions, and then discuss the similarities and differences in their approaches.

▶ **Concept Extension**

▶ **Concept Extension**

Use the associative property to make a ten and add within 20.

- Write the problem 9 + 6 on the board.

- Have children work in pairs to make a ten and add. Have one pair describe what they did.

- When they tell how they made 10, write 9 + 1 on the board.

- When they explain how they added the remaining 5 to get 15, write + 5 to make the expression 9 + 1 + 5.

- Ask: *What happens if you add 9 + 1 first, then add 5?* [We get 10 + 5 = 15.] Ask: *What happens if you add 1 + 5 first, then add 9?* [We get 6 + 9 = 15.]

- Lead children to conclude that grouping the addends differently does not change the total.

▶ **Mathematical Discourse**

2 *Why is the sum of 9 + 6 and 10 + 5 the same?*

Children need to understand that as a number is decomposed and composed in different ways, the total stays the same. Responses should reflect the idea that some quantity has been taken from one addend and moved to the other, decreasing one addend and increasing the other by the same amount. So the overall quantity has not changed.

Differentiated Instruction

▶ Quick Check and Remediation

Materials For each child: 16 counters

- Ask children to solve $8 + 7 = ?$ by making a ten. [Add $8 + 2$ to make a 10. Then $10 + 5 = 15$, so $8 + 7 = 15$.]

- For children who are still struggling, use the chart below to guide remediation.

- After providing remediation, check children's understanding using the following problem: *Solve $9 + 4 = ?$ by making a ten.* [Add $9 + 1$ to make a 10. Then $10 + 3 = 13$, so $9 + 4 = 13$.]

If the error is . . .	Children may . . .	To remediate . . .
$8 + 2$ is 10, so $8 + 7 = 17$	not understand the need to decompose the second addend.	Ask: *Where did you get the 2?* Use counters to model the problem with children. Elicit that the 2 comes from the 7, leaving 5 more to add.
14 or 16	be counting on instead of making a ten, and making a mistake in counting.	Have children demonstrate how they added. If they are counting on from 8, explain that it's easy to lose track when counting on more than 2 or 3. Guide children to use a make a ten approach.
any other teen number, or one of the addends	not have decomposed the addend correctly to make a ten, or may have simply used an addend as the sum.	Have children model "10 and some more," using counters, for 12, 13, 15, and 16. Then have them model $8 + 7$ using counters. Ask: *How can you change this model to show "10 and some more"?*

▶ Hands-On Activity

Use connecting cubes to model making a 10.

Materials For each pair: 20 connecting cubes (10 each in two different colors)

- Provide pairs of children with 10 connecting cubes in each of 2 different colors. Give them an addition problem with a teen number sum, such as $8 + 6$.

- Children write the problem and model it with two trains of different color connecting cubes, one for each addend.

- Children take cubes from one train and connect them to the other train to make a ten. Then they say how many are still left on the first train and solve the problem as "10 and 4 more," or 14. They write $10 + 4 = 14$ and $8 + 6 = 14$.

- Have pairs explain their work. You may wish to repeat the activity with other numbers.

▶ Challenge Activity

Write and solve addition word problems.

Materials For each pair: 20 counters (optional)

- Have children work in pairs to write word problems involving teen numbers. They may wish to use counters to act out their ideas while they write.

- Circulate and offer support and feedback. When the pairs are finished, put the problems in a pile.

- Pairs take turns picking a problem, reading it, and solving by making a ten. The rest of the group listens to see if they are correct. Children may ask questions or recommend strategies as appropriate.

- For extra challenge, see if children can solve the problems without using manipulatives or even paper and pencil.

Teacher Notes

Teacher-Toolbox.com

Overview

Assign the Lesson 14 Quiz and have children work independently to complete it.

Use the results of the quiz to assess children's understanding of the content of the lesson and to identify areas for reteaching. See the Lesson Pacing Guide at the beginning of the lesson and the Differentiated Instruction activities for suggested instructional resources.

Tested Skills

Assesses 1.OA.C.6

Problems on this quiz require children to be able to add two one-digit numbers by decomposing one addend to make a ten, applying the make-a-ten strategy to add numbers within 20. Children will also need to be familiar with number partners for 10 and understand teen numbers as "10 and some more."

Ready® Mathematics

Lesson 14 Quiz Answer Key

Name _____

Solve.

1 $7 + 8 = ?$

$7 + \underline{3} = \underline{10}$

$10 + \underline{5} = \underline{15}$

$7 + 8 = \underline{15}$

2 $5 + 9 = ?$ | 5 | 6 | 7 | 8 | 9 | 10 | 11 | 12 | 13 | 14 | 15 |

$5 + \underline{5} = \underline{10}$

$10 + \underline{4} = \underline{14}$

$5 + 9 = \underline{14}$

3 $? = 8 + 8$

Possible work: $8 + 2 = 10; 10 + 6 = 16$

$\underline{16} = 8 + 8$

Grade 1 **Lesson 14** Make a Ten to Add   1   ©Curriculum Associates, LLC
Copying permitted for classroom use.

Common Misconceptions and Errors

Errors may result if children:

- do not decompose the second addend or decompose it incorrectly.

- confuse the sum with an addend.

- incorrectly apply the make-a-ten strategy.

- do not understand the concept of equivalent expressions.

Lesson 14 Quiz Answer Key continued   Name _____

Solve.

④ 7 + 9 = ?

Possible work: 7 + 3 = 10; 10 + 6 = 16

<u>16</u> = 7 + 9

⑤ Amy buys 8 red cups and 5 blue cups.
How many cups in all?

Possible work: 8 + 2 = 10; 10 + 3 = 13

8 + 5 = <u>13</u>

Grade 1 Lesson 14 Make a Ten to Add   2   ©Curriculum Associates, LLC
Copying permitted for classroom use.

Lesson 15
Add Three Numbers

CCSS Focus

Domain
Operations and Algebraic Thinking

Cluster
A. Represent and solve problems involving addition and subtraction.

Standard
1.OA.A.2 Solve word problems that call for addition of three whole numbers whose sum is less than or equal to 20, e.g., by using objects, drawings, and equations with a symbol for the unknown number to represent the problem.

Additional Standards
1.OA.B.3, 1.OA.C.6 (See page B3 for full text.)

Standards for Mathematical Practice (SMP)

1 Make sense of problems and persevere in solving them.

2 Reason abstractly and quantitatively.

3 Construct viable arguments and critique the reasoning of others.

4 Model with mathematics.

7 Look for and make use of structure.

8 Look for and express regularity in repeated reasoning.

Lesson Objectives

Content Objectives
- Write addition expressions with three addends to represent word problems.
- Find the total of three addends, using strategies such as making a ten and using doubles.
- Use the associative and commutative properties to group addends in order to find known sums.

Language Objectives
- Draw jumps on number paths or use 10-frames to find the total of three addends.
- Use connecting cubes to show that changing the order or the grouping of addends does not change the sum.
- Explain how making a ten can be used to find the total of three numbers.

Prerequisite Skills

- Write addition sentences to solve word problems.
- Use doubles to add.
- Make a ten to add.
- Understand sums greater than 10.

Lesson Vocabulary

- **Associative Property of Addition** when the grouping of 3 or more addends is changed, the total does not change.

Review the following key term.

- **addend** a number being added.

Learning Progression

In Kindergarten children solve addition and subtraction word problems and add and subtract within 10, using objects and drawings.

In Grade 1 children first learn to solve word problems that call for addition of two whole numbers. They learn strategies such as counting on, making ten, and creating equivalent but easier or known sums to add. Children also apply properties of operations as strategies to add and subtract.

In this lesson children solve word problems that involve three addends. They use the associative property to group addends to make a ten and then add the third addend.

In Grade 2 children continue to use the addition strategies they learned in Grade 1. They work with totals to 20 and then extend this understanding to solve problems involving addition and subtraction within 100, using diagrams and number sentences.

Lesson Pacing Guide

Whole Class Instruction

Day 1
45–60 minutes

Introduction

Use What You Know
- Explore It *25 min*
- Try It *20 min*

Day 2
45–60 minutes

Modeled Instruction

Explore Together
- Example Problem *5 min*
- Model It *20 min*
- Hands-On Activity *20 min*

Practice and Problem Solving
Assign pages 131–132.

Day 3
45–60 minutes

Guided Instruction

Learn Together
- Example Problem *5 min*
- Model It *15 min*
- Talk About It *10 min*
- Hands-On Activity *15 min*

Practice and Problem Solving
Assign pages 133–134.

Day 4
45–60 minutes

Guided Practice

Practice Together
- Example Problem *10 min*
- Problems 1–2 *20 min*
- Fluency Practice *15 min*

Practice and Problem Solving
Assign pages 135–136.

Day 5
45–60 minutes

Independent Practice

Practice by Myself
- Problems 3–5 *10 min*
- Concept Extension *10 min*
- Quick Check and Remediation *10 min*
- Hands-On or Challenge Activity *15 min*

Teacher-Toolbox: Lesson Quiz
Lesson 15 Quiz

Materials for Lesson Activities

Per child: 17 counters (8 red, 6 yellow, 4 blue), 18 connecting cubes (6 one color, 4 a second color, and 8 a third color), 12 blocks (6 red, 4 blue, 2 green) Activity Sheet 11, Activity Sheet 21

Per pair: pattern blocks (6 each in three different shapes)

For display: 14 pencils

Small Group Differentiation

Teacher-Toolbox.com

Reteach
Ready Prerequisite Lessons *45–90 min*

- Lesson 18 Add Within 10
- Lesson 23 Make Teen Numbers

Teacher-led Activities
Tools for Instruction *15–20 min*

Grade 1 *(Lesson 15)*
- Make a Ten to Add Within 20
- Number Pairs for Sums to 10
- Find Missing Addends for Sums to 10

Student-led Activities
Math Center Activities *30–40 min*

Grade K *(Lessons 18 and 23)*
- K.24 Tell Addition Stories
- K.29 Roll and Make Teen Numbers

Grade 1 *(Lesson 15)*
- 1.26 Add Three Numbers
- 1.27 Three Addends

Personalized Learning

i-Ready.com

Independent
i-Ready Lessons* *10–20 min*

Grade 1 *(Lesson 15)*
- Addition Facts for 10
- Adding Three Numbers
- Counting On to Add
- Acting Out Addition and Subtraction

* i-Ready lessons may be updated during the 2016–2017 school year. Updated references will be on the Teacher-Toolbox.

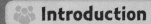

Introduction

Activity A Word Problem with Three Addends

Objective
Model writing a number sentence with three addends to solve an addition word problem.

Materials for each child
• 12 blocks: 6 red, 4 blue, and 2 green (optional)

Materials for display
• 14 pencils

Overview
Children act out an addition problem with three addends. They identify ways to group two addends to find an easier or known sum.

Step By Step

Explore It

Pose the problem.
• Tell children to imagine that someone has dropped a container of pencils and the pencils are scattered on the ground. Then read aloud the problem from the Student Book page: *Joe picks up 7 pencils. Carla picks up 3 pencils. Pete picks up 4 pencils. How many pencils do the children pick up?*

Act out the problem.
• Have three children stand at the front of the classroom. Give each child the appropriate number of pencils as you say: *Here are the 7 pencils that Joe picks up. Here are the 3 pencils that Carla picks up. Here are the 4 pencils that Pete picks up.*

• Have the three children hold up their pencils. Ask: *How can you find how many pencils all 3 children pick up?* [Count all the pencils or add together the number of pencils that each child has.]

Write an addition sentence with three addends to represent the problem.
• Ask: *What number sentence can you write to show how to find the total number of pencils?* [7 + 3 + 4 = ?] Write the addition sentence on the board. Have children record the

---

Add Three Numbers

Explore It

Joe picks up 7 pencils. Carla picks up 3 pencils. Pete picks up 4 pencils. How many pencils do the children pick up?

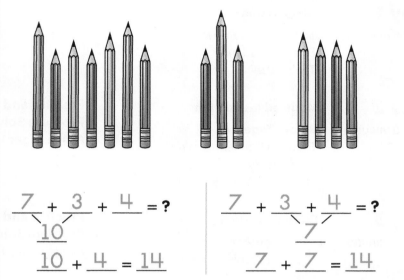

$$\underline{7} + \underline{3} + \underline{4} = ?$$
$$\underline{10}$$
$$\underline{10} + \underline{4} = \underline{14}$$

$$\underline{7} + \underline{3} + \underline{4} = ?$$
$$\underline{7}$$
$$\underline{7} + \underline{7} = \underline{14}$$

The children pick up __14__ pencils.

94

---

addition sentence in the left column of their Student Book page.

• Ask: *Why do you add the numbers?* [You are looking for the total number of pencils in all, so you need to add.]

Talk about and solve the addition sentence.
• Ask: *What do the three addends in the number sentence stand for?* [the number of pencils each child picks up]

• Direct children's attention to the addition sentence on the board. Ask if anyone sees a way to make a ten with any of the numbers. Circle the 7 and 3 and write 10 on the board under these two numbers. Have children write 10 below 7 + 3.

• Discuss why making a ten makes it easier to find the total. Then have children identify the next step in finding the total. [10 + 4 = 14] Write this number sentence on the board. Then have children write this number sentence.

• Again, write 7 + 3 + 4 = ? on the board. Have children record the number sentence in the right column of their Student Book page. Circle 3 and 4 and have children add these numbers first and give the total. Write 7 under the 3 and 4 and have children do the same.

• Ask: *What strategy can you use to find the total of the remaining two numbers?* Guide children to see that they can use doubles to add 7 + 7 = 14. Have them write this number sentence.

• Discuss the idea that you used different groupings to add the numbers and still ended up with the same total.

Try It

Ana has 6 red blocks, 4 blue blocks, and 2 green blocks. How many blocks does she have in all?

> Children's drawings should show 6 red blocks, 4 blue blocks, and 2 green blocks.

6 + 4 + 2 = ?
__10__

__10__ + __2__ = __12__

6 + 2 + 4 = ?
__6__

__6__ + __6__ = __12__

Ana has __12__ blocks in all.

95

Step By Step

Try It

Pose the problem.

• Say: *Ana has 6 red blocks, 4 blue blocks, and 2 green blocks. How many blocks does she have in all?*

Model the problem and write addition sentences.

• Have children draw blocks to model the problem. Optionally, you can provide children with 6 red, 4 blue, and 2 green blocks to model the problem.

Solve the addition sentences.

• Ask children to look for a way to group the addends to make a ten and a way to group the addends to make doubles. Have them write the 10 and the double below the corresponding number sentences. Then have children write number sentences to solve the problem using the 10 and the double.

Lead the class in discussion.

• Discuss why making a ten or finding doubles makes it easier to find the total.

• Have children explain how they can use different groupings to add the numbers and still have the same total.

• Ask children to share which strategy they prefer and why.

Modeled Instruction

Step By Step

- Explain that this page is about solving a word problem with three addends. Read aloud the problem at the top of the page. Encourage children to identify the three items that need to be added.

- Use Hands-On Activity 1 to connect writing and solving a number sentence with three addends to the problem on the page.

▶ **Hands-On Activity 1**

Model It

- Direct children's attention to Model It. Ask: *What do the 8 red counters stand for in the problem?* [8 cans that Pat collects] *What do the 2 yellow counters stand for?* [2 cans that Max collects] *What do the 4 blue counters stand for?* [4 cans that May collects]

- Relate the three addends, 8 + 2 + 4, to the counters. Discuss the strategy of making a ten with two of the addends, 8 and 2. Help children recognize that 4 more need to be added to the 10.

- Ask: *How many cans do all three children collect?* Have children write the total in the blank.

▶ **Mathematical Discourse 1**

SMP TIP Model with Mathematics
Continuing to emphasize the relationship between a real-life mathematical situation, a model, and a number sentence helps children develop skills that involve abstract reasoning. *(SMP 4)*

 **Mathematics**
PRACTICE AND PROBLEM SOLVING

Assign *Practice and Problem Solving* **pages 131–132** after students have completed this section.

Add Three Numbers

Pat collects 8 cans of food.
Max collects 2 cans. May collects 4 cans.
How many cans do they collect in all?

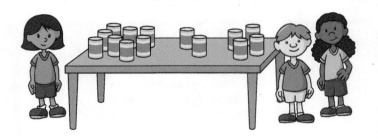

Model It   Find 8 + 2 + 4. ....

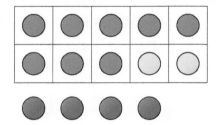

$$8 + 2 + 4$$
$$10 + 4 = \underline{14}$$

96

▶ **Mathematical Discourse**

1 *How does making a ten make it easier to find the total of three numbers?*

If you make a ten with two of the three addends, you are left with two addends to add. The two addends are 10 and the other number. It's easy to add 10 and the other number because they make a teen number whose parts are the 10 and the other number.

▶ **Hands-On Activity 1**

Use counters and a 10-frame to add three addends.

Materials For each child: 14 counters (8 red, 2 yellow, and 4 blue), 10-Frame (Activity Sheet 11)

- Have children place the 8 red counters and 2 yellow counters in the 10-frame and place 4 blue counters in a row beneath the 10-frame.

- Ask: *How many counters are in the 10-frame?* [10] *What are the parts that make 10?* [8 and 2] *How many do you add to 10?* [4]

Learn Together
Add Three Numbers

Adam plants 6 flowers. Kate plants 4 flowers.
Yuri plants 8 flowers. How many flowers?
How do you know?

Model It Find 6 + 4 + 8. ....

⑥ 7 8 9 10 11 12 13 14 15 16 17 18

6 + 4 = __10__

10 + __8__ = __18__

Talk About It Do you agree? Why or why not? ....

Boom writes 6 + 4 + 8.
Buzz writes 4 + 6 + 8.
Buzz says both are correct.

97

▶ Hands-On Activity 2

Model the commutative and associative properties of addition.

Materials For each child: 18 connecting cubes (6 one color, 4 a second color, and 8 a third color)

- Ask children to count the connecting cubes, identifying that there are 18 in all.

- Have children use the connecting cubes to model putting the addends 6, 4, and 8 in different orders. Discuss how the total number of cubes is the same for each arrangement.

▶ Mathematical Discourse

2 *Is the total of 6 + 4 + 8 the same as the total of 4 + 6 + 8? How do you know?*

Yes, the totals are the same. Both 6 + 4 = 10 and 4 + 6 = 10, so in both cases you add 10 + 8 to find the total of 18.

3 *Is there another way you could write the addends? If so, explain whether the total remains the same.*

Yes, you can write 6 + 8 + 4. You can still add 6 + 4 = 10; 10 + 8 = 18, so the total remains the same. Children may give other ways to write the expression, such as 8 + 6 + 4 and 4 + 8 + 6 and say that the total remains the same for any order in which the addends are placed.

Step By Step

- Read aloud the problem at the top of the page. Have children match each group of flowers in the picture to the numbers in the word problem.

Model It

- Direct attention to Model It. Read aloud: *Find 6 + 4 + 8.* Relate the three addends to the picture above and to the numbers in the word problem. Then relate the three addends to the number path model.

- Ask: *Which two numbers do you add first to make a ten?* [6 + 4 = 10.] *What number do you add to the 10 to find the total?* [8] Have children complete the number sentences.

> **SMP TIP Repeated Reasoning**
> Children have found partners of 10 and have learned to use the make a ten strategy to add 2 one-digit numbers. Emphasize the benefit in making a ten to add 3 one-digit numbers. This important calculation will be repeated as children learn to add two-digit numbers and as they learn later concepts. *(SMP 8)*

Talk About It

- Read aloud Talk About It. Encourage discussion by having children tell what is the same and what is different about the way Boom and Buzz write the addends for the problem.

- Use Mathematical Discourse questions 2 and 3 to engage children in a discussion about the commutative and associative properties of addition.

▶ **Mathematical Discourse 2 and 3**

▶ **Hands-On Activity 2**

> 📦 **Ready** Mathematics
> PRACTICE AND PROBLEM SOLVING
>
> Assign *Practice and Problem Solving* **pages 133–134** after students have completed this section.

👥 Guided Practice

Step By Step

- Read the example problem at the top of the page. Discuss with children that this is another situation in which you add three numbers to find the total.

- Ask children to identify the number of apples that each person has. As they do, write the addends $7 + 3 + 5$ on the board.

- Direct children's attention to the number path. Ask: *What number do you start with?* [7] *Why do you first add 3?* [to make 10] Relate to the number sentence $7 + \underline{3} = \underline{10}$.

- Ask: *How do you know how many more to add?* [Look at the third addend, so add 5 more.] Connect this to the number sentence $10 + \underline{5} = \underline{15}$. Then guide children to recognize that these two number sentences are the two separate additions needed to find $7 + 3 + 5$.

▶ **Mathematical Discourse 1**

- Work together with children to complete Problem 1. Make sure they see the connection between the numbers in the problem, the circles in the model, and the numbers in the number sentences.

- In Problem 2, children make a ten with the second and third addends. Continue to emphasize that the order and grouping of the addends does not change the total.

▶ **Fluency Practice**

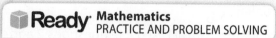

Assign *Practice and Problem Solving* **pages 135–136** after students have completed this section.

Practice Together
Add Three Numbers

Jon has 7 apples. Tom has 3 apples. Bo has 5 apples. How many apples do they have?

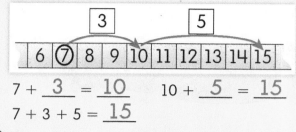

$7 + \underline{3} = \underline{10}$ $10 + \underline{5} = \underline{15}$

$7 + 3 + 5 = \underline{15}$

1 Ann has 9 red balls and 1 green ball. She has 2 blue balls. How many balls does she have?

$\underline{9} + \underline{1} = \mathbf{10}$

$\mathbf{10} + \underline{2} = \underline{12}$

2 Deb has 8 round stickers. She has 4 square stickers and 6 triangle stickers. How many stickers does Deb have?

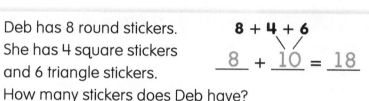

$\mathbf{8 + 4 + 6}$

$\underline{8} + \underline{10} = \underline{18}$

98

▶ **Mathematical Discourse**

1 *Are there other ways you could solve the word problem at the top of the page instead of using a number path to add the numbers? Tell about the other ways.*

You could use counters or cubes to stand for each group of apples and then count to find the total. You could draw a picture or use 10-frames.

▶ **Fluency Practice**

Practice finding partners of 10.

Materials For each child: Number Bond Practice for 10 (Activity Sheet 21)

- Have children complete Activity Sheet 21 (Number Bond Practice for 10).

- Then have pairs work together to review the facts. One child reads the given addend and the other child tells the partner that makes 10.

Practice by Myself
Add Three Numbers

3 Bob has 5 books. Jill gives him 3 more books. Then he gets 5 more books. How many books does Bob have now?

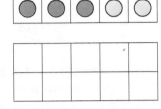

| 5 | 6 | 7 | 8 | 9 | 10 | 11 | 12 | 13 | 14 |

10

5 + 3 + 5 = __13__

4 8 children are on the bus.
2 more children get on.
9 children get on next.
How many children are on the bus now?

10

8 + 2 + 9 = __19__

5 There are 6 marbles in a jar. Len puts 3 marbles in. Pam puts 7 marbles in. How many marbles are in the jar now?

6 + 3 + 7 = __16__

99

Step By Step

- Read each problem aloud, then have children work independently to solve.

- Remind children to look for ways to add numbers whose sums they already know. They may use the strategy of making a ten or adding doubles to help them add two of the three addends in the number sentences for each word problem.

- In Problem 3, children may use the number path to make a ten and find the total. Some children may notice that the two addends that make a ten (5 + 5) are also doubles. These two addends are not next to each other in the number sentence. Use Mathematical Discourse question 2 to discuss grouping addends in a different order.

▶ **Mathematical Discourse 2**

- In Problem 4, some children might draw in the 10-frames, while others just add 10 + 9.

- If children struggle with Problem 5, encourage them to find an easier way to add by grouping addends that make a ten.

▶ **Concept Extension**

▶ **Concept Extension**

Solve word problems with zero as an addend.

- Adapt the word problems on this page to have one addend of zero. For example, 8 children on the bus; no children get on at the next stop; then 9 children get on.

- Work with children to write the number sentence with a zero addend, 8 + 0 + 9, and find the total.

- Provide more examples for children to complete.

▶ **Mathematical Discourse**

2 *To solve Problem 3, Boom added 5 + 3 + 5. Buzz added 5 + 5 + 3. Do you think they both got the same total? Why or why not?*

Both ways give the same total. You are adding the same numbers, so the totals are the same. Changing the way you add the numbers together still gives you the same total.

Differentiated Instruction

▶ Quick Check and Remediation

Materials For each child: 17 counters, 17 connecting cubes

• Ask children to find the total number of pets if there are 4 dogs, 7 cats, and 6 fish. [17 pets]

• For children who are still struggling, use the chart below to guide remediation.

• After providing remediation, check children's understanding using the following problem: *Sam finds 7 shells. Brian finds 5 shells. Timmy finds 3 shells. How many shells do they find in all?* [15 shells]

If the error is ...	Children may ...	To remediate ...
10	have used the make a ten strategy to add 4 + 6 and then forgot to add the third addend, 7.	Have children use counters to show the number of each kind of pet. Then write a number sentence for the counters: 4 + 7 + 6 = ____. Have them combine the groups of 4 and 6 to make a ten, write the expression 10 + 7, and add to find the total, 17.
11	have added only the first two addends, 4 + 7, and then forgot to add the third addend, 6.	Have children draw a picture showing how many of each animal and then write the number beneath each picture. Ask them to write a number sentence to find the total.
16	have used the make a ten strategy to add 4 + 6, and then added 6 again instead of adding 7.	Have children use connecting cubes to model each addend. Have them join the 4-cube stick and 6-cube stick to make a stick of 10 cubes. Children use the 10-cube stick and the 7-cube stick to write the number sentence to find the total: 10 + 7 = 17.

▶ Hands-On Activity

Use shapes to model adding three numbers.

Materials For each pair: pattern blocks (6 each in three different shapes)

• One partner uses any number of each of the three different shapes to make three separate groups.

• The other partner writes the addition number sentence using three addends to represent the number of shapes in each group.

• Partners talk about what strategies they can use and then select an appropriate strategy to find the total number of shapes in all three groups.

▶ Challenge Activity

Use strategies to add four addends to find sums less than 20.

• Have children use strategies such as making a ten and using doubles to solve addition number sentences with four addends:

9 + 7 + 1 + 2 = ____ [19]   4 + 5 + 4 + 5 = ____ [18]

8 + 6 + 2 + 3 = ____ [19]   3 + 5 + 2 + 3 = ____ [13]

7 + 4 + 3 + 5 = ____ [19]   7 + 0 + 3 + 7 = ____ [17]

8 + 1 + 8 + 2 = ____ [19]   9 + 4 + 2 + 1 = ____ [16]

6 + 3 + 2 + 7 = ____ [18]   5 + 4 + 3 + 2 = ____ [14]

Teacher Notes

Teacher-Toolbox.com

Overview

Assign the Lesson 15 Quiz and have children work independently to complete it.

Use the results of the quiz to assess children's understanding of the content of the lesson and to identify areas for reteaching. See the Lesson Pacing Guide at the beginning of the lesson and the Differentiated Instruction activities for suggested instructional resources.

Tested Skills

Assesses 1.OA.A.2

Problems on this quiz require children to be able to solve word problems involving three addends using the associative and commutative properties to group addends and strategies such as making a ten and using doubles. Children will also need to be familiar with writing addition sentences and finding sums greater than 10.

Ready® Mathematics

Lesson 15 Quiz Answer Key

Name _____

Solve.

1 Aba has 6 hens. She has 5 pigs and 4 cows. How many animals does she have in all?

| 5 | 6 | 7 | 8 | 9 | 10 | 11 | 12 | 13 | 14 | 15 |

10

$6 + 5 + 4 = \underline{15}$

Aba has $\underline{15}$ animals.

2 There are 9 frogs on a log. 1 more frog hops on the log. Then 7 more frogs hop on. How many frogs are on the log now?

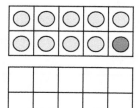

10

$9 + 1 + 7 = \underline{17}$

There are $\underline{17}$ frogs on the log.

Common Misconceptions and Errors

Errors may result if children:

• use the make-a-ten strategy but then forget to add the third addend.

• add only two addends.

• incorrectly apply the associative and commutative properties when grouping addends.

Lesson 15 **Quiz Answer Key** continued   Name _____

Solve.

3 There are 2 blue boats and 8 red boats in the pond.
There are 6 green boats in the pond.
How many boats are in the pond?

2 + 8 + 6 = _16_

There are _16_ boats in the pond.

4 Luke feeds the bunnies 4 carrots.
Deb feeds the bunnies 7 carrots.
Ravi feeds the bunnies 6 carrots.
How many carrots do the bunnies get?

4 + 7 + 6 = _17_

The bunnies get _17_ carrots.

5 Bob sees 8 black bugs and 5 green bugs.
He sees 5 red bugs.
How many bugs does Bob see?

8 + 5 + 5 = _18_

Bob sees _18_ bugs.

Grade 1 Lesson 15 Add Three Numbers

2

©Curriculum Associates, LLC
Copying permitted for classroom use.

Lesson 16
Make a Ten to Subtract

CCSS Focus

Domain
Operations and Algebraic Thinking

Cluster
C. Add and subtract within 20.

Standard
1.OA.C.6 Add and subtract within 20, demonstrating fluency for addition and subtraction within 10. Use strategies such as counting on; making ten (e.g., $8 + 6 = 8 + 2 + 4 = 10 + 4 = 14$); decomposing a number leading to a ten (e.g., $13 - 4 = 13 - 3 - 1 = 10 - 1 = 9$); using the relationship between addition and subtraction (e.g., knowing that $8 + 4 = 12$, one knows $12 - 8 = 4$); and creating equivalent but easier or known sums (e.g., adding $6 + 7$ by creating the known equivalent $6 + 6 + 1 = 12 + 1 = 13$).

Additional Standard
1.OA.B.3 (See page B3 for full text.)

Standards for Mathematical Practice (SMP)
1 Make sense of problems and persevere in solving them.
2 Reason abstractly and quantitatively.
3 Construct viable arguments and critique the reasoning of others.
4 Model with mathematics.
7 Look for and make use of structure.
8 Look for and express regularity in repeated reasoning.

Lesson Objectives

Content Objectives
• Recognize that teen numbers can be decomposed and composed to subtract.
• Use the make-a-ten strategy to subtract single-digit numbers from teen numbers.

Language Objectives
• Explain how to use the make-a-ten strategy to subtract.
• Use 10-frames and number paths to decompose teen numbers to make a ten and find a difference.
• Justify answers and communicate the results to others.

Prerequisite Skills

• Count on to add and subtract.
• Add and subtract in word problems.
• Know number partners for numbers within 10.
• Understand teen numbers.
• Understand totals greater than 10.
• Make a ten to add.

Lesson Vocabulary

There is no new vocabulary. Review the following key terms.

• **make a ten** a strategy that uses combinations of numbers that add to ten when finding totals greater than 10.
• **teen number** a ten and some number of ones from 1 to 9. The numbers 11–19.

Learning Progression

In Kindergarten children add and subtract within 10, know decompositions for all numbers within 10, and know the partner that makes 10 for numbers within 10. Children understand teen numbers as 10 and some ones.

In Grade 1 children add and subtract within 20. They solve addition problems with two single-digit addends and solve related subtractions.

In this lesson children use the make-a-ten strategy to subtract single-digit numbers from teen numbers. They use 10-frames and number paths to decompose a teen number, subtract in parts that allow them to make a ten, and then subtract the other part to find the difference.

In Grade 2 children add and subtract within 100 using strategies based on place value, properties of operations, and the relationship between addition and subtraction.

Lesson Pacing Guide

Whole Class Instruction

Day 1
45–60 minutes

Introduction
Use What You Know
• Explore It *25 min*
• Try It *20 min*

Day 2
45–60 minutes

Modeled Instruction
Explore Together
• Example Problem *5 min*
• Model It *20 min*
• Hands-On Activity *20 min*

Practice and Problem Solving
Assign pages 139–140.

Day 3
45–60 minutes

Guided Instruction
Learn Together
• Example Problem *5 min*
• Model It *25 min*
• Talk About It *15 min*

Practice and Problem Solving
Assign pages 141–142.

Day 4
45–60 minutes

Guided Practice
Practice Together
• Example Problem *10 min*
• Problems 1–2 *20 min*
• Visual Model *15 min*

Practice and Problem Solving
Assign pages 143–144.

Day 5
45–60 minutes

Independent Practice
Practice by Myself
• Problems 3–5 *10 min*
• Fluency Practice *10 min*
• Quick Check and Remediation *10 min*
• Hands-On or Challenge Activity *15 min*

Teacher-Toolbox: Lesson Quiz
Lesson 16 Quiz

Materials for Lesson Activities

Per child: 16 two-color counters, 16 dried beans or other small objects, 17 triangle shapes, 14 connecting cubes, number path showing the numbers 1 to 16
Activity Sheet 11*

Per pair: none

For display: 16 markers, transparent bag
Activity Sheet 22

* Used for more than one activity.

Small Group Differentiation

Teacher-Toolbox.com

Reteach
Ready Prerequisite Lessons *45–90 min*

Grade K
• Lesson 18 Add Within 10
• Lesson 19 Subtract Within 10

Teacher-led Activities
Tools for Instruction *15–20 min*

Grade 1 *(Lesson 16)*
• Make a Ten to Add Within 20
• Find the Rule
• Find Missing Addends for Sums to 10
• Subtraction Number Sentences

Student-led Activities
Math Center Activities *30–40 min*

Grade K *(Lessons 18 and 19)*
• K.24 Tell Addition Stories
• K.25 Subtract and Match

Grade 1 *(Lesson 16)*
• 1.09 Make a Ten to Subtract

Personalized Learning

i-Ready.com

Independent
i-Ready Lessons* *10–20 min*

Grade 1 *(Lesson 16)*
• Part 1: Addition and Subtraction Fact Families
• Part 2: Addition and Subtraction Fact Families
• Acting Out Addition and Subtraction

* i-Ready lessons may be updated during the 2016–2017 school year. Updated references will be on the Teacher-Toolbox.

Introduction

Make a Ten to Subtract

Activity Make a Ten to Subtract

Objective
Model solving a subtraction problem.

Materials for each child
• 16 counters

Materials for display
• 16 markers
• transparent bag

Overview
Children solve subtraction problems and write number sentences to represent them. They discuss making a ten to help them subtract.

Step By Step

Explore It

Pose the problem.

• Tell children to imagine that Maria packed her bag for school this morning. Then read the problem from the Student Book page aloud: *Maria has 16 markers. 9 markers fall out of her bag. How many markers are left? How can you think about 10 as you subtract?*

Solve the problem.

• Allow children to use any strategy they choose to solve the problem. Make counters available for children to use as they work.

• Observe as children work to see if they make a 10 or use another strategy to help them solve the problem.

Talk about and solve the problem.

• Use the transparent bag with the 16 markers inside to act out the situation. Say: *One way you can find how many markers are left is to count back.* Count back aloud from 16 to 7 as you remove 9 markers, one by one, from the bag. Ask children to share whether they used this strategy.

• Say: *Another way you can find out how many markers are left is to start at 9 and then count up from 9 to 16.* Display the 9 markers that were taken out of the bag. Say: *Nine.* Then

Explore It

Maria has 16 markers. 9 fall out of her bag. How many markers are left?

$$\underline{\ 16\ } - \underline{\ 9\ } = \underline{\ 7\ }$$

100

pick up and display each of the 7 markers inside the bag and count aloud, one by one: *10, 11, 12, 13, 14, 15, 16.* Ask children to share whether they used this strategy.

• Place all of the markers back in the bag. Say: *You could also subtract by making a ten. How many markers would you need to subtract from 16 to get 10?* [6] Remove 6 markers from the bag. Say: *We've subtracted 6 markers. How many more do we still need to subtract?* [3] Remove 3 markers from the bag. *What is 10 minus 3?* [7] Ask children to share whether they used this strategy.

Write and solve a subtraction number sentence to represent the problem.

• Say: *Let's write a number sentence to solve the problem. Should we write an addition sentence or a subtraction sentence?* [subtraction] Have children explain their reasoning.

• Write $16 - 9 = ?$ on the board.

• Discuss with children what the 16 in the number sentence stands for. [the number of markers Maria put in her bag] Then ask what the 9 in the number sentence stands for. [the number of markers that fall out of Maria's bag]

• Ask children to tell why 9 is subtracted from 16 in the number sentence. [to find how many markers are left in the bag]

• Complete the number sentence on the board and have children record it on their Student Book page. [$16 - 9 = 7$]

Use What You Know
Make a Ten to Subtract

 Try It

Rina has 13 apples. She gives away 6 apples.
How many apples does she have left?

_13_ – _6_ = _7_

101

Try It

Pose the problem.

- Read the problem from the Student Book page aloud: _Rina has 13 apples. She gives away 6 apples. How many apples does she have left?_

Solve the problem.

- Have the children count the number of apples in the basket. [13]

- Then have children write the number sentence and solve the problem. Children can use any strategy, but should be able to understand that this is a take-away situation, and that 6 needs to be subtracted from 13. Provide counters to children who are struggling.

Discuss children's strategies.

- Invite volunteers to share their strategies with the class. Listen for children who used counting how many are left, counting on, and making a ten to subtract.

- Write the number sentence on the board. [13 − 6 = 7]

- Ask if there are children who did not write the number sentence this way and discuss.

Modeled Instruction

Step By Step

• Explain that this page is about solving a subtraction problem, just like the Activity in the Introduction. Read aloud the problem at the top of the page.

Model It

• Direct children's attention to Model It. Remind children that they can use what they know about addition to help them subtract. Read aloud: *15 − 7 = ? is the same as 7 + ? = 15.*

▶ **Mathematical Discourse 1**

▶ **Hands-On Activity**

• Discuss which number to start with. [the number being subtracted, or 7] Have children count up 3 to make 10; then count 5 more to reach 15.

• Point out how the 3 and 5 they just counted make 8. Then ask children how many they counted in all to get from 7 to 15. [8] Relate the numbers to the subtraction number sentence 15 − 7 = 8.

SMP TIP Repeated Reasoning
Algebraic ideas underlie what children are doing when they create equivalent expressions to solve a problem. Children begin to consider the relationship between the parts. Provide children with physical models such as counters, 10-frames, connecting cubes, and number paths to strengthen the connections they are making between objects and abstract reasoning. *(SMP 8)*

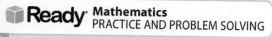 **Ready** Mathematics
PRACTICE AND PROBLEM SOLVING

Assign *Practice and Problem Solving* **pages 139–140** after students have completed this section.

Make a Ten to Subtract

Ava has 15 beads. She gives away 7 beads. How many beads are left?

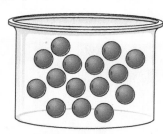

Model It Find 15 − 7.

$15 − 7 = ?$ is the same as $7 + ? = 15$

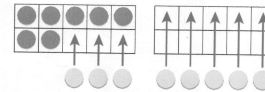

Start with 7.
How many more to 10? __3__
How many more to 15? __5__
So, 15 − 7 = __8__

▶ Mathematical Discourse

1 *How can you use the idea of parts and the whole to explain that 15 − 7 = ? is the same as 7 + ? = 15?*

15 is the whole. 7 and another number are the parts. You can add the parts together to get the whole. You can also subtract one part from the whole to get the other part.

▶ Hands-On Activity

Use 10-frames to subtract.

Materials For each child: 10-Frame (Activity Sheet 11), 15 two-color counters

• Distribute the counters and have children count to confirm there are 15 in all.

• Have children place 7 red counters in a 10-frame and tell how many more counters are needed to fill it. [3] Have children place 3 yellow counters in the 10-frame and discuss their understanding that 7 and 3 make 10.

• After children place the remaining counters (yellow side up) in the second 10-frame, ask: *How many counters are in the other 10-frame?* [5] *How many do 5 and 3 make?* [8] Guide children to see that the 8 yellow counters and 7 red counters make 15 counters in all.

• To connect the number of counters to the subtraction, conclude by saying: *15 counters minus 7 counters is 8 counters. 15 minus 7 is 8.*

Learn Together
Make a Ten to Subtract

Coach has 14 hats. He gives out 6 hats.
How many hats are left?

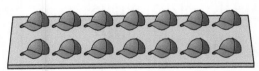

Model It Find 14 − 6. Think: 6 = 2 + 4. ⋯⋯⋯⋯⋯⋯

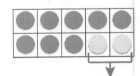 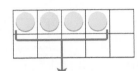

$$14 - 4 = \underline{10}$$
$$10 - 2 = \underline{8}$$
$$14 - 6 = \underline{8}$$

Take away 2.   Take away 4.

💬 Talk About It **What is wrong?** ⋯⋯⋯⋯⋯⋯

Buzz finds 13 − 5.

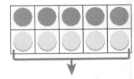 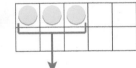

Take away 5.   Take away 3.

103

©Curriculum Associates, LLC   Copying is not permitted

▶**English Language Learners**

Create language cards for *subtract, take away,* and *minus.* For the number sentence 14 − 4 = 10, show: "fourteen minus four equals ten"; "take away four from fourteen to make ten"; "subtract four from fourteen to get ten."

▶**Mathematical Discourse**

2 *How does making a ten make it easier to subtract from a teen number?*

You can think of a teen number as 10 and some ones. You can subtract the ones to get to 10. Then you subtract from the 10 as many more ones as you need to subtract in all. It's easier to subtract from 10 because you know the number partners that make 10.

Step By Step

- Read aloud the problem at the top of the page. Ask children what operation they can use to solve the problem. [subtraction] Have them explain their reasoning.

▶**English Language Learners**

Model It

- Direct attention to Model It. Read aloud: *Find 14 − 6.* Relate the 14 hats to the 14 counters in the two 10-frames.

- Ask children what strategies they would use to help them subtract. Listen for children who suggest making a ten. Point out the 10-frames on the page and discuss how they can be used to make a ten to subtract.

- Have children identify which number to start with. [14] Ask: *How can you make a ten?* [take away 4] Point out that the bracket under the 4 counters indicates they are taken away. Relate the number sentence 14 − 4 = 10 to the 4 taken-away counters and the 10-frame that contains 10 counters.

- Ask: *How many more do you need to take away?* [2] *Why?* [You need to take away 6 and you already took away 4; 4 and 2 are 6.] *How many counters are left?* [8] Relate 10 − 2 = 8 to the 2 taken-away counters and the 8 counters remaining in the 10-frame.

- Reinforce children's understanding by asking how many counters they started with [14], how many were taken away [6 in all], and how many are left [8]. Then direct attention to the final number sentence and discuss.

▶**Mathematical Discourse 2**

Talk About It

- Read aloud Talk About It. Children may recognize that 2 counters, not 5, need to be taken away from the left 10-frame. Discuss that 5 need to be taken away in all.

📦**Ready** Mathematics
PRACTICE AND PROBLEM SOLVING

Assign *Practice and Problem Solving* **pages 141–142** after students have completed this section.

👥👥 Guided Practice

Step By Step

- Read aloud the problem at the top of the page. Discuss what strategies children could use to solve subtraction problems.

- Direct attention to the number path. Ask what strategy it shows. [make a ten] Guide them to name the number to start with when using this strategy. [16] Ask: *How many from 16 to 10 on the number path?* [6]

- Connect this 6 to the box above the number path and to the first number sentence beneath the number path.

- Ask: *How many more do you need to subtract?* [1] *How do you know?* [You need to subtract 7 altogether.] Relate this to the jump from 10 to 9 on the number path and to the second number sentence.

- Ask: *What number do you end at after two jumps on the number path?* [9] Connect this to the final number sentence, 16 − 7 = 9.

▶ **Visual Model**

- Work together with children to complete Problem 1 using the same strategy.

- For Problem 2, children use 10-frames and counters to find 17 − 8. Ask whether they prefer to use a number path or 10-frames to make a ten to subtract. Help children understand that neither model is "better" than the other by discussing how both methods give the same answer.

▶ **Mathematical Discourse 1 and 2**

> **SMP TIP Look for and Use Structure**
> Children use number paths and number sentences to represent decompositions when subtracting from teen numbers. Connecting the two strategies, making a ten to subtract and counting back to subtract, helps children look for and make use of structure. *(SMP 7)*

Make a Ten to Subtract

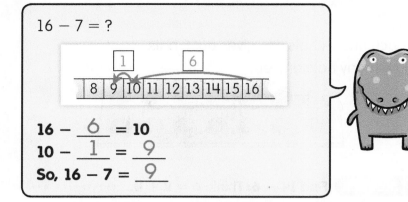

16 − 7 = ?

16 − __6__ = 10
10 − __1__ = 9
So, 16 − 7 = __9__

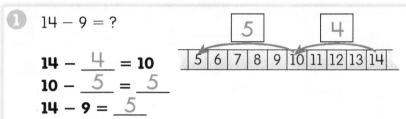

1 14 − 9 = ?

14 − __4__ = 10
10 − __5__ = __5__
14 − 9 = __5__

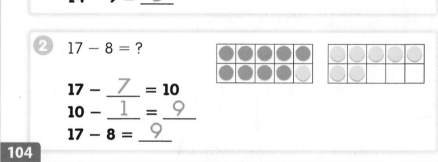

2 17 − 8 = ?

17 − __7__ = 10
10 − __1__ = __9__
17 − 8 = __9__

104

▶ **Mathematical Discourse**

1 *How is making a ten to subtract on a number path like counting back to subtract?*

It's like counting back two times to subtract. First you count back to 10 on the number path. Then you count back a second time, from 10.

2 *How do you know how many to count back each time?*

Break the number you are subtracting into two parts. Count back to subtract one part to get to 10 on the number path. Then count back to subtract the other part from 10.

▶ **Visual Model**

Visualize subtraction on a number path.

Materials For each child: 16 dried beans or other small objects, number path showing numbers 1 to 16

- Have children use dried beans to help them visualize subtraction on the number path.

- For 16 − 7 = 9, have children place 1 bean beneath each number on the number path.

- Children first take away 6 beans and then take away 1 bean to model taking away 7 beans in all.

Make a Ten to Subtract

 $13 - 7 = ?$

Possible work: $7 + 3 = 10$; $10 + 3 = 13$

$13 - 7 =$ _6_

---

4 $15 - 8 = ?$

| 6 | 7 | 8 | 9 | 10 | 11 | 12 | 13 | 14 | 15 |

Possible work: $15 - 5 = 10$; $10 - 3 = 7$

$15 - 8 =$ _7_

---

5 $14 - 5 = ?$

Possible work: $14 - 4 = 10$; $10 - 1 = 9$

$14 - 5 =$ _9_

105

Step By Step

- Before children work on this page, review the models used in this lesson. Emphasize that children are free to use whatever way helps them solve the problem.

- Read each problem aloud, then have children work independently to solve.

- As children work, walk around to assess their progress and understanding.

- In Problem 3, some children may choose to solve the problem by drawing 3 counters to make a ten, then 3 more to make 13. You may wish to pose Mathematical Discourse questions 3 and 4 to discuss other ways children could solve the problem.

▶ **Mathematical Discourse 3 and 4**

- Ask children who solve Problem 5 without showing their work to explain the strategy they used.

▶ **Fluency Practice**

▶ **Fluency Practice**

Break apart teen numbers into a 10 and some ones.

Materials For display: Teen Number Cards (Activity Sheet 22)

Use Activity Sheet 22 (Teen Number Cards) to provide children with practice breaking apart teen numbers into a 10 and some ones. Display a card and have children call out 10 and the number that together make the teen number. For example, hold up a card marked 17. Children call out: *10 and 7 make 17.*

▶ **Mathematical Discourse**

3 *Explain a strategy you could use to find 13 − 7 in Problem 3.*

You have 7 counters in one 10-frame. You need to know how many more counters to make 13. You can draw 3 more counters to make 10. Then you can draw 3 more counters to make 13. You put together the 3 counters and 3 counters to get 6. So you know you need 6 counters to get from 7 to 13. So you know that $13 − 7 = 6$.

4 *Did anyone else use the same strategy? If not, how did you find 13 − 7?*

Children may say they used the same method or that $13 − 3 = 10$ and $10 − 3 = 7$, so $13 − 7 = 6$.

Lesson 16
Make a Ten to Subtract

Differentiated Instruction

▶ Quick Check and Remediation

Materials For each child: 14 counters, 14 connecting cubes, Activity Sheet 11 (10-Frame), number path showing numbers 1 to 14

• Ask children to find $14 - 8$. [6]

• For children who are still struggling, use the chart below to guide remediation.

• After providing remediation, check children's understanding using the following problem: $13 - 6$. [7]

If the error is . . .	Children may . . .	To remediate . . .
2	have taken away 4 to make 10 and then, instead of taking away 4 more, taken away 8 more to find $14 - 12 = 2$.	Provide children with 14 counters and two 10-frames to model the problem so that they can count the 8 counters to take away.
7	have included 8 as one of the numbers they counted as they counted up from 8 to 14.	Have children use a number path to draw individual jumps from 8 to 14 and then count the number of jumps (6) to find the difference between 14 and 8.
10	have decomposed 14 into 10 and 4 and taken away 4 to get 10 without continuing on to take away another 4 from 10 to get 6.	Have children connect 14 cubes and break them apart to make a ten-train and a train of 4 ones. Have them take away 8 cubes, 4 from the 4 ones and 4 from the ten-train, and count what's left to find how many cubes remain.

▶ Hands-On Activity

Use shapes to make a ten to subtract.

Materials For each child: 17 triangle shapes

• Distribute triangle shapes. Write the subtraction $16 - 9$ on the board. Have children count out 16 triangles in a horizontal row.

• Have children move 6 triangles into a second row. Discuss how 10 and 6 still show 16 in all.

• Point to the problem on the board and ask how many they need to take away. [9] Have them take away the 6 triangles in the second row.

• Tell children they can count on from 6 to find out how many more triangles they need to take away from the 10 to take away 9 in all.

• Have them count 7, 8, 9 as they take away 3 triangles from the 10. Say: *Now you've taken away 9 triangles. Count how many are left.* [7]

• Repeat for other subtraction problems such as $17 - 9$, $15 - 9$, $15 - 6$, $14 - 8$, and $13 - 9$.

▶ Challenge Activity

Use number bonds to make a ten to subtract.

• Have children solve subtraction problems using number bonds. Present the first problem, showing the decomposition of both 15 and 9. Guide children to recognize that breaking the teen number into a ten and some ones helps them decide how to break apart the other number.

$$15 \quad - \quad 9 \quad = \underline{\quad}$$
$$\diagdown \quad \diagdown$$
$$10 \quad 5 \qquad 5 \quad 4$$

• Give children the subtraction problems $14 - 6$ and $17 - 9$. Ask them to break apart the numbers like you did in the example to solve.

Teacher Notes

Overview

Assign the Lesson 16 Quiz and have children work independently to complete it.

Use the results of the quiz to assess children's understanding of the content of the lesson and to identify areas for reteaching. See the Lesson Pacing Guide at the beginning of the lesson and the Differentiated Instruction activities for suggested instructional resources.

Tested Skills

Assesses 1.OA.C.6

Problems on this quiz require children to be able to subtract one-digit numbers from teen numbers using the make a ten strategy. Children will also need to be familiar with counting on and making a ten to add, number partners for 10, and how to add and subtract in word problems.

Ready® Mathematics

Lesson 16 Quiz Answer Key

Name _____

Solve.

1 $13 - 4 = ?$

Possible work: $4 + 6 = 10$; $10 + 3 = 13$; $6 + 3 = 9$

$13 - 4 = \underline{9}$

2 $16 - 8 = ?$

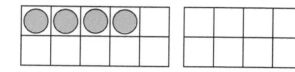

Possible work: $16 - 6 = 10$; $10 - 2 = 8$

$16 - 8 = \underline{8}$

Common Misconceptions and Errors

Errors may result if children:

• do not recognize that teen numbers can be decomposed and composed to subtract.

• decompose the lesser number and make a ten but subtract the wrong partner.

• count on from the lesser number using the lesser number as the first count.

Lesson 16 Quiz Answer Key continued

Name _____

Solve.

3 $17 - 9 = ?$

Possible work: $17 - 7 = 10; 10 - 2 = 8$

$17 - 9 =$ $\underline{8}$

4 $15 - 6 = ?$

Possible work: $15 - 5 = 10; 10 - 1 = 9$

$15 - 6 =$ $\underline{9}$

5 Pablo has 14 books.
He gives away 8 books.
How many books does he have left?

Possible work: $14 - 4 = 10; 10 - 4 = 6$

$14 - 8 =$ $\underline{6}$

Pablo has $\underline{6}$ books left.

Grade 1 **Lesson 16** Make a Ten to Subtract

2

©Curriculum Associates, LLC
Copying permitted for classroom use.

Assessment

Step By Step

- Have children solve the problems individually and show their work. Emphasize that children are free to use whatever way helps them solve the problems.

- Observe as children work. Watch for those who struggle with the idea of "1 ten and some number of ones." Help these children identify the ten and ones in each teen number. Have them write, draw, and talk about making a ten as they add.

Unit 3 Review

Solve the problems.

1 8 blocks are big. 7 blocks are small.
How many in all?

$8 + \underline{2} = \underline{10}$
$10 + \underline{5} = \underline{15}$
$8 + 7 = \underline{15}$

---

2 Max has 14 stickers. He gives away 5 stickers.
How many stickers are left?

$14 - \underline{4} = 10$
$10 - \underline{1} = \underline{9}$
$14 - 5 = \underline{9}$

| 6 | 7 | 8 | 9 | 10 | 11 | 12 | 13 | 14 | 15 |

---

3 4 green balls. 7 red balls. 3 blue balls. How many in all?

$4 + 7 + 3 = \underline{14}$

4 $\underline{7} = 13 - 6$

---

5 16 is the same as

$\underline{1}$ ten and $\underline{6}$ ones

6 $17 = 10 + \underline{7}$

$17 = \underline{9} + 8$

106

Teacher Notes

7 6 children are on the bus.
5 more children get on.
4 children get on next.
How many children are
on the bus now?

$$\overset{10}{6 + 5 + 4} = \underline{15}$$

There are __15__ children on the bus now.

Step By Step

- For Problem 8, children find number partners for 11, starting with 10 and 1, and then moving to 9 and 2 in order to solve the word problem. For children who struggle, point out that the first number bond shows 1 one and ask: *What else does 11 have?* [1 ten] Then remind children that they can find another partner of 11 by subtracting 1 from one addend and adding 1 to the other addend.

8 Cam has 11 apples.
9 are red. The rest are green.
Complete the number bonds.
Then write two addition sentences.

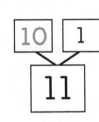

__10__ + 1 = 11

9 + __2__ = 11

Cam has __2__ green apples.

107

Teacher Notes

Assessment

Step By Step

Put It Together

- On this page, children start with 10 and then add some ones to make a teen number. Then they subtract 7 from the number they made.

- Read the directions and task aloud. Make sure children understand what they need to do to complete the task.

- Direct children to complete problem 9 on their own.

- As children work on their own, observe their progress and understanding. Respond to their questions and provide additional support as needed.

- If time permits, have children share their drawings and solutions with the class. Have them show the partners of 7 that they used to do their subtraction.

- Ask: *How did you know those were the partners of 7 to use?* [The first partner should be the same as the number of ones in their teen number.]

- Have children return to the Unit Opener page and complete the *After* column of the progress chart.

Put It Together

9 **Make a teen number.**

Then make a ten to subtract.

Draw more stickers to make 11, 12, 13, 14, or 15. Then subtract 7 from your number.

Possible answer: Child draws 3 stars to make 13.

$$\underline{13} - \underline{3} = 10$$

$$10 - \underline{4} = \underline{6}$$

So, $\underline{13} - 7 = \underline{6}$

108

Teacher Notes

Scoring Rubric

Points	Expectations
4	The child: • creates a teen number. • correctly uses the "make a ten" strategy to subtract.
3	The child: • may create a teen number. • may have a minor error when subtracting 7.
2	The child: • may create a teen number. • may incorrectly identify the partners of 7 or the difference.
1	The child: • may show errors in creating a teen number. • may make multiple errors when subtracting.
0	The child: • does not attempt to complete the task.

Which lessons are students building upon?

Kindergarten, Lesson 21
Understand Teen Numbers
K.NBT.A.1

Kindergarten, Lesson 22
Count Teen Numbers
K.CC.A.3, K.CC.B.5

Kindergarten, Lesson 22
Count Teen Numbers
K.CC.A.3, K.CC.B.5

Kindergarten, Lesson 24
Count to 100 by Tens
K.CC.A.1, K.CC.A.2

Kindergarten, Lesson 25
Count to 100 by Ones
K.CC.A.1, K.CC.A.2

Kindergarten, Lesson 22
Count Teen Numbers
K.CC.A.3, K.CC.B.5

Kindergarten, Lesson 23
Make Teen Numbers
K.NBT.A.1

Kindergarten, Lesson 24
Count to 100 by Tens
K.CC.A.1, K.CC.A.2

Kindergarten, Lesson 21
Understand Teen Numbers
K.NBT.A.1

Kindergarten, Lesson 22
Count Teen Numbers
K.CC.A.3, K.CC.B.5

Kindergarten, Lesson 24
Count to 100 by Tens
K.CC.A.1, K.CC.A.2

Unit 4

Lesson 17
Understand Tens
1.NBT.B.2a, 1.NBT.B.2c

Lesson 18
The 120 Chart
1.OA.C.5, 1.NBT.A.1

Lesson 19
Understand 10 More and 10 Less
1.NBT.C.5

Lesson 20
Add and Subtract Tens
1.NBT.C.6

Which lessons are students preparing for?

Grade 2, Lesson 10
Understand Three-Digit Numbers
2.NBT.A.1a, 2.NBT.A.1b,
2.NBT.A.2

Grade 2, Lesson 11
Read and Write Three-Digit Numbers
2.NBT.A.3

Grade 2, Lesson 7
Add Two-Digit Numbers
2.NBT.B.5, 2.NBT.B.8

Grade 2, Lesson 8
Subtract Two-Digit Numbers
2.NBT.B.5, 2.NBT.B.8

Grade 2, Lesson 7
Add Two-Digit Numbers
2.NBT.B.5, 2.NBT.B.8

Grade 2, Lesson 8
Subtract Two-Digit Numbers
2.NBT.B.5, 2.NBT.B.8

Grade 2, Lesson 7
Add Two-Digit Numbers
2.NBT.B.5, 2.NBT.B.8

Grade 2, Lesson 8
Subtract Two-Digit Numbers
2.NBT.B.5, 2.NBT.B.8

Unit 4
Tens

Unit 4 – Number and Operations in Base Ten
Tens

60 cherries and 50 grapes. The cherries and grapes are in bags of 10. Ben gives Emma some of the bags. What math questions could Ben ask about the bags of fruit?

In this unit, you will learn about tens and how to add and subtract tens. Then you will be able to solve problems like Ben's.

✓ Self Check

Check off the skills you know now. Then see how many more you can check off after each lesson!

I can:	Before this unit	After this unit
show numbers as tens.	☐	☐
count on a 120 chart.	☐	☐
find 10 more and 10 less than a number.	☐	☐
subtract 10 in my head.	☐	☐
add tens.	☐	☐
subtract tens.	☐	☐

Ready Mathematics
PRACTICE AND PROBLEM SOLVING

Practice and Problem Solving Resources

Use the following resources from **Practice and Problem Solving** to engage students and their families and to extend student learning.

- **Family Letters** Send Family Letters home separately before each lesson or as part of a family communication package.

- **Unit Games** Use partner Unit Games at classroom centers and/or send them home for play with family members.

- **Unit Practice** Assign Unit Practice as homework, as independent or small group practice, or for whole class discussion.

- **Fluency Practice** Assign Fluency Skills Practice and Fluency Repeated Reasoning Practice worksheets throughout the unit.

At A Glance

- This page introduces children to the general ideas behind working with tens.

- The checklist allows them to see what skills they will be learning and take ownership of their progress.

Step By Step

- Explain to children that they are going to begin a new unit of lessons. Tell them that in all the lessons in this unit they will be learning about tens and how to add and subtract tens.

- Read the introduction to the unit together as a class. Invite children to suggest questions that could be asked about the problem situation. Discuss the questions children pose without the expectation that they are to solve them.

- Then take a few minutes to have each child independently read through the list of skills.

- Ask children to consider each skill and check the box in the *Before* column if it is a skill they think they already have. Remind children that these skills are likely to all be new to them, but it's still possible some children have some of the skills.

- Engage children in a brief discussion about the skills. Invite children to comment on which ones they would most like to learn, or which ones seem similar or related to something they already know. Remind them that the goal is to be able to check off all the skills they have learned by the end of the unit.

- At the end of the unit, have children complete the *After* column. As time allows, pose questions about the problem situation at the top of the page and solve as a class.

Lesson 17
Understand Tens

CCSS Focus

Domain
Number and Operations in Base Ten

Cluster
B. Understand place value.

Standards
1.NBT.B.2 Understand that the two digits of a two-digit number represent amounts of tens and ones. Understand the following as special cases:
a. 10 can be thought of as a bundle of ten ones—called a "ten."
c. The numbers 10, 20, 30, 40, 50, 60, 70, 80, 90 refer to one, two, three, four, five, six, seven, eight, or nine tens (and 0 ones).

Standards for Mathematical Practice (SMP)
2 Reason abstractly and quantitatively.
3 Construct viable arguments and critique the reasoning of others.
5 Use appropriate tools strategically.
7 Look for and make use of structure.
8 Look for and express regularity in repeated reasoning.

Lesson Objectives

Content Objectives
- Understand that the base-ten system is made up of groups of tens and ones.
- Organize 10 ones into a group of ten.
- Express 10 ones as 1 ten and 1 ten as 10 ones.
- Identify and write two-digit numbers in terms of tens and ones.

Language Objectives
- Use connecting cubes to show that one 10-cube bar represents 10 ones or the number 10 and not the number 1.
- Circle groups of 10 objects in a group containing a multiple of 10 objects.
- Count groups of 10 objects and write the total as the number of tens.

Prerequisite Skills
- Count to 100.
- Add within 10.
- Understand teen numbers as 1 group of ten and some ones.

Lesson Vocabulary

Review the following key terms.
- **ones** single units or objects.
- **tens** groups of ten ones.

Learning Progression

In Kindergarten children count by tens to 100 and write numbers to 20, observing place value.

In Grade 1 children explore tens by making a ten to add and subtract and by recognizing teen numbers as a composition of a ten and some ones.

In this lesson children explore the concept of ten as 10 ones by counting, recording, and comparing multiple groups of ten. They reason that 10 can be shown as one group of 10 or as 10 individual ones and compare numbers expressed in the two forms. Concepts in this lesson lay groundwork for understanding the idea that the two digits in two-digit numbers represent a number of tens and ones and for adding and subtracting multiples of ten.

In Grade 2 children use their understanding of the base-ten system to add and subtract two-digit numbers and extend the concept of place value to understand three-digit numbers.

Lesson Pacing Guide

Whole Class Instruction

Day 1 *45–60 minutes*	**Introduction** **Use What You Know** • Explore It *25 min* • Try It *20 min*	
Day 2 *45–60 minutes*	**Modeled Instruction** **Explore Together** • Opening Question *5 min* • Think *15 min* • Talk About It *10 min* • Hands-On Activity *15 min*	**Practice and Problem Solving** Assign pages 155–156.
Day 3 *45–60 minutes*	**Guided Instruction** **Explore Together** • Hands-On Problem *5 min* • Problems 1–3 *15 min* • Talk About It *10 min* • Visual Model *15 min*	**Practice and Problem Solving** Assign pages 157–158.
Day 4 *45–60 minutes*	**Guided Practice** **Connect It** • Problems 4–6 *15 min* **Independent Practice** **Show What I Know** • Problem 7 *15 min* • Intervention, On-Level, or Challenge Activity *15 min*	**Practice and Problem Solving** Assign pages 159–160.
	Teacher-Toolbox: Lesson Quiz Lesson 17 Quiz	

Materials for Lesson Activities

Per child: 23 connecting cubes (13 in one color, 10 in another color),
11 to 29 dry beans, crayons, base-ten blocks
Activity Sheet 11, Activity Sheet 19*

Per pair: 60 connecting cubes, 1-6 number cube

For display: none

*Used for more than one activity.

Small Group Differentiation

Teacher-Toolbox.com

Reteach
Ready Prerequisite Lessons *45–90 min*

Grade K
• Lesson 21 *Understand* Teen Numbers
• Lesson 22 Count Teen Numbers

Teacher-led Activities
Tools for Instruction *15–20 min*

Grade 1 *(Lesson 17)*
• Patterns on the Hundred Chart
• Making a Set Up to 10 Objects
• Counting Up to 20 Objects

Student-led Activities
Math Center Activities *30–40 min*

Grade K **(***Lessons 21 and 22***)**
• K.28 Teen Number Vocabulary
• K.08 Pick and Write

Grade 1 *(Lesson 17)*
• 1.21 Groups of 10

Personalized Learning

i-Ready.com

Independent
i-Ready Lessons* *10–20 min*

Grade 1 *(Lesson 17)*
• Grouping into Tens and Ones
• Regrouping Tens as Ones

* i-Ready lessons may be updated during the 2016–2017 school year. Updated references will be on the Teacher-Toolbox.

👥 Introduction

Activity Make a Ten

Objective

Explore groups of ten as a way to express 10 ones.

Materials for each child

• 23 connecting cubes (13 in one color, 10 in another color)

Overview

Children explore the concept of tens beyond teen numbers by building groups of 10 connecting cubes and describing the total number of cubes.

Step By Step

Explore It

Introduce the activity.

• Distribute connecting cubes to children. Write the number 6 on the board. Have children place 6 cubes on their 10-frames. Explain that children will add cubes to the 10-frame to build groups of 10.

Build one group of 10.

• Ask children how many more cubes need to be added in order to make 10. Then have them add that number of cubes of a different color to the 10-frame. Reinforce addition by stating the sum: *6 + 4 = 10. 10 cubes on the frame.* Write the sum on the board and have children complete the number sentence on the Student Book page.

• When the 10-frame is full, tell children to connect the 10 ones (cubes) to make 1 ten. Have them place the ten to the left of the 10-frame.

• Discuss that children now have one group of 10 (pointing to the connected cubes) and 0 ones (pointing to an empty 10-frame).

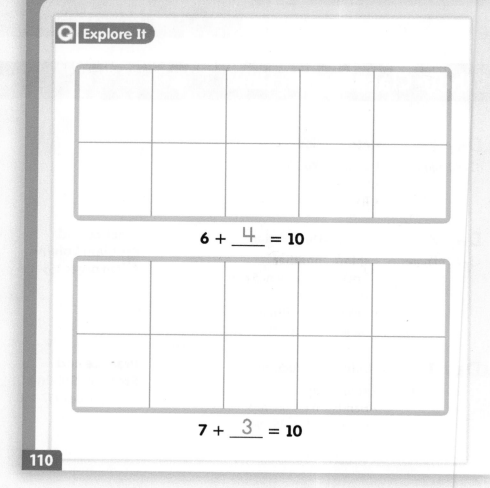

🔄 Explore It

$6 + \underline{\quad 4 \quad} = 10$

$7 + \underline{\quad 3 \quad} = 10$

110

• To emphasize that 1 ten is the same as 10 ones, ask children to break apart the ten, place the individual cubes in the 10-frame, and then connect the cubes again to make a ten. Again, have children put the ten to the left of the 10-frame.

Build another group of 10

• Repeat the process, starting with the number 7.

• When children have completed building ten both ways, invite children to share how they are alike and how they are different.

Use What You Know
Understand Tens

>> Try It

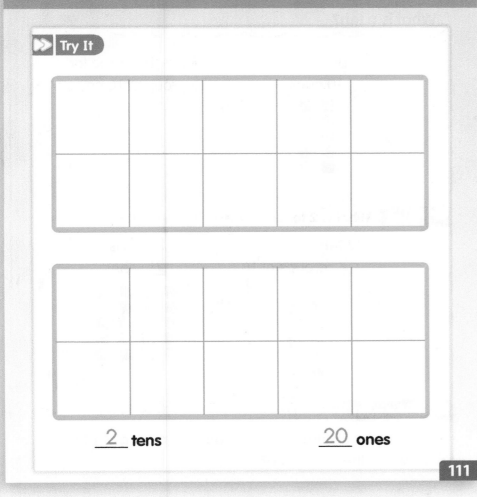

___2___ tens   ___20___ ones

111

Try It

Build two groups of 10.

- Have children use the cubes to build one ten-train. Ask: *How many ones are in the ten-train?* [10]

- Then have children use connecting cubes to build a second ten-train. Ask: *How many cubes are in this ten-train?* [10]

- Then ask: *How many tens do you have in all?* [2 tens] *How many ones are in 2 tens?* [20 ones] Have children take apart each ten and place the individual cubes in the two 10-frames on the Student Book page to verify that there are 20 cubes. Have children write the number of tens and the number of ones.

- As children build and break apart tens, look for an understanding that 1 ten and a group of 10 ones are the same and that 2 tens and 20 ones are the same. Some children may think of a ten as a one and count 1, 2 instead of 1 ten, 2 tens. Children will have opportunities to develop this thinking as they work through the lesson. Additional support is provided in the Hands-On Activity and the Visual Model in the lesson.

Modeled Instruction

Step By Step

- Read aloud the question at the top of the page. Then direct attention to the 10 ones and 1 ten on the Student Book page. Ask: *How can you tell that both pictures show ten cubes?*

Think

- Read Think aloud. As children explain their thinking, reinforce the idea that when the cubes are separate, they are expressed as *ones* and when they are connected, they are expressed as *tens*.

▶ **Mathematical Discourse 1 and 2**

- Display a train of 10 cubes and 3 single cubes. Ask: *Would it make sense to count these as* [point to the ten-train] *1,* [point to each of the 3 single cubes as you count] *2, 3, 4 cubes? Why or why not?* Make sure children understand that the ten and the ones are counted differently because they represent different quantities.

Talk About It

- Read Talk About It. Encourage discussion by asking questions, such as: *Do you agree with what [child's name] said? Does someone have a different way to tell how the pictures are the same?* [Both pictures have 10 cubes. The cubes are connected in the ten and separate in the ones.]

▶ **Hands-On Activity**

SMP TIP   Construct Arguments
Asking children to express and justify mathematical ideas reinforces understanding of concepts and promotes mathematical reasoning. Validate and support the way they express their ideas, and help them develop their reasoning skills through further questioning. *(SMP 3)*

 **Mathematics**
PRACTICE AND PROBLEM SOLVING

Assign *Practice and Problem Solving* **pages 155–156** after students have completed this section.

Understand Tens

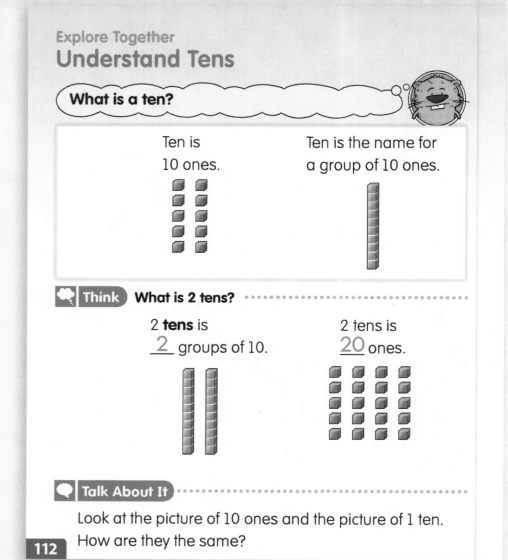

What is a ten?

Ten is 10 ones.

Ten is the name for a group of 10 ones.

Think   What is 2 tens?

2 **tens** is __2__ groups of 10.

2 tens is __20__ ones.

Talk About It

Look at the picture of 10 ones and the picture of 1 ten. How are they the same?

112

▶ **Mathematical Discourse**

1 *When you make tens as shown in Think, how can you tell for sure that each group has ten cubes in it?*

Some children will count the cubes in each group. Others may count the number in one group and compare the others to it.

2 *If you had a lot of cubes to count, how might making tens help you count them?*

If you make groups of ten, you can count the cubes by tens. If you count lots of cubes one by one, it could take a long time and you may lose count. Counting by tens is faster and you won't lose count as easily.

▶ **Hands-On Activity**
Model tens with connecting cubes.

Materials   For each pair: 50 connecting cubes

- Have children work in pairs. One child counts out a group of 20 cubes, while the other counts out a group of 30 cubes.

- Ask partners to switch groups of cubes and connect them to form tens. Together partners count the tens (by ten) and verify that 20 is 2 tens and 30 is 3 tens.

Explore Together
Understand Tens

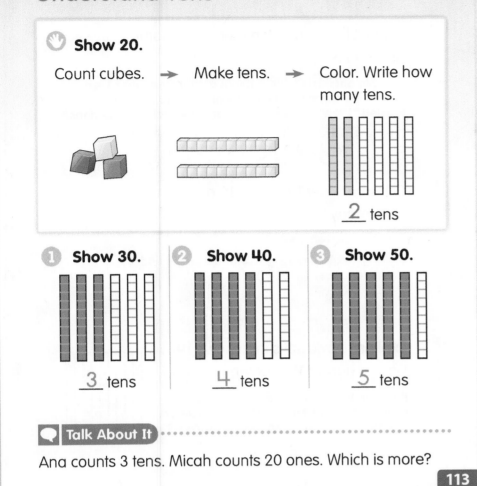

✋ **Show 20.**

Count cubes. → Make tens. → Color. Write how many tens.

__2__ tens

1 **Show 30.**

__3__ tens

2 **Show 40.**

__4__ tens

3 **Show 50.**

__5__ tens

💬 **Talk About It** •

Ana counts 3 tens. Micah counts 20 ones. Which is more?

113

Step By Step

- Explain the directions at the top of the page. Have children follow the model by counting out 20 cubes and making groups of 10. Ask why 2 groups of cubes are colored. Ensure that children make the connection between the physical model and the picture.

- Allow children time to complete Problems 1–3. Watch to make sure they count, color, and record the number of tens, not the number of cubes, on the lines.

- Discuss the structure of the numbers 20, 30, 40, 50, connecting each one to the number of tens recorded. Make sure children understand that the zero shows there are only tens and no extra ones.

- Write the number 30 on the board and cover the zero. Ask: *If I told you to show this number of cubes, what would you do?* Children should see that without the zero, the number is read as 3 ones, not as 3 tens.

▶ **Mathematical Discourse 3**

Talk About It

- Read the Talk About It question aloud. Encourage children to justify their decision. Ask Mathematical Discourse question 4 to extend the idea of comparing tens.

▶ **Mathematical Discourse 4**

▶ **Visual Model**

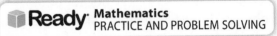 **Ready**· **Mathematics** PRACTICE AND PROBLEM SOLVING

Assign *Practice and Problem Solving* **pages 157–158** after students have completed this section.

▶ **Visual Model**

Recognize rows of a hundreds chart as tens.

Materials For each child: Hundreds Chart (Activity Sheet 19), crayons

- Display a hundreds chart. Ask children to find the row of squares showing 1–10 on their own charts and color it. Demonstrate on the displayed chart.

- Have children shade in the next row of ten with a different color. Ask how many rows are shaded and how many squares are shaded. Encourage children to justify their answers by counting, or by recognizing that the numbers on the chart tell how many in all.

- Continue to have children shade in rows and find totals. Discuss how each row is like a ten they made with connecting cubes.

- Point out that the numbers in the rightmost column are the numbers you say when you count by tens.

▶ **Mathematical Discourse**

3 *How could you see that 40 is more than 30 just by looking at the numbers?*

Look for an understanding that the digits 3 and 4 in 30 and 40 indicate a number of tens. Since 4 is more than 3, 4 tens or 40 is more than 3 tens or 30.

4 *How did you decide whether Ana or Micah has more cubes?*

Some children might suggest building each group of cubes and counting them. Others may suggest thinking of 3 tens as 30 ones and comparing 20 ones to 30 ones or thinking of 20 as 2 tens and comparing 3 tens to 2 tens.

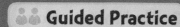
Guided Practice

Step By Step

- Discuss each Connect It problem as a class using the discussion points outlined below.

Draw

- If children need help, provide a set of 10 cubes linked together to help them remember what is meant by 1 ten.

- Invite children to share their drawings. Ask questions, such as: *Why did you draw your tens the way you did? Does anyone have a question about [child's name]'s drawing?*

- Encourage children to answer questions about their drawings. You may wish to have them modify their drawings or make new ones based on the questions from others.

- Revisit the earlier discussion about why it makes sense to group 10 ones as 1 ten. Remind children that counting by tens makes sense when there are many items to count.

Reason

- Circulate the room to check understanding by asking questions like: *What does your picture show? How is the picture of 1 ten different from the picture of 10 ones?*

- Invite children to share their drawings and explain how they found the number of tens in all. Encourage them to comment on the drawings and explanations of others.

Explain

- Ask children to talk to a partner about the problem. After a few minutes, start a class discussion about the counting method David may have used.

- Point to each ten on the student page as you say: *10, 11, 12, 13, 14.* Then ask: *Why doesn't David's counting on strategy work?* Children should recognize that he counted the first ten correctly, but then he counted all the other tens as if they were ones instead of tens.

- Invite volunteers to show the correct way to count the tens. Then ask children to make a drawing that correctly shows 14 using base-ten blocks.

Connect It
Understand Tens

④ Draw Show why 1 ten means the same as 10 ones.

Possible answer: Children might demonstrate that 1 ten means the same as 10 ones by drawing 10 single cubes labeled "1 ten" and 1 group of ten cubes labeled "10 ones."

⑤ Reason Draw 1 ten and 10 more ones. How many tens in all?

Possible answer: 2 tens

Children might draw 1 group of ten cubes and 10 single cubes.

⑥ Explain David says this shows 14. Do you agree? Why or why not?

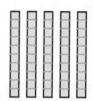

Possible answer: I do not agree. David counted this as 1 ten and 4 ones. There are 5 groups of ten, or 5 tens, so this shows 50.

114

SMP TIP Look for Structure
As children learn to see a set of multiple parts (ten individual items) as one single part (one ten) they are building understanding of the structure and power of the base ten counting system. Provide multiple opportunities for children to compose and decompose tens to reinforce this concept. *(SMP 7)*

Ready Mathematics
PRACTICE AND PROBLEM SOLVING

Assign *Practice and Problem Solving* **pages 159–160** after students have completed this section.

Show What I Know
Understand Tens

7 **Think about making tens.**

A: Circle groups of 10.
Write how many.

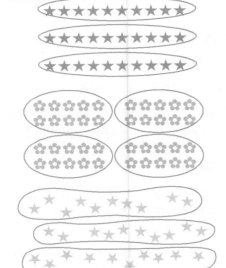

How many groups? __3__
How many stars? __30__

How many groups? __4__
How many flowers? __40__

How many groups? __3__
How many stars? __30__

B: Draw 21 beach balls.
Show how you know you have 21.

Possible answer: Children might show 21 by drawing
21 beach balls or circles, ringing 2 groups of ten to
show 2 tens and 1 left over.

115

Step By Step

• Tell children that they will complete this page independently.

• Read the directions and questions aloud, making sure children understand what they are expected to do.

• In Part A, children circle groups of ten, write how many groups of ten there are, and tell how many objects there are in all.

• In Part B, children make 2 tens and 1 one.

• Observe children as they work. Ask questions such as the following to encourage thinking and problem-solving strategies:

How can you be sure you have circled ten?

How can you check that you have the correct number of stars?

What does 21 mean? How many tens does 21 have? How many ones?

Is there a way to show 21 that makes it easy to count?

Scoring Rubrics

Expectations for 4–3 Points

Points	Expectations
4	The child: • accurately circles groups of ten and identifies the number of groups and totals. • draws the correct number of balls and justifies by labeling each ball, or groups balls into tens and ones and gives the total.
3	The child: • may circle groups of ten, but show minor errors in the number of groups and totals. • may show the correct number of balls, but presents a justification that is inaccurate or incomplete.

Expectations for 2–0 Points

Points	Expectations
2	The child: • may circle groups of ten in some, but not all of the sets and does not accurately identify all groups or totals. • shows the correct number of balls, but provides no justification.
1	The child: • attempts to circle groups of ten and show the correct number of balls, but there is no evidence of a strategy or understanding of the problems.
0	The child: • does not attempt to solve the problems.

Differentiated Instruction

▶ Intervention Activity

Record groups of ten and ones.

Materials For each child: 10-Frame (Activity Sheet 11), for each pair: 60 connecting cubes, 1–6 number cube

- Organize children into pairs and explain that they will play a game.

- Give children the target number 30. Tell them that when one of them reaches this number or gets beyond it, the game is over and they play again.

- To play, children take turns rolling the number cube and placing that number of cubes on their 10-frame. After each roll, children add cubes to the 10-frame and record the total number of cubes. When the 10-frame is full, they connect the cubes to make a ten and place it to the left of the frame. Instruct children to record the total by counting and writing the tens (outside of the frame) and the ones (inside the frame). For example: 2 tens and 3 ones.

▶ On-Level Activity

Record tens and some ones.

Materials For each child: 11 to 29 dry beans

- Put children into groups of 2 or 3 and give each child a different numbers of beans. Use amounts greater than 10 but less than 30. Have each child arrange his or her beans into groups of 10 and extra ones.

- Encourage children to record the number of tens they made. Ask each group to count by tens to determine the total number of tens they have.

- Groups then combine the leftover beans to see if they can create additional groups of ten and again find the total number of tens.

- You may want to have children put all beans together in a large group, redistribute them among members, and repeat the activity.

▶ Challenge Activity

Make more than 9 tens.

Materials Optional: Hundreds Chart (Activity Sheet 19), base-ten blocks

- As a preview to the next lesson, challenge children to find out how many cubes are equal to 10 tens, 11 tens, 12 tens. You might give them a hundreds chart and base-ten blocks, or suggest that they make drawings.

- Encourage them to think about the strategies they used to find the total number of cubes and share these ideas with the class.

Teacher Notes

Teacher-Toolbox.com

Overview

Assign the Lesson 17 Quiz and have children work independently to complete it.

Use the results of the quiz to assess children's understanding of the content of the lesson and to identify areas for reteaching. See the Lesson Pacing Guide at the beginning of the lesson and the Differentiated Instruction activities for suggested instructional resources.

Tested Skills

Assesses 1.NBT.B.2a, 1.NBT.B.2c

Problems on this quiz require children to be able to organize ones into groups of ten, express 10 ones as 1 ten and 1 ten as 10 ones, and identify and write two-digit numbers as tens and ones. Children will also need to be familiar with adding within 10, counting to 100, and understand teen numbers as one group of ten and some ones.

Ready **Mathematics**

Lesson 17 Quiz Answer Key

Name _____

Solve.

1 Show 90.

_9_ tens

2 Show 70.

_7_ tens

3 Draw 2 tens and 10 ones. Then fill in the blank.

Possible answer: Children might draw 2 groups of ten cubes and 10 single cubes.

There are _3_ tens in all.

Grade 1 Lesson 17 *Understand Tens*   1   ©Curriculum Associates, LLC
Copying permitted for classroom use.

Common Misconceptions and Errors

Errors may result if children:

- miscounts groups of ten and inaccurately identifies the total.
- circle groups containing more than or less than 10 items.
- circle groups of ten but then miscount the number of groups.

Lesson 17 **Quiz Answer Key** continued

Name ____________________

Solve.

4 Circle groups of 10.
Write how many.

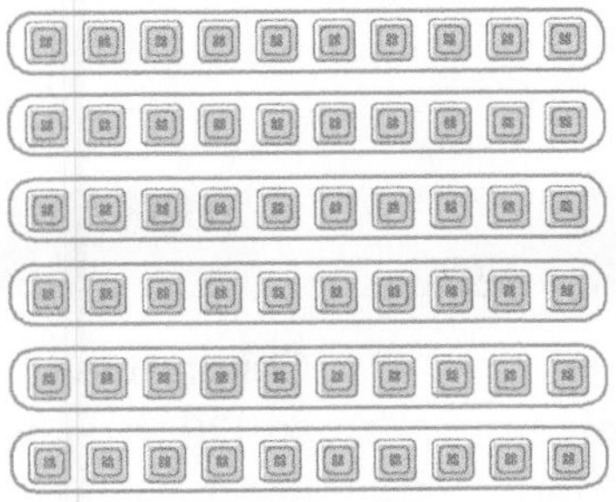

How many groups? 6

How many buttons? 60

5 Below are Keb's stickers.
How many groups of ten? 4
How many stickers? 40

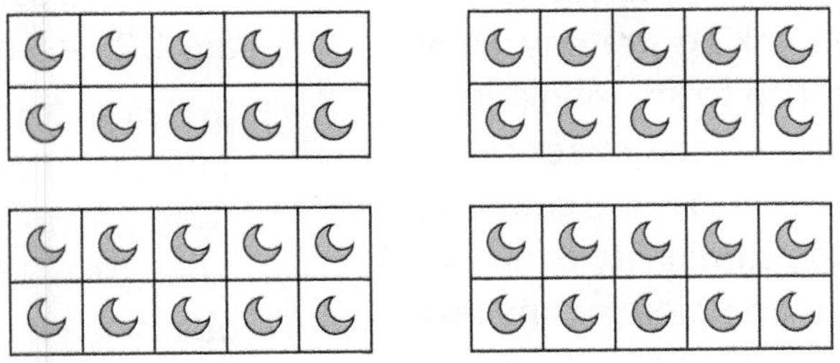

Grade 1 Lesson 17 *Understand* Tens   2   ©Curriculum Associates, LLC Copying permitted for classroom use.

CCSS Focus

Domain
Operations and Algebraic Thinking

Cluster
C. Add and subtract within 20.

Standards
1.OA.C.5 Relate counting to addition and subtraction (e.g., by counting on 2 to add 2).
1.NBT.A.1 Count to 120, starting at any number less than 120. In this range, read and write numerals and represent a number of objects with a written numeral.

Additional Standard
1.OA.3.6 (See page B3 for full text.)

Standards for Mathematical Practice (SMP)

2 Reason abstractly and quantitatively.
3 Construct viable arguments and critique the reasoning of others.
5 Use appropriate tools strategically.
7 Look for and make use of structure.
8 Look for and express regularity in repeated reasoning.

Lesson Objectives

Content Objectives

• Count on from any number on the 120 chart.
• Connect counting on to addition.
• Count by 1s, 2s, and 5s within 120.

Language Objectives

• Read and circle numbers in a 120 chart and describe patterns.
• Draw arrows or use a finger to count by 1s, 2s, or 5s from any number on a 120 chart.
• Tell how to start from a given number to find 1, 2, and 5 more than that number.

Prerequisite Skills

• Count by ones.
• Count by twos.
• Count on to add.

Lesson Vocabulary

• **120 chart** a chart labeled with numbers from 1 to 120 set across 10 columns and down 12 rows.
• **row** a horizontal arrangement of items in a chart.
• **column** a vertical arrangement of items in a chart.

Review the following key term.

• **tens** groups of ten ones.

Learning Progression

In Kindergarten children learn the relationship between a quantity of objects and the number representing the quantity. They understand that the last number name said tells the number of objects counted. They count to 100 by 1s and 10s, count up from a given number, and write numbers from 0 to 20.

In Grade 1 children understand counting as a thinking strategy. They relate counting on to addition and subtraction and counting back to subtraction. They relate the counting sequence to the cardinality of numbers: each number is one more or one less than the number after or before.

Children read and write numbers from 1 to 120 and use strategies that involve 10 as a benchmark number.

In this lesson children use a 120 chart to count up from any given number within 120. They look for patterns in the 120 chart that show relationships between numbers. They count up by 1s, 2s, and 5s and identify numbers that are 1, 2, or 5 more than a given number.

In Grade 2 children count within 1,000 and skip count by 5s, 10s, and 100s. Children read and write numbers to 1,000. They identify groups as having an odd or even number of objects.

Lesson Pacing Guide

Whole Class Instruction

Day 1
45–60 minutes

Introduction

Use What You Know
• Explore It *25 min*
• Try It *20 min*

Day 2
45–60 minutes

Modeled Instruction

Explore Together
• Opening Question *5 min*
• Model It *20 min*
• Hands-On Activity *20 min*

Practice and Problem Solving
Assign pages 163–164.

Day 3
45–60 minutes

Guided Instruction

Learn Together
• Opening Question *5 min*
• Model It *20 min*
• Talk About It *10 min*
• Visual Model *10 min*

Practice and Problem Solving
Assign pages 165–166.

Day 4
45–60 minutes

Guided Practice

Practice Together
• Example Problem *5 min*
• Problems 1–2 *25 min*
• Concept Extension *15 min*

Practice and Problem Solving
Assign pages 167–168.

Day 5
45–60 minutes

Independent Practice

Practice by Myself
• Problems 3–4 *15 min*
• Fluency Practice *10 min*
• Quick Check and Remediation *10 min*
• Hands-On or Challenge Activity *10 min*

Teacher-Toolbox: Lesson Quiz
Lesson 18 Quiz

Materials for Lesson Activities

Per child: 1 blue crayon, 1 yellow crayon
Activity Sheet 23*

Per pair: crayons
Activity Sheet 23

For display: Activity Sheet 23*

*Used for more than one activity.

Small Group Differentiation

Teacher-Toolbox.com

Reteach
Ready Prerequisite Lessons *45–90 min*

Grade K
• Lesson 24 Count to 100 by Tens
• Lesson 25 Count to 100 by Ones

Teacher-led Activities
Tools for Instruction *15–20 min*

Grade 1 *(Lesson 18)*
• Patterns on the Hundred Chart
• Identifying Numerals to 10
• Count Forward by 1s

Student-led Activities
Math Center Activities *30–40 min*

Grade K *(Lessons 24 and 25)*
• K.30 Count by Tens
• K.31 Tens Bingo
• K.32 Count by Ones Vocabulary
• K.33 Keep Counting

Grade 1 *(Lesson 18)*
• 1.28 Counting Vocabulary
• 1.29 Count to 120

Personalized Learning

i-Ready.com

Independent
i-Ready Lessons* *10–20 min*

Grade 1 *(Lesson 18)*
• Counting On: 1 to 100
• One More
• One Less

* i-Ready lessons may be updated during the 2016–2017 school year. Updated references will be on the Teacher-Toolbox.

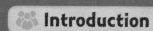 **Introduction**

Activity The 120 Chart

Objective

Count on from any given number within 120.

Materials for display

• 120 Chart (Activity Sheet 23)

Overview

Children act out counting numbers from 1 to 10. They count on a 120 chart from given numbers and fill in missing numbers in sections of the 120 chart.

Step By Step

Explore It

Act out counting 1 to 10.

• Arrange 10 chairs in a row at the front of the classroom. Have 10 children stand in front of the chairs.

• Together with the class, count aloud from 1 to 10 as the children sit down in the chairs one by one.

• When the number 10 is reached, the class repeats "10" again and the last child stands back up. Have the class count aloud back from 10 to 1 as the children stand back up one by one.

• Repeat the activity, this time having children clap on each number as the class counts up from 1 to 10 and back from 10 to 1.

Display the 120 chart.

• Cover the bottom two rows of a displayed 120 chart so children see the numbers 1 to 100 on the chart.

• Point to the first row on the chart and ask children how it relates to the activity they just completed. [You can count up from 1 to 10 and back from 10 to 1 on it.]

• Have children name the numbers that the displayed chart starts and ends with [1 and 100] Ask: *How do you think you can count numbers greater than 100?* [Start over with 1, 2, 3, and so on, but say "one hundred" in front of each number: 101, 102, 103, and so on.]

Explore It

How can you count on a 120 chart?

1	2	3	4	5	6	7	8	9	10
11	12	13	14	15	16	17	18	19	20
21	22	23	24	25	26	27	28	29	30
31	32	33	34	35	36	37	38	39	40
41	42	43	44	45	46	47	48	49	50
51	52	53	54	55	56	57	58	59	60
61	62	63	64	65	66	67	68	69	70
71	72	73	74	75	76	77	78	79	80
81	82	83	84	85	86	87	88	89	90
91	92	93	94	95	96	97	98	99	100
101	102	103	104	105	106	107	108	109	110
111	112	113	114	115	116	117	118	119	120

116

Talk about the 120 chart.

• Uncover the bottom two rows of the chart and direct children's attention to the 120 chart on the Student Book page. Discuss how the two rows at the bottom are different from the rest of the chart. [They have 3 digits; they show numbers in the hundreds.]

• Count aloud from 100 to 120 with children, pointing to each number on the displayed chart as the class counts it.

Use the 120 chart to count on from a given number.

• Direct children's attention back to the 120 chart on the Student Book page.

• Ask children how the chart might be used to help them count. [You can start counting at any number on the chart. You can stop counting at any number.] Count aloud from 21 to 30 with children. Encourage children to touch the numbers on their 120 chart as they count.

• Repeat counting aloud together with the class, starting at and ending on different numbers. For example, count from 11 to 25, 27 to 40, 52 to 56, 58 to 60, 84 to 91, 95 to 104, and so on.

Use What You Know
The 120 Chart

>> **Try It**

Write the missing numbers.

31	32	33	34	35	36	37	38	39	40
41	42	43	44	45	46	47	48	49	50
51	52	53	54	55	56	57	58	59	60

81	82	83	84	85	86	87	88	89	90
91	92	93	94	95	96	97	98	99	100
101	102	103	104	105	106	107	108	109	110

117

Step By Step

Try It

Find missing numbers.

- Point to the first blank in the first chart on the Student Book page. Ask: *What number is missing?* [34] Have children write that number to fill in the blank. Encourage children to share how they decided.

- Have children name the number that comes before the missing number [33] and the one that comes after. [35] Count the three numbers aloud as a class.

- Repeat for the remaining missing numbers in both charts on the Student Book page.

Check for understanding.

- Direct children's attention back to the displayed 120 chart. Ask them the following questions: *How many numbers are across the first row of the 120 chart?* [10] *How do you know?* [The numbers go from 1 to 10.] *Do you think there are 10 numbers in the next row?* [Yes.] *Why?* [There are the same amount of boxes in the next row.]

- Observe to see that children recognize that the last number in each row makes a ten.

Modeled Instruction

Step By Step

- Begin by asking children what they remember about the Activity in the Introduction. Explain that this page is also about the 120 chart. Read aloud the question.

▶ **English Language Learners**

Model It

- Have children look at the first column in the 120 chart, then ask what is the same about the numbers in the column. [Each number ends with "1;" each number has 1 one.]

- Read the numbers in the column aloud. Then ask what is different about the numbers. [They each begin with a different number; the tens increase by one.]

- Have children look at the third row in the chart and describe how the numbers are alike and how they are different.

- Children should notice that all the numbers in the row begin with 2, or 2 tens, except for the last number, which begins with 3, or 3 tens. They should also notice that each number ends with a different number and may see that the ones increase by one.

▶ **Mathematical Discourse 1**

- Read the directions aloud and have children color and circle. Then discuss the patterns they see. Guide children to see that the same patterns repeat in all the columns and rows of the chart.

▶ **Hands-On Activity**

SMP TIP Look for Structure
Studying the relationship between the numbers in the columns and rows of the 120 chart helps children connect the numbers in the chart to the place-value concepts of tens and ones. *(SMP 7)*

Ready Mathematics
PRACTICE AND PROBLEM SOLVING

Assign *Practice and Problem Solving* **pages 163–164** after students have completed this section.

The 120 Chart

How does the 120 chart show numbers?

Model It Find numbers.

Use blue. Color the numbers that have 2 ones.
Use red. Circle the numbers that have 3 tens.

1	2	3	4	5	6	7	8	9	10
11	12	13	14	15	16	17	18	19	20
21	22	23	24	25	26	27	28	29	(30)
(31)	(32)	(33)	(34)	(35)	(36)	(37)	(38)	(39)	40
41	42	43	44	45	46	47	48	49	50
51	52	53	54	55	56	57	58	59	60
61	62	63	64	65	66	67	68	69	70
71	72	73	74	75	76	77	78	79	80
81	82	83	84	85	86	87	88	89	90
91	92	93	94	95	96	97	98	99	100
101	102	103	104	105	106	107	108	109	110
111	112	113	114	115	116	117	118	119	120

118

▶ **Mathematical Discourse**

1 *How do the numbers change in each row? In each column?*
Children may say that in each row the ones change from 1 to 9 (1, 2, 3, 4, 5, 6, 7, 8, 9), until the last number, which ends in zero. They may also recognize that in the rows, the ones go up by 1. Children may say that as you go down each column, the tens go up by 1.

▶ **English Language Learners**

To present visual language support for children who need help distinguishing between a row and a column, provide a 120 chart labeled with the words "column" and "row." The labels should each include an arrow pointing to a column and a row.

▶ **Hands-On Activity**
Find patterns on the 120 chart.

Materials For each pair: 120 Chart (Activity Sheet 23), crayons

- Provide pairs of children with a 120 chart. Have them work together to color to find patterns on the 120 chart.

- Have children share their ideas with the class, explaining the patterns they have discovered.

- Different children will describe the same pattern differently. Guide the discussion to be sure all the ideas being suggested are understood.

Learn Together
The 120 Chart

How can you count on the 120 chart?

Model It Count up.

Count up 1 from 5. Then count up 1 from 18.

5 and 1 more is __6__.

18 and 1 more is __19__.

1	2	3	4	⑤	**6**	7	8	9	10
11	12	13	14	15	16	17	⑱	**19**	20

Count up 2 from 62. Then count up 2 from 75.

62 and 2 more is __64__.

75 and 2 more is __77__.

61	㉖62	63	**64**	65	66	67	68	69	70
71	72	73	74	⑦⑤	76	**77**	78	79	80

Count up 5 from 85. Then count up 5 from 90.

85 and 5 more is __90__.

90 and 5 more is __95__.

81	82	83	84	㊙85	86	87	88	89	⑨⓪
91	92	93	94	**95**	96	97	98	99	100

Talk About It Who is right? How do you know?

Boom says 70 and 5 more is 74.

Buzz says 70 and 5 more is 75.

119

▶ **Visual Model**

Count on with the 120 chart.

Materials For display: 120 Chart (Activity Sheet 23)

• Use the displayed 120 chart to reinforce the concept of counting on by 1 and 2.

• Draw a circle around 43 on the chart. Say: *Let's count up by 1.* Move your finger one space to the right and stop on 44 as the children count: *43, 44.*

• Then demonstrate counting up by 2 by drawing a circle around 58 and moving your finger to point to 59 and 60. Have children count: *58, 59, 60.*

• Repeat, beginning at different numbers on the chart. Include starting at numbers such as 89, to give children practice transitioning between the decades on the chart.

▶ **Mathematical Discourse**

2 *How is counting on 2 like adding 2?*

They are both about 2 more. When you count on 2, you move two spaces on the number chart and stop at the number that is 2 more than the number you start with. When you add 2, you get the number that is 2 more than the number.

Step By Step

• Read aloud the question at the top of the page.

Model It

• Direct attention to Model It. Read the first two sentences. Have children count up 1 from 5 by first having them place their finger on the circled number (5), then have them move their finger along the arrow to the colored number (6). Have children count aloud as they do so: *5, 6.*

• Ask: *How many numbers are colored next to the 5?* [1] *How many more than 5 is 6?* [1 more] Have children complete the sentence "5 and 1 more is 6." Relate the sentence to the circled 5 and the one colored square. Repeat for 18.

• Guide children as they complete the remaining sentences by asking questions such as: *When you start at 62 (or 75) and count up 2, how many numbers are colored?* [2] *When you start at 85 (or 90) and count up 5, how many numbers are colored?* [5] *How many more than 75 is 77?* [2] *How many more than 90 is 95?* [5] *How do you know?* [I counted up.]

▶ **Mathematical Discourse 2**

• After children complete the sentences have them point to additional numbers and tell the number that is 1, 2, or 5 more. Ask them to explain their reasoning.

Talk About It

• Read aloud Talk About It.

Error Alert Children who think Boom is correct may have difficulty with the transition between the tens on the number chart. They may have counted 70 as one of the five counts: *70, 71, 72, 73, 74.*

▶ **Visual Model**

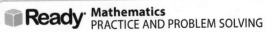

Ready Mathematics
PRACTICE AND PROBLEM SOLVING

Assign *Practice and Problem Solving* **pages 165–166** after students have completed this section.

Step By Step

- Have children look at the section of the 120 chart at the top of the page. Discuss the numbers it shows.

- Direct children's attention to Problem 1. Have children circle the number 40 on the number chart. As children find 1 more, 2 more, and 5 more than 40, encourage them to see the relationship between the number they start with and the number of counts they make for each.

- As children find 1 more, 2 more, and 5 more than 55, ask them to explain how they know which number to stop at. [by counting up 1, 2, or 5; by counting the number of squares]

- For Problem 2, encourage children to move their fingers along the rows and columns of the chart at the top of the page as they count by 1, 2, and 5.

- As children begin, ask: *What number is 1 more than 33?* [34] *than 35?* [36] *How does using the number chart help you count?* [It can help me keep track of my counts. I know that the numbers in a row go up by one.]

- As children count by 2 and then 5, have them discuss the patterns they see. For counting by 2, they may say that they count every other number. For counting by 5, they may recognize that the ones number is either a 5 or a 0.

▶ **Concept Extension**

SMP TIP Repeated Reasoning
By discussing and connecting relationships on the 120 chart, children begin to see how the sequence of numbers is related to the numeric relationships in the numbers. *(SMP 8)*

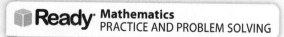 **Mathematics**
PRACTICE AND PROBLEM SOLVING

Assign *Practice and Problem Solving* **pages 167–168** after students have completed this section.

Practice Together
The 120 Chart

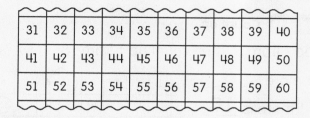

Fill in the blanks. Use the chart.

31	32	33	34	35	36	37	38	39	40
41	42	43	44	45	46	47	48	49	50
51	52	53	54	55	56	57	58	59	60

① **Start at 40.**   **Start at 55.**

1 more than 40 is <u>41</u>.   1 more than 55 is <u>56</u>.

2 more than 40 is <u>42</u>.   2 more than 55 is <u>57</u>.

5 more than 40 is <u>45</u>.   5 more than 55 is <u>60</u>.

② **Count by 1:** 33, <u>34</u>, 35, <u>36</u>, 37, <u>38</u>

Count by 2: 42, <u>44</u>, <u>46</u>, <u>48</u>, 50

Count by 5: 40, 45, <u>50</u>, <u>55</u>, <u>60</u>

▶ **Concept Extension**
Count by 2s and 5s on the 120 chart.

Materials For each child: 120 Chart (Activity Sheet 23)

Distribute the 120 chart. Ask questions like the following and have children use their 120 charts to respond. Have them tell the answers without counting on the chart.

- *What number is 2 more than 16?* [18] *2 more than 70?* [72] *2 more than 109?* [111]

- *What number is 5 more than 35?* [40] *5 more than 41?* [46] *5 more than 76?* [81]

Practice by Myself
The 120 Chart

Fill in the blanks. Use the chart.

91	92	93	94	95	96	97	98	99	100
101	102	103	104	105	106	107	108	109	110
111	112	113	114	115	116	117	118	119	120

3 **Start at 100.**   **Start at 115.**

1 more than 100 is <u>101</u>.   1 more than 115 is <u>116</u>.

2 more than 100 is <u>102</u>.   2 more than 115 is <u>117</u>.

5 more than 100 is <u>105</u>.   5 more than 115 is <u>120</u>.

4 **Count by 1:** 104, <u>105</u>, 106, <u>107</u>, 108, <u>109</u>

Count by 2: 98, <u>100</u>, <u>102</u>, <u>104</u>, 106

Count by 5: 95, 100, <u>105</u>, <u>110</u>, <u>115</u>

121

Step By Step

- Before children work on this page, review some of the ways they have used the 120 chart when counting. Emphasize that children are free to use whatever way helps them solve the problem.

- Read each problem aloud, then have children work independently to solve.

- For both Problems 3 and 4, observe to see if some children are having difficulty with numbers greater than 100.

- After children have completed their work, use the Mathematical Discourse question to encourage discussion about the strategies they used.

▶ **Mathematical Discourse**

▶ **Fluency Practice**

▶ **Fluency Practice**

Practice counting by 1s, 2s, and 5s.

Materials For display: 120 Chart (Activity Sheet 23)

Display the 120 chart. Have the class count on by 1, 2, and 5, using examples like the following.

- count by 1:
  start at 11 and end at 20
  start at 56 and end at 70

- count by 2:
  start at 2 and end at 30
  start at 88 and end at 110

- count by 5:
  start at 5 and end at 120
  start at 45 and end at 70

▶ **Mathematical Discourse**

How did you know what numbers to write to complete the sentences in Problem 3?

For finding "1 more," children may say they used the number chart and looked at the number to the right of the given number, or that they counted on by 1. For finding "2 more," children may share that they counted on by 2, or looked at every other number. For finding "5 more," children may suggest counting on by 5 or looking for numbers that end in either 5 or 0 as strategies.

Differentiated Instruction

▶ Quick Check and Remediation

Materials For each child: 120 Chart (Activity Sheet 23)

• Ask children to tell which number on the 120 chart is 5 more than 65. [70]

• For children who are still struggling, use the chart below to guide remediation.

• After providing remediation, check children's understanding using the following problem: *Which number is 2 more than 34?* [36]

If the error is . . .	Children may . . .	To remediate . . .
66	have counted by 1 instead of 5.	Provide children with a 120 chart and have them circle 65 and 66. Guide them to see that 66 is 1 more than 65. Ask children to count up 5 to find 5 more than 65.
67	have counted by 2 instead of 5.	Provide children with a 120 chart and have them circle 65, color the five numbers to the right, and count the numbers. Then have them write: *5 more than 65 is 70.*
69	have started with 65 as the first counting number.	Provide children with a 120 chart and have them circle 65, then count on 5 as they touch and say each number: *66, 67, 68, 69, 70.*

▶ Hands-On Activity

Use a 120 chart to count by 2s and 5s.

Materials For each child: one blue and one yellow crayon, 120 Chart (Activity Sheet 23)

• Distribute the 120 chart and two crayons to each child.

• Have children count by 2 from 2 to 120 on the chart and color each square the same color.

• Have children count by 5 from 5 to 120 and color each square the same color.

• Tell children that some squares will be colored with more than one color.

• Discuss the patterns children see.

▶ Challenge Activity

Find the difference between two numbers on a 120 chart.

Materials For each child: 120 Chart (Activity Sheet 23)

• Have children find 16 and 27 on the 120 chart. Ask: *How many more is 27 than 16?* [11] Have children explain the strategy they use to find the answer. Ask them whether they found the difference without counting.

• Have children find the differences for other pairs of numbers:

25 and 34 [9]	101 and 114 [13]
48 and 60 [12]	52 and 96 [44]
57 and 87 [30]	39 and 44 [5]
63 and 89 [26]	75 and 107 [32]
78 and 92 [14]	6 and 106 [100]

Teacher Notes

Teacher-Toolbox.com

Overview

Assign the Lesson 18 Quiz and have children work independently to complete it.

Use the results of the quiz to assess children's understanding of the content of the lesson and to identify areas for reteaching. See the Lesson Pacing Guide at the beginning of the lesson and the Differentiated Instruction activities for suggested instructional resources.

Tested Skills

Assesses 1.OA.C.5

Problems on this quiz require children to be able to count up by 1s, 2s, and 5s from any number within 120 and identify numbers that are 1, 2, or 5 more than a given number. Children will also need to be familiar with counting on to add.

Ready® **Mathematics**

Lesson 18 Quiz Answer Key

Name _____

Solve.

Fill in the blanks. Use the chart.

91	92	93	94	95	96	97	98	99	100
101	102	103	104	105	106	107	108	109	110
111	112	113	114	115	116	117	118	119	120

1 Start at 105.

1 more than 105 is __106__.

2 more than 105 is __107__.

5 more than 105 is __110__.

Start at 110.

1 more than 110 is __111__.

2 more than 110 is __112__.

5 more than 110 is __115__.

2 Count by 1: 92, __93__, 94, __95__, 96, __97__

Count by 2: 94, __96__, __98__, __100__, 102

Count by 5: 100, 105, __110__, __115__, __120__

Grade 1 **Lesson 18** The 120 Chart

1

©Curriculum Associates, LLC
Copying permitted for classroom use.

Common Misconceptions and Errors

Errors may result if children:

• count up from a number using the number as the first count.

• do not understand that a given number is one more or one less than the number before or after.

• incorrectly sequence the numbers when counting by 1s, 2s, or 5s.

Name _____

Fill in the blanks. Use the chart.

61	62	63	64	65	66	67	68	69	70
71	72	73	74	75	76	77	78	79	80
81	82	83	84	85	86	87	88	89	90

3 Count by 1: _82_, 83, _84_, _85_, 86, _87_

Count by 2: 68, _70_, _72_, 74, _76_, 78

Count by 5: 70, _75_, _80_, 85, _90_

4 Start at 80.

1 more than 80 is _81_.

2 more than 80 is _82_.

5 more than 80 is _85_.

Start at 75.

1 more than 75 is _76_.

2 more than 75 is _77_.

5 more than 75 is _80_.

Grade 1 **Lesson 18** The 120 Chart

 2

©Curriculum Associates, LLC
Copying permitted for classroom use.

Lesson 19
Understand 10 More and 10 Less

CCSS Focus

Domain
Number and Operations in Base Ten

Cluster
C. Use place value understanding and properties of operations to add and subtract.

Standard
1.NBT.C.5 Given a two-digit number, mentally find 10 more or 10 less than the number, without having to count; explain the reasoning used.

Additional Standards
1.NBT.B.2a, 1.NBT.B.2c (See page B3 for full text.)

Standards for Mathematical Practice (SMP)

2 Reason abstractly and quantitatively.

3 Construct viable arguments and critique the reasoning of others.

5 Use appropriate tools strategically.

7 Look for and make use of structure.

8 Look for and express regularity in repeated reasoning.

Lesson Objectives

Content Objectives

- Mentally add and subtract 10 from any number within 120.

- Recognize that adding or subtracting a ten results in a change in the tens digit alone.

Language Objectives

- Use connecting cubes, digit cards, or a 120 chart to show how only the tens digit changes when 10 is added to or subtracted from a number.

- Tell how finding 10 more or 10 less is like and how it is different from finding 1 more or 1 less.

- Write numbers that are 10 more and 10 less than a given number.

Prerequisite Skills

- Count to 120 by 10s.
- Understand that 10 ones can be represented as 1 ten.

Lesson Vocabulary

- **10 less** 1 less ten or 10 less ones than a given number.
- **10 more** 1 more ten or 10 more ones than a given number.

Learning Progression

In Kindergarten children explore 10 as a group of objects within a teen number and count by tens to 100.

In Grade 1 children view 10 ones as a unit called a ten. They build on their "counting by tens" skills by mentally finding 10 more and 10 less than a number.

In this lesson children mentally add and subtract 10 to any number within 120. As they explore "10 more" and "10 less" with connecting cubes and on a 120 chart, they use the mental image formed to recognize that when adding or subtracting a ten, the tens digit increases or decreases by one respectively.

In Grade 2 children build on this concept, using it to add and subtract two-digit numbers. They extend the use of mental imagery through open number lines.

Lesson Pacing Guide

Whole Class Instruction

Day 1
45–60 minutes

Introduction

Use What You Know
- Explore It *25 min*
- Try It *20 min*

Day 2
45–60 minutes

Modeled Instruction

Explore Together
- Opening Question *5 min*
- Think *15 min*
- Talk About It *15 min*
- Hands-On Activity *10 min*

Practice and Problem Solving
Assign pages 171–172.

Day 3
45–60 minutes

Guided Instruction

Explore Together
- Hands-On Problem *15 min*
- Problems 1–2 *10 min*
- Talk About It *10 min*
- Fluency Practice *10 min*

Practice and Problem Solving
Assign pages 173–174.

Day 4
45–60 minutes

Guided Practice

Connect It
- Problems 3–5 *15 min*

Independent Practice

Show What I Know
- Problem 6 *15 min*
- Intervention, On-Level, or Challenge Activity *15 min*

Practice and Problem Solving
Assign pages 175–176.

Teacher-Toolbox: Lesson Quiz
Lesson 19 Quiz

Materials for Lesson Activities

Per child: 52 connecting cubes, 3 small objects to use as markers, 30 counters, Challenge Activity worksheet
Activity Sheet 22, Activity Sheet 23*, Activity Sheet 25, Activity Sheet 42

Per pair: 52 connecting cubes, base-ten blocks
Activity Sheet 23, Activity Sheet 25, Activity Sheet 42, Activity Sheet 43

For display: Activity Sheet 23

*Used for more than one activity.

Small Group Differentiation

Teacher-Toolbox.com

Reteach
Ready Prerequisite Lessons *45–90 min*

Grade K
- Lesson 24 Count to 100 by Tens

Teacher-led Activities
Tools for Instruction *15–20 min*

Grade 1 *(Lesson 19)*
- Patterns on the Hundreds Chart
- Using Models to Subtract 10
- One More
- One Less

Student-led Activities
Math Center Activities *30–40 min*

Grade K *(Lesson 24)*
- K.30 Count by Tens
- K.31 Tens Bingo

Grade 1 *(Lesson 19)*
- 1.30 Use Vocabulary for Ten More, Ten Less
- 1.31 Ten More, Ten Less

Personalized Learning

i-Ready.com

Independent
i-Ready Lessons* *10–20 min*

Grade 1 *(Lesson 19)*
- Counting On: 1 to 100
- One More
- One Less

i-Ready lessons may be updated during the 2016–2017 school year. Updated references will be on the Teacher-Toolbox.

👥 Introduction

Activity Build 10 More or 10 Less

Objective

Explore the concept of 10 more and 10 less.

Materials for each pair

• 52 connecting cubes

Overview

Children model a problem finding 10 more than a given number. They then explore the meaning of and strategies for finding 10 more and 10 less.

Step By Step

Explore It

Pose the problem.

• Read the problem from the Student Book page aloud: *There are 27 monkeys living at the zoo. There are 10 more birds than monkeys. How many birds live at the zoo?*

Solve the problem.

• Have children work in pairs to solve the problem using any strategy. Tell them to model the problem and solution with connecting cubes. Then have children draw their model on the workmat on the Student Book page and write the number of monkeys and the number of birds.

• Watch as children complete the problem, ensuring they understand that to find the number of birds, 10 must be added to the number of monkeys.

Share strategies.

• Invite volunteers to share their results and explain the strategy they used by demonstrating it for the class to observe.

• Make sure that children share many different strategies. If no children organized the cubes by making ten-trains, you may want to demonstrate this strategy yourself.

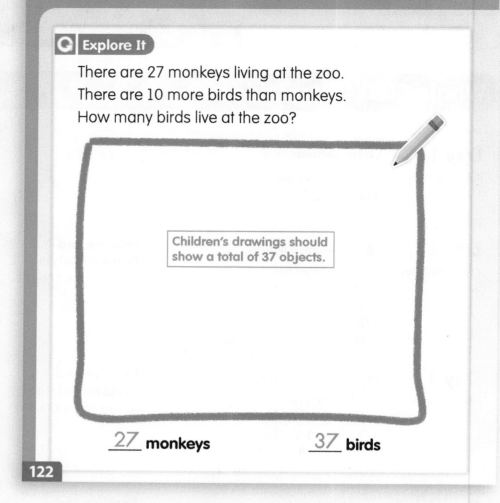

🔵 **Explore It**

There are 27 monkeys living at the zoo.
There are 10 more birds than monkeys.
How many birds live at the zoo?

Children's drawings should show a total of 37 objects.

<u>27</u> **monkeys**   <u>37</u> **birds**

122

• Encourage children to ask each other questions. Model this by asking questions about the strategies students explain, such as: *Why do you have 2 ten-trains and 7 extra cubes instead of 27 cubes? Why did you add 10 ones to 27? Or: Why did you add 1 ten instead of 10 ones?*

Explore and extend.

• Compare the strategies children used. Discuss how adding 10 single cubes and 1 ten-train resulted in the same answer.

• Tell children to show 42 with connecting cubes. Have them show 10 more in two different ways. Discuss how "10 more" implies adding 10, and explore the concept that 1 ten is composed of 10 ones, so adding 10 ones results in the same total, 52, as adding 1 ten.

• Have children show 42 again. Discuss how 10 was taken away from 52—either as 10 ones or as 1 ten—therefore 42 is "10 less" than 52.

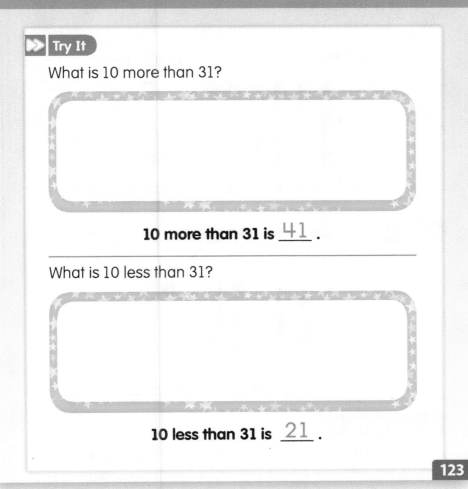

>> Try It

What is 10 more than 31?

10 more than 31 is 41 .

What is 10 less than 31?

10 less than 31 is 21 .

123

Step By Step

Try It

Pose additional problems.

- Provide the students with 41 connecting cubes. Read aloud the problems on the Student Book page: *What is 10 more than 31? What is 10 less than 31?*

Model the problems.

- Have children model the problems with connecting cubes on the workmats, then record their answers.

- Watch children as they work, observing the strategies they employ. Some children might use ten-trains and 1 extra cube to show 31. Others may count out 31 cubes.

- To find 10 more, some children may add another ten-train, with others adding 10 separate cubes and recounting.

- To find 10 less, some children may take away a ten-train, while others may take away 10 individual cubes and recount.

Discuss answers.

- After children have written their answers, ask them to explain how they solved the problems. Encourage children to show each number using tens and extra ones, but do not expect every child to see 10 more as adding a ten and 10 less as subtracting a ten.

- Use the Hands-On Activity in the lesson as extra support for children who were unable to represent the problems or find the answers correctly.

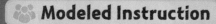

Modeled Instruction

Step By Step

- Read aloud the question at the top of the page. Ask children why it is important to know about 10 more or 10 less than a number.

- Direct attention to the "42 and 10 more" on the Student Book page. Ask children to describe how the pictures are like what they did in the Activity in the Introduction. Ask: *How can you tell that 42 and 10 more is the same as 4 tens, 2 ones, and 1 ten?*

▶ **English Language Learners**

Think

- As children explain their reasoning, reinforce the idea of "10 more" as 1 ten. Discuss how this relates to the addition sentence in Think (42 + 10 = 52) and to the picture of tens and ones below. Guide children to see that the two pictures of tens and ones show the same quantity.

▶ **Mathematical Discourse 1**

Talk About It

- Present the Talk About It question. Encourage discussion by asking questions such as: *Do you agree or disagree? Why? How could you use a model to help you explain?*

▶ **Hands-On Activity**

SMP TIP Repeated Reasoning
As children model 10 more and 10 less by adjusting digit cards, they recognize the repeated reasoning that allows them to increase or decrease the digit in the tens place. They then can connect it to the process of adding or subtracting 1 in single digit operations. *(SMP 8)*

Ready Mathematics
PRACTICE AND PROBLEM SOLVING

Assign *Practice and Problem Solving* **pages 171–172** after students have completed this section.

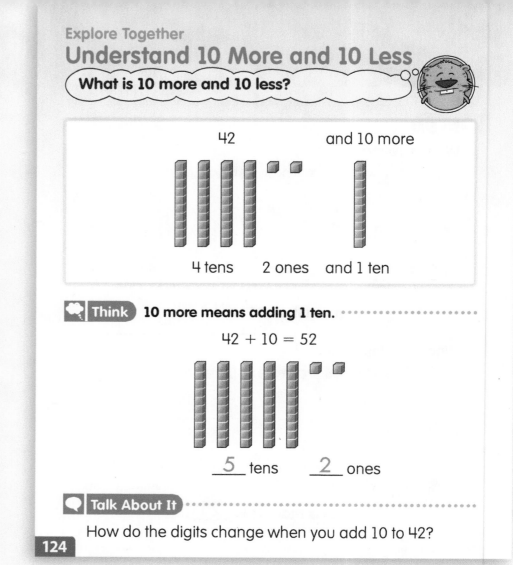

Explore Together
Understand 10 More and 10 Less

What is 10 more and 10 less?

42   and 10 more

4 tens   2 ones   and 1 ten

Think 10 more means adding 1 ten.

$$42 + 10 = 52$$

__5__ tens   __2__ ones

Talk About It

How do the digits change when you add 10 to 42?

124

▶ **Mathematical Discourse**

1 *How is adding 10 to 40 like adding 1 to 4? How is it different?*
   Children may recognize that 40 + 10 is 50 and 4 + 1 is 5; 40 becomes 50 and 4 becomes 5, and in each case a 4 and 5 are used. They are different because 40 and 50 include a zero. Other children may focus on the number of tens. Adding 40 + 10 is like adding 4 tens and 1 ten which is like 4 + 1, the difference being they are tens and not ones.

▶ **English Language Learners**

In some languages the words for multiples of ten are more explicit than the English words. Many languages use words that describe them as 2 tens, 3 tens, etc. Help children relate the terms used in their native language to English by saying: *42 is 4 tens and 2. When you add a ten, you have 5 tens and 2, or 52.*

▶ **Hands-On Activity**
   Model tens and ones with connecting cubes.

   Materials For each child: 52 connecting cubes, Number Cards 0 to 11 (Activity Sheet 25)

- Ask children to show 42 cubes as tens and ones. Have them place the number card "4" under the 4 ten-trains and "2" under the 2 ones. Discuss how the 4 tells the number of tens shown.

- Tell children to add another ten-train to their group of cubes and adjust the cards to show how many tens and ones they have now. Ask: *What card did you change? Why? Why didn't you need to change the card showing the ones?* Discuss how adding 1 ten to a number increases the tens by 1.

- Repeat the activity using other two-digit numbers, then for finding 10 less than a number.

Explore Together
Understand 10 More and 10 Less

 Find 10 less than 37.

Use a 120 chart. → Color the → __27__ is 10
Color 37.   number   less than 37.
                   above 37.

21	22	23	24	25	26	27	28	29	30
31	32	33	34	35	36	37	38	39	40
41	42	43	44	45	46	47	48	49	50

1 Find 10 more than 62. Color both numbers.

__72__ is 10 more than 62.

2 Find 10 less than 69. Color both numbers.

__59__ is 10 less than 69.

51	52	53	54	55	56	57	58	59	60
61	62	63	64	65	66	67	68	69	70
71	72	73	74	75	76	77	78	79	80

💬 **Talk About It**

How does the 120 chart help you find 10 less and 10 more? Why does this work?

125

▶ Fluency Practice

Find 10 more and 10 less on the 120 chart.

Materials For each child: 120 Chart (Activity Sheet 23)

- Use the 120 chart to reinforce the concept of 10 more and 10 less.
- Have children color the number 86. Then have them circle the number that is 10 more and put an X on the number that is 10 less.
- Repeat for additional numbers.

▶ Mathematical Discourse

2 *How is finding 10 more and 10 less on the 120 chart like adding and subtracting 10 cubes?*

Children should notice that, in both cases, the tens digit changes by 1 while the ones digit remains the same. Some may recognize that moving down on the chart is like adding 10 ones, just as adding a ten-train is like adding 10 ones. The inverse is true for 10 less.

Step By Step

- Provide each child with Activity Sheet 23 (120 Chart) and 3 objects to use as markers. Ask children to place a marker on the number 13. Have them count on 10 and place a marker where they land.
- Then ask children to place a marker on the number 76 and ask: *Where do you think you can find 10 more than 76? How do you know?*
- Discuss how the number that is 10 more is directly below the original number on the chart. Ask: *Do you think this will work for finding 10 more than any number? Explain.*
- Have children find 10 more than several numbers. Help them see that, as they move down on the chart, the tens place increases by 1 and the ones place is unchanged.
- Then have children find 10 less than the same numbers. Make sure they see that when moving up a row the tens digit decreases by 1 and the ones digit remains unchanged.
- Direct attention to the example problem. Explain that only a section of a 120 chart is shown. Display the rows shown. Stress the difference between adding 1 one and adding 1 ten by moving your finger from 37 to 38 and asking: *What happens when I move over one in this direction? How is it different from moving down one?*
- Help children see that moving to the right shows 1 more, so the change occurs in the ones digit while the digit in the tens place stays the same. Contrast this to the change that occurs in "10 more" and "10 less" as children complete Problems 1 and 2.

Talk About It

- Read Talk About It. Encourage children to justify their responses.

▶ **Mathematical Discourse 2**

▶ **Fluency Practice**

 Ready· Mathematics
PRACTICE AND PROBLEM SOLVING

Assign *Practice and Problem Solving* **pages 173–174** after students have completed this section.

👥👥 Guided Practice

Step By Step

- Discuss each Connect It problem as a class using the discussion points outlined below.

Identify

- This problem extends the concept of 10 more to numbers beyond 100. Ask children to retell how they found 10 more and 10 less in the previous activity. Then ask if it is possible to use the same strategy to find 10 more than a number beyond 100. Encourage them to explain their thinking.

- Compare and contrast the results of finding 10 more than a number beyond 100 by asking: *When you move down one, what changes? What stays the same?*

- After children have completed the sentence, help them see that the tens increase by 1 by having them cover the 6 in both numbers to reveal the 9 and 10. •

- Display a 120 chart. Shade in the number 108. Have children find 10 more on the chart. Discuss how both the 1 (in the hundreds place) and the 8 remain unchanged while the zero changed to a 1. Challenge children to think beyond the chart by asking: *If you added another row of numbers to this chart, what number do you think will be below 118? How do you know?*

> **SMP TIP Use Structure**
> The structure of the 120 chart enables children to mentally see "10 more" and "10 less" than a number. Ask them to close their eyes and "see" the number that is 10 more than 57; 10 less than 81. *(SMP 7)*

Choose

- Have children look at the numbers that end each sentence and the numbers in the yellow box. Ask them what they notice about these numbers. [The ones are all the same; some of the tens are different.]

- As children complete each sentence, encourage them to explain how they decided which number to use. Ask questions such as: *How did you know to choose the number you did in the first sentence? How are the last two sentences alike? How are they different?*

Connect It
Understand 10 More and 10 Less

3 **Identify** What is 10 more than 96?

81	82	83	84	85	86	87	88	89	90
91	92	93	94	95	96	97	98	99	100
101	102	103	104	105	106	107	108	109	110

10 more than 96 is <u>106</u>.

4 **Choose** Fill in the blanks. Use the numbers in the box.

<u>68</u> is 10 more than 58.

<u>48</u> is 10 less than 58.

<u>98</u> is 10 more than 88.

<u>78</u> is 10 less than 88.

> 78
> 48
> 68
> 98

5 **Explain** Buzz says 10 less than 84 is 83. Do you agree? Why or why not?

Possible answer: I don't agree. 10 less than 84 is 74. You subtract 1 ten. Buzz subtracted 1 one.

126

Explain

- You may wish to have children answer the questions in pairs before discussing them as a class. As they talk to each other, remind them of what they learned about the difference between adding 1 more and adding 10 more.

- Support children who offer explanations during class discussion with questions such as: *How is finding 10 less different from finding 1 less? What happens to the tens and the ones when you find 10 less? 1 less?*

📦 **Ready** Mathematics
PRACTICE AND PROBLEM SOLVING

Assign *Practice and Problem Solving* **pages 175–176** after students have completed this section.

Show What I Know

Understand 10 More and 10 Less

6 **Think about 10 more and 10 less.**

A: Use digit cards to make numbers.

0	1	2	3	4	5	6	7	8	9

Write a number. Find 10 less and 10 more than your number.

Possible answer:

3	6

10 less than _36_ is _26_.

10 more than _36_ is _46_.

Write a different number. Find 10 less and 10 more than your number.

Possible answer:

8	9

10 less than _89_ is _79_.

10 more than _89_ is _99_.

B: Find 93 + 10. Tell how you know.

93 + 10 = _103_

Possible answer:
On the 120 chart, 103 is 10 more than 93.

127

Step By Step

- Tell children that they will complete this page independently.

- Read the directions aloud, making sure children understand what is expected.

- In Part A, children make 2 two-digit numbers, then write the numbers that are 10 more and 10 less.

- In Part B, children find 93 + 10 and explain the strategy they used.

- Observe as children work. Ask questions such as the following to encourage thinking and problem-solving strategies:

  How many digits should you write on each card? Why?

  Does thinking about the cubes or the 120 chart help you find 10 more or 10 less? How?

  What happens to a number when you add or subtract 10? Why does that happen?

  What is the easiest way for you to think about 10 more than 93? Can you draw a picture of it?

  Do you think 10 more than 93 will be more than 100 or less than 100? Why?

Scoring Rubrics

Expectations for 4–3 Points

Points	Expectations
4	The child: • writes one digit on each card and accurately records 10 more and 10 less. • correctly identifies 103 as the total and provides an accurate explanation of the strategy employed.
3	The child: • writes one digit on each card and records 10 more and 10 less but may request to use cubes or a 120 chart to check accuracy. • correctly identifies 103 as the total but provides only a partial or unclear explanation of the strategy used.

Expectations for 2–0 Points

Points	Expectations
2	The child: • writes digits on the cards, but inaccurately records 10 more and 10 less. • correctly identifies 103 as the total but provides an unclear explanation of the strategy used.
1	The child: • may write digit(s) on the cards, but does not connect the numbers shown on the cards and the 10 more or 10 less that is recorded. • does not find the correct total and may not attempt to provide an explanation.
0	The child: • does not attempt to write digits or complete the problems.

Differentiated Instruction

▶ Intervention Activity

Build 10 more or 10 less.

Materials For each child: Dot Cards—Small (Activity Sheet 42), Teen Number Cards (Activity Sheet 22), 30 counters

• Provide each child with a set of counters, teen number cards, and the "10 more" and "10 less" cards from Activity Sheet 42.

• Have children select a card containing a teen number and instruct them to model the number with counters. Encourage them to line up the group of ten counters.

• Children then randomly select a "10 more" or "10 less" card. They create another model next to the original showing 10 more or 10 less than that number. Remind them to line up the tens.

• Have children record on paper or a whiteboard the two numbers and write either "10 more" or "10 less" next to the number that shows the result of the addition or subtraction they performed.

▶ On-Level Activity

Model 10 more and 10 less.

Materials For each pair: Two-Digit Number Mats (Activity Sheet 43), 2 copies of Number Cards 0 to 11 (Activity Sheet 25), Dot Cards—Small (Activity Sheet 42), 120 Chart (Activity Sheet 23), base-ten blocks

• Place children in pairs. Provide each pair with a blank two-digit number mat, 2 sets of cards showing the digits 0–9, "10 more" and "10 less" cards, base-ten blocks, and Activity Sheet 23 (120 Chart).

• One child selects two digit cards and places them in the boxes on the two-digit number mat to show a two-digit number. The partner chooses a "10 more" or "10 less" card. The first child selects a digit card to make the number show 10 more or 10 less by placing the new digit on top of the original one.

• Partners work together to model both numbers and/or find them in the 120 chart to check the answer. If correct, they clear the board and roles are reversed.

• If incorrect, they find the digit card that will make the number correct and place it on the workmat. The board is cleared, roles are reversed and play resumes.

▶ Challenge Activity

Find multiples of 10 more and 10 less.

Materials For each child: worksheet including several problems such as: Find 20 more than 36, Find 40 less than 95, and challenge problems such as: Find 30 more than 127. For more advanced children, include adding and subtracting multiples of 10 to numbers in the 200–1,000 range.

• Distribute a worksheet to each child, instructing them to find the solutions and show the strategy they used for each one. Challenge them to utilize a variety of strategies, reminding them to draw a picture of what they "see" in their brain when finding each sum or difference.

• Challenge children to complete the work mentally without the support of physical models or a 120 chart. Tell them that they can draw pictures of either of those models, if that is what they "see" in their brain, but to rely on the mental rather than physical image.

Teacher Notes

Teacher-Toolbox.com

Overview

Assign the Lesson 19 Quiz and have children work independently to complete it.

Use the results of the quiz to assess children's understanding of the content of the lesson and to identify areas for reteaching. See the Lesson Pacing Guide at the beginning of the lesson and the Differentiated Instruction activities for suggested instructional resources.

Tested Skills

Assesses 1.NBT.C.5

Problems on this quiz require children to be able to mentally add and subtract 10 from any number within 120, recognizing that adding or subtracting 10 increases or decreases the tens digit by 1 respectively. Children will also need to be familiar with counting to 120 by 10s and representing 10 ones as 1 ten.

***Ready*® Mathematics**

Lesson 19 Quiz Answer Key

Name _____

Solve.

1 What is 10 more than 94?

81	82	83	84	85	86	87	88	89	90
91	92	93	94	95	96	97	98	99	100
101	102	103	104	105	106	107	108	109	110

10 more than 94 is <u>104</u>.

2 Fill in the blanks. Use the numbers in the box.

<u>54</u> is 10 more than 44.

<u>34</u> is 10 less than 44.

<u>64</u> is 10 less than 74.

<u>84</u> is 10 more than 74.

84
64
54
34

Grade 1 Lesson 19 *Understand* 10 More and 10 Less

1

Common Misconceptions and Errors

Errors may result if children:

- increase the ones digit by 1 instead of the tens digit when adding 10.
- decrease the ones digit by 1 instead of the tens digit when subtracting 10.
- increase the tens digit by 1 when subtracting 10 or decrease the tens digit by 1 when adding 10.

Lesson 19 Quiz Answer Key continued   Name _____

Solve.

3 Find 10 less and 10 more than 62.

10 less than __62__ is __52__.

10 more than __62__ is __72__.

4 Find 95 + 10. Tell how you know.

Possible answer:

On the 120 chart, 105 is 10 more than 95.

95 + 10 = __105__

5 Mark has 27 stickers.
Tala has 10 more stickers than Mark.
How many stickers does Tala have?

Tala has __37__ stickers.

Grade 1 **Lesson 19** *Understand* 10 More and 10 Less   **2**   ©Curriculum Associates, LLC
Copying permitted for classroom use.

Lesson 20
Add and Subtract Tens

CCSS Focus

Domain
Number and Operations in Base Ten

Cluster
C. Use place value understanding and properties of operations to add and subtract.

Standard
1.NBT.C.6 Subtract multiples of 10 in the range 10–90 from multiples of 10 in the range 10–90 (positive or zero differences), using concrete models or drawings and strategies based on place value, properties of operations, and/or the relationship between addition and subtraction; relate the strategy to a written method and explain the reasoning used.

Additional Standards
1.NBT.B.2a, 1.NBT.B.2b, 1.NBT.B.2c, 1.NBT.C.4 (See page B3 for full text.)

Standards for Mathematical Practice (SMP)

1 Make sense of problems and persevere in solving them.

2 Reason abstractly and quantitatively.

3 Construct viable arguments and critique the reasoning of others.

4 Model with mathematics.

5 Use appropriate tools strategically.

6 Attend to precision.

7 Look for and make use of structure.

8 Look for and express regularity in repeated reasoning.

Lesson Objectives

Content Objectives
- Count tens as 1 ten, 2 tens, 3 tens, . . . tens or as 10, 20, 30 . . .
- Add multiples of 10 to multiples of 10 and subtract multiples of 10 from multiples of 10.
- Relate adding tens to adding ones.

Language Objectives
- Use connecting cubes and quick-draw diagrams to model and represent tens in word problems.
- Complete number sentences based on models to solve word problems involving adding and subtracting tens.
- Draw arrows or use a finger on a 120 chart to find the unknown in a number sentence.
- Restate what information a word problem is asking for and orally describe how to solve.

Prerequisite Skills

- Count by tens to 100.
- Represent a multiple of 10 as a number of groups of ten.

Lesson Vocabulary

There is no new vocabulary. Review the following key term.

- **tens** groups of ten ones.

Learning Progression

In Kindergarten children organize 10 objects into a group of 10 and count by tens to 100.

In Grade 1 children view 10 ones as a unit called a ten. They compose two-digit numbers into groups of tens and some ones.

In this lesson children model the relationship between groups of 10 and an equal number of units of 10 and apply it to adding and subtracting multiples of 10. Children compare physical/visual representations to number sentences

and analyze the ways in which the models relate to each other. As they recognize how adding tens and adding ones correlate to each other, children move beyond physical and visual models to compute mentally.

In Grade 2 children apply concepts of adding and subtracting within place values to number sentences involving regrouping where a ten may be composed or decomposed to add or subtract a two-digit number.

Lesson Pacing Guide

Whole Class Instruction

Day 1
45–60 minutes

Introduction
Use What You Know
- Explore It *25 min*
- Try It *20 min*

Day 2
45–60 minutes

Modeled Instruction
Explore Together
- Example Problem *10 min*
- Model It *10 min*
- Hands-On Activity *15 min*
- Visual Model *10 min*

Practice and Problem Solving
Assign pages 179–180.

Day 3
45–60 minutes

Guided Instruction
Learn Together
- Example Problem *5 min*
- Model It *15 min*
- Talk About It *10 min*
- Concept Extension *15 min*

Practice and Problem Solving
Assign pages 181–182.

Day 4
45–60 minutes

Guided Practice
Practice Together
- Example Problem *5 min*
- Problems 1–2 *10 min*
- Visual Model *15 min*
- Fluency Practice *15 min*

Practice and Problem Solving
Assign pages 183–184.

Day 5
45–60 minutes

Independent Practice
Practice by Myself
- Problems 3–5 *15 min*
- Quick Check and Remediation *15 min*
- Hands-On or Challenge Activity *15 min*

Teacher-Toolbox: Lesson Quiz
Lesson 20 Quiz

Materials for Lesson Activities

Per child: 7 tens blocks, crayons (2 colors)
Activity Sheet 23*, Activity Sheet 24*

Per pair: 50 foam shapes or beads, 50 counters, 50 base-ten blocks or connecting cubes, workmats containing an addition and a subtraction open number sentence, 12 tens blocks
Activity Sheet 23*, Activity Sheet 24*

For display: 60 connecting cubes

*Used for more than one activity.

Small Group Differentiation

Teacher-Toolbox.com

Reteach
Ready Prerequisite Lessons *45–90 min*

Grade K
- Lesson 24 Count to 100 by Tens

Teacher-led Activities
Tools for Instruction *15–20 min*

Grade 1 *(Lesson 20)*
- Using Models to Subtract 10
- Sums of Ten
- Add and Subtract 1 and 2

Student-led Activities
Math Center Activities *30–40 min*

Grade K *(Lesson 24)*
- K.30 Count by Tens
- K.31 Tens Bingo

Grade 1 *(Lesson 20)*
- 1.32 Add and Subtract Tens
- 1.33 Subtract Tens Bingo

Personalized Learning

i-Ready.com

Independent
i-Ready Lessons* *10–20 min*

Grade 1 *(Lesson 20)*
- Part 1: Addition and Subtraction Fact Families
- Part 2: Addition and Subtraction Fact Families
- Part 1: Addition Facts
- Part 2: Addition Facts

* i-Ready lessons may be updated during the 2016–2017 school year. Updated references will be on the Teacher-Toolbox.

Introduction

Activity One Ten, Ten Ones

Objective

Relate counting groups of 10 to adding multiples of 10.

Materials for each pair

- 50 foam shapes, beads, or counters
- 50 base-ten blocks or connecting cubes
- 120 Chart (Activity Sheet 23)

Overview

Children solve a problem, model the addition with base-ten blocks, and connect counting tens to addition of multiples of 10.

Step By Step

Explore It

Pose the problem.

- Tell children to imagine that Buzz is working on an art project using foam shapes. Then read the problem on the Student Book page aloud: *Buzz uses 30 foam shapes. He then uses 20 more. How many shapes does Buzz use in all?*

Solve the problem.

- Have children work with a partner to find a solution to the problem. Make varied counters and 120 charts available. Remind children to use whatever materials they need to help them solve the problem, and that there is a workmat for them to use on the Student Book page.

- Watch children as they work, taking note of the strategies and/or materials they use.

Share strategies.

- Invite volunteers to share their solution and strategy with the class. Make sure all the strategies children used are represented.

- Help children recognize that not only do all the strategies lead to the same solution, but some of the strategies also use the same reasoning. For instance, finding 30 on a 120 chart and counting on 2 more tens is similar to starting with 3 tens and counting on 2 more tens.

Use What You Know

Add and Subtract Tens

Explore It

Buzz uses 30 foam shapes. He then uses 20 more. How many shapes does Buzz use in all?

Buzz uses __50__ shapes in all.

Connect counting methods.

- Display a group of 30 objects, organize them into groups of 10, and lay a tens block above one of the groups. Ask: *How is this ten the same as the group of 10? How is it different?* Discuss that both show a group of 10, but the tens block is one piece. Lay a tens block above the each of the remaining groups.

- Count the groups of objects together (10, 20, 30), writing the numbers on cards as children count. Place these cards below the groups. Then count the tens blocks together (1 ten, 2 tens, 3 tens), recording on cards as you count, and placing them below the tens blocks.

- Compare the recorded numbers, asking how they are the same and how they are different. Switch the cards, placing 10, 20, 30 below the tens blocks and 1 ten, 2 tens, 3 tens below the groups. Ask: *How do the numbers shown count these groups?*

- Ask: *If I add 2 more tens blocks, how many tens blocks will I have?* [5] *If I add 2 more groups of 10 (objects), how many (objects) will I have?* [50] *How many groups will I have?* [5]

- Lead children to see that since both the objects and tens blocks are in groups of 10, they can be counted either way.

Use What You Know
Add and Subtract Tens

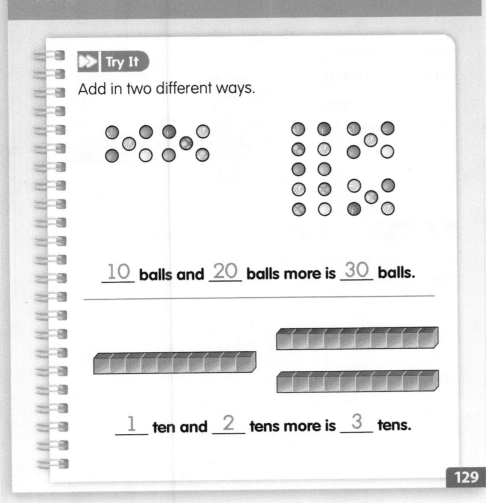

▶▶ Try It

Add in two different ways.

__10__ balls and __20__ balls more is __30__ balls.

__1__ ten and __2__ tens more is __3__ tens.

129

Step By Step

Try It

Connect counting to adding.

- Direct children's attention to the Student Book page. Have children add numbers of objects in two different ways. Then have them complete the sentences to record the results.

- Ask how the two sentences are alike and how they are different. Children should explain that one sentence describes the single balls and the other describes groups of ten. The numbers in each situation are equal, but represented differently (as ones and tens).

Solve another problem.

- Provide children with the following problem: *Show 20 and 20 more with either counters or tens blocks. Tell the total number of blocks (or counters) both ways.* [40, 4 tens]

- As children work, observe those who connect adding tens to adding ones. Use the Hands-On Activity and Visual Models in the lesson for children who may require additional support to solidify this concept.

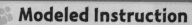

Modeled Instruction

Step By Step

- Revisit the Activity in the Introduction discussing how tens can be counted as 10, 20, 30, . . . or as 1 ten, 2 tens, 3 tens, ... Have children retell the strategies they used to find 20 and 20 more. Ask them to describe how they used the two counting methods to find a solution to the problem.

- You may wish to engage children in a quick counting-by-10s warm-up. Display a tens block and invite children to count with you as you add 1 tens block at a time up to 10 tens blocks, or 100. Then count back to 0 as each tens block is removed.

- Direct attention to the erasers shown at the top of the page. Ask children how they might make this problem easier to solve. Listen for suggestions of grouping erasers into tens or using tens blocks to count. Ask Mathematical Discourse question 1 to reinforce the idea of modeling with tens blocks.

▶ **Mathematical Discourse 1**

Model It

- Discuss how Model It represents the erasers. Use the Hands-On Activity to help children connect adding tens blocks to adding multiples of 10 as they complete the number sentence.

▶ **Hands-On Activity**

▶ **Visual Model**

Ready Mathematics
PRACTICE AND PROBLEM SOLVING

Assign *Practice and Problem Solving* **pages 179–180** after students have completed this section.

Add and Subtract Tens

Tess has 30 erasers in a jar.
She gets 20 more.

How many erasers
does she have now?

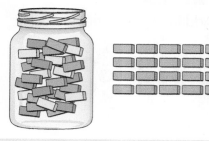

Model It Find 30 + 20.

Write the numbers as tens.
Then add the tens.

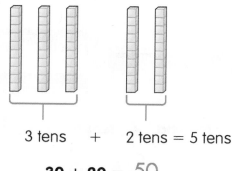

3 tens + 2 tens = 5 tens

30 + 20 = __50__

130

▶ **Mathematical Discourse**

1 *Why might it be easier to add tens blocks rather than add all the erasers?*

The tens blocks are already grouped into 10, which is easier than circling groups of 10 erasers. It is easier to see how many tens blocks there are than how many erasers there are. Some children may notice that 5 tens show 50, which is easier than seeing 50 erasers.

▶ **Hands-On Activity**

Relate adding tens to adding ones.

Materials For each child: 5 tens blocks, Tens Cards (Activity Sheet 24)

Have children model the addition problem 30 + 20 with tens blocks, placing the tens cards under each group. Ask: *What part of the number on the card tells how many tens blocks there are?* Then have children place a finger over the zero in each number. Ask: *What is 3 + 2? What is 30 + 20? How do the digits help you add tens?* Repeat the above activity using several other addition sentences.

▶ **Visual Model**

Show tens with connecting cubes.

Materials For display: 60 connecting cubes

- Display 2 trains of 10 connecting cubes each and ask: *How many cubes do you see?* [20] *How many ten-trains?* [2] Add 3 more ten-trains and ask: *How many cubes did I add?* [30] *How many trains did I add?* [3]

- Recite together: *2 tens and 3 tens makes 5 tens; 20 and 30 is 50.*

- Display groups of 4 ten-trains and 2 ten-trains, encouraging children to recite together: *4 tens and 2 tens makes 6 tens; 40 and 20 is 60.* Repeat with varied multiples of ten.

Learn Together
Add and Subtract Tens

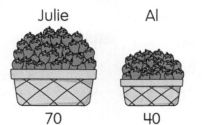

Julie picks 70 berries.
Al picks 40 berries.

How many more
does Julie pick?

Julie   Al

70   40

 **Model It** Find 70 − 40.

Use addition to subtract.
Write as tens.
Then add the tens.

$40 + ? = 70$

4 tens + _3_ tens = _7_ tens

70 − 40 = _30_

4 tens	+	3 tens	

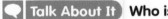 **Talk About It** Who is right? How do you know?

Buzz says 60 − 20 = 40.

Boom says 6 tens − 2 tens = 4 tens.

131

Step By Step

- Read aloud the problem at the top of the page. Say: *I don't see 7 tens.'I just see lots of berries.* Ask: *How is 70 equal to 7 tens when there are no tens showing?* Reinforce the concept that within 70 are 7 groups of ten.

Model It

- Direct children's attention to Model It. Explain that the picture shows quick drawings of tens, where each stick represents one tens block. Review how both the addition and subtraction number sentences model the problem by encouraging children to share how they used addition to help them subtract in previous lessons.

- Prior to completing Model It, use the Concept Extension to reinforce the connection between subtraction and finding a missing addend.

▶ **Concept Extension**

▶ **Mathematical Discourse 2**

Talk About It

- As children discuss Talk About It, suggest that they model both subtractions to justify their responses. Emphasize that "60" is another way to describe "6 tens," making both Buzz and Boom correct.

> **SMP TIP Model with Mathematics/Look for Structure**
> As children explore the many ways to model the problems in this lesson, they recognize that physical and visual models help them understand the number sentences that represent a problem. They also recognize the structure involved in representing a subtraction problem as a missing addend problem. *(SMP 4 and 7)*

▶ **Concept Extension**
Model a missing addend.

Materials For each child: 120 Chart (Activity Sheet 23), crayons (2 colors)

- Give each child a 120 chart and two crayons. Have children circle the number on the chart that tells how many berries Julie picks. Demonstrate how to use one color to draw a line through each row up to 70. Discuss how this shows all of Julie's berries.

- Then have children circle the number that shows how many berries Al picks and use the other color to draw a line through each row up to 40.

- Ask: *What shows how many more berries Julie picks? How can you find out how many more there are?* Relate counting the groups of 10 that fall between 40 and 70 to finding a missing addend and discuss how it models subtraction.

- Use an interactive whiteboard or a clean 120 chart and repeat the activity using other numbers.

▶ **Mathematical Discourse**

2 *What are some other ways to find the answer to the problem on this page?*
Some children may count on using their fingers to keep track of the number of tens between 40 and 70. Others may count backwards from 70 to 40. Some may suggest putting 4 tens blocks on top of 4 of the 7 tens blocks and count the tens blocks that aren't covered.

 **Ready** Mathematics
PRACTICE AND PROBLEM SOLVING

Assign *Practice and Problem Solving* **pages 181–182** after students have completed this section.

👥👥 Guided Practice

Step By Step

- Read the example problem aloud. Use tens blocks to model both operations shown and ask the Mathematical Discourse question to help children see how the two number sentences represent the same situation.

▶ **Mathematical Discourse**

- Use the Visual Model to help children connect a familiar model to the problem situations found on this page.

▶ **Visual Model**

- For Problem 1, reinforce children's understanding that both number sentences represent the 3 groups of flowers by displaying counting cards showing 10, 20, 30 and 1 ten, 2 tens, 3 tens. Ask questions such as: *Which cards could I place below the blue flowers?* [10 or 1 ten] *The groups of yellow flowers?* [20 or 2 tens] *Are there any cards I could place below all the flowers?* [30 or 3 tens] *Why?* [There are 30 flowers in all.]

- For Problem 2, encourage children to use the space provided to show how they thought about the problem. Have children share their strategies with the class, explaining what they did.

▶ **Fluency Practice**

 **Ready·** Mathematics
PRACTICE AND PROBLEM SOLVING

Assign *Practice and Problem Solving* **pages 183–184** after students have completed this section.

Practice Together
Add and Subtract Tens

50 gray birds.
30 red birds.

How many more gray birds?

50 − 30 = __20__

$30 + ? = 50$

| | | | | |

3 tens   2 tens

---

1 10 blue flowers.
20 yellow flowers.

How many flowers in all?

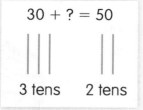

10 + 20 = __30__   __1__ ten + __2__ tens = __3__ tens

---

2 Find 90 − 40.

$4 + ? = 9$

4 tens + __5__ **tens = 9 tens**

40 + __50__ **= 90**   **90 − 40 =** __50__

132

▶ **Mathematical Discourse**

How do the number sentences describe the problem?

Since there are 50 gray birds, when you take away the number of red birds, what is left are how many more gray birds there are. Since there are 30 red birds, you can put together the number of red birds and how many more gray birds to make 50 gray birds in all.

▶ **Fluency Practice**

Add and subtract multiples of 10.

Materials For each child: Tens Cards (Activity Sheet 24)

- Distribute all of the cards except the cards showing < and >. Have children use two numbers and an operation to write a number sentence. Encourage children to use any method or strategy to complete the number sentence.

- Then have them repeat the activity, making sure that each number sentence is different.

▶ **Visual Model**

Use number bonds to relate subtracting tens to subtracting ones.

- Show children the number bond:

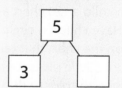

- Remind children that they used number bonds in previous lessons to subtract. Review methods they used to find the missing number.

- Show the number bond:

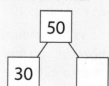

- Discuss how the numbers compare to those in the first bond. Relate 50 to 5 tens and 30 to 3 tens and ask: *How does knowing how to solve the first number bond help you solve the second one?*

Practice by Myself
Add and Subtract Tens

3 60 paper clips.
50 are in a box.

How many are not
in the box?

$50 + ? = 60$

| | | | | |

$60 - 50 = \underline{10}$

4 30 footballs and 30 basketballs.

What is the total number of balls?

$30 + 30 = \underline{60}$

$\underline{3}$ tens + $\underline{3}$ tens = $\underline{6}$ tens

5 Find $80 - 20$.

$2 + ? = 8$

2 tens + $\underline{6}$ tens = 8 tens

$20 + \underline{60} = 80$ $80 - 20 = \underline{60}$

133

Step By Step

- Before children work on this page, review how they can use tens blocks, number bonds, and the 120 chart to help them add groups of ten. Emphasize that children are free to use whatever way helps them solve the problem.

- Point out that the problems on this page are similar to the problems the children solved together on the previous page.

- Read each problem aloud, then have children work independently to solve.

▶ **English Language Learners**

- You may wish to draw attention to the model in Problem 3, asking children how the tens are related to the paper clips described in the problem.

- For Problem 4, observe if children are drawing 30 basketballs or using quick drawings or other representations of ten to model the problem.

- For those children who count on by ones and make 10 marks for each count, suggest that they circle the group of ten marks to represent one ten.

- Encourage children to use the space provided to show the strategy they used to solve Problem 5. Ask those who used a strategy other than a visual model to explain the strategy they employed.

SMP TIP Attend to Precision
As children work to add multiples of ten in Problem 4, encourage those children who draw 30 balls to organize them in a way that makes it easy to count accurately and check the precision of their calculation. *(SMP 6)*

▶ **English Language Learners**

Some children may struggle with comprehending the language used in a word problem. You may wish to write each sentence of the two word problems on this page on a separate line followed by a picture that represents it. Then underline the important words.

Differentiated Instruction

▶ Quick Check and Remediation

Materials For each child: 120 Chart (Activity Sheet 23), 7 tens blocks

- Ask children to solve the addition sentence $20 + \underline{\quad} = 70$ and show their thinking. [50]

- For children who are still struggling, use the chart below to guide remediation.

- After providing remediation, check children's understanding using the following problem: *Find the answer to 60 − 20 in two ways.* [40; Methods will vary.]

If the error is . . .	Children may . . .	To remediate . . .
90	have added 20 + 70.	Have children model the addition with base-ten blocks or on a 120 chart, reminding them of the meaning of the equal sign. Compare the model to their solution, discussing how their answer is one of the two numbers whose sum is 70.
60	have included 20 in their counts when counting on by tens.	Show children a 120 chart. Circle 20 and have children draw a line through each row to 20. Circle 70 and have children count on with you as you swipe your finger along each row. Explain that the row of 20 has already been counted so it isn't part of the counts when counting on.
5	have found the solution for $2 + \underline{\quad} = 7$.	Write: 2 tens + 5 tens = 7 tens. Praise the strategy children used, but point out that the 5 they found is actually 5 tens or 50. Return to their solution and ask if it makes sense. Have them calculate 20 + 5 to find that 25 is not equal to 70.

▶ Hands-On Activity
Construct number sentences.

Materials For each pair: 120 Chart (Activity Sheet 23), 2 copies of Tens Cards (Activity Sheet 24), workmats containing an addition and a subtraction open number sentence, extra blank cards, 12 tens blocks

- Place children with a partner and give each child a set of cards showing multiples of ten from 10 to 120.

- One partner chooses two cards to create an addition or subtraction sentence, placing them in the appropriate open number sentence. The other partner finds the solution to the sentence and places it on the mat. Check using tens blocks or the 120 chart.

- The first partner reorganizes the numbers to create the inverse sentence. Together, partners check that the sentence is correct.

- Children may challenge themselves with sums greater than 120 by writing the sum on a blank card.

▶ Challenge Activity
Construct advanced number sentences.

Materials For each pair: 2 copies of Tens Cards (Activity Sheet 24), workmats containing an addition and a subtraction open number sentence, extra blank cards

- Place children with a partner and give each child a set of cards showing multiples of ten from 10 to 200. Instruct them to complete the activity as in the Hands-On Activity on the left.

- Children will notice their cards include numbers beyond 120. Tell them that their challenge is to work with those larger numbers. If they require a greater challenge, provide them with multiples-of-ten cards greater than 200. They may use the blank cards to record sums that exceed the numbers on their cards.

- Challenge children to compute without the aid of tens blocks or 120 charts; however, allow children to use them if needed.

Teacher Notes

Teacher-Toolbox.com

Overview

Assign the Lesson 20 Quiz and have children work independently to complete it.

Use the results of the quiz to assess children's understanding of the content of the lesson and to identify areas for reteaching. See the Lesson Pacing Guide at the beginning of the lesson and the Differentiated Instruction activities for suggested instructional resources.

Tested Skills

Assesses 1.NBT.C.6

Problems on this quiz require children to be able to add multiples of 10 to multiples of 10 and subtract multiples of 10 from multiples of 10. Children will also need to be familiar with counting by 10s to 100 and understand that multiples of 10 represent groups of 10.

Ready® **Mathematics**

Lesson 20 Quiz Answer Key

Name _____

Solve.

1 60 books.
40 are on the shelf.
How many are not on the shelf?

60 − 40 = __20__

$40 + ? = 60$

|||| ||||||

4 tens   6 tens

2 10 small boats and 40 big boats.
How many boats in all?

10 + 40 = __50__

$10 + 40 = ?$

| ||||

1 ten   4 tens

3 40 green apples and 40 red apples.
What is the total number of apples?
$40 + 40 = ?$

__4__ tens + __4__ tens = __8__ tens

40 + 40 = __80__

Grade 1 **Lesson 20** Add and Subtract Tens   1   ©Curriculum Associates, LLC
Copying permitted for classroom use.

Common Misconceptions and Errors

Errors may result if children:

- ignore the zeros and add/subtract the tens place digits as ones.
- count on by 10s from a number using the number as the first count.
- do not recognize that multiples of 10 are groups of 10.

Name _____

Solve.

4 Find $70 - 20$.

$2 + ? = 7$

2 tens + _5_ tens = 7 tens

20 + _50_ = 70   **70 − 20 = _50_**

5 Taro has 20 balloons.
Pam has 60 balloons.
How many balloons in all?

20 + 60 = _80_

There are _80_ balloons in all.

  2

Assessment

Step By Step

- Have children solve the problems individually and show their work. Emphasize that children are free to use whatever way helps them solve the problems.

- Circulate and observe children's work. Problems 1 and 2 are based on the 120 Chart. For children who struggle, discuss the ways to count by ones, twos, and tens on the chart.

  Error Alert Look for children who add or subtract 1 instead of 10 in Problems 2, 3, and 4. Guide them to understand that 1 ten is the same as 10 ones. Have them identify where in the number the tens are written. Emphasize the difference between the tens and ones places.

Unit 4 Review

Solve the problems.

1 35 ducks and 2 more ducks.

2 more than 35 is ___37___.

23	24	25	26	27	28
33	34	35	36	37	38
43	44	45	46	47	48

---

2 52 paper clips. 10 are in a box. How many are not in the box?

41	42	43	44	45	46	47	48	49	50
51	52	53	54	55	56	57	58	59	60
61	62	63	64	65	66	67	68	69	70

52 − 10 = ___42___

---

3 **86 + 10 =** ___96___ | **4** ___70___ **= 80 − 10**

---

5 **Count by 1: 108,** _109_**, 110,** _111_**,** _112_**, 113**

134

Teacher Notes

6 The number of birds is the same as 6 tens.

Draw 6 tens.

Children draw six tens.

6 tens is __6__ groups of 10.   6 tens is __60__ ones.

There are __60__ birds.

---

7 Jo has 24 markers.

24 is __2__ tens and __4__ ones.

Bo has 10 more than Jo.   Mo has 10 fewer than Jo.

__34__ = 24 + 10   24 − 10 = __14__

Bo has __34__ markers.   Mo has __14__ markers.

135

Step By Step

- If children have difficulty drawing tens for Problem 6, review that 1 ten is 10 ones. Consider showing children a tens block and and having them brainstorm fast ways to draw tens using lines or rectangles.

  Error Alert Look for children who add or subtract 1 instead of 10 in Problems 7 and 8. Guide them to understand that 1 ten is the same as 10 ones. Have them identify where in the number the tens are written. Emphasize the difference between the tens and ones places.

Teacher Notes

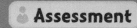 **Assessment**

Step By Step

Put It Together

- On this page, children draw several tens, then use this number to complete a problem that involves subtracting 10.

- Read the directions and task aloud. Make sure children understand what they need to do to complete the task.

- Direct children to complete problem 8 on their own.

- As children work on their own, observe their progress and understanding. Respond to their questions and provide additional support as needed.

- Have children share their drawing and problem with the class. Guide them to make a connection between their drawing and the numbers they wrote in the word problem.

- Have children demonstrate and justify the strategies they used to solve the problem.

- Have children return to the Unit Opener page and complete the *After* column of the progress chart.

Put It Together

8 **Subtract tens.**

Draw 5, 6, 7, 8, or 9 tens. Complete the problem using your number.

Possible answer: Children may draw base-ten blocks to represent 7 tens.

There are __70__ shapes. 30 of them are squares. The rest are circles. How many are circles? Show your work.

Possible answer:

70 = 7 tens and 30 = 3 tens

3 tens + 4 tens = 7 tens

4 tens = 40

__40__ shapes are circles.

136

Teacher Notes

Scoring Rubric

Points	Expectations
4	The child: • draws the same number of tens as the number in the problem. • uses an appropriate strategy to subtract 30 and correctly solves the problem.
3	The child: • may draw the same number of tens as their number in the problem. • may use an appropriate strategy to subtract 30, but with a minor computation error.
2	The child: • may not draw the same number of tens as the number in the problem. • may show signs of using a strategy to subtract 30, but the work has some errors.
1	The child: • may not draw the same number of tens as the number in the problem or does not draw any tens. • may not show signs of using a strategy to subtract 30 and the work has many errors.
0	The child: • does not attempt to complete the task.

Unit 5 Tens and Ones

Which lessons are students building upon?

Kindergarten, Lesson 21
Understand Teen Numbers
K.NBT.A.1

Kindergarten, Lesson 24
Count to 100 by Tens
K.CC.A.1, K.CC.A.2

Kindergarten, Lesson 25
Count to 100 by Ones
K.CC.A.1, K.CC.A.2

Kindergarten, Lesson 5
Compare Within 5
K.CC.B.4c, K.CC.C.6, K.CC.C.7

Kindergarten, Lesson 12
Compare Within 10
K.CC.B.4c, K.CC.C.6, K.CC.C.7

Kindergarten, Lesson 25
Count to 100 by Ones
K.CC.A.1, K.CC.A.2

Kindergarten, Lesson 22
Count Teen Numbers
K.CC.A.3, K.CC.B.5

Kindergarten, Lesson 24
Count to 100 by Tens
K.CC.A.1, K.CC.A.2

Kindergarten, Lesson 25
Count to 100 by Ones
K.CC.A.1, K.CC.A.2

Kindergarten, Lesson 23
Make Teen Numbers
K.NBT.A.1

Kindergarten, Lesson 24
Count to 100 by Tens
K.CC.A.1, K.CC.A.2

Kindergarten, Lesson 25
Count to 100 by Ones
K.CC.A.1, K.CC.A.2

Kindergarten, Lesson 23
Make Teen Numbers
K.NBT.A.1

Kindergarten, Lesson 24
Count to 100 by Tens
K.CC.A.1, K.CC.A.2

Kindergarten, Lesson 25
Count to 100 by Ones
K.CC.A.1, K.CC.A.2

Unit 5

Lesson 21
Understand Tens and Ones
1.NBT.B.2a, 1.NBT.B.2c

Lesson 22
Compare Numbers
1.NBT.B.3

Lesson 23
Add Tens to Any Number
1.NBT.C.4

Lesson 24
Add Tens and Add Ones
1.NBT.C.4

Lesson 25
Add and Regroup
1.NBT.C.4

Which lessons are students preparing for?

Grade 2, Lesson 10
Understand Three-Digit Numbers
2.NBT.A.1a, 2.NBT.A.1b, 2.NBT.A.2

Grade 2, Lesson 11
Read and Write Three-Digit Numbers
2.NBT.A.3

Grade 2, Lesson 11
Read and Write Three-Digit Numbers
2.NBT.A.3

Grade 2, Lesson 12
Compare Three-Digit Numbers
2.NBT.A.4

Grade 2, Lesson 13
Add Three-Digit Numbers
2.NBT.B.7, 2.NBT.B.9

Grade 2, Lesson 15
Add Several Two-Digit Numbers
2.NBT.B.6

Grade 2, Lesson 13
Add Three-Digit Numbers
2.NBT.B.7, 2.NBT.B.9

Grade 2, Lesson 15
Add Several Two-Digit Numbers
2.NBT.B.6

Grade 2, Lesson 13
Add Three-Digit Numbers
2.NBT.B.7, 2.NBT.B.9

Grade 2, Lesson 15
Add Several Two-Digit Numbers
2.NBT.B.6

Unit 5
Tens and Ones

Unit 5 – Number and Operations in Base Ten
Tens and Ones

Jack has 27 cards. Kim has 34 cards. Owen has 20 cards. Jack wants to compare the numbers of cards. He wants to trade some cards. What math questions could Jack ask could about the cards?

In this unit, you will learn to compare numbers and to add two-digit numbers. Then you will be able to solve problems like Jack's!

✓ **Self Check**

Check off the skills you know now. Then see how many more you can check off after each lesson!

I can:	Before this unit	After this unit
rename numbers as tens and ones.	☐	☐
compare two-digit numbers.	☐	☐
add tens to any number.	☐	☐
add tens and ones.	☐	☐
regroup to add two-digit numbers.	☐	☐

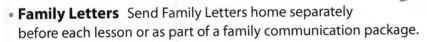

Ready Mathematics
PRACTICE AND PROBLEM SOLVING

Practice and Problem Solving Resources

Use the following resources from *Practice and Problem Solving* to engage students and their families and to extend student learning.

- **Family Letters** Send Family Letters home separately before each lesson or as part of a family communication package.

- **Unit Games** Use partner Unit Games at classroom centers and/or send them home for play with family members.

- **Unit Practice** Assign Unit Practice as homework, as independent or small group practice, or for whole class discussion.

- **Fluency Practice** Assign Fluency Skills Practice and Fluency Repeated Reasoning Practice worksheets throughout the unit.

At A Glance

- This page introduces children to the general ideas behind working with two-digit numbers.

- The checklist allows them to see what skills they will be learning and take ownership of their progress.

Step By Step

- Explain to children that they are going to begin a new unit of lessons. Tell them that in all the lessons in this unit they will be learning to compare numbers and to add two-digit numbers.

- Read the introduction to the unit together as a class. Invite children to suggest questions that could be asked about the problem situation. Discuss the questions children pose without the expectation that they are to solve them.

- Then take a few minutes to have each child independently read through the list of skills.

- Ask children to consider each skill and check the box in the *Before* column if it is a skill they think they already have. Remind children that these skills are likely to all be new to them, but it's still possible some children have some of the skills.

- Engage children in a brief discussion about the skills. Invite children to comment on which ones they would most like to learn, or which ones seem similar or related to something they already know. Remind them that the goal is to be able to check off all the skills they have learned by the end of the unit.

- At the end of the unit, have children complete the *After* column. As time allows, pose questions about the problem situation at the top of the page and solve as a class.

Lesson 21
Understand Tens and Ones

CCSS Focus

Domain
Number and Operations in Base Ten

Cluster
B. Understand place value.

Standards
1.NBT.B.2 Understand that the two digits of a two-digit number represent amounts of tens and ones. Understand the following as special cases:
a. 10 can be thought of as a bundle of ten ones—called a "ten."
c. The numbers 10, 20, 30, 40, 50, 60, 70, 80, and 90 refer to one, two, three, four, five, six, seven, eight, or nine tens (and 0 ones).

Standards for Mathematical Practice (SMP)
2 Reason abstractly and quantitatively.
3 Construct viable arguments and critique the reasoning of others.
5 Use appropriate tools strategically.
6 Attend to precision.
7 Look for and make use of structure.
8 Look for and express regularity in repeated reasoning.

Lesson Objectives

Content Objectives
• Represent two-digit numbers as tens and ones.
• Decompose a two-digit number as some tens and some ones in multiple ways.
• Model a two-digit number in multiple ways.

Language Objectives
• Use connecting cubes and draw diagrams to model a two-digit number as a group of ones and as a group of tens plus ones.
• Write given two-digit numbers as different tens and ones.
• Justify conclusions and communicate the conclusions to others.

Prerequisite Skills

• Count by tens to 100.
• Represent 10 ones as 1 ten.

Lesson Vocabulary

• **digit** any of the ten symbols used in the base-ten numeration system 0, 1, 2, 3, 4, 5, 6, 7, 8, 9.
• **place value** the value of the place of a digit, such as tens and ones.

Review the following key terms.
• **ones** single units or objects.
• **tens** groups of ten ones.

Learning Progression

In Kindergarten children decompose numbers from 11–19 using objects or drawings, understanding that these numbers are composed of a group of 10 ones and 1 to 9 additional ones.

In Grade 1 children extend their understanding of two-digit numbers to include those beyond 19. They also learn to see 10 as 10 ones or 1 ten.

In this lesson children decompose two-digit numbers into groups of tens and ones, representing them in multiple ways. They recognize that the digit in the

tens place of a two-digit number denotes a number of tens and they write two-digit numbers by placing each digit in the appropriate place-value location. The focus on tens and ones continues in Grade 2 as children learn to compare and add two-digit numbers.

In Grade 2 children build on place-value concepts as they decompose two- and three-digit numbers and apply the decomposition to add and subtract numbers with regrouping.

Lesson Pacing Guide

Whole Class Instruction

Day 1
45–60 minutes

Introduction
Use What You Know
• Explore It *25 min*
• Try It *20 min*

Day 2
45–60 minutes

Modeled Instruction
Explore Together
• Opening Question *5 min*
• Think *15 min*
• Talk About It *10 min*
• Hands-On Activity *15 min*

Practice and Problem Solving
Assign pages 195–196.

Day 3
45–60 minutes

Guided Instruction
Explore Together
• Hands-On Problem *10 min*
• Problems 1–2 *15 min*
• Talk About It *10 min*
• Visual Model *10 min*

Practice and Problem Solving
Assign pages 197–198.

Day 4
45–60 minutes

Guided Practice
Connect It
• Problems 3–5 *15 min*

Independent Practice
Show What I Know
• Problem 6 *15 min*
• Intervention, On-Level, or Challenge Activity *15 min*

Practice and Problem Solving
Assign pages 199–200.

Teacher-Toolbox: Lesson Quiz
Lesson 21 Quiz

Materials for Lesson Activities

Per child: 1 paper bag, 45 connecting cubes, number cube, base-ten blocks (10 tens blocks and 32 ones blocks)
Activity Sheet 19*, Activity Sheet 25, Activity Sheet 43

Per pair: whiteboard

For display: Activity Sheet 25, Activity Sheet 43

*Used for more than one activity.

Small Group Differentiation

Teacher-Toolbox.com

Reteach
Ready Prerequisite Lessons *45–90 min*

• Lesson 21 *Understand* Teen Numbers
• Lesson 25 Count to 100 by Ones

Teacher-led Activities
Tools for Instruction *15–20 min*

Grade 1 *(Lesson 21)*
• Making a Set Up to 10 Objects

Student-led Activities
Math Center Activities *30–40 min*

Grade K *(Lessons 21 and 25)*
• K.28 Teen Number Vocabulary
• K.32 Count by Ones Vocabulary
• K.33 Keep Counting

Grade 1 *(Lesson 21)*
• 1.24 Tens and Ones
• 1.25 Tens and Ones Match

Personalized Learning

i-Ready.com

Independent
i-Ready Lessons* *10–20 min*

Grade 1 *(Lesson 21)*
• Grouping into Tens and Ones
• Regrouping Tens as Ones

* i-Ready lessons may be updated during the 2016–2017 school year. Updated references will be on the Teacher-Toolbox.

Introduction

Activity Counting with Tens

Objective

Explore the many ways to count and represent two-digit numbers.

Materials for each child

- 1 paper bag
- 45 connecting cubes

Overview

Children count a set of cubes by combining groups of ten and counting the remaining cubes. Then they show a two-digit number using different numbers of tens and ones.

Step By Step

Explore It

Set the stage.

- Distribute a bag containing 32 connecting cubes to each child. Cubes should not be connected into groups. Children should not know how many cubes are in the bags.

- Ask children to guess the number of cubes they have and record the number in their Student Books.

- Have children open their bags. Discuss the many ways they might count the cubes (for example, by ones, twos, fives, tens). Remind them of previous lessons where they made ten-trains.

Pose the problem.

- Explain to children that for this problem they will count their cubes by making different numbers of tens.

- First they make 1 ten-train, count the tens, and then count the ones that remain. Ask children to record the number of tens and ones they counted on the Student Book page.

- Have children continue the activity by next making 2 ten-trains, and finally 3 ten-trains. Each time, they record the number of tens and ones they count.

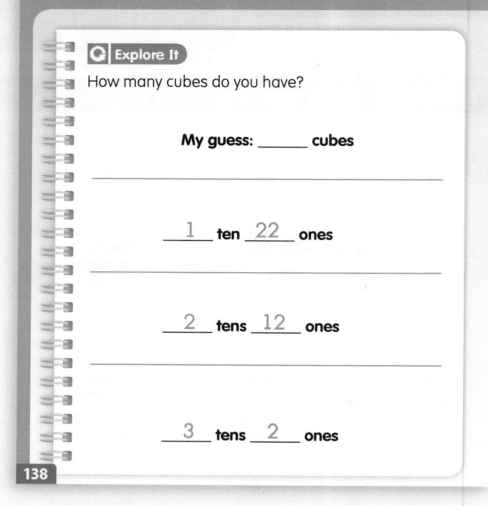

Inside the image:

⊙ Explore It

How many cubes do you have?

My guess: _____ cubes

_____1_____ ten _____22_____ ones

_____2_____ tens _____12_____ ones

_____3_____ tens _____2_____ ones

138

Share work.

- Invite volunteers to share the different numbers of tens and ones they counted. Discuss how making tens helps them count the cubes. Invite volunteers to share how their guess compared to the actual number of cubes in the bag.

- Write "32 cubes" on the board. Under that write the headings "Tens" and "Ones." In the tens column write 0. Ask children how many ones cubes they have if they make no ten-trains. Record 32 in the ones place.

- Now record a 1 in the tens column and ask children how many extra ones there are if they make 1 ten. Record 22 in the ones column. Repeat with 2 and 3 tens.

- Discuss how these can all be ways to show 32 cubes. Lead children to notice that each time you add 1 to the "Tens" column, you take 10 from the "Ones" column. Ask: *Which of these ways makes it easiest to count all the cubes? Why?*

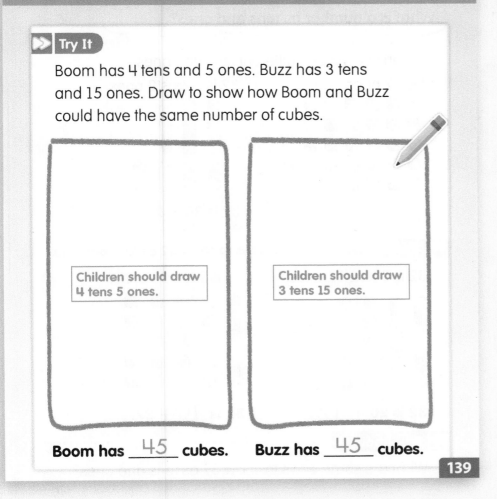

⟩⟩ Try It

Boom has 4 tens and 5 ones. Buzz has 3 tens and 15 ones. Draw to show how Boom and Buzz could have the same number of cubes.

Children should draw 4 tens 5 ones.

Children should draw 3 tens 15 ones.

Boom has __45__ cubes.   Buzz has __45__ cubes.

139

Step By Step

Try It

Pose the problem.

• Tell children that Boom and Buzz both have some cubes. Then read the problem on the Student Book page aloud: *Boom has 4 tens and 5 ones; Buzz has 3 tens and 15 ones. Draw to show how Boom and Buzz could have the same number of cubes.*

Model and solve the problem.

• Allow children to model with cubes, if necessary, before drawing pictures and completing the sentences. Some children may be able to model this situation with cubes, but may struggle to draw pictures. The lesson provides many opportunities to further develop this understanding.

• Invite volunteers to share their drawings and explain their reasoning on how Boom and Buzz both have 45 cubes. Listen to their explanations on how the drawings show 45 in different ways, helping them articulate using the terms *tens* and *ones*.

Modeled Instruction

Step By Step

- Read the question at the top of the page and ask children how the base-ten blocks in the example on the Student Book page remind them of the Activity in the Introduction. Have them circle groups of ten in the single ones to recognize that the number of blocks in each group is the same; they are just organized differently.

Think

- Read Think with children and ask them to describe the difference between the base-ten blocks on the left and on the right. Guide them to recognize that these show the same total number of blocks with different numbers of bundled tens. Have children circle all the groups of 10 that they see.

▶ **Mathematical Discourse 1**

Talk About It

- For Talk About It, children should be able to use what they have learned to find that 37 is 3 tens 7 ones, 2 tens 17 ones, and 1 ten 27 ones.

▶ **Hands-On Activity**

SMP TIP Use Structure

Children look for and make use of structure as they repeatedly count 10 objects and bundle them into one group of ten. The Hands-On Activity presents an opportunity for doing this. Allow children to also use connecting cubes as they discuss the Talk About It question and whenever the opportunity arises throughout the lesson. *(SMP 7)*

 **Mathematics**
PRACTICE AND PROBLEM SOLVING

Assign *Practice and Problem Solving* **pages 195–196** after students have completed this section.

Understand Tens and Ones

What is a number as tens and ones?

You can show 32 as different tens and ones.

32 is 32 ones.

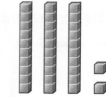

32 is 3 tens 2 ones.

32 is 30 + 2.

 Think There are other ways to show **32** as tens and ones.

32 is 2 tens 12 ones.   32 is 1 ten 22 ones.

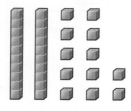 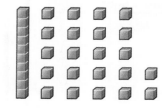

32 is 20 + _12_ .   **32 is _10_ + 22.**

Talk About It ·····························

140 What are some ways to show 37 as tens and ones?

▶ **Mathematical Discourse**

1 *How do you know that all these groups of blocks show 32 blocks in all?*
Some children may respond that they counted them all. Others may notice that each group has a total of 3 tens and 2 extra ones.

▶ **Hands-On Activity**

Model tens and ones with base-ten blocks.

Materials For each child: Hundreds Chart (Activity Sheet 19), base-ten blocks (3 tens blocks, 32 ones blocks)

- Instruct children to count out 32 ones blocks and place one in each box of the chart from 1 to 32.

- Discuss how children can find groups of ten within the chart. Have them identify one group of ten, then two groups of ten and finally three groups of ten. As a class, count the total number of blocks, counting tens first then counting on the ones.

- Tell children to replace the ones blocks in the top row with a tens block to show a group of ten. Ask: *How many tens blocks do you have? How many ones blocks are left?* Count the blocks by tens and ones. Have children replace another set of ten and finally the last set of ten, counting the tens and remaining ones blocks after each row is replaced.

Explore Together
Understand Tens and Ones

 Show 23 as different tens and ones.
Use base-ten blocks.

Make 23 one way. → Make 23 another way.
Write the tens and ones.   Write the tens and ones.

__2__ tens __3__ ones   __1__ ten __13__ ones

1 **Show 45 as tens and ones two ways.**
Possible answers

__4__ tens __5__ ones

__3__ tens __15__ ones

2 **Show 54 as tens and ones two ways.**
Possible answers

__5__ tens __4__ ones

__3__ tens __24__ ones

💬 **Talk About It**

What are other ways you can show these numbers?

141

▶ Visual Model

Decompose numbers into tens and ones.

Materials For display: Two-Digit Number Mats (Activity Sheet 43), Number Cards 0 to 11 (Activity Sheet 25)

- Cover the 0 on the 20 card with a 3 and display it above a number bond showing 23 in the top box.

- Show how 23 can be "broken apart" into tens and ones by separating the cards, placing 20 in one part of the bond and 3 in the other part.

- Connect this model to the tens and ones children wrote on their papers.

- Repeat for other two-digit numbers as needed throughout the lesson.

▶ Mathematical Discourse

2 Can 54 be shown as 4 tens and 5 ones? Explain.

No. The 5 in 54 means 5 tens not 5 ones. The 4 means 4 ones not 4 tens.

3 *Why do you think there are more ways to show 54 than 45?*

Some children may say that 54 is a greater number. Others may point out that there are more tens in 54 than in 45, so there are more ways to combine tens and ones.

Step By Step

- Have children model 23 with base-ten blocks on a piece of paper, showing 2 tens blocks and 3 ones blocks. Tell them to write the number of tens and ones on the piece of paper.

▶ Visual Model

- Next have children trade 1 tens block for 10 ones blocks and count the tens and ones in this model. Ask them to write this number of tens and ones on the paper. Then direct attention to the problem at the top of the page.

- Work through Problems 1 and 2 with children. Write 45 and 54 on the board. Ask: *How are these numbers the same? How are they different?* Model 45 and 54 with base-ten blocks and discuss the meaning of the 5 in each number. Emphasize that in the number 54, the 5 refers to 5 groups of ten.

▶ Mathematical Discourse 2

Talk About It

- Present the Talk About It question, revisiting the many ways children decomposed 32 on the previous page. Have them work in pairs to find as many ways as possible to represent 45 and 54. Allow them to use blocks for support. Record their findings on the board and ask Mathematical Discourse question 3.

▶ Mathematical Discourse 3

Ready Mathematics
PRACTICE AND PROBLEM SOLVING

Assign *Practice and Problem Solving* **pages 197–198** after students have completed this section.

👥👥 Guided Practice

Step By Step

- Discuss each Connect It problem as a class using the discussion points outlined below.

Draw

- This problem provides children with an opportunity to demonstrate their understanding of the meaning of tens and ones. Remind them that it is like problems they completed on previous pages.

- Allow children to use base-ten blocks for support and remind them how to make quick drawings to represent tens and ones.

- Ask children to demonstrate and explain how their drawing shows an equality using questions such as: *Why did you circle these blocks? How can you show that 1 ten is the same as 10 of these blocks?*

Identify

- You may want children to work in pairs, using base-ten blocks to model the choices before deciding which ones represent 76.

- As children work, ask questions such as: *I see a 6 and a 7 in 60 + 7 just like the 6 and 7 in 76, so why didn't you circle 60 + 7? How do you know that 6 tens and 16 ones is the same as 76?*

- You may want to challenge some children to find as many other ways as possible to represent 76 and tell how they found them.

Explain

- A common misconception among children is that each digit in a two-digit number is a separate entity and that they are therefore interchangeable. This problem focuses on this misconception by asking children to analyze the value given to each digit by its label or placement.

- As children explain their reasoning to the class, encourage them to support it with physical and/or visual models. Ensure that they explain what is wrong with the presented reasoning.

Connect It
Understand Tens and Ones

3 **Draw** Show why 36 ones is the same as 3 tens 6 ones.

Possible answer: Children's drawings might show 36 objects with groups of ten circled to show 3 tens and 6 ones.

4 **Identify** Circle all the ways that show 76.

(7 tens 6 ones)   6 tens 7 ones

60 + 7   (70 + 6)

(5 tens 26 ones)   (6 tens 16 ones)

5 **Explain** Buzz says 5 tens 8 ones = 5 + 80. Do you agree? Tell why or why not.

Possible answer: I do not agree. 5 tens 8 ones is 50 + 8.

- Rewrite each value as 50 + 8 and 80 + 5 and have children write the two-digit number for each of them. Then write 8 + 50 and 5 + 80 and have them write the two-digit numbers. Model how the order of the addends doesn't affect the number but the order of the digits does.

> **SMP TIP Construct Arguments and Critique Reasoning/Attend to Precision**
> Prompt children with questions in order to elicit clear, concise explanations of their actions. Encourage them to use accurate mathematical language in their descriptions and justification for the drawings or choices they made. Lead them to use these explanations and justification to argue why Buzz is or is not correct in his thinking. *(SMP 3 and 6)*

 Ready Mathematics
PRACTICE AND PROBLEM SOLVING

Assign *Practice and Problem Solving* **pages 199–200** after students have completed this section.

Show What I Know
Understand Tens and Ones

6 Think about how you can show numbers as different tens and ones.

A: Circle some tens and ones.

Possible answer: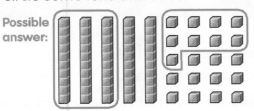

Write the number as tens and ones in two different ways. Write the two-digit number.

___3___ tens __9__ ones   __2__ tens _19_ ones   __39__

B: Use the two digits from A. Write a different number. Show this number as tens and ones in two different ways.

Possible answer:

Children may draw or write to show 93 as 9 tens 3 ones and 8 tens 13 ones.

143

Step By Step

- Read the directions aloud and make sure children understand that they are to make a two-digit number by circling any number of tens blocks and any number of ones blocks in the diagram. Encourage them to circle at least 3 tens.

- For Part B, make sure children reverse the order of the digits from the number they made in Part A.

- As children work, support them with questions such as:

  How can you make sure all these ways show the number of blocks you circled?

  Can you think of a different number of tens to use?

  Why did you write this digit as ones in the first part and as tens in the second part?

  Which number can be shown in more ways, the one from Part A or the one from Part B? Why?

Scoring Rubrics

Expectations for 4–3 Points

Points	Expectations
4	The child: • represents the blocks circled in multiple ways and writes the corresponding number. • reverses the order of the digits and accurately represents the tens and ones.
3	The child: • accurately represents the blocks circled as a group of tens and some ones in only one way (e.g., 3 tens 4 ones). • reverses the digits and accurately represents the two-digit number.

Expectations for 2–0 Points

Points	Expectations
2	The child: • represents the blocks circled as a two-digit number, but may not represent it in any other way. • reverses the order of the digits and may use a drawing to represent the value.
1	The child: • may attempt to represent the blocks circled, but that representation may not correspond to the number of blocks that are circled. • writes a number that does not correspond to the blocks circled or to any other number.
0	The child: • does not attempt to represent blocks as tens and ones.

Differentiated Instruction

▶ Intervention Activity

Model tens and ones digits.

Materials For each child: base-ten blocks (10 tens blocks and 10 ones blocks), Number Cards 0 to 11 (Activity Sheet 25), Two-Digit Number Mats (Activity Sheet 43)

• Place the two-digit number mats and cards showing the numbers 1–9 faceup on the desk.

• Have children select a two-digit number mat, place it on the desk, and show the number using tens blocks.

• Children then select a number card, place it over the zero on the two-digit number mat and place the corresponding number of ones blocks on the desk. Repeat the activity, having children select a different two-digit number mat and a different number card, until all cards have been used.

• Optional: Have children build some tens and ones, then find the corresponding cards to model the number they built.

▶ On-Level Activity

Cover a hundreds chart.

Materials For each child: Hundreds Chart (Activity Sheet 19), base-ten blocks (10 tens blocks and 12 ones blocks), number cube

• Place children in pairs. Tell them their goal is to fill their hundreds chart with base-ten blocks.

• Children take turns rolling a number cube and placing the corresponding number of ones blocks on their hundreds chart, starting with 1 and continuing consecutively. After each turn, the child says: *I have ___ cubes.*

• When a row of ten is filled, the child removes the ones blocks and lays a tens block across that row. As they accumulate tens, they describe the number of cubes in more than one way, such as: *1 ten 13 ones, and 2 tens 3 ones, are each 23 cubes.*

• Play continues until one child fills the chart.

• The game may be expedited by having the children roll two number cubes and use the sum of the numbers to determine how many ones blocks to place on the hundreds chart.

▶ Challenge Activity

Play "Guess My Number."

Materials For each pair: whiteboard

• Place children in pairs. One child writes a two-digit number on the whiteboard without revealing it to the partner. He or she gives a clue, such as: *My number has more than 3 tens.* The partner writes a guess on a whiteboard. The first child indicates if the number is correct and if not, provides other clues until the partner writes the correct number on the whiteboard.

• Encourage children to think of many different kinds of clues, such as using "greater than" or "less than" for the digits [the ones digit is greater than the tens digit], using tens and ones [there are more tens than ones; there are three more tens than ones]. Challenge them to use a variety of clues.

• When the number has been guessed, the other partner takes a turn writing a number and giving clues.

• Allow children to play until time has expired.

• Optional: You may want to write two-digit numbers on cards for children to randomly select instead of making up their own. Play then continues until all the cards have been used.

Teacher Notes

Teacher-Toolbox.com

Overview

Assign the Lesson 21 Quiz and have children work independently to complete it.

Use the results of the quiz to assess children's understanding of the content of the lesson and to identify areas for reteaching. See the Lesson Pacing Guide at the beginning of the lesson and the Differentiated Instruction activities for suggested instructional resources.

Tested Skills

Assesses 1.NBT.B.2a, 1.NBT.B.2c

Problems on this quiz require children to be able to decompose two-digit numbers into groups of tens and ones, representing the numbers in multiple ways. Children will also need to be familiar with counting by 10s to 100 and representing 10 ones as 1 ten.

Ready® **Mathematics**

Lesson 21 Quiz Answer Key

Name _____

Solve.

1. Show 76 as tens and ones two ways.

   Possible answers:

   __7__ tens __6__ ones

   __6__ tens __16__ ones

2. Show why 47 ones is the same as 4 tens 7 ones.
   Possible answer: Children's drawings might show 47 objects with groups of ten circled to show 4 tens and 7 ones.

3. Circle all the ways that show 63.

   30 + 6   (4 tens 23 ones)

   (6 tens 3 ones)   3 tens 6 ones

   (5 tens 13 ones)   (60 + 3)

Common Misconceptions and Errors

Errors may result if children:

• think that each digit in a two-digit number is interchangeable.

• do not recognize that 10 can be expressed as 10 ones or 1 ten.

• do not recognize that the digit in the tens place of a two-digit number denotes a number of tens and the digit in the ones place denotes a number of ones.

Lesson 21 **Quiz Answer Key** continued

Name _____

Solve.

4. Use the numbers on the cards. Write a two-digit number. Show this number as tens and ones in two different ways.

| 5 | | 8 |

Possible answers:

The number is __85__.

__8__ tens __5__ ones
__6__ tens __25__ ones

5. There are 3 boxes of pencils and 2 more pencils on one table.
There is 1 box of pencils and 22 more pencils on another table.
Each box has 10 pencils.
Show that both tables have the same number of pencils.
Possible answer: Child might draw 3 tens and 2 ones to show the 32 pencils on one table. Child might draw 1 ten and 22 ones (with 2 groups of 10 circled) to show the 32 pencils on the second table.

Grade 1 Lesson 21 *Understand* Tens and Ones

2

©Curriculum Associates, LLC
Copying permitted for classroom use.

Lesson 22
Compare Numbers

CCSS Focus

Domain
Number and Operations in Base Ten

Cluster
B. Understand place value.

Standard
1.NBT.B.3 Compare two two-digit numbers based on meanings of the tens and ones digits, recording the results of comparisons with the symbols >, =, and <.

Additional Standards
1.NBT.B.2a, 1.NBT.B.2b, 1.NBT.B.2c
(See page B3 for full text.)

Standards for Mathematical Practice (SMP)
3 Construct viable arguments and critique the reasoning of others.
4 Model with mathematics.
6 Attend to precision.
7 Look for and make use of structure.

Lesson Objectives

Content Objectives
• Understand the meaning of the symbols < and >.
• Compare the value of 2 two-digit numbers using tens and ones.
• Write the symbols <, >, and = to compare 2 two-digit numbers.

Language Objectives
• Orally describe and write the symbols used to represent *is greater than, is less than,* and *is the same as.*
• Use quick-draw diagrams and base-ten blocks to model two-digit numbers in comparison problems.
• Rewrite given pairs of two-digit numbers as tens and ones and determine which number is greater than, less than, or equal to the other.

Prerequisite Skills

• Understand concepts of *less than, more than,* and *the same as.*
• Understand the equal sign.
• Understand two-digit numbers as tens and ones.

Lesson Vocabulary

• **<** symbol that means *is less than.*
• **>** symbol that means *is greater than.*
• **greater than** number with a greater value or quantity.
• **less than** number with a smaller value or quantity.
• **more than** more in quantity or amount.

Review the following key terms.

• **compare** to decide if amounts or sizes are greater than, less than, or equal to each other.
• **equal sign (=)** a symbol that means *is the same as.*
• **fewer** indicating a lesser quantity or amount.
• **more** indicating a greater quantity or amount.

Learning Progression

In Kindergarten children use matching or counting strategies to identify the number of objects in a group as less than, equal to, or greater than the number of objects in another group. Children compare two numbers within 10 written as numerals.

In Grade 1 children understand that the 2 digits in a two-digit number represent tens and ones. They understand 10, 20, 30, 40, 50, 60, 70, 80, 90, and 100 as bundles of tens and zero ones.

In this lesson children use models of base-ten blocks to compare the number of tens and ones in 2 two-digit numbers. They use quick drawings and draw their own representations to compare 2 two-digit numbers. Children write <, >, or = to record their comparisons.

In Grade 2 children compare three-digit numbers based on the place-values hundreds, tens, and ones. They use the symbols <, >, and = to record comparisons.

Lesson Pacing Guide

Whole Class Instruction

Day 1
45–60 minutes

Introduction
Use What You Know
- Explore It *25 min*
- Try It *20 min*

Day 2
45–60 minutes

Modeled Instruction
Explore Together
- Example Problem *5 min*
- Model It *25 min*
- Hands-On Activity *15 min*

Practice and Problem Solving
Assign pages 203–204.

Day 3
45–60 minutes

Guided Instruction
Learn Together
- Example Problem *5 min*
- Model It *15 min*
- Talk About It *10 min*
- Fluency Practice *15 min*

Practice and Problem Solving
Assign pages 205–206.

Day 4
45–60 minutes

Guided Practice
Practice Together
- Example Problem *10 min*
- Problems 1–2 *25 min*
- Visual Model *10 min*

Practice and Problem Solving
Assign pages 207–208.

Day 5
45–60 minutes

Independent Practice
Practice by Myself
- Problems 3–5 *15 min*
- Quick Check and Remediation *15 min*
- Hands-On or Challenge Activity *15 min*

Teacher-Toolbox: Lesson Quiz
Lesson 22 Quiz

Materials for Lesson Activities

Per child: base-ten blocks
Activity Sheet 1, Activity Sheet 23, Activity Sheet 26, Activity Sheet 27*

Per pair: base-ten blocks
Activity Sheet 25*

For display: none

*Used for more than one activity.

Small Group Differentiation

Teacher-Toolbox.com

Reteach
Ready Prerequisite Lessons *45–90 min*

Grade K
- Lesson 5 Compare Within 5
- Lesson 12 Compare Within 10

Teacher-led Activities
Tools for Instruction *15–20 min*

Grade 1 *(Lesson 22)*
- Compare Two-Digit Numbers
- One More
- One Less

Student-led Activities
Math Center Activities *30–40 min*

Grade K *(Lessons 5 and 12)*
- K.11 1 More
- K.12 Compare Vocabulary
- K.13 Which Group Is More?
- K.14 Count and Compare
- K.15 Which Is More?
- K.16 Compare and Color

Grade 1 *(Lesson 22)*
- 1.34 Comparison Vocabulary
- 1.35 Compare Numbers

Personalized Learning

i-Ready.com

Independent
i-Ready Lessons* *10–20 min*

Grade 1 *(Lesson 22)*
- Comparing Numbers to 100 Using Symbols
- Comparing Sets

i-Ready lessons may be updated during the 2016–2017 school year. Updated references will be on the Teacher-Toolbox.

 **Introduction**

Activity Compare Numbers

Objective
Model to compare two-digit numbers.

Materials for each child
• base-ten blocks

Overview
Children use base-ten blocks to model comparison problems with two-digit numbers. They use phrases such as *more*, *greater than*, *less than*, and *fewer* to talk about quantities.

Step By Step

Explore It

Pose the problem.

• Ask the children to imagine that a class needs to move some books to the school library, and that two children each make a few trips carrying books to the library. Say: *Rosa carried 24 books. Ryan carried 37 books. Who carried more books? Who carried fewer?* Ask children to suggest ways they can compare the number of books Rosa and Ryan each carried.

Model the problem with base-ten blocks.

• Write the two numbers on the board: 24 and 37.

• Ask: *How can you show 24 using base-ten blocks?* [2 tens 4 ones] Direct children's attention to the Student Book page. Have children model 24 with their blocks on the workmat labeled *Rosa*.

• Ask: *How can you show 37 using base-ten blocks?* [3 tens 7 ones] Have children model 37 with their blocks on the workmat labeled *Ryan*.

Compare the models.

• Direct attention to the model for 24. Ask: *How many tens are there?* [2] *How many ones?* [4]

• Now direct attention to the model for 37. Ask: *How many tens are there?* [3] *How many ones?* [7]

Ⓖ Explore It

Rosa carried 24 books. Ryan carried 37 books. Who carried more books? Who carried fewer?

Rosa	Ryan

Ryan carried (more) / fewer books than Rosa.

Rosa carried more / (fewer) books than Ryan.

144

• Discuss with children which number has more tens. Guide them to understand that when one number has more tens than another, it is the "bigger" number.

Talk about the models and the problem.

• Tell children that since 37 has more tens than 24, 37 is greater than 24. Say: *Ryan carried 37 books and Rosa carried 24 books. What can you say about the number of books Ryan carried?* [Ryan carried more books than Rosa.] Have children circle the word *more* in the first sentence below the workmat.

• Explain that you can compare two numbers in a different way. Say: *24 is less than 37.* Ask: *What can you say about the books Rosa carried?* [Rosa carried fewer books than Ryan.] Have children circle the word *fewer* in the second sentence below the workmat.

• Discuss how the words *fewer* and *less* describe smaller quantities and the words *greater* and *more* describe larger quantities.

• Have children name some words they use when quantities are the same. Look for responses such as *equal, the same amount*, and *as many as.*

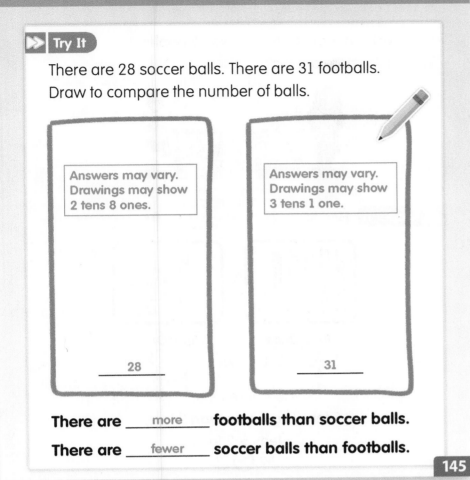

>> **Try It**

There are 28 soccer balls. There are 31 footballs.
Draw to compare the number of balls.

Answers may vary.
Drawings may show
2 tens 8 ones.

Answers may vary.
Drawings may show
3 tens 1 one.

28

31

There are __more__ footballs than soccer balls.

There are __fewer__ soccer balls than footballs.

145

Step By Step

Try It

Pose the problem.

• Tell children to imagine the balls stored in a school gym. Then read the problem from the Student Book page aloud: *There are 28 soccer balls. There are 31 footballs. Draw to compare the number of balls.*

Model the problem.

• Allow children time to model the numbers. Some children may need to use base-ten blocks before making a drawing.

Compare the models.

• Ask: *Which number has more tens?* [31] *How does that help you know which number is greater?* [The number with more tens is the greater number.]

• Say: *There are 28 soccer balls and 31 footballs. What can you say about the number of footballs?* [There are more footballs than soccer balls.]

• Then ask: *What can you say about the number of soccer balls?* [There are fewer soccer balls than footballs.]

• Have children complete the comparison statements on the Student Book page.

• Note whether children accurately use the words *more, greater, less,* and *fewer* in their descriptions.

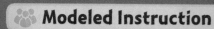
Modeled Instruction

Step By Step

- Explain that this page is about comparing two amounts to find which is more. Read the problem aloud.

Model It

- Direct children's attention to the base-ten blocks and place-value charts in Model It.

▶ **Hands-On Activity**

- Remind children they can use what they know about tens and ones to compare 52 and 25. Ask: *Which have a greater value, tens or ones?* [tens]

- Explain that since tens have a greater value, you first look at the tens when comparing two-digit numbers. Have children look at the place value charts that show 25 and 52 Ask: *How many tens are in 52?* [5] *How many tens are in 25?* [2] *Which number has more tens?* [52] Guide children to recognize that if one number has more tens than the other, then there is no need to look at the ones.

▶ **Mathematical Discourse 1 and 2**

- Relate the concept of *more* to the phrase *is greater than* on the page. Tell children you can write the symbol > to mean *is greater than*. Write 52 > 25 on the board and point out that the wide end of the symbol points to the greater number.

- Invite children to tell who picked more apples and to explain how they know.

> **SMP TIP Attend to Precision**
> When children understand the meanings of symbols used in mathematics and are able to use them to relate quantities appropriately, they recognize that the symbols are a precise and shorter way of recording these relationships. *(SMP 6)*

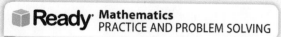
Mathematics
PRACTICE AND PROBLEM SOLVING

Assign *Practice and Problem Solving* **pages 203–204** after students have completed this section.

Compare Numbers

Nora picks 52 apples. Nick picks 25 apples. Who picks more apples?

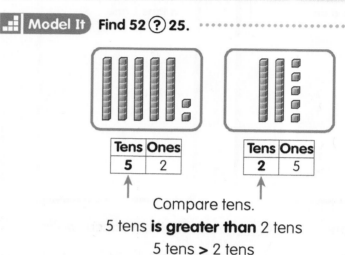

Model It Find 52 ⑦ 25.

Tens	Ones
5	2

Tens	Ones
2	5

Compare tens.

5 tens **is greater than** 2 tens

5 tens > 2 tens

52 ⊘ 25

▶ **Mathematical Discourse**

1 *How are the numbers 52 and 25 the same? How are they different?*

They have the same two digits, 2 and 5. In 52, the 5 is in the tens place; in 25, the 5 is in the ones place. In 52, the 2 is in the ones place; in 25, the 2 is in the tens place.

2 *How does changing the position of the 2 change the value of the number?*

In 25, 2 is in the tens place and has a value of 20. In 52, 2 is in the ones place and has a value of 2. So 2 has a greater value when it is in the tens place than when it is in the ones place.

▶ **Hands-On Activity**

Use base-ten blocks to compare numbers.

Materials For each child: Place-Value Mat (Activity Sheet 27), base-ten blocks

- Have children model 52 and 25 with base-ten blocks, placing the blocks for each number in the appropriate columns of the place-value mat.

- Ask children to record each number on the place-value mat. Discuss that 52 has more tens and therefore is greater than 25.

Learn Together
Compare Numbers

Gabe collects 35 rocks.
Rose collects 39 rocks.
Who collects fewer rocks?

Model It Find 35 (?) 39.

Compare tens.
Tens are the same.
Compare ones.

Tens	Ones
3	**5**

Tens	Ones
3	**9**

5 ones **is less than** 9 ones
5 ones < 9 ones

35 (<) 39   5 (<) 9

Talk About It Do you agree? Why or why not?

Fred collects 35 rocks.
Buzz says Fred collects more rocks than Gabe.

147

▶ Fluency Practice

Find 10 more and 10 less with base-ten blocks.

Materials For each child: 10 More, 10 Less (Activity Sheet 26), base-ten blocks

- Display 2 tens blocks and ask: *How many?* [20] Show another tens block. Ask: *How many now?* [30] *What is the addition sentence?* [20 + 10 = 30]
- Remove one tens block. Ask: *How many now?* [20] *What is the subtraction sentence?* [30 − 10 = 20]
- Continue with other numbers of tens.
- Have children use Activity Sheet 26 (10 More, 10 Less) and base-ten blocks to practice adding and subtracting tens.

▶ Mathematical Discourse

3 *You know that 35 is less than 39. What else do you know about 35 and 39?*

Children might say that 39 is greater than 35 and that 35 is not equal to 39.

Step By Step

- Read aloud the problem at the top of the page. Ask children whether they need to find the number that is greater or less. Make the connection between *fewer* and *less than*.

Model It

- Direct children's attention to the place-value charts in Model It. Challenge children to describe how to use the charts to determine which number is less.
- Read aloud the text on the page. Explain that since both numbers have the same tens, you need to compare the ones.
- Encourage children to describe how they might compare the ones to see which number is less. Lead them to understand that since both numbers have 3 tens, the number with fewer ones is less.

> **SMP TIP Use Structure**
> As children work with tens and ones to compare two-digit numbers, they begin to build general mathematical rules. Using the concept of place-value to compare two numbers deepens their understanding of the structure within the number system. *(SMP 7)*

- Write 35 < 39 on the board. Show that the narrow end of the symbol points to the lesser number. Say: *35 is less than 39; Gabe collects fewer rocks than Rose.*

▶ **Mathematical Discourse 3**

Talk About It

- Read aloud Talk About It. Children may realize that Fred collects the same number of rocks as Gabe. Ask children what symbol to use to compare the numbers. [The equal sign; 35 = 35.]

▶ **Fluency Practice**

Ready Mathematics
PRACTICE AND PROBLEM SOLVING

Assign *Practice and Problem Solving* **pages 205–206** after students have completed this section.

Step By Step

- Read aloud the problem at the top of the page. Ask: *Do you find the number that is greater or less?* [greater] *How do you know?* [The question has the word "more" which relates to a greater number.]

- Direct children's attention to the quick drawing. Explain that a quick drawing is a fast way to show tens and ones. Each line stands for a ten and each circle is a one.

- Invite a volunteer to describe what the quick drawing shows. Ask a different child to explain why 48 is greater than 14.

▶ **Visual Model**

- Guide children to understand that since 48 is greater than 14, Jen has more coins than Kim. Ask Mathematical Discourse question 1 to look at this answer in a different way.

▶ **Mathematical Discourse 1**

- Work together with children to complete Problem 1. Children may quickly recognize that the number of tens and ones are the same in both numbers. Ask children what symbol they write for the phrase "is the same as." [The equal sign, =.]

- In Problem 2, children can make their own quick drawings to show that 23 < 27. Invite children to tell what their quick drawings show and how the drawings helped them to compare the numbers.

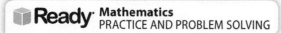
Ready Mathematics
PRACTICE AND PROBLEM SOLVING

Assign *Practice and Problem Solving* **pages 207–208** after students have completed this section.

Practice Together
Compare Numbers

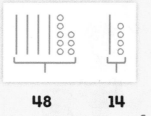

Jen has 48 coins. Kim has 14 coins. Who has more coins?

48   **14**

__4__ tens is greater than __1__ ten

48 ⊘ **14**

---

① Fill in the blanks, then write <, >, or = in the circle.

__7__ tens __2__ ones   __7__ tens __2__ ones

72 ⊜ **72**

---

② Write <, >, or = in the circle.

23 ⊘ **27**

148

▶ **Mathematical Discourse**

1 *Which girl has fewer coins? How do you know?*

Since 48 is greater than 14, 14 is less than 48. Since Kim's number of coins is less than Jen's, she has fewer coins.

▶ **Visual Model**

Compare numbers with the 120 chart.

Materials For each child: 120 Chart (Activity Sheet 23)

- Distribute Activity Sheet 23 (120 Chart).

- Explain that numbers are greater as you go across each row and then down each column.

- Show how to use the chart to verify that 48 is greater than 14. Explain that the row with 48 is closer to the bottom of the chart than the row with 14, so 48 is greater than 14.

- Allow children to use the chart to check answers to other problems in the lesson.

Practice by Myself
Compare Numbers

③ Fill in the blanks, then write <, >, or = in the circle.

<u>9</u> tens <u>3</u> ones   <u>4</u> tens <u>8</u> ones

93 ⟩ 48

④ Fill in the blanks, then write <, >, or = in the circle.

<u>1</u> tens <u>6</u> ones   <u>6</u> tens <u>0</u> ones

16 ⟨ 60

⑤ Write <, >, or = in the circle.

42 ⟨ 45

29 ⟩ 29

50 ⟩ 36

149

Step By Step

- Have children complete Problems 3 through 5 on their own. Remind them to compare tens first, then ones if the tens are the same.

▶ **English Language Learners**

- In Problem 3, children compare to find 93 > 48. Support is provided for children to write the number of tens and ones in each number.

▶ **Mathematical Discourse 2**

- In Problem 4, children compare 16 and 60. Children encounter a number with zero ones as they find 16 < 60.

- Supports are removed in Problem 5. Children choose a strategy to use to compare the number pairs.

▶ **English Language Learners**

Provide sentence frames for children to refer to as they work. Write the sentence frames on the board or on index cards:

___ is greater than ___

___ is less than ___

___ is equal to ___

As children gain familiarity with the language, they may discontinue using the frames.

▶ **Mathematical Discourse**

2 *In Problem 3, you found 93 > 48. How could you use the digits 9 and 3 to make a two-digit number that is less than 48? Explain your thinking.*

If you put 3 in the tens place and 9 in the ones place, you get a number that has 3 tens. Since 3 tens is less than 4 tens, 39 is less than 48.

Differentiated Instruction

▶ Quick Check and Remediation

Materials For each child: base-ten blocks, Number Paths (Activity Sheet 1), Place-Value Mat (Activity Sheet 27)

• Ask children to tell which number is greater, 54 or 38. [54]

• For children who are still struggling, use the chart below to guide remediation.

• After providing remediation, check children's understanding using the following problem: *Which number is greater, 46 or 62?* [62]

If the error is . . .	Children may . . .	To remediate . . .
38	have compared the digits in the ones place (8 > 4) instead of the digits in the tens place (5 > 3).	Provide children with base-ten blocks and Activity Sheet 27 (Place-Value Mat) to model 54 and 38 as tens and ones. Have them compare the number of tens to find 54 > 38.
38	have compared the digits in the tens place and incorrectly found 3 > 5.	Provide children with Activity Sheet 1 (Number Paths) that they can use to see the order of numbers from least to greatest (3 < 5 and 5 > 3).
38	have confused the meaning of greater and lesser.	Remind children of the relationship among *is greater than, more,* and >, and among *is less than, fewer,* and <. Have them use base-ten blocks to model 54 and 38 and try again to answer the question.

▶ Hands-On Activity

Model a two-digit number that is <, >, or = a given number.

Materials For each pair: 2 copies of Number Cards 0 to 11 (Activity Sheet 25), base-ten blocks

• Use Activity Sheet 25 (Number Cards 0 to 11) to make two sets of number cards for each pair of children: 0–9 and 1–9.

• Partners shuffle the sets of cards separately and place them facedown in two stacks: 1–9 for tens digits and 0–9 for ones digits. The symbol cards >, <, and = go in a separate facedown stack.

• Partner A turns over a number from each stack and models the two-digit number with base-ten blocks.

• Partner B turns over a symbol card and places it next to Partner A's two-digit number. Partner B uses base-ten blocks to model a number that makes a true comparison.

• Partners record the number sentence and repeat the activity, switching roles.

▶ Challenge Activity

Order two-digit numbers from least to greatest and greatest to least.

Materials For each pair: 2 copies of Number Cards 0 to 11 (Activity Sheet 25)

• Distribute number cards showing the numbers 0–9, and cards showing the symbols <, =, and > to pairs.

• Have children mix up the number cards and place them facedown. Have children put the symbol cards faceup.

• Have one child pick 6 number cards. Challenge the other child to build 3 two-digit numbers and use the symbol cards to show the three numbers in order from least to greatest. For example, the cards 2, 4, 1, 7, 8, and 6 can be arranged as 16 < 24 < 78. If the children agree on the comparison, have them record it.

• Have children reshuffle and redraw number cards. This time have them build 3 two-digit numbers and use symbols to order them from greatest to least. Then have children switch roles and continue playing as long as time allows.

Teacher Notes

Teacher-Toolbox.com

Overview

Assign the Lesson 22 Quiz and have children work independently to complete it.

Use the results of the quiz to assess children's understanding of the content of the lesson and to identify areas for reteaching. See the Lesson Pacing Guide at the beginning of the lesson and the Differentiated Instruction activities for suggested instructional resources.

Tested Skills

Assesses 1.NBT.B.3

Problems on this quiz require children to be able to compare two two-digit numbers based on the value of the tens and ones digits and write the *less than* (<), *greater than* (>), and *equal to* (=) symbols to record the comparisons. Children will also need to be familiar with the concepts "less than," "more than," and "the same as" and the equal sign (=) and understand two-digit numbers as tens and ones.

Ready® **Mathematics**

Lesson 22 Quiz Answer Key

Name _____

Solve.

1 Fill in the blanks, then write <, >, or = in the circle.

__5__ tens __6__ ones   __6__ tens __5__ ones

56 ⊘ 65

2 Fill in the blanks, then write <, >, or = in the circle.

__7__ tens __4__ ones   __2__ tens __9__ ones

74 ⊘ 29

Common Misconceptions and Errors

Errors may result if children:

- confuse the symbols $<$, $>$, and $=$ or their meaning.
- compare digits in the tens place only or the ones place only.
- compare digits in the ones place first.

Name _____

3 Fill in the blanks, then write $<$, $>$, or $=$ in the circle.

__5__ tens __0__ ones   __2__ tens __5__ ones

50 $\gt$ 25

4 Write $<$, $>$, or $=$ in the circle.

48 $\gt$ 46

57 $=$ 57

86 $\lt$ 90

5 Mel has 27 shells.
Ann has 72 shells.
Who has more shells?

Mel   Ann

__2__ tens __7__ ones   __7__ tens __2__ ones

27 $\lt$ 72

Ann has more shells.

2

LESSON OVERVIEW

Lesson 23
Add Tens to Any Number

CCSS Focus

Domain
Number and Operations in Base Ten

Cluster
C. Use place value understanding and properties of operations to add and subtract.

Standard
1.NBT.C.4 Add within 100, including adding a two-digit number and a one-digit number, and adding a two-digit number and a multiple of 10, using concrete models or drawings and strategies based on place value, properties of operations, and/or the relationship between addition and subtraction; relate the strategy to a written method and explain the reasoning used. Understand that in adding two-digit numbers, one adds tens and tens, ones and ones; and sometimes it is necessary to compose a ten.

Additional Standards
1.NBT.B.2a, 1.NBT.B.2c, 1.NBT.B.3 (See page B3 for full text.)

Standards for Mathematical Practice (SMP)
2 Reason abstractly and quantitatively.

3 Construct viable arguments and critique the reasoning of others.

4 Model with mathematics.

6 Attend to precision.

7 Look for and make use of structure.

8 Look for and express regularity in repeated reasoning.

Lesson Objectives

Content Objectives
- Add multiples of ten to any two-digit number.
- Apply strategies to addition of two-digit numbers.
- Model addition involving tens.

Language Objectives
- Use base-ten blocks, quick-draw diagrams, number bonds, or place value charts to decompose two-digit numbers into tens and ones.
- Tell how the different approaches used by others to add tens to any number are alike and how they are different.

Prerequisite Skills

- Find 10 more and 10 less than a given number.
- Distinguish between the tens and ones places in a two-digit number.

Lesson Vocabulary

There is no new vocabulary. Review the following key terms.

- **ones** single units or objects.
- **tens** groups of ten ones.

Learning Progression

In Kindergarten children decompose teen numbers into a ten and some ones, understanding that 10 ones can be seen as a group of ten.

In Grade 1 children further their work in the base-ten system by computing sums within 100. Concrete and visual models support their understanding of place value and help them make a connection between the visual tens and the digit that represents a group of tens.

In this lesson children build on prior work with finding 10 more and 10 less by adding multiples of ten to a given two-digit number. They become increasingly flexible in their use of strategies, representing sums in many forms and justifying them with physical and visual models.

In Grade 2 children expand their work in the base-ten system. They add and subtract multi-digit numbers, building on their understanding of place value and the strategies they developed in Grade 1.

Lesson Pacing Guide

Whole Class Instruction

Day 1
45–60 minutes

Introduction

Use What You Know
• Explore It *25 min*
• Try It *20 min*

Day 2
45–60 minutes

Modeled Instruction

Explore Together
• Example Problem *5 min*
• Model It *20 min*
• Hands-On Activity *20 min*

Practice and Problem Solving
Assign pages 211–212.

Day 3
45–60 minutes

Guided Instruction

Learn Together
• Example Problem *5 min*
• Model It *10 min*
• Talk About It *15 min*
• Visual Model *15 min*

Practice and Problem Solving
Assign pages 213–214.

Day 4
45–60 minutes

Guided Practice

Practice Together
• Example Problem *5 min*
• Problems 1–2 *10 min*
• Concept Extension *15 min*
• Fluency Practice *15 min*

Practice and Problem Solving
Assign pages 215–216.

Day 5
45–60 minutes

Independent Practice

Practice by Myself
• Problems 3–5 *15 min*
• Quick Check and Remediation *15 min*
• Hands-On or Challenge Activity *15 min*

Teacher-Toolbox: Lesson Quiz
Lesson 23 Quiz

Materials for Lesson Activities

Per child: 37 counters, base-ten blocks
Activity Sheet 3, Activity Sheet 23*, Activity Sheet 25, Activity Sheet 27*, Activity Sheet 28

Per pair: base-ten blocks, set of cards containing varied two-digit numbers
Activity Sheet 24, Activity Sheet 25, Activity Sheet 27

For display: none

*Used for more than one activity.

Small Group Differentiation

Teacher-Toolbox.com

Reteach
Ready Prerequisite Lessons *45–90 min*

Grade K
• Lesson 22 Count Teen Numbers
• Lesson 24 Count to 100 by Tens

Teacher-led Activities
Tools for Instruction *15–20 min*

Grade 1 *(Lesson 23)*
• Two-Digit Addition Without Regrouping
• Counting Up to 20 Objects
• Count Forward by 1s

Student-led Activities
Math Center Activities *30–40 min*

Grade K *(Lessons 22 and 24)*
• K.08 Pick and Write
• K.30 Count by Tens
• K.31 Tens Bingo

Grade 1 *(Lesson 23)*
• 1.36 Add Tens to a Number

Personalized Learning

i-Ready.com

Independent
i-Ready Lessons* *10–20 min*

Grade 1 *(Lesson 23)*
• Regrouping Tens as Ones
• Part 1: Counting to 20
• Part 2: Counting to 20

* i-Ready lessons may be updated during the 2016–2017 school year. Updated references will be on the Teacher-Toolbox.

Introduction

Activity Add Multiples of Ten

Objective

Relate adding a multiple of ten to finding 10 more.

Materials for each child

• base-ten blocks

• 37 counters

• 120 Chart (Activity Sheet 23)

Overview

Children solve problems and recognize how their strategies lead to adding a 10.

Step By Step

Explore It

Pose the problem.

• Tell children that Maria has a collection of sea shells and is going to the beach to collect some more shells. Then read the problem on the Student Book page aloud: *Maria has 17 shells. She finds 20 more. How many shells does Maria have now?*

Solve the problem.

• Tell children they may use counters, base-ten blocks, 120 charts, or drawings on the workmat on the Student Book page to help them solve the problem.

• Observe as children work to see if they apply what they know about 10 more to find 20 more.

• Some children may add 20 counters and recount. Others may count on by tens or by ones from 17, while some children may recognize that adding 2 tens increases the tens digit by 2.

Share strategies.

• Have children present their solutions and strategies to the class. Use your observations of their work to help guide the discussion as children share their reasoning.

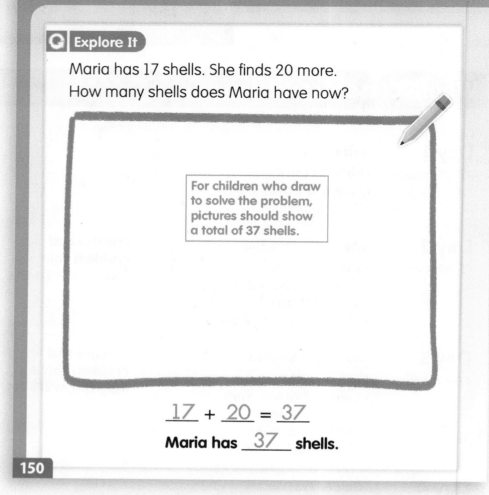

Explore It

Maria has 17 shells. She finds 20 more. How many shells does Maria have now?

For children who draw to solve the problem, pictures should show a total of 37 shells.

17 + 20 = 37

Maria has ___37___ shells.

150

• Encourage multiple children to share, ensuring that the strategies presented are representative of the different ways children solved the problem.

Explore the concept.

• Have children model 17 as tens and ones with base-ten blocks.

• Write "17 + 20" on the board and discuss how this addition represents the problem. Show two additional ten blocks and ask: *When I add 1 ten to 17, how many tens are there?* [2] *When I add a second ten, how many tens are there then?* [3]

• Relate adding 20 to adding 10 (or finding 10 more than a number). Help children count on by tens from 17, saying 27 when 1 ten is added, then 37 when 1 more ten is added.

• Have children write the number sentence and complete the statement to show how many shells Maria has in her collection.

Use What You Know

Add Tens to Any Number

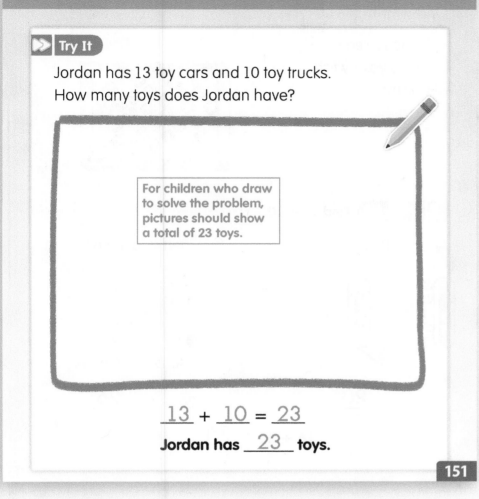

>> Try It

Jordan has 13 toy cars and 10 toy trucks.
How many toys does Jordan have?

For children who draw
to solve the problem,
pictures should show
a total of 23 toys.

$\underline{13} + \underline{10} = \underline{23}$

Jordan has __23__ toys.

151

Step By Step

Try It

Pose the problem.

- Read the problem on the Student Book page aloud: *Jordan has 13 toy cars and 10 toy trucks. How many toys does Jordan have?*

Solve the problem.

- Allow children sufficient time to solve the problem using any strategy they prefer. Encourage children to use counters, base-ten blocks, 120 charts, or drawings on the workmat on the Student Book page to help them solve the problem.

Explore the concept.

- Help children write a number sentence to represent the problem. Ask them to share the strategy they used to find their solution, then complete the sentence on the page.

- Look for the ways in which children solve the problem without expectation that all children will be successful. Use the Hands-On Activity and the Visual Model in the lesson as additional supports for those children who struggle with the concept of adding tens to a number.

- Allowing children to model the addition in multiple ways will help them connect the model to the problem and number sentence.

Modeled Instruction

Step By Step

- Read the problem aloud. Ask children how adding 10 is like finding 10 more than a number.

- Complete the Hands-On Activity to reinforce the concept of adding tens and adding ones.

▶ **Hands-On Activity**

Model It

- Draw attention to Model It. Compare the process shown to how children used blocks to add in the Hands-On Activity. Discuss with children how the blocks and the number sentences below them are related.

- Remind children that there are many ways to think about finding a sum. Ask Mathematical Discourse question 1 to engage children in utilizing and sharing mental strategies.

▶ **Mathematical Discourse 1**

SMP TIP Look for and Use Structure
Consistently emphasizing the structure of the base-ten system of numeration helps children gradually internalize that structure. This enables them to use this understanding to add tens and ones in two-digit numbers, and later as they explore addition and subtraction involving composing and decomposing a ten. *(SMP 7)*

Ready Mathematics
PRACTICE AND PROBLEM SOLVING

Assign *Practice and Problem Solving* **pages 211–212** after students have completed this section.

Explore Together
Add Tens to Any Number

Eli has 16 red fish
and 10 yellow fish.
How many fish in all?

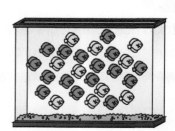

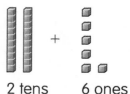 **Model It** Find 16 + 10.

Add the tens.   Then add the ones.

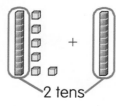

2 tens   2 tens   6 ones

$10 + 10 = \underline{20}$ $20 + 6 = \underline{26}$

$$16 + 10 = \underline{26}$$

152

▶ **Mathematical Discourse**

1 *What are some ways you can add 16 + 10 in your head?*

Some children may respond that it is like finding 10 more so you just make the tens in 16 one more. Others may remember using a 120 chart and "see" 26 right below 16.

▶ **Hands-On Activity**

Model two-digit numbers on a place-value mat.

Materials For each child: base-ten blocks, Place-Value Mat (Activity Sheet 27), Number Cards 0 to 11 (Activity Sheet 25)

- Distribute Activity Sheet 27 (Place-Value Mat), cards showing the digits 0 to 9 from Activity Sheet 25 (Number Cards 0 to 11), 2 tens blocks, and 16 ones blocks to each child.

- Have children model 16 on the place-value mat with base-ten blocks. If children use 16 ones blocks, have

---

them compose a ten by removing 10 ones from the ones column and adding a tens block to the tens column. Then have them place the corresponding digit card under each place to indicate how many tens and ones there are.

- Tell children to add ten more ones blocks. Ask: *How are adding 1 ten and adding 10 ones alike?* Reinforce that when 10 ones are added, the ones can be composed into a ten. Have children compose a ten by removing 10 ones from the ones column and placing a tens block in the tens column.

- Have children place digit cards to represent the number in each place. Discuss that adding 10 increases the tens place by 1 ten, so the digit increases by one. There were no additional ones added, so the ones digit does not change.

Learn Together
Add Tens to Any Number

50 blue balloons
and 13 red balloons.

How many balloons altogether?

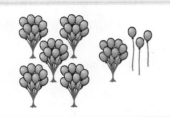

🔲 **Model It** Find 50 + 13. ·········

Write the tens and ones.

50 + [13]

[10] [3]

(50 + 10)+ 3

Add the tens.
Then add the ones.

50 + 10 = 60

60 + __3__ = __63__

50 + 13 = __63__

💬 **Talk About It** What is wrong? ·········

20 baseballs and 12 footballs. How many balls?

What's wrong?   2 + 10 + 2 = 14

▶ Show the right way.   __20__ + __10__ + __2__ = __32__

153

Step By Step

- Read aloud the problem at the top of the page.

▶ **Mathematical Discourse 2**

- Engage children in sharing strategies they could use to solve this problem. Listen for ideas expressed that are explored in the Visual Model, then use the Visual Model activity to validate the strategies and to provide children a way to "see" the strategies discussed.

▶ **Visual Model**

Model It

- Direct children's attention to Model It. Discuss how decomposing 13 in the number bond is like breaking it apart in the number sentence addition.

Talk About It

- Allow children to discuss Talk About It with a partner before discussing it as a class. Encourage children to clearly describe the error and justify a correct solution strategy.

📖 **Ready** Mathematics
PRACTICE AND PROBLEM SOLVING

Assign *Practice and Problem Solving* **pages 213–214** after students have completed this section.

▶ **Visual Model**

Explore strategies to add 2 two-digit numbers.

Materials For each child: 1 counter, 120 Chart (Activity Sheet 23)

- Have children place a counter on the number 13 in the 120 chart. Tell them to move their finger to show 10 more. Write:

+10
13 → 23

- Have children move their fingers to show 10 more, continuing to add to the model until 5 tens are added.

+10 +10 +10 +10 +10
13 23 33 43 53 63

- Discuss how adding 5 tens is like adding 1 ten five times. Recognizing the repeated reasoning involved provides children with a mental strategy for adding multiples of ten to any number.

- Have children place a counter on the number 50 in their charts. Lead them to explore ways to add 13.

- Ask: *Do you think it is easier to start at 50 and count on 13, or start at 13 and count on to 50? Why?* [Some children may think it is easier to start at 50 and then count on 1 ten and then 3 ones. Others may think it is easier to start at 13 as then they only need to count on 5 tens and 0 ones.]

- Write 13 + 50 = 63 and 50 + 13 = 63 on the board. Help children recognize that the commutative property applies to multi-digit numbers just as it does to single-digit numbers.

▶ **Mathematical Discourse**

2 *How is this problem the same as and how is it different from 16 + 10?*

Children should say a teen number is an addend in both sentences, however the other addend in this problem is greater than ten. Some children may notice that both problems involve adding a teen number and a tens number.

👥 Guided Practice

Step By Step

- Read the example problem aloud. Ask children which number sentence the quick drawing represents. [10 + 19] After sharing their ideas, ask children how to change the quick drawing to show 20 + 9.

- Read Problem 1 and discuss the way 32 is decomposed in the number bond. Reinforce the commutative property by asking: *Would the sum be different if we added 32 to 20? Explain.* Ask Mathematical Discourse question 1 to support previous work adding multiples of ten.

▶ **Mathematical Discourse 1**

- Present Problem 2 and engage children in describing the strategies and/or models that help them solve the problem. Ask each child to draw a picture of the way they thought about the problem.

> **SMP TIP Model with Mathematics**
> Relate the models children have explored to each other, to the problems they model, and to a number sentence. This facilitates children's ability to independently model a problem situation. *(SMP 4)*

▶ **Concept Extension**

▶ **Fluency Practice**

Ready **Mathematics**
PRACTICE AND PROBLEM SOLVING

Assign *Practice and Problem Solving* **pages 215–216** after students have completed this section.

Practice Together
Add Tens to Any Number

> 10 blue marbles and 19 green marbles. How many marbles in all?
>
> $10 + 10 = \underline{20}$
>
> $20 + 9 = \underline{29}$
>
> $10 + 19 = \underline{29}$

1 20 black cars and 32 white cars. What is the total number of cars?

$20 + 32 = \underline{52}$

2 29 small ants and 10 big ants. How many ants are there?

$\underline{39} = 29 + 10$

▶ **Mathematical Discourse**

1 *How does knowing how to add 30 + 20 help you add 32 + 20?*
Children may say 30 + 20 is 50 and 32 is 2 more than 30, so add 2 to 50.

▶ **Fluency Practice**
Practice adding tens.

Materials For each child: Practice Adding Tens (Activity Sheet 28); optional: counters, base-ten blocks, Place-Value Mat (Activity Sheet 27), Number Bond Mat (Activity Sheet 3), 120 Chart (Activity Sheet 23)

- Provide children with Activity Sheet 28 for practice adding multiples of ten.

- Make base-ten blocks, place-value mats, number bond mats, counters, and 120 charts available for children to use. Remind children to show their thinking in the box provided or to draw a picture showing their thinking.

▶ **Concept Extension**

Explore patterns involved in adding multiples of ten.

Write the additions vertically on the board:

24	34	44		
+ 10	+ 10	+ 10	+	+

Have children solve the first two and then challenge them to find the missing numbers for the other addition problems. Lead them to see the patterns that evolve when 10 is added repeatedly.

Extend this pattern to adding multiples of 10:

24	24	24		
+ 10	+ 20	+ 30	+	+

Compare the two models discussing similarities and differences. Refer to adding tens on a 120 chart, reinforcing the concept that adding one ten 2, 3, 4, . . . times is like adding 2, 3, 4, . . . tens to a number.

Practice by Myself
Add Tens to Any Number

3 70 small paper clips
and 14 big paper clips.
How many paper clips?

||||||| + :::

__84__ = 70 + 14

4 40 green frogs and 25 yellow frogs.
How many frogs?

40 + 25 = __65__

5 17 triangles and 20 squares.
How many shapes?

17 + 20 = __37__

155

©Curriculum Associates, LLC   Copying is not permitted

Step By Step

- Before children begin work on this page, review the models used in this lesson. Emphasize that children are free to use whatever way helps them solve the problems.

- Read each problem aloud, pointing out that these problems are similar to the ones children solved on previous pages.

▶ **English Language Learners**

- You may wish to build on previous discussions about equality by discussing the position of the totals in the number sentences in each of the problems. Ask children to explain why it is all right to show the totals these two ways.

- Have children work independently to solve each problem, offering support when necessary.

- For Problem 4, observe to see if any children record the total as 605. Support those children by asking how 60 and 5 more would look as a quick drawing or how it would look in a 120 chart.

- Ask children who solve Problem 5 without showing their work to explain the strategy they used.

▶ **Mathematical Discourse 2**

▶ **English Language Learners**

Reinforce the vocabulary used for the models shown on this page by replicating the quick drawing from Problem 3 on the board and writing the words "quick drawing" above it. Then draw the number bond in Problem 4 on the board and write "number bond" above it.

▶ **Mathematical Discourse**

2 *What are some different ways to add 17 + 20?*

Children might suggest adding 1 ten, 2 tens, and 7 ones to get 37. Others might count on by tens: 17, 27, 37. Another possible strategy is to decompose 17: 10 + 7 + 20 = 37.

Differentiated Instruction

▶ Quick Check and Remediation

Materials For each child: base-ten blocks, 120 Chart (Activity Sheet 23), Place-Value Mat (Activity Sheet 27)

• Ask children to show the sum and strategy they used for finding 46 + 30. [76]

• For children who are still struggling, use the chart below to guide remediation.

• After providing remediation, check children's understanding using the following problem: *Find 50 + 37.* [87]

If the error is . . .	Children may . . .	To remediate . . .
706	have combined 70 and 6 without attending to place value.	Have children model the problem with base-ten blocks on a place-value mat. Remove the ones and ask children how many tens and ones there are. Place a 7 and 0 in the proper place-value locations. Add the 6 ones and ask how many ones there are. Place the digit 6 in the ones place. Help children see that 70 + 6 = 76 since 0 + 6 = 6.
49	have added 30 as 3 ones rather than as 3 tens.	Have children model the addition using a 120 chart, breaking 30 into 10 + 10 + 10. Help children see that 3 groups of ten, not 3 ones, are added.

▶ Hands-On Activity

Model addition sentences.

Materials For each pair: base-ten blocks, Tens Cards (Activity Sheet 24), Number Cards 0 to 11, (Activity Sheet 25), Place-Value Mat (Activity Sheet 27), and a set of cards containing varied two-digit numbers

• Provide children with tens cards showing the numbers 10–100, number cards showing the digits 0–9, and the other materials.

• Set the tens cards and the two-digit number cards facedown next to each other. Have one child pick a number from one pile, model it with base-ten blocks on Activity Sheet 27 (Place-Value Mat), and place digit cards under each place to show the number. The partner chooses a number from the other pile and adds base-ten blocks to the place-value mat to model it.

• Together, children adjust the digit cards to show the sum of their two numbers. If a sum is greater than 100, allow children to attempt the challenge, or place the cards under the piles and draw again. Repeat switching the starting partner until all cards have been used.

• Optional: Have children record the additions on a whiteboard or paper.

▶ Challenge Activity

Explore patterns.

• Challenge children to expand on the Concept Extension activity earlier in the lesson, in which they explored the patterns when multiples of ten are added to a number.

• Have children create as many different patterns as they can, such as: consistently adding 20 (or 30, 40, etc.); what the pattern looks like using numbers in the hundreds; finding patterns when multiples of 100 are added, etc.

• Encourage children to be creative in finding patterns and have them record the patterns they discover.

Teacher Notes

Teacher-Toolbox.com

Overview

Assign the Lesson 23 Quiz and have children work independently to complete it.

Use the results of the quiz to assess children's understanding of the content of the lesson and to identify areas for reteaching. See the Lesson Pacing Guide at the beginning of the lesson and the Differentiated Instruction activities for suggested instructional resources.

Tested Skills

Assesses 1.NBT.C.4

Problems on this quiz require children to be able to add multiples of ten to any two-digit number using different models and strategies. Children will also need to be familiar with finding 10 more and 10 less than a number and distinguishing between the tens and ones place in a two-digit number.

Ready® **Mathematics**

Lesson 23 Quiz Answer Key

Name _____

Solve.

1. 60 blue butterflies and 12 yellow butterflies.
   How many butterflies?

   60 + 12 = <u>72</u>

2. 46 small fish and 50 big fish.
   How many fish?

   <u>96</u> **= 46 + 50**

Common Misconceptions and Errors

Errors may result if children:

- ignore the zero in a multiple of ten and add the digit in the tens place to the digit in the ones place.

- ignore or do not attend to place value.

Name _____

Solve.

3 38 brown cows and 20 spotted cows.
How many cows?

38 + 20 = _58_

4 23 circles and 60 squares.
How many shapes?

_83_ **= 23 + 60**

5 One day Li's hens lay 32 eggs.
The next day the hens lay 30 eggs.
How many eggs do the hens lay in all?

32 + 30 = _62_

The hens lay _62_ eggs in all.

CCSS Focus

Domain
Number and Operations in Base Ten

Cluster
C. Use place value understanding and properties of operations to add and subtract.

Standard
1.NBT.C.4 Add within 100, including adding a two-digit number and a one-digit number, and adding a two-digit number and a multiple of 10, using concrete models or drawings and strategies based on place value, properties of operations, and/or the relationship between addition and subtraction; relate the strategy to a written method and explain the reasoning used. Understand that in adding two-digit numbers, one adds tens and tens, ones and ones; and sometimes it is necessary to compose a ten.

Additional Standard
1.OA.A.2 (See page B3 for full text.)

Standards for Mathematical Practice (SMP)
2 Reason abstractly and quantitatively.

4 Model with mathematics.

6 Attend to precision.

7 Look for and make use of structure.

8 Look for and express regularity in repeated reasoning.

Lesson Objectives

Content Objectives
- Model addition of two-digit numbers.
- Add two-digit numbers without regrouping.

Language Objectives
- Use base-ten blocks, quick-draw diagrams, number bonds, or place value charts to decompose two-digit numbers into tens and ones.
- Record the sum of the tens and the sum of the ones and then add these sums together to find the total when adding two-digit numbers.
- Talk with a partner about strategies used to solve a problem.

Prerequisite Skills
- Add ten to any number.
- Model a two-digit number as tens and ones.

Lesson Vocabulary
There is no new vocabulary. Review the following key terms.
- **ones** single units or objects.
- **tens** groups of ten ones.

Learning Progression

In Kindergarten children decompose teen numbers into 10 ones and some additional ones, laying the foundation for using tens and ones.

In Grade 1 children fluently add within 10 and then 20 using concrete models, drawings, and strategies. They apply addition skills to problem solving situations.

In this lesson children compute sums within 100 with attention to place value and the base-ten system of numeration. Adding tens and ones separately reinforces previous work with place value and prepares children for finding sums of any two-digit numbers. Strategies used for single-digit computations and for adding tens to any number support the methods children use for two-digit addition and provide a basis for understanding adding tens and adding ones.

In Grade 2 children work toward fluency with addition and subtraction within 100 and extend this work to addition and subtraction within 1,000, including situations where composing or decomposing a ten is required.

Lesson Pacing Guide

Whole Class Instruction

Day 1
45–60 minutes

Introduction
Use What You Know
• Explore It *25 min*
• Try It *20 min*

Day 2
45–60 minutes

Modeled Instruction
Explore Together
• Example Problem *5 min*
• Model It *25 min*
• Visual Model *15 min*

Practice and Problem Solving
Assign pages 219–220.

Day 3
45–60 minutes

Guided Instruction
Learn Together
• Example Problem *5 min*
• Model It *15 min*
• Talk About It *10 min*
• Visual Model *15 min*

Practice and Problem Solving
Assign pages 221–222.

Day 4
45–60 minutes

Guided Practice
Practice Together
• Example Problem *10 min*
• Problems 1–2 *15 min*
• Fluency Practice *20 min*

Practice and Problem Solving
Assign pages 223–224.

Day 5
45–60 minutes

Independent Practice
Practice by Myself
• Problems 3–5 *10 min*
• Hands-On Activity *10 min*
• Quick Check and Remediation *10 min*
• Hands-On or Challenge Activity *15 min*

Teacher-Toolbox: Lesson Quiz
Lesson 24 Quiz

Materials for Lesson Activities

Per child: 1 bag, 21–44 counters, base-ten blocks
Activity Sheet 19, Activity Sheet 29

Per pair: base-ten blocks, 10 cards containing two-digit addition problems
Activity Sheet 3, Activity Sheet 19, Activity Sheet 27

For display: none

Small Group Differentiation

Teacher-Toolbox.com

Reteach
Ready Prerequisite Lessons *45–90 min*

Grade K
• Lesson 24 Count to 100 by Tens
• Lesson 25 Count to 100 by Ones

Teacher-led Activities
Tools for Instruction *15–20 min*

Grade 1 *(Lesson 24)*
• Two-Digit Addition Without Regrouping
• Identifying Numerals to 10
• Counting Up to 20 Objects

Student-led Activities
Math Center Activities *30–40 min*

Grade K *(Lessons 24 and 25)*
• K.30 Count by Tens
• K.31 Tens Bingo
• K.32 Count by Ones Vocabulary
• K.33 Keep Counting

Grade 1 *(Lesson 24)*
• 1.37 Add Tens and Ones

Personalized Learning

i-Ready.com

Independent
i-Ready Lessons* *10–20 min*

Grade 1 *(Lesson 24)*
• Regrouping Tens as Ones
• Joining Sets to Add

* i-Ready lessons may be updated during the 2016–2017 school year. Updated references will be on the Teacher-Toolbox.

Introduction

Activity How Many Counters?

Objective
Apply known strategies to add two-digit numbers.

Materials for each child
• bag containing 21–44 counters

Overview
Children solve a problem, share strategies, and compare the problem to previous ones.

Step By Step

Explore It

Pose the problem.

• Provide each child with a bag containing 21–44 counters. To avoid regrouping situations, the number of counters in each bag should have a ones digit that is between 1 and 5. Tell children that this activity involves three steps:

1) First have children find the number of counters in their bag, place them on the workmat on the Student Book page, and record the number.

2) Next have children work with a partner. Have the partners tell the number of counters they each have and record that number on the Student Book page.

3) Then have partners combine their counters, find the number of combined counters, and record the total on the Student Book page.

Solve the problem.

• Observe the strategies children use. Do they count individual counters or group them into tens and ones? Do they combine both sets of counters and recount? Do they recount using tens and ones or count all the counters? Do they add the numbers from each bag? Observe without giving suggestions, allowing children to use their own methods. Use your observations to question groups during class discussion.

Use What You Know
Add Tens and Add Ones

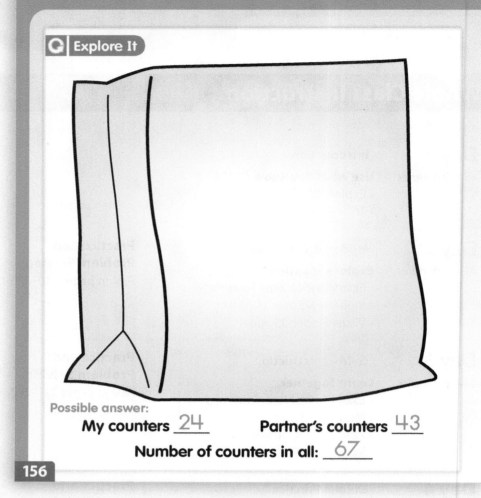

Explore It

Possible answer:

My counters 24   **Partner's counters** 43

Number of counters in all: 67

156

Share solution strategies.

• Invite children to share the ways they counted the number of counters in their individual bags. Discuss the advantages of grouping them in tens and ones.

• Have pairs of children share the strategies they used to find the total of all counters in *both* bags, recording on the board those that involve writing a number sentence and finding the total. Compare the various strategies, discussing the similar elements of each one.

Compare addends in addition problems.

• Examine the number sentences on the board. Make sure children notice that each is an addition sentence.

• Write a number sentence on the board that shows adding a multiple of ten to a two-digit number, such as 20 + 27 = 47. Briefly discuss the strategies children used in the previous lesson to solve this type of problem.

• Compare the number sentences and strategies used in this activity to the problems children solved when adding tens to any number. Point out that in these problems, both addends have numbers other than 0 in the ones place. Discuss how with all of these problems, you add the tens to tens and ones to ones.

Use What You Know
Add Tens and Add Ones

>> Try It

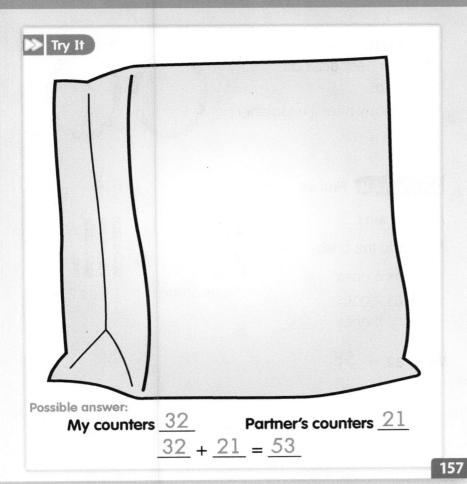

Possible answer:

My counters 32 **Partner's counters** 21

32 + 21 = 53

157

Step By Step

Try It

Pose the problem.

• Have pairs of children switch bags with other pairs to create a situation that is different from the problem they solved during the activity.

• Tell children that they will once again:

  1) find and record the number of counters in their own bag;

  2) record the number of counters in their partner's bag;

  3) combine their counters with those of their partner, and find and record the total number of counters in both bags.

Solve the problem.

• Ask children to write a number sentence to represent the number of counters in both bags and the total.

• Scan the room as children work, taking note of those who add numerically and those who count all counters. Be prepared to support children who need additional help in seeing and combining tens and ones. Discuss what each number in the number sentences represents.

Modeled Instruction

Step By Step

- Read aloud the problem at the top of the page. Have children solve the problem using any strategy they want.

- Invite volunteers to share solutions and strategies. Prompt children with questions such as: *Why did you choose that strategy? Where did those extra ones you added come from?* Engage the class to ask questions of or challenge peers to justify a strategy.

Model It

- Draw attention to Model It. Point out that the base-ten blocks model how to break the two-digit numbers into tens and ones, so the tens can be added together and the ones can be added together.

- Show children how the vertical addition sentence helps group tens together and ones together. Ask them to solve the problem by writing "5 tens 8 ones" as a number.

▶ **Visual Model 1**

▶ **Mathematical Discourse 1**

> **SMP TIP Repeated Reasoning**
> As children explore different models for addition, they begin to see repeatedly that when tens and ones are present, tens are added to tens and ones are added to ones. As they work on problems in the lesson, emphasize the reasoning that when tens are added to tens the result is a greater number of tens; and that the same applies to the ones. *(SMP 8)*

 Mathematics
PRACTICE AND PROBLEM SOLVING

Assign *Practice and Problem Solving* **pages 219–220** after students have completed this section.

Explore Together
Add Tens and Add Ones

> A necklace has 26 beads.
> Another necklace has
> 32 beads.
> How many beads altogether?

Model It **Find 26 + 32.**

Add the tens.

Then add the ones.

$$\begin{array}{r} 2 \text{ tens } 6 \text{ ones} \\ + \ 3 \text{ tens } 2 \text{ ones} \\ \hline 5 \text{ tens } 8 \text{ ones} = \underline{58} \end{array}$$

26 + 32 = <u>58</u>

 +

2 tens 6 ones   3 tens 2 ones

158

▶ **Mathematical Discourse**

1 *How is adding tens and adding ones like adding tens to any number? How is it different?*

In both types of problems you add tens to tens and ones to ones. When you add tens to any number, one of the addends has 0 ones.

▶ **Visual Model 1**

Count on with the hundreds chart.

Materials For each child: Hundreds Chart (Activity Sheet 19), 3 counters

- Present the strategy of using a hundreds chart to count on. Display 26 + 32 and 32 = 3 tens 2 ones.

- Have children place a counter on the 26 in the chart. Model on the board counting on the 3 tens in 32. Children use a second counter to show the same jumps on the hundreds chart.

26   36   46   56

- Then children use a third counter to show counting on 2 more, and record:

56   57   58

- Repeat with other addition problems.

Learn Together
Add Tens and Add Ones

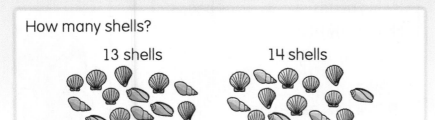

How many shells?

13 shells   14 shells

▦ Model It Find 13 + 14.

Add the tens.
Then add the ones.

10 + 3
10 + 4
‾‾‾‾‾
20 + 7 = _27_

13 + 14 = _27_

💬 Talk About It Who is right? How do you know?

Boom: 2 tens 5 ones
       + 1 ten 3 ones
       3 tens 8 ones

Buzz: 20 + 5
     10 + 3
     30 + 8

159

▶ Visual Model 2

Help children build a visual strategy for adding.

- Write the addition sentence 13 + 14 on the board. Ask children to look at the number bonds on the Student Book page, tell what parts are added together, and explain why. Model adding ones to ones and tens to tens on the board by drawing:

13 + 14

- Ask: *When you add the two ones digits, what are you really adding? Why? Would it make sense to add a 1 to the 4? Explain.*

- Write several other addition problems and have children model adding tens, then adding ones.

▶ Mathematical Discourse

2 *What way makes it easiest for you to add? Why?*

Listen for sound reasoning in the choices children make. If they respond that "it is easier" press them to explain what makes it easier than the other methods. Make sure their choices demonstrate an understanding of addition within place values.

Step By Step

- Read the example problem aloud and ask children to model it with a number sentence. Discuss the reason for using addition, and emphasize that you can add in any order.

Model It

- Direct attention to Model It. Ask how the number bonds are like the base-ten blocks on the previous page. Emphasize that both models show ways to break numbers into tens and ones.

- Ask children to compare the vertical addition sentence on this page with the one on the previous page. Guide them to recognize that both show adding tens and adding ones. On the previous page, the words "tens" and "ones" are used. This page uses numbers that show the value of the tens and ones.

- Have children fill in the blanks.

Talk About It

- Allow children to discuss Talk About It with a partner before sharing ideas with the class. Guide the class to conclude that both Buzz and Boom are correct.

> **Misconception Alert**
> Some children may think that there is only one correct way to show adding tens and adding ones.

▶ **Visual Model 2**

▶ **Mathematical Discourse 2**

> **SMP TIP Look for Structure**
> Help children see how closely the different representations are related to reinforce the structure of mathematics and build a strong sense of number. *(SMP 7)*

Ready Mathematics
PRACTICE AND PROBLEM SOLVING

Assign *Practice and Problem Solving* **pages 221–222** after students have completed this section.

👥 **Guided Practice**

Step By Step

- Read the example problem aloud. Ask children how the 34 beads are modeled. Lead them to see that 34 is modeled as 30 + 4 and with a quick drawing. Repeat for 55.

> **SMP TIP Reason Abstractly**
> Reinforce the importance of adding sticks to sticks and circles to circles (tens to tens and ones to ones). As children internalize that 1 stick + 2 circles results in 12 and not 3, they practice abstract reasoning about adding like terms. Children will encounter other types of like terms, such as denominators of fractions and variables in number sentences, in later math courses. *(SMP 2)*

- Read Problem 1, pointing out that this model is like the number sentence in the example problem with some numbers missing. Discuss what numbers belong in the blanks, making sure children record 1 ten as 10.

- Have children complete the number bonds in Problem 2 and ask them to describe ways they can use the bonds to find the total.

- Remind children that they are free to use models or strategies not shown on this page that help them think about addition of two-digit numbers.

- If children struggle to get started, suggest that they make quick drawings to picture the tens and ones in each number.

▶ **Mathematical Discourse 1**

▶ **Fluency Practice**

Ready· Mathematics
PRACTICE AND PROBLEM SOLVING

Assign *Practice and Problem Solving* **pages 223–224** after students have completed this section.

Add Tens and Add Ones

34 big beads and 55 small beads.
How many beads?

30 + 4
50 + 5

$\boxed{80} + \boxed{9} = \boxed{89}$

34 + 55 = __89__

① 47 brown cows and
12 black cows.
How many cows in all?

47 + 12 = __59__

40 + $\boxed{7}$
$\boxed{10}$ + **2**
$\boxed{50}$ + $\boxed{9}$ = $\boxed{59}$

② 17 green pencils and
21 yellow pencils.
How many pencils?

__38__ = **17 + 21**

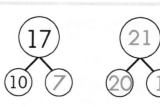

160

▶ **Mathematical Discourse**

1 *How do picture models help you think about an addition?*

Children may respond that the picture helps them "see" the parts that need to be added. Some may say that the sticks help them think of the digit for the tens place. Others may like the way the arrows show jumps when they count on.

▶ **Fluency Practice**

Choose strategies to solve addition problems.

Materials For each child: Practice Adding Tens and Ones (Activity Sheet 29)

Distribute the activity sheet and tell children that they are free to use any of the models from this or other lessons to help them solve the additions.

Practice by Myself
Add Tens and Add Ones

③ 52 oak trees
and 35 pine trees.
How many trees in all?

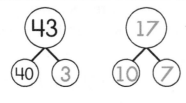

$$50 + 2$$
$$30 + 5$$
$$80 + 7 = 87$$

52 + 35 = 87

④ Manny has 43 cards.
Mark has 17 cards.
What is the total
number of cards?

43
40   3

17
10   7

43 + 17 = 60

⑤ 31 green grapes and 23 red grapes.
How many grapes altogether?

31 + 23 = 54

161

▶ Hands-On Activity

Use base-ten blocks to add multi-digit numbers.

Materials For each child: base-ten blocks

- Have children use base-ten blocks to add 43 + 17. First ask them to identify the tens and ones in each number, then model the tens and ones with base-ten blocks. [4 tens 3 ones and 1 ten 7 ones]

- Ask children to combine the tens and tell how many there are in all. [5 tens]

- Then have children combine the ones. Guide them to realize that the ones make an additional ten for a total of 6 tens, or 60.

▶ Mathematical Discourse

2 *What is another way to find the total in Problem 3?*

Children might describe writing 52 as 5 tens 2 ones and 35 as 3 tens 5 ones, then adding tens and adding ones to get 8 tens 7 ones, or 87. Others may see that the sum of the tens digits is 8 and the sum of the ones digits is 7, and instinctively know that this represents 87.

Step By Step

- Before children work on this page, review the models used in this lesson. Emphasize that children are free to use whatever way helps them solve the problems. Discuss with them that by completing the model shown in each problem they are demonstrating that they know how to solve these problems in many ways.

- Read each problem aloud, then have children work independently to solve.

- In Problem 3, watch children to ensure they are recording 5 tens and 8 tens as 50 and 80, respectively. Prompt them with questions such as: *What is another way to write 5 tens?*

▶ **Mathematical Discourse 2**

- In Problem 4, if children struggle with the concept of decomposing a number into tens and ones numerically, suggest they use base-ten blocks or connecting cubes to decompose each two-digit number and record numbers for each place value in the number bonds. Then use the Hands-On Activity to help children understand how to compose a ten in this problem.

▶ **Hands-On Activity**

- Encourage children to show the model or explain the strategy they used to solve Problem 5.

Differentiated Instruction

▶ Quick Check and Remediation

Materials For each child: base-ten blocks

- Ask children to find the sum of 27 and 62 and show or describe the model or strategy they used. [Possible answer: 20 + 7 + 60 + 2 = 80 + 9, or 89]

- For children who are still struggling, use the chart below to guide remediation.

- After providing remediation, check children's understanding using the following problem: *Find the sum of 43 and 32.* [75]

If the error is . . .	Children may . . .	To remediate . . .
87 or 82	have added 2 tens but failed to add the additional ones.	Compare the model or strategy children used to the addition problem. Check to see that both addends are modeled correctly and lead them to see that both groups of ones must be added.
17	have counted 8 tens and 9 ones and added 8 + 9.	Have children model the addends with base-ten blocks. Reinforce the concept that each ten equals 10 ones by pointing to each tens block and counting aloud by tens, and then pointing to each ones block and counting aloud by ones.
any other number	have miscounted.	Have children check their work using a different model or strategy to identify the error.

▶ Hands-On Activity

Model two-digit addition problems.

Materials For each pair: Place-Value Mat (Activity Sheet 27), Hundreds Chart (Activity Sheet 19), Number Bond Mat (Activity Sheet 3), base-ten blocks, 10 cards containing two-digit addition problems

- Children place the addition problem cards facedown. One child draws a card, places it faceup, models the addition using one of the materials provided and finds the sum.

- The partner solves the problem using a different model. Compare answers. If they are the same, a new card is drawn and the addition is modeled in two different ways.

- If the sums are different, partners exchange models, work the problem again, and determine which sum is correct and where the error was made.

▶ Challenge Activity

Explore the effects of rearranging digits in addends.

- Write the expressions "24 + 53" and "23 + 54" and have children find the sums. Guide them to recognize that the sum is the same for both problems. Ask children how the number sentences are the same and how they are different.

- Tell children that their challenge is to find out if the sums will ALWAYS be the same when the digits in the ones place are switched and if it works when the digits in the tens place are switched. Encourage them to justify their conclusion using words and pictures. [Because 24 + 53 = 20 + 4 + 50 + 3, swapping the tens digits (or the ones digits) of the 2 two-digit numbers is the same as rearranging the order of the addends in the sum and will always result in the same sum.]

- Challenge them further to determine if this works when the ones and tens digits are switched in each number and justify why or why not (for example: 24 + 53 and 42 + 35). You may need to help children see that swapping the ones and tens digits may change the value of the sum (for example, 29 + 32 ≠ 92 + 23).

Teacher Notes

Teacher-Toolbox.com

Overview

Assign the Lesson 24 Quiz and have children work independently to complete it.

Use the results of the quiz to assess children's understanding of the content of the lesson and to identify areas for reteaching. See the Lesson Pacing Guide at the beginning of the lesson and the Differentiated Instruction activities for suggested instructional resources.

Tested Skills

Assesses 1.NBT.C.4

Problems on this quiz require children to be able to add tens and add ones and add two two-digit numbers without regrouping. Children will also need to be familiar with decomposing a two-digit number into tens and ones and adding 10 to any number.

Ready **Mathematics**

Lesson 24 Quiz Answer Key

Name _____

Solve.

1 43 tall flowers and 21 short flowers.
How many flowers?

$$\boxed{40} + 3$$
$$20 + \boxed{1}$$
_____
$$\boxed{60} + \boxed{4} = \boxed{64}$$

43 + 21 = __64__

2 36 soccer balls and 14 footballs.
How many balls?

36 + 14 = __50__

36		14	
30	6	10	4

Common Misconceptions and Errors

Errors may result if children:

- add only the tens digits or only the ones digits.
- add both tens digits and include a ones digits without adding the other ones digit.
- add both ones digits and include a tens digits without adding the other tens digit.

Name _____

Solve.

③ 23 red stars and 51 blue stars.
How many stars?

$\underline{74} = 23 + 51$

④ 48 triangles and 21 squares.
How many shapes?

$48 + 21 = \underline{69}$

⑤ One week a class collects 31 cans.
The next week the class collects 67 cans.
How many cans in all does the class collect?

$31 + 67 = \underline{98}$

The class collects $\underline{98}$ cans.

Grade 1 Lesson 24 Add Tens and Add Ones

2

CCSS Focus

Domain
Number and Operations in Base Ten

Cluster
C. Use place value understanding and properties of operations to add and subtract.

Standard
1.NBT.C.4 Add within 100, including adding a two-digit number and a one-digit number, and adding a two-digit number and a multiple of 10, using concrete models or drawings and strategies based on place value, properties of operations, and/or the relationship between addition and subtraction; relate the strategy to a written method and explain the reasoning used. Understand that in adding two-digit numbers, one adds tens and tens, ones and ones; and sometimes it is necessary to compose a ten.

Standards for Mathematical Practice (SMP)

1 Make sense of problems and persevere in solving them.

2 Reason abstractly and quantitatively.

3 Construct viable arguments and critique the reasoning of others.

4 Model with mathematics.

6 Attend to precision.

7 Look for and make use of structure.

8 Look for and express regularity in repeated reasoning.

Lesson Objectives

Content Objectives
- Add two-digit numbers with regrouping.
- Compose a ten when adding ones.
- Relate two-digit addition with regrouping to two-digit addition without regrouping and to the make-a-ten strategy.

Language Objectives
- Draw quick-draw diagrams to show how to add two-digit numbers with regrouping.
- Rewrite two 2-digit numbers as tens and ones to add with regrouping.
- Tell how adding two-digit numbers with regrouping is like and how it is different from adding two-digit numbers without regrouping.
- Listen to the ideas of others and compare their strategies.

Prerequisite Skills
- Add two-digit numbers without regrouping.
- Utilize the make-a-ten strategy.

Lesson Vocabulary
- **make a ten** a strategy that uses combinations of numbers that add to ten when finding totals greater than 10.

Learning Progression

In Kindergarten children find number partners to make a ten and decompose teen numbers into ten ones and some more ones.

In Grade 1 children develop concepts related to the base ten system as they make a ten when adding two numbers whose sum is greater than ten and as they add tens to tens and ones to ones in double-digit addition.

In this lesson children expand on prior work with two-digit addition by recognizing that when adding ones to ones the sum may be greater than ten. Children apply models and strategies explored in previous lessons to addition with regrouping, developing an understanding of the process of making a ten from the sum of the ones digits to add to the existing tens.

In Grade 2 children continue work with two-digit addition and subtraction and extend base-ten computations to three-digit numbers.

Lesson Pacing Guide

Whole Class Instruction

Day 1
45–60 minutes

Introduction
Use What You Know
• Explore It *25 min*
• Try It *20 min*

Day 2
45–60 minutes

Modeled Instruction
Explore Together
• Example Problem *5 min*
• Model It *15 min*
• Hands-On Activity *15 min*
• Visual Model *10 min*

Practice and Problem Solving
Assign pages 227–228.

Day 3
45–60 minutes

Guided Instruction
Learn Together
• Example Problem *5 min*
• Model It *10 min*
• Talk About It *10 min*
• Hands-On Activity *15 min*
• Visual Model *5 min*

Practice and Problem Solving
Assign pages 229–230.

Day 4
45–60 minutes

Guided Practice
Practice Together
• Example Problem *5 min*
• Problems 1–2 *20 min*
• Fluency Practice *20 min*

Practice and Problem Solving
Assign pages 231–232.

Day 5
45–60 minutes

Independent Practice
Practice by Myself
• Problems 3–5 15 min
• Quick Check and Remediation *15 min*
• Hands-On or Challenge Activity *15 min*

Teacher-Toolbox: Lesson Quiz
Lesson 25 Quiz

Materials for Lesson Activities

Per child: base-ten blocks, 25 counters (7 red and 18 blue)
Activity Sheet 11, Activity Sheet 19*, Activity Sheet 30

Per pair: 2 number cubes, base-ten blocks

For display: 25 counters (7 red, 18 blue)

*Used for more than one activity.

Small Group Differentiation

Teacher-Toolbox.com

Reteach
Ready Prerequisite Lessons *45–90 min*

Grade K
• Lesson 24 Count to 100 by Tens
• Lesson 25 Count to 100 by Ones

Teacher-led Activities
Tools for Instruction *15–20 min*

Grade 1 *(Lesson 25)*
• Two-Digit Addition Without Regrouping

Student-led Activities
Math Center Activities *30–40 min*

Grade K *(Lessons 24 and 25)*
• K.30 Count by Tens
• K.31 Tens Bingo
• K.32 Count by Ones Vocabulary
• K.33 Keep Counting

Grade 1 *(Lesson 25)*
• 1.38 Add and Regroup

Personalized Learning

i-Ready.com

Independent
i-Ready Lessons* *10–20 min*

Grade 1 *(Lesson 25)*
• Adding a Two-Digit Number and a One-Digit Number
• Joining Sets to Add

* i-Ready lessons may be updated during the 2016–2017 school year. Updated references will be on the Teacher-Toolbox.

Introduction

Activity Explore Addition Strategies

Objective
Build the concept of regrouping with addition.

Materials for each child
- Hundreds Chart (Activity Sheet 19)
- base-ten blocks
- counters

Overview
Children explore, justify, and apply strategies for addition involving composing a ten in the ones place.

Step By Step

Explore It

Pose the problem.
- Tell children that Buzz and Boom both solved the problem "16 + 8" in different ways.
- Read each strategy one at a time, allowing children time to think about the first strategy before reading the next one.
- *Buzz said he added 16 + 4 to make 20 and then added 4 more.*
- *Boom said he broke 16 into 10 and 6. He added 6 + 4 to make ten, added 4 more, and then added the other 10.*

Model strategies.
- Have children work with a partner to model each strategy using blocks, hundreds charts, or other tools of their choice on the workmat on the Student Book page. Ask children if both strategies led to the same answer. [Yes, 24.]
- Ask each pair to decide which strategy they think was easier to use or which they like better. Ask several groups to explain their decisions.

Add and Regroup

Explore It

Buzz and Boom each find 16 + 8.

Buzz said he added 16 + 4 to make 20 and then added 4 more.

Boom said he broke 16 into 10 and 6. He added 6 + 4 to make ten, added 4 more, and then added the other ten. Show each strategy. Find each sum.

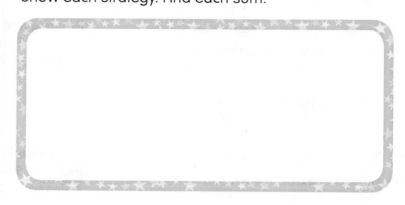

Buzz's sum: 24   **Boom's sum:** 24

162

Justify strategies.
- Invite volunteers to justify each strategy by demonstrating it with a model. Ask children to explain why each strategy works.
- Compare the two strategies, asking children to tell how they are different and how they are alike.

Apply strategies.
- Discuss with children how adding these numbers is like or different from the addition problems they have done in previous lessons. Focus on the fact that in this problem, the total of the digits in the ones place is greater than 10.
- Encourage children to work with a partner to find a different way to solve the problem and share it with the class.

Use What You Know
Add and Regroup

>> Try It

Draw a picture to show how to find 17 + 5.

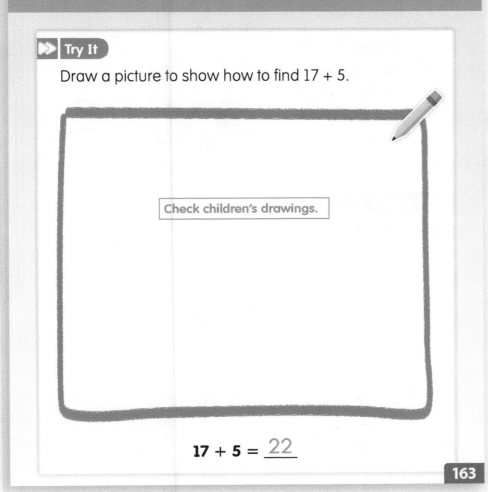

Check children's drawings.

17 + 5 = __22__

163

Step By Step

Try It

Pose the problem.

• Provide the children with the following problem: *Draw a picture to show how to find 17 + 5.*

Model and apply strategies.

• Encourage children to think about how they can model the situation with blocks, hundreds charts, or other tools.

• Some children might be able to make quick drawings that represent taking 3 ones from 5 ones and adding it to the 7 ones in 17 to make 2 tens. Others may make a drawing and count all. Support the latter group by allowing them to work with connecting cubes to physically create a 10 with the ones from both numbers.

Share drawings.

• Have pairs of children show and describe their drawings to each other.

• Invite volunteers to share their drawings with the class. Discuss how the drawings are similar and different, and how they each represent the problem.

Modeled Instruction

Step By Step

- Read the problem aloud. Ask children to relate this situation to the Activity in the Introduction by discussing ways to organize the erasers in a way that makes it easier to find the total.

- Use Hands-On Activity 1 to prepare children for the diagram shown in Model It.

▶ **Hands-On Activity 1**

> **SMP TIP Look for Structure**
> Display 18 blue counters and 7 red counters. Move two of the red counters into the blue group to demonstrate the viability of reorganizing addends to make a ten and to reinforce the application of the associative property of addition. *(SMP 7)*

Model It

- Draw attention to the diagram shown in Model It. Relate the diagram to Hands-On Activity 1 with questions such as: *How are the pictures shown like the 10-frames you filled? What is the arrow telling you to do? Why is it helpful to move 2 of the 7 ones over to the group of 18?*

▶ **Visual Model 1**

- Connect the process shown here to the making a ten strategy by asking Mathematical Discourse question 1.

▶ **Mathematical Discourse 1**

 Mathematics
PRACTICE AND PROBLEM SOLVING

Assign *Practice and Problem Solving* **pages 227–228** after students have completed this section.

Add and Regroup

Lou has some erasers.
18 are blue. 7 are red.
How many erasers in all?

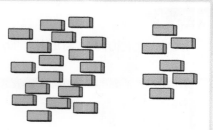

Model It Find 18 + 7.

Make the next ten.

Then add the tens and ones.

18   +   7

18 + 2 + 5

$20 + 5 = \underline{25}$

$18 + 7 = \underline{25}$

20 + 5

164

▶ **Mathematical Discourse**

1 *How is adding 18 + 7 like using the "make a ten" strategy?*

Children should notice that in adding 8 ones and 7 ones, the total is greater than 10, so composing a ten helps find the sum. In this problem, there is another ten to add so the sum has 2 tens, not one.

▶ **Visual Model 1**

Use quick number bonds to make the next ten.

Demonstrate the use of a quick number bond to help children see the numbers involved in making a ten.

$$18 + 7 =$$
2   5

▶ **Hands-On Activity 1**

Model addition with counters.

Materials For each child: two copies of 10-Frame (Activity Sheet 11), 25 counters (7 red and 18 blue)

Have children model 18 with blue counters on two 10-frames and 7 using red counters on a third 10-frame. Ask them to reorganize the counters to make it easier to count the total. Guide children to take 2 counters from 7 and place them with 8 to complete another frame of 10. Remind children that the total in addition is not affected by moving the parts being added.

Learn Together
Add and Regroup

How many marbles?

35 marbles 27 marbles

Model It Find 35 + 27. ⋯⋯⋯⋯⋯⋯⋯⋯⋯⋯⋯⋯

Add the tens and ones.

5 tens   12 ones
50   +   12
50   +   10 + 2 = __62__

35 + 27 = __62__

💬 **Talk About It** Who is right? How do you know? ⋯⋯⋯⋯⋯

Buzz: 25 + 16 = 41   Boom: 25 + 16 = 31

165

- Read the problem aloud and compare it to the problem from Model It on the previous page. Guide children to recognize that this addition problem involves 2 two-digit numbers.

- Use Hands-On Activity 2 to allow children to explore different strategies. Justify all reasonable methods, emphasizing that there are many ways to find the sum.

▶ **Hands-On Activity 2**

Model It

- Explore the model shown in Model It, helping children relate it to other models and strategies they have used. Point out that the sum of the ones digits is decomposed into a ten and some ones, so you can add all tens, then add ones.

▶ **Visual Model 2**

▶ **Mathematical Discourse 2**

Talk About It

- Read Talk About It. Have children work with a partner to find 25 + 16. Allow some pairs to present their work and tell who is right. After children understand that Buzz did the problem correctly, ask children to describe what they think Boom did wrong.

📦 **Ready**® Mathematics
PRACTICE AND PROBLEM SOLVING

Assign *Practice and Problem Solving* **pages 229–230** after students have completed this section.

▶ **Hands-On Activity 2**

Add two-digit numbers using a hundreds chart.

Materials For each child: Hundreds Chart (Activity Sheet 19), 12 counters

- Have children model 35 in the hundreds chart by shading in 3 rows of ten and then adding 5 more counters. Ask them to add 27 to the chart in whatever way makes it easiest for them to count the total.

- Observe the strategies children use to find the total. Look for strategies such as: coloring 2 more rows and adding 7 counters; coloring 2 rows, filling the row of 5 counters with 5 more and adding the other 2 at the end; counting on 2 tens from 35 and then adding 7 ones, etc.

- Encourage children to share their strategies with the class. Pose questions such as: *How is your strategy like . . . ? Why can you put 5 of the 7 counters next to the other 5?*

▶ **Mathematical Discourse**

2 *How is adding 35 + 27 like adding 35 + 23? How is it different?*

In both problems, you add tens to tens and ones to ones. When you add 35 and 27, the total of the ones is greater than 10. When you add 35 and 23, the total of the ones is less than 10.

▶ **Visual Model 2**

Use number bonds to see tens and ones.

Reinforce the addition of tens to tens and ones to ones by showing 35 and 27 in number bonds:

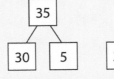

30 + 20 = 50; 5 + 7 = 12; 50 + 12 = 62

👥👥 Guided Practice

Step By Step

- Read the example problem aloud. Ask children to describe the strategy that is used to add 27 and 64.

- Encourage children to describe or demonstrate other strategies that might be used to solve the example problem.

- Some children may suggest counting on by tens and then adding the ones. Reinforce the concept of the commutative property by asking: *Is it easier to start with 27 or 64 when counting on? Why? Why doesn't it matter which number you start with?*

- Have children use the model shown for Problem 1 as a guide, but encourage them to use whatever strategies or models they prefer to show the addition. Allow pairs to compare strategies they used.

> **SMP TIP Use Structure**
> Draw attention to the tens and ones shown in Problem 2. Ask children if it would make sense to write the answer for 3 tens and 15 ones as 315 and why or why not. This allows children to apply the structure they have learned with the base-ten system. *(SMP 7)*

- Use Mathematical Discourse question 1 to engage children in describing strategies and models. Stress the importance of each child utilizing a strategy that is comfortable and effective for that individual. Make sure children understand that for any problem, the strategy they find most effective may be different from what other people choose, and that's okay. Remind children that in the Activity in the Introduction, Buzz and Boom used different strategies to get the same answer.

▶ **Mathematical Discourse 1**

▶ **Fluency Practice**

Ready Mathematics
PRACTICE AND PROBLEM SOLVING

Assign *Practice and Problem Solving* **pages 231–232** after students have completed this section.

Practice Together
Add and Regroup

27 flower stickers. 64 star stickers.
How many stickers?

$$2 \text{ tens } 7 \text{ ones}$$
$$+ \ 6 \text{ tens } 4 \text{ ones}$$
$$8 \text{ tens } 11 \text{ ones} = 80 \ + \ 11$$
$$80 \ + 10 + 1$$

27 + 64 = <u>91</u>

① 38 soccer balls and 46 kickballs.
How many balls?

<u>84</u> **= 38 + 46**

② 17 yellow flowers and 28 white flowers.
How many flowers altogether?

17 + 28 = <u>45</u>

$$1 \text{ ten } \ 7 \text{ ones}$$
$$+ \ 2 \text{ tens } 8 \text{ ones}$$
$$\underline{3} \text{ tens } \underline{15} \text{ ones}$$

166

▶ **Mathematical Discourse**

1 *What strategy or model makes it easiest for you to add with regrouping? Why?*
Listen to children's responses, encouraging them to justify specifically rather than saying, "It's easier." Responses should refer to combining tens and ones and accounting for composing and regrouping a ten.

▶ **Fluency Practice**

Choose strategies to add with regrouping.

Materials For each child: Practice Regrouping to Add (Activity Sheet 30)

Distribute Activity Sheet 30 (Practice Regrouping to Add). Instruct children to find the total for each addition problem. Tell them to show their work using drawings, number bonds, or numbers and words.

Practice by Myself
Add and Regroup

3 33 math books and 27 reading books.
What is the total number of books?

33 + 27 = <u>60</u>

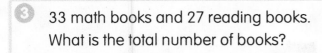

4 48 circles and 35 squares.
How many shapes?

<u>83</u> **= 48 + 35**

$$\begin{array}{r} 4 \text{ tens } 8 \text{ ones} \\ +\ 3 \text{ tens } 5 \text{ ones} \\ \hline \underline{7} \text{ tens } \underline{13} \text{ ones} \end{array}$$

5 17 gold stars and 29 silver stars.
How many stars in all?

17 + 29 = <u>46</u>

167

Step By Step

- Before children work on this page, review the models used in this lesson. Emphasize that children are free to use whatever way helps them solve the problems. Tell them that they may use a different strategy for each problem if they choose.

- Read each problem aloud, then have children work independently to solve.

- Observe children as they complete Problem 3, paying attention to the methods children use to find the sum. Do they combine the ones, compose a ten, and count all the tens? Do they count all the blocks individually? Do they count all the tens and then count on all the ones? Do they ignore the model and mentally find the sum? Use these observations to provide each child the appropriate tools or support he or she needs to be successful.

- Watch for children who fail to interpret 7 tens as 70 in Problem 4. Encourage them to use base-ten blocks to model the problem and check their answer.

▶ **English Language Learners**

▶ **Mathematical Discourse 2**

- Remind children to show the strategy they used in Problem 5 with a drawing or other type of model, or by describing the strategy.

- Use Mathematical Discourse question 3 to start a discussion about the different strategies children used to solve the problems on this page.

▶ **Mathematical Discourse 3**

▶ **English Language Learners**

Some English language learners may need support with the vocabulary in Problem 4. Write the word *Shapes* on the board and invite children to draw or write the names of shapes that they know. Reinforce the idea that circles and squares (and others) are all kinds of shapes.

▶ **Mathematical Discourse**

2 *How are the models shown in Problems 3 and 4 alike? How are they different?*
Both models show breaking up the addends into tens and ones. Problem 3 does this with drawings of tens and ones. Problem 4 does this with numbers and words.

3 *How did you choose a strategy for each problem? Did you use the same strategy for all the problems?*
Allow children to describe and justify the strategies they used. Discuss why some strategies might make more sense for certain problems (for example, making a ten in Problem 3 leaves no leftover ones to add). Encourage children to find a balance between choosing a strategy they are comfortable with and a strategy that "works well" for a specific problem.

Differentiated Instruction

▶ Quick Check and Remediation

Materials For each child: base-ten blocks

- Ask children to find the sum of 27 and 58 and show their work. [85]
- For children who are still struggling, use the chart below to guide remediation.
- After providing remediation, check children's understanding using the following problem: *Find the sum of 15 and 49.* [64]

If the error is . . .	Children may . . .	To remediate . . .
715	have recorded 7 tens and 15 ones as 715.	Have children model the problem with base-ten blocks. Write 7 tens as 70 and 15 as 10 + 5. Ask children how they would add 70 + 10 + 5 and compare it to their answer. Discuss which answer is correct and why. Encourage them to recognize the error they made by having them tell what is wrong with the original answer.
75	have failed to add the composed ten to the 7 tens.	Isolate the ones digits and have children calculate. Ask them to write 15 as tens and ones. Lead children to see that the 10 from 15 needs to be combined with the other tens to find the sum.
any other sum	have miscalculated.	Tell children to check their answers using a physical model.

▶ Hands-On Activity

Build and solve problems involving regrouping.

Materials For each pair: 2 number cubes (1–6 and 4–9), base-ten blocks

- Place children in pairs. One partner rolls the number cubes and forms a two-digit number using the numbers rolled as digits. The number is recorded on a whiteboard or paper. The other partner rolls the number cubes and forms a two-digit number to add to the first number.
- Partners work together to find the sum, then check using base-ten blocks. If their sum is not correct, they must find their error before rolling again.
- If the addition requires regrouping, the partners earn a point. The activity ends when the partners have earned 5 points or when time expires.

▶ Challenge Activity

Explore strategies involving subtraction.

Materials For each child: Hundreds Chart (Activity Sheet 19), base-ten blocks

- Remind children of the strategies they used during this lesson. Tell them that you thought of another strategy for adding 18 + 7: Add 10 to 18 and then subtract 3.
- Challenge children to:
  - try the strategy with at least 10 different addition problems involving a two-digit and a one-digit number.
  - justify why this strategy works.
  - determine if it will work for adding other numbers.
- Allow children to share their work.

Teacher Notes

Teacher-Toolbox.com

Overview

Assign the Lesson 25 Quiz and have children work independently to complete it.

Use the results of the quiz to assess children's understanding of the content of the lesson and to identify areas for reteaching. See the Lesson Pacing Guide at the beginning of the lesson and the Differentiated Instruction activities for suggested instructional resources.

Tested Skills

Assesses 1.NBT.C.4

Problems on this quiz require children to be able to add tens and add ones and to add two two-digit numbers with regrouping. Children will also need to be familiar with adding two two-digit numbers without regrouping and the make a ten strategy.

Ready **Mathematics**

Lesson 25 Quiz Answer Key

Name _____

Solve.

1 36 white eggs and 25 brown eggs.
How many eggs?

$\underline{61}$ = 36 + 25

2 35 black bugs and 47 red bugs.
How many bugs in all?

35 + 47 = $\underline{82}$

    3 tens 5 ones
+ 4 tens 7 ones
$\underline{7}$ tens $\underline{12}$ ones

3 56 small dogs and 17 big dogs.
What is the total number of dogs?

$\underline{73}$ = 56 + 17

Grade 1 **Lesson 25** Add and Regroup   1   ©Curriculum Associates, LLC
Copying permitted for classroom use.

Common Misconceptions and Errors

Errors may result if children:

- do not add the composed ten from the ones place in the tens place.
- ignore or confuse place value when writing the sum.
- incorrectly decompose a two-digit number into tens and ones.

Name _____

Solve.

4 38 white socks and 48 black socks.
How many socks?

<u>86</u> = 38 + 48

5 There are 63 apple trees on the farm.
There are 29 pear trees.
How many trees are on the farm?

63 + 29 = <u>92</u>

There are <u>92</u> trees on the farm.

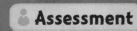
Assessment

Step By Step

- Have children solve the problems individually and show their work. Emphasize that children are free to use whatever way helps them solve the problems.

- Monitor children's comfort and ability to move flexibly between different representations of tens and ones—visual model of base ten blocks, tens and ones chart, number bond, words, and mathematical expressions.

- Some models refer to a number of tens, while others represent tens numerically (as 20 or 30, for example). Children should be able to explain the meaning of a ten [10 ones] and use their knowledge of tens and ones to add two-digit numbers.

Unit 5 Review

Solve the problems.

1. Ali picks 73 pears.
   Greg picks 37 pears.
   Who picks more pears?

   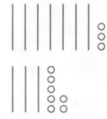

   73 $>$ 37

   _____Ali_____ picks more pears.

2. 25 pink shells.
   34 brown shells.
   How many shells in all?

   25 + 34 = __59__

   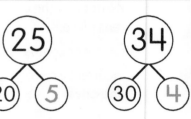

3. Circle ways to show 38.

   (3 tens 8 ones) (30 + 8)

   80 + 3   (2 tens 18 ones)

4. **20 + 51 = _71_**

5. Write <, >, or = in the circle.

   54 $<$ 56   **19 $=$ 19**

6. _68_ **= 45 + 23**

Teacher Notes

7 42 red birds. 46 blue birds.

Are there fewer red birds or blue birds?

Write the tens and ones.

Then write <, >, or = in the circle.

Tens	Ones
4	2

Tens	Ones
4	6

42 46

There are ___fewer___ red birds than blue birds.

---

8 27 circles and 29 triangles.

How many shapes in all?

```
   2 tens 7 ones
 + 2 tens 9 ones
```

_4_ tens _16_ ones

_56_ = 27 + 29

There are _56_ shapes in all.

169

- For Problems 7 and 8, children need to apply knowledge of tens and ones to a context and use their understanding of numbers in base ten to solve problems.

- If children struggle with the representation in Problem 8, have them relate it to the charts shown in Problem 7. Then guide them to add the tens and add the ones. Finally, elicit that the tens and ones must be written as a number. You may wish to have some children use base ten blocks or a visual representation of base ten blocks.

Teacher Notes

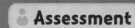

Step By Step

Put It Together

- On this page, children write a two-digit number and set up an addition problem involving regrouping. They add, using any approach that makes sense to them.

- Read the directions and task aloud. Make sure children understand what they need to do to complete the task.

- Direct children to complete problem 9 on their own.

- As children work on their own, observe their progress and understanding. Respond to their questions and provide additional support as needed.

- Have children share their problem and solution with the class. Ask them to explain the strategy they used.

- Have the class ask questions about each child's work. Encourage children to justify their work and tell how they added and regrouped.

- Have children return to the Unit Opener page and complete the *After* column of the progress chart.

Put It Together

9 **Add two numbers.**

Use the digits 5 and 7 to write a number.
Add your number to 28.
Show your work.

Children write either 57 or 75. They might make a quick drawing to show their number and 28.

Possible answer:

$$5 \text{ tens } 7 \text{ ones}$$
$$+\ \underline{2 \text{ tens } 8 \text{ ones}}$$
$$7 \text{ tens } 15 \text{ ones} = 8 \text{ tens } 5 \text{ ones}$$

$$57 + 28 = 85$$

170

Teacher Notes

Scoring Rubric

Points	Expectations
4	The child: • writes 57 or 75. • uses an appropriate strategy to add either 57 or 75 to 28; all work is accurate.
3	The child: • writes 57 or 75. • uses an appropriate strategy to add either 57 or 75 to 28; work might have minor errors.
2	The child: • writes 57 or 75. • shows work with some indication of a strategy for adding either 57 or 75 to 28 that contains some computational errors.
1	The child: • may write a number other than 57 or 75, for example just 7 or 5. • shows work with no clear strategy for adding either 57 or 75 to 28 that is inaccurate and/or incomplete.
0	The child: • does not attempt to complete the task.

Unit 6 Shapes

Which lessons are students building upon?

Kindergarten, Lesson 29
See Position and Shape
K.G.A.1

Kindergarten, Lesson 30
Name Shapes
K.G.A.2, K.G.A.3

Kindergarten, Lesson 31
Compare Shapes
K.G.B.4

Kindergarten, Lesson 30
Name Shapes
K.G.A.2, K.G.A.3

Kindergarten, Lesson 31
Compare Shapes
K.G.B.4

Kindergarten, Lesson 32
Build Shapes
K.G.B.5, K.G.B.6

Kindergarten, Lesson 30
Name Shapes
K.G.A.2, K.G.A.3

Kindergarten, Lesson 31
Compare Shapes
K.G.B.4

Kindergarten, Lesson 32
Build Shapes
K.G.B.5, K.G.B.6

Unit 6

Lesson 26
Understand Shapes
1.G.A.1

Lesson 27
Understand Putting Shapes Together
1.G.A.2

Lesson 28
Understand Breaking Shapes
into Parts
1.G.A.3

Which lessons are students preparing for?

Grade 2, Lesson 26
Recognize and Draw Shapes
2.G.A.1

Grade 2, Lesson 26
Recognize and Draw Shapes
2.G.A.1

Grade 2, Lesson 27
Understand Tiling in Rectangles
2.G.A.2

Grade 2, Lesson 26
Recognize and Draw Shapes
2.G.A.1

Grade 2, Lesson 28
Understand Halves, Thirds, and
Fourths in Shapes
2.G.A.3

Unit 6
Shapes

Unit 6 – Geometry
Shapes

Eve has some shapes. She wants to put shapes together to make a new shape. She wants to make equal parts. What math questions could Eve ask about the shapes?

In this unit, you will learn about shapes and about equal parts of shapes. Then you will be able to solve problems like Eve's.

✓ Self Check

Check off the skills you know now. Then see how many more you can check off after each lesson!

I can:	Before this unit	After this unit
use sides and corners to name shapes.	☐	☐
put shapes together to make new shapes.	☐	☐
break shapes into halves.	☐	☐
break shapes into fourths.	☐	☐

Ready Mathematics
PRACTICE AND PROBLEM SOLVING

Practice and Problem Solving Resources

Use the following resources from **Practice and Problem Solving** to engage students and their families and to extend student learning.

- **Family Letters** Send Family Letters home separately before each lesson or as part of a family communication package.

- **Unit Games** Use partner Unit Games at classroom centers and/or send them home for play with family members.

- **Unit Practice** Assign Unit Practice as homework, as independent or small group practice, or for whole class discussion.

- **Fluency Practice** Assign Fluency Skills Practice and Fluency Repeated Reasoning Practice worksheets throughout the unit.

At A Glance

- This page introduces children to the general ideas behind working with shapes.

- The checklist allows them to see what skills they will be learning and take ownership of their progress.

Step By Step

- Explain to children that they are going to begin a new unit of lessons. Tell them that in all the lessons in this unit they will be learning about shapes and about equal parts of shapes.

- Read the introduction to the unit together as a class. Invite children to suggest questions that could be asked about the problem situation. Discuss the questions children pose without the expectation that they are to solve them.

- Then take a few minutes to have each child independently read through the list of skills.

- Ask children to consider each skill and check the box in the *Before* column if it is a skill they think they already have. Remind children that these skills are likely to all be new to them, but it's still possible some children have some of the skills.

- Engage children in a brief discussion about the skills. Invite children to comment on which ones they would most like to learn, or which ones seem similar or related to something they already know. Remind them that the goal is to be able to check off all the skills they have learned by the end of the unit.

- At the end of the unit, have children complete the *After* column. As time allows, pose questions about the problem situation at the top of the page and solve as a class.

CCSS Focus

Domain
Geometry

Cluster
A. Reason with shapes and their attributes.

Standard
1.G.A.1 Distinguish between defining attributes (e.g., triangles are closed and three-sided) versus non-defining attributes (e.g., color, orientation, overall size); build and draw shapes to possess defining attributes.

Additional Standard
1.MD.C.4 (See page B3 for full text.)

Standards for Mathematical Practice (SMP)

2 Reason abstractly and quantitatively.

3 Construct viable arguments and critique the reasoning of others.

6 Attend to precision.

7 Look for and make use of structure.

Lesson Objectives

Content Objectives

• Identify the defining attributes of a shape.

• Distinguish between defining and non-defining attributes.

• Classify a shape based on its defining attributes.

Language Objectives

• Draw a shape based on given attributes or its name.

• Use an index card as a tool to determine if a shape has a square corner and to compare the shape's side lengths.

• Orally describe what is the same and what is different about a given group of shapes.

Prerequisite Skills

• Recognize and name basic shapes.

• Recognize similarities and differences among shapes.

• Draw basic shapes.

Lesson Vocabulary

• **corner** a point where two or more lines meet.

• **hexagon** a shape with 6 sides and 6 corners.

• **rectangle** a shape with 4 sides and 4 square corners that has opposite sides the same length.

• **rhombus** a shape with 4 sides and 4 corners that has all sides the same length.

• **side** a line segment that is part of a shape.

• **square** a shape with 4 sides and 4 square corners that has all sides the same length.

• **trapezoid** a quadrilateral with at least one pair of parallel sides.

• **triangle** a shape with 3 sides and 3 corners.

Learning Progression

In Kindergarten children explore basic shapes in their world by naming and describing them by their visible attributes.

In Grade 1 children build on the concept of shapes by classifying, composing, and partitioning them.

In this lesson children analyze shapes based on defining attributes and recognize attributes that do not affect the shape—non-defining attributes. They recognize that some quadrilaterals are named by attributes other than the number of sides and corners and utilize those attributes in classifying them.

In Grade 2 children extend their understanding of shapes to include pentagons and draw shapes based on specific attributes.

Lesson Pacing Guide

Whole Class Instruction

Day 1
45–60 minutes

Introduction
Use What You Know
• Explore It *25 min*
• Try It *20 min*

Day 2
45–60 minutes

Modeled Instruction
Explore Together
• Opening Question *10 min*
• Think *10 min*
• Talk About It *15 min*
• Concept Extension *10 min*

Practice and Problem Solving
Assign pages 243–244.

Day 3
45–60 minutes

Guided Instruction
Explore Together
• Hands-On Problem *10 min*
• Problems 1–2 *15 min*
• Talk About It *15 min*
• Concept Extension *5 min*

Practice and Problem Solving
Assign pages 245–246.

Day 4
45–60 minutes

Guided Practice
Connect It
• Problems 3–5 *15 min*

Independent Practice
Show What I Know
• Problem 6 *15 min*
• Intervention, On-Level, or Challenge Activity *15 min*

Practice and Problem Solving
Assign pages 247–248.

Teacher-Toolbox: Lesson Quiz
Lesson 26 Quiz

Materials for Lesson Activities

Per child: 1 index card
Activity Sheet 31

Per pair: two 3-foot lengths of yarn or string
Activity Sheet 31*

For display: tape, square piece of paper
Activity Sheet 31

*Used for more than one activity.

Small Group Differentiation

Teacher-Toolbox.com

Reteach
Ready Prerequisite Lessons *45–90 min*

Grade K
• Lesson 30 Name Shapes
• Lesson 31 Compare Shapes

Teacher-led Activities
Tools for Instruction *15–20 min*

Grade 1 *(Lesson 26)*
• Plane Shapes: Defining Attributes
• Shapes and Position of Objects
• Describing and Comparing Shapes by Attributes

Student-led Activities
Math Center Activities *30–40 min*

Grade K *(Lessons 30 and 31)*
• K.42 I Spy Shapes
• K.43 Shape Match
• K.44 Is It Flat or Solid?
• K.45 Match and Name Shapes
• K.46 Find and Tell
• K.47 Alike and Different

Grade 1 *(Lesson 26)*
• 1.39 Draw Two Shapes
• 1.40 Shape Attributes

Personalized Learning

i-Ready.com

Independent
i-Ready Lessons* *10–20 min*

Grade 1 *(Lesson 26)*
• Classifying Plane Shapes by Attributes
• Identifying Two-Dimensional Shapes
• Comparing Two-Dimensional Shapes

* i-Ready lessons may be updated during the 2016–2017 school year. Updated references will be on the Teacher-Toolbox.

Introduction

Activity What Belongs?

Objective

Build the concept of defining attributes.

Materials for each pair

• Shapes 1 (Activity Sheet 31)

Materials for display

• two copies of Shapes 1 (Activity Sheet 31)

• tape

Overview

Children find a common attribute among shapes and determine whether other shapes belong in the same group.

Step By Step

Explore It

Sort closed shapes.

• Display two cards with closed shapes. Include one shape that has only straight sides and one that has both straight and curved sides.

• Tell children that these shapes belong together in a special way. Give them time to think about this and then display a card containing an open shape.

• Explain that this shape does not belong with the others. Have children talk to a partner about what makes it different.

• Discuss that the first two shapes are *closed*. Relate these shapes to fenced areas, explaining that there is no opening for anyone to get in or out. The other shape is *open* (or not closed) so anyone could get in or out.

• Display several other shapes, both open and closed, having children determine whether or not each one belongs to the group of *closed* shapes.

Sort closed shapes with straight sides.

• Repeat the activity above, first displaying two polygons, then two shapes with curved sides. Challenge children to explain why the polygons belong together.

• Emphasize that in the first two shapes, all sides are straight, and that a shape with any curved sides does not belong to the group.

• As you display other shapes (including open ones), have children tell whether they belong to the group *straight sides*.

Sort by attribute.

• Give each pair of children a set of shape cards.

• Draw a large circle on the board. Write the word *closed* above it. Tell children that only shapes that are closed belong in the circle.

• Have pairs sort the shapes and place all of the closed shapes in the circle workmat on the Student Book page.

• Display one set of shape cards. Then invite children one at a time to put a shape from the display in the circle drawn on the board. Allow the class to agree or disagree and then come to a consensus. Save this display for children to refer to later in the lesson.

• Draw a second circle on the board and label *straight sides*. Then repeat the activity for shapes with straight sides.

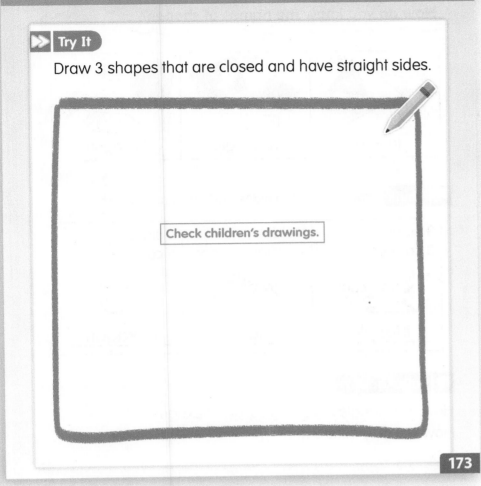

>> **Try It**

Draw 3 shapes that are closed and have straight sides.

Check children's drawings.

173

Step By Step

Try It

Evaluate defining attributes.

- Scatter all the shapes on the floor or display them on the board. Have children identify and justify the shapes that belong to both the *closed* group and the *straight sides* group. You may want to identify all these shapes as polygons, but don't expect mastery of the term.

- Ask children to describe other ways that the shapes are alike and different. Discuss that the shapes are different sizes and colors. Encourage children to think about whether shapes of different size and color can still belong to the groups *closed* and *straight sides*.

Pose another problem.

- Ask children to draw 3 shapes that are closed and have straight sides.

Solve the problem.

- Allow children time to draw 3 shapes.

- Encourage children who are struggling to look at the shapes displayed inside the circle labeled *closed* and the circle labeled *straight sides*. Ask: *Which shapes are in both circles?*

- Have children discuss with a partner how their drawings are alike and how they are different. Listen for children who use the words *closed* and *straight sides* in their descriptions.

👥 **Modeled Instruction**

Step By Step

• Explain that in this lesson children will only be working with shapes that are closed and have straight sides.

• Read aloud the opening question. Then direct attention to the group of triangles. Ask children what is the same about the shapes. Then draw a square on the board and ask if it belongs and why. Help children focus on the fact that triangles have 3 sides and 3 corners. Then guide children to recognize that rectangles have 4 sides and 4 square corners and hexagons have 6 sides and 6 corners.

Think

• Read Think aloud. Have children fill in the blanks with the name of each type of shape. Emphasize that color is not a defining attribute. Point out that the red triangle, rectangle, and hexagon are all the same color but not the same shape.

Talk About It

• Discuss the Talk About It questions. Guide children to recognize that all the shapes are closed and have straight sides. Triangles, rectangles, and hexagons have different numbers of sides and corners.

▶ **Mathematical Discourse 1**

> **Misconception Alert** Some children may associate the name of a shape with a particular figure they have seen before. Exposing children to a variety of shapes allows them to examine them analytically.

▶ **Concept Extension 1**

SMP TIP Attend to Precision
As children describe shapes, encourage them to communicate precisely about defining attributes. *(SMP 6)*

📖 **Ready**· **Mathematics**
PRACTICE AND PROBLEM SOLVING

Assign *Practice and Problem Solving* **pages 243–244** after students have completed this section.

Explore Together
Understand Shapes

How do you know the names of shapes?

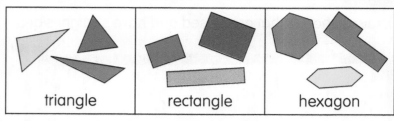

| triangle | rectangle | hexagon |

💬 **Think** You look at the sides and corners.

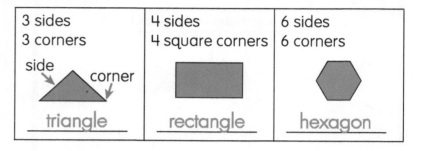

| 3 sides 3 corners | 4 sides 4 square corners | 6 sides 6 corners |
| triangle | rectangle | hexagon |

💬 **Talk About It**

How are triangles, rectangles, and hexagons alike?
How are they different?

174

▶ **Mathematical Discourse**

1 *Boom says the pink shape in the hexagon box can't be a hexagon because it has square corners and the other ones don't. What do you think?*

The kind of corners doesn't make a difference. If a shape has 6 sides and 6 corners it is considered a hexagon.

▶ **Concept Extension 1**

Explore the concept of non-defining attributes.

• Draw several triangles of different size, color, and orientation. Ask children to describe the differences in the shapes.

• Make a dot in one corner of each shape to use as a starting point. Slide a pointer along each side of a triangle as you count the sides. Then touch each corner, counting each one.

• Guide children to understand that a change in the color, orientation, or size doesn't affect the shape. In this case, the number of sides and corners is what defines the shape.

Explore Together
Understand Shapes

✋ **Sort shapes with 4 sides and 4 corners.**

Make a dot •
if true.
Make an ✗
if not true.

→ Describe these rectangles.

✗ 4 sides the same length

• 4 square corners

• opposite sides the same length

---

1 **Describe these squares.**

• 4 sides the same length

• 4 square corners

• opposite sides the same length

2 **Describe these rhombuses.**

• 4 sides the same length

✗ 4 square corners

• opposite sides the same length

💬 **Talk About It** •

How are these shapes alike? How are they different?   **175**

▶ **Concept Extension 2**
Explore trapezoids.

• Display the three trapezoids shown.

• Tell children that this is another type of shape called a trapezoid. Ask: *How many sides does a trapezoid have?* [4] Ask: *How many corners does a trapezoid have?* [4]

• Ask: *Are the opposite sides the same length?* [Sometimes.] Help children see that one pair of opposite sides of the first trapezoid shown above are the same length, but that opposite sides of the other 2 trapezoids are not the same length.

▶ **Mathematical Discourse**

2 *What is the same about all the shapes on this page? What is different about them?*

All the shapes have 4 sides and 4 corners, but some of the sides are different lengths. Some of the corners are square corners and some are not.

▶ **English Language Learners**

Materials For display: square piece of paper

Hold up the square paper. Explain that a "square corner" is any corner that looks like the corners of a square. Then tape the paper to the board and point out the "opposite" sides. Ask children to identify square corners and opposite sides in the shapes on the student page.

Step By Step

• Begin by having children examine the shapes shown on the page.

▶ **Mathematical Discourse 2**

• Explain to the children that shapes with 4 sides and 4 corners have many different names. Each group of shapes has common attributes that make them belong together.

• Provide each child with an index card. As they complete the activity on this page, model for them how to use the card to check for square corners and to mark it with a pencil to compare side lengths.

▶ **English Language Learners**

• Read the directions aloud. Walk through the completed example. Invite volunteers to explain why there is an *X* next to the first attribute and dots next to the others.

• Make sure children understand that they need to decide whether each of the attributes fit with a square in Problem 1 and then with a rhombus in Problem 2.

▶ **Concept Extension 2**

Talk About It

• Have children look at all 9 shapes as they start discussing the Talk About It questions. Expand the discussion by asking: *How is a square like a rhombus? How is it different? How is a rectangle like a rhombus? How is it different?*

• Guide children to recognize that if two (or more) shapes have a dot for the same attribute, they share this attribute.

> **SMP TIP Reason Abstractly**
> Children focus on defining attributes and reason abstractly by discussing similarities and differences between shapes. *(SMP 2)*

 Ready **Mathematics**
PRACTICE AND PROBLEM SOLVING

Assign *Practice and Problem Solving* **pages 245–246** after students have completed this section.

👥👥 Guided Practice

Step By Step

- Discuss each Connect It problem as a class using the discussion points outlined below.

Classify

- You may want to place children in pairs to talk about the shapes. Remind them that some shapes may not belong to any of the groups listed.

- Display a copy of the shapes shown on the page and invite volunteers to point out the shapes they colored red and ask for justification. Encourage children to articulate the defining attributes. Repeat with the remaining shapes.

- Ask children to identify the shapes that they did not color and explain why.

Create

- Allow children to work with a partner to describe each shape and provide support to those who struggle to connect a name with its shape. After the discussion, each child draws shapes independently.

- Encourage children to draw their shapes as carefully as possible. Do not expect precision in their drawings; however, allow children who are concerned about precision to use a straight edge.

- Invite a volunteer to display the shapes they drew and justify them. Ask others to display shapes that are different in some way from those already shown.

- Discuss how some attributes may be different, such as the size of the entire shape or lengths of some sides, yet all the shapes within each category have defining attributes that put them in the group. The one common attribute among them all is that they each have 4 sides and 4 corners.

Evaluate

- Discuss the questions as a group. Encourage children to focus on attributes, prompting them with questions such as: *Why do you think Eve might have thought this is a rectangle? Why is it important to know all the things that give a shape its name?*

Connect It
Understand Shapes

3 **Classify** Color the shapes.

triangles ■ hexagons ■ rectangles ■ rhombuses ■

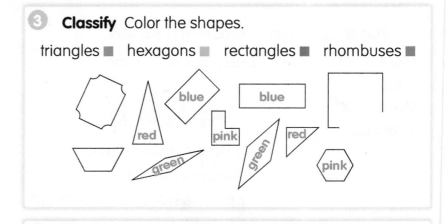

4 **Create** Draw the shape named in each box.
Possible answers:

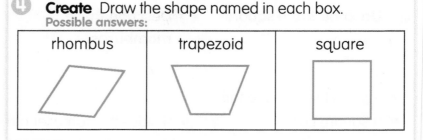

| rhombus | trapezoid | square |

5 **Evaluate** Eve says this shape is a rectangle.
Do you agree?
Why or why not?

176

- Emphasize the fact that for a shape to be given a specific name it must possess all the attributes of the shape, not just one or two.

- Stimulate further evaluation of the attributes of shapes by asking: *Boom says this shape looks like a rhombus because it is slanted. What do you think?*

- You may want to extend this concept by having children evaluate other shapes. For example, draw a rectangle in the box labeled "rhombus" and ask children if they think it belongs there and why.

Ready· **Mathematics**
PRACTICE AND PROBLEM SOLVING

Assign *Practice and Problem Solving* **pages 247–248** after students have completed this section.

Show What I Know
Understand Shapes

6 **Make the same shape in different ways.**

A: Choose a shape to draw. Circle its name.

hexagon (triangle) rectangle
rhombus square trapezoid

Draw 3 of your shapes. Make each one different in some way.

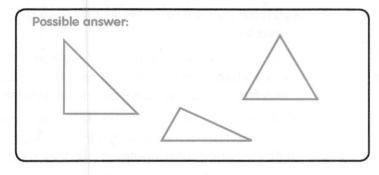

Possible answer:

B: How are your shapes different? How are they alike?

Possible answer: They all have 3 sides and 3 corners.
The sides are different lengths. One has a square corner.
The rest have no square corners.

177

Step By Step

- Read the directions aloud. Make sure children understand that they must draw shapes that all have the name they selected.

- In Part A, make sure children understand that they can choose any shape on the list. They draw three different examples of that shape.

- In Part B, children compare and contrast the shapes they drew.

- As children work, prompt them with the following questions:

  What are some things you could do to make each shape a little different from the others?

  Can you find more than one way to make your shapes different from each other?

  What makes your shape different from the other shapes listed?

  How can you make sure all your shapes have the same name?

Scoring Rubrics

Expectations for 4–3 Points

Points	Expectations
4	The child: • draws three shapes that have the defining attribute of the shape selected and alters each one with varied non-defining attributes. • identifies all non-defining attributes as the differences and all defining attributes as the similarities.
3	The child: • draws three shapes that have the defining attributes of the shape selected; however, the non-defining attribute may be the same for each shape (e.g., all are different sizes). • describes similarities using some defining attributes and describes differences based on the one non-defining attribute.

Expectations for 2–0 Points

Points	Expectations
2	The child: • draws three basic shapes of the name circled, some of which may not be different from the others. • may describe similarities in a general way such as "all the same shape" and differences as "all different."
1	The child: • may draw shapes that do not all match the circled name. • may identify similarities and differences as either "all different" or "all the same."
0	The child: • does not attempt to draw shapes or answer the questions.

Lesson 26 *Understand* Shapes   **177**

Differentiated Instruction

▶ Intervention Activity
Match shapes and attributes.

Materials For each child: Shapes 1 (Activity Sheet 31)

- Have children place an attribute card at the top of their desks. They then examine each shape card and compare it to each of the attributes on the attribute card.

- If the shape fits all attributes, the shape card is kept faceup under the attribute card. Unused shape cards are placed in a pile.

- Repeat with each of the other attribute cards.

▶ On-Level Activity
Classify shapes by name.

Materials For each pair: Shapes 1 (Activity Sheet 31), a 3-foot length of yarn or string

- Place children in pairs and show them how to form a circle with the string. Have them lay out the shape cards faceup and stack the attribute cards facedown.

- Children turn up an attribute card, set it next to the circle, and take turns selecting a shape card. If the shape matches the attribute card, it goes in the circle.

- When all the shapes are placed, children discuss why they all belong in the circle. Then they remove the shapes, select a different attribute card, and repeat the activity.

▶ Challenge Activity
Classify shapes that belong to multiple groups.

Materials For each group: Shapes 1 (Activity Sheet 31), two 3-foot lengths of yarn or string

- Allow children to work in groups of 2 to 4. Show them how to make two overlapping circles with the yarn, creating an intersection. Model the activity by placing the attribute cards for rectangle and square above each circle. Discuss how the intersection means that a shape could belong to both groups, square and rectangle.

- Select some shape cards and place them in the proper section of the overlapping circles. Point out that some shapes do not belong to either group, so they go outside the circles. Discuss why the squares are in the intersection.

- After modeling the activity, tell children to place their attribute cards facedown and divide the shape cards among themselves. They randomly choose two attribute cards and place them above each circle. Then they take turns placing one of their shape cards in an appropriate section of the circles (or outside), justifying the placement.

- The group decides if the shape is placed correctly and either keeps it there or removes it. Then the next child has a turn. Continue until all shapes are placed.

- Children can redistribute the shape cards, select two different attribute cards, and repeat the activity.

Teacher Notes

Teacher-Toolbox.com

Overview

Assign the Lesson 26 Quiz and have children work independently to complete it.

Use the results of the quiz to assess children's understanding of the content of the lesson and to identify areas for reteaching. See the Lesson Pacing Guide at the beginning of the lesson and the Differentiated Instruction activities for suggested instructional resources.

Tested Skills

Assesses 1.G.A.1

Problems on this quiz require children to be able to identify defining attributes of a shape and classify or draw a shape based on its attributes. Children will also need to be familiar with identifying, naming, and drawing basic shapes and recognizing similarities and differences among shapes.

Ready® Mathematics

Lesson 26 Quiz Answer Key

Name _____

Solve.

1 Describe these hexagons.
Make a dot • if true.
Make an x if not true.

_•_ 6 corners
_•_ 6 sides
_x_ 6 sides the same length

2 Mark each triangle with an x.
Mark each rhombus with a •.
Circle each rectangle.
Color in each hexagon.

Grade 1 **Lesson 26** *Understand Shapes*

1

©Curriculum Associates, LLC
Copying permitted for classroom use.

Common Misconceptions and Errors

Errors may result if children:

- do not recognize or incorrectly name basic shapes.
- are unable to distinguish between defining and non-defining attributes.
- cannot determine whether a shape has all or only some given attributes.

Lesson 26 **Quiz Answer Key** continued

Name _____

Solve.

3 Draw the shape named in each box.
Possible answer:

Triangle 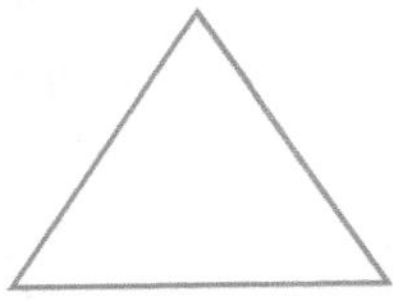	Rectangle 

4 Draw 3 triangles.
Make each one different in some way.
Possible answer:

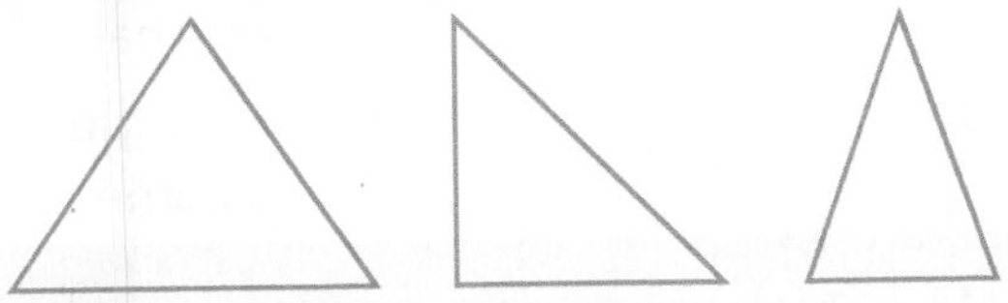

5 Cara draws a shape with 4 sides.
Circle each shape she could draw.

triangle   (trapezoid)   hexagon

(rectangle)   (rhombus)   (square)

Grade 1 Lesson 26 *Understand* Shapes

2

CCSS Focus

Domain
Geometry

Cluster
A. Reason with shapes and their attributes.

Standard
1.G.A.2 Compose two-dimensional shapes (rectangles, squares, trapezoids, triangles, half-circles, and quarter-circles) or three-dimensional shapes (cubes, right rectangular prisms, right circular cones, and right circular cylinders) to create a composite shape, and compose new shapes from the composite shape.

Standards for Mathematical Practice (SMP)

2 Reason abstractly and quantitatively.

3 Construct viable arguments and critique the reasoning of others.

4 Model with mathematics.

5 Use appropriate tools strategically.

6 Attend to precision.

7 Look for and make use of structure.

Lesson Objectives

Content Objectives

- Compose two-dimensional shapes to create composite shapes and then compose new shapes from the composite shape.

Language Objectives

- Use pattern blocks to create composite shapes.
- Identify and describe everyday situations or objects involving composite shapes.
- Draw composite shapes using given smaller shapes.

Prerequisite Skills

- Identify and describe squares, circles, triangles, rectangles, hexagons, trapezoids, and rhombuses.

Lesson Vocabulary

- **circle** a figure with no sides and no corners.
- **compose** to combine two or more shapes to create a new shape.
- **composite shape** a figure that is made up of two or more shapes.
- **decompose** to break apart a shape into smaller shapes.
- **half-circle** one of two equal parts of a circle.
- **quarter-circle** one of four equal parts of a circle.

Review the following key terms.

- **corner** a point where two or more lines meet.
- **hexagon** a shape with 6 sides and 6 corners.
- **rectangle** a shape with 4 sides and 4 square corners that has opposite sides the same length.
- **rhombus** a shape with 4 sides and 4 corners that has all sides the same length.
- **side** a line segment that is part of a shape.
- **square** a shape with 4 sides and 4 square corners that has all sides the same length.
- **trapezoid** a quadrilateral with at least one pair of parallel sides
- **triangle** a shape with 3 sides and 3 corners.

Learning Progression

In Kindergarten children compose shapes to build pictures and designs.

In Grade 1 children compose and decompose different shapes, building an understanding of part-whole relationships.

In this lesson children put together two or more shapes to create a composite shape. They learn to perceive a combination of shapes as a single new

shape. As a result, children begin to notice shapes within an already existing shape. These ideas are extended in the next lesson in which children break circles and squares into two or four equal parts.

In Grade 2 children continue to partition circles and squares into 2 and 4 equal parts. They also extend the concept to rectangles and 3 equal parts.

Lesson Pacing Guide

Whole Class Instruction

Day 1
45–60 minutes

Introduction
Use What You Know
• Explore It *25 min*
• Try It *20 min*

Day 2
45–60 minutes

Modeled Instruction
Explore Together
• Opening Question *10 min*
• Think *15 min*
• Talk About It *10 min*
• Visual Model *10 min*

Practice and Problem Solving
Assign pages 251–252.

Day 3
45–60 minutes

Guided Instruction
Explore Together
• Hands-On Problem *5 min*
• Problems 1–2 *10 min*
• Talk About It *15 min*
• Concept Extension *15 min*

Practice and Problem Solving
Assign pages 253–254.

Day 4
45–60 minutes

Guided Practice
Connect It
• Problems 3–5 *15 min*

Independent Practice
Show What I Know
• Problem 6 *15 min*
• Intervention, On-Level, or Challenge Activity *15 min*

Practice and Problem Solving
Assign pages 255–256.

Teacher-Toolbox: Lesson Quiz
Lesson 27 Quiz

Materials for Lesson Activities

Per child: pattern blocks, tangram pictures, 7 tangram pieces
Activity Sheet 32*, Activity Sheet 33*, Activity Sheet 44

Per pair: none

For display: 27 connecting cubes

*Used for more than one activity.

Small Group Differentiation

Teacher-Toolbox.com

Reteach
Ready Prerequisite Lessons *45–90 min*

Grade K
• Lesson 30 Name Shapes
• Lesson 32 Build Shapes

Teacher-led Activities
Tools for Instruction *15–20 min*

Grade 1 *(Lesson 27)*
• Plane Shapes: Making New Shapes
• Shape and Position of Objects
• Making Shapes

Student-led Activities
Math Center Activities *30–40 min*

Grade K *(Lessons 30 and 32)*
• K.42 I Spy Shapes
• K.44 Is It Flat or Solid?
• K.45 Match and Name Shapes
• K.48 Match and Draw
• K.50 Make a Shape
• K.51 Shape Shift

Grade 1 *(Lesson 27)*
• 1.41 Shape Match
• 1.42 Put Shapes Together

Personalized Learning

i-Ready.com

Independent
i-Ready Lessons* *10–20 min*

Grade 1 *(Lesson 27)*
• Parts 1 and 2: Decomposing Two-Dimensional Shapes
• Identifying Two-Dimensional Shapes

*i-Ready lessons may be updated during the 2016–2017 school year. Updated references will be on the Teacher-Toolbox.

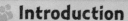
Introduction

Activity Make New Shapes

Objective
Explore ways to put together shapes to make other known shapes.

Materials for each child
- pattern blocks or
  Pattern Blocks (Activity Sheet 33)

Overview
Children explore putting together shapes to make new shapes by placing different pattern blocks together to form the shape of another pattern block.

Step By Step

Explore It

Introduce the activity.

- Distribute Activity Sheet 33 or pattern blocks that match those shapes to children. Hold up the different shapes and have children identify the shape names. Then tell children that they will investigate ways to put shapes together to make other shapes.

Combine two shapes to make a new shape.

- Direct children's attention to the workmat on their Student Book page. Ask them to put together two triangles on the workmat so that one full side of each shape is touching. Then invite children to find a block shape that is the same shape as the new shape. Children should see that these two triangle shapes form a rhombus.

- You may wish to have children place the triangles on top of the rhombus to see that the two shapes match.

- Ask children to put together two trapezoids so that they form one of the other block shapes. Guide children to join corresponding sides of the trapezoids and find the block that it matches. Children should see that they could combine two trapezoids to make a hexagon.

Explore It

Make shapes.

178

Combine like shapes to make new shapes.

- Tell children that they can put together more than two blocks to create other block shapes. Have pairs of children use only triangles to match the given trapezoid piece. Ask: *How many triangles did you use to make a trapezoid?* [3]

- Examine different ways to make a hexagon. Ask: *How many trapezoids did you use to make a hexagon?* [2] *If three triangles make a trapezoid, how many triangles are needed to make a hexagon?* [6] Ask three children to combine triangles to make a hexagon and verify their answers.

- Ask children how they might put together rhombuses to make a hexagon. Encourage children to place a rhombus block on top of a hexagon block, aligning two sides. Then have children place a second rhombus block. Ask: *How can you make a hexagon using only rhombuses?* [put together three rhombuses]

>> Try It

Use 3 different shapes to make a hexagon.
Then trace the shapes you used.

Possible answer:

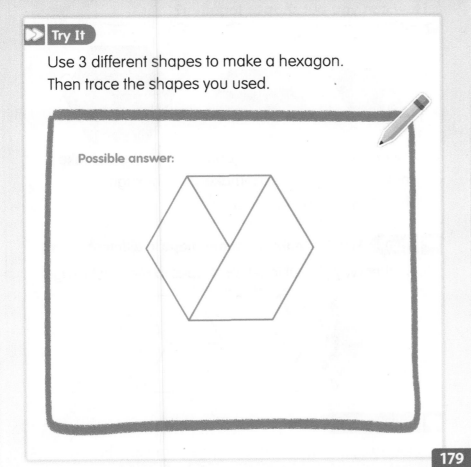

179

Step By Step

Try It

Pose the problem.

- Challenge children to use three different block shapes to make a hexagon.

Solve the problem.

- As children work, look for understanding that a triangle and rhombus can be combined to make a trapezoid and that two trapezoids combine to make a hexagon. Children will have opportunities to develop understanding as they work through the activities of the lesson.

- Once children have found three different shapes that combine to make a hexagon, have them record their work by tracing the individual pattern blocks they used.

Modeled Instruction

Step By Step

- Introduce the question at the top of the page. Discuss with children why they think it is important to know about putting shapes together.

- Direct attention to the shapes shown at the top of the page. Invite children to describe how the pictures remind them of what they did in the Activity in the Introduction.

- Ask children to identify the shapes that have been put together to make the new shape. Then have children name each new shape. Point out that triangles are used to make all three shapes.

Think

- Read Think with children. Direct attention to the hexagon on the left and have children identify the blue shape as a rhombus. Tell children to draw other shapes they can add to the rhombus to make a hexagon. Then challenge them to show another way to make a hexagon that is different from the two ways shown on the page.

▶ **Visual Model**

Talk About It

- Present the Talk About It question. Encourage children to share the different ways they put together shapes.

▶ **Mathematical Discourse 1**

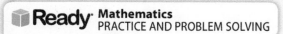 **Mathematics**
PRACTICE AND PROBLEM SOLVING

Assign *Practice and Problem Solving* **pages 251–252** after students have completed this section.

Understand Putting Shapes Together

How can you put shapes together?

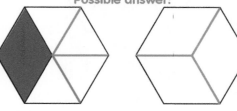

| 2 triangles make a rhombus | 1 rhombus and 1 triangle make a trapezoid | 6 triangles make a hexagon |

💬 **Think** **You can make the same shape in different ways.**

Show other ways to put together shapes to make a hexagon.

Possible answer:

💬 **Talk About It** ·······································

180 How did you put together shapes to make a hexagon?

▶ **Mathematical Discourse**

1 *How did you decide what shapes to show in your hexagon drawings?*
Look for an understanding of which pattern block shapes were combined to make hexagons and which shapes can be combined to make a trapezoid, which is essentially half of a hexagon.

▶ **Visual Model**

Combine shapes to make hexagons.

- Draw 3 regular hexagons on the board. As you complete the activity, use different colors to represent the different shapes that you draw.

- Start with a hexagon that shows six triangles. Then ask children what shape can be made with 2 triangles.

- In the second drawing, replace 2 triangles with 1 rhombus. Continue the process until the second hexagon shows three rhombuses.

- Refer children back to the hexagon with six triangles. Ask them what shape can be made with 3 triangles. In the third hexagon, show how 2 trapezoids can be put together to make a hexagon.

Understand Putting Shapes Together

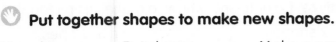 **Put together shapes to make new shapes.**

Use shapes. → Put shapes together. Trace each shape. → Make a new shape. Trace each shape.

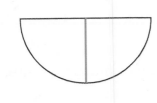   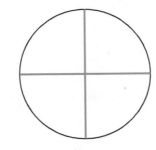

1 Make this.

2 Then make this.

💬 **Talk About It**
What other shapes can you make with shape pieces?

181

Step By Step

• Review the directions at the top of the page. Explain to children that they will put together shapes to make a new shape, and then they will use that new shape to make another new shape.

• Cut out the pieces from Activity Sheet 32 (Shapes 2) and distribute to children. Lead them through the steps of the model at the top of the page, tracing the lines within the rectangle to show the shapes that were put together.

• Have children put together shapes to make the half-circle shown in Problem 1. Tell them to draw the shapes they used.

• Then have them use the shape made in Problem 1 to make the shape in Problem 2, drawing the shapes that were put together to make the circle. Talk about how many quarter-circles were used to make the half-circle and circle.

Talk About It

• Read aloud the Talk About It question. Allow children to use all the shape pieces to see what other composite shapes they can make. Encourage them to describe the shapes they create.

▶ **Mathematical Discourse 2**

▶ **Concept Extension**

> **SMP TIP Look for Structure**
> As children compose shapes, they are building understanding of patterns and iterating units. Encourage children to see not just the composite shape, but the shapes that form the composite shape. *(SMP 7)*

📦 **Ready**· Mathematics
PRACTICE AND PROBLEM SOLVING

Assign *Practice and Problem Solving* **pages 253–254** after students have completed this section.

▶ **Concept Extension**
Put together 3-dimensional shapes.

Materials For display: 27 connecting cubes

• Display a connecting cube and have children name its shape.

• Put together 8 cubes to create a larger cube. Ask: *What shapes did I put together to make another shape?* [cubes]

• Then make several rectangular prisms. Show children how to combine those rectangular prisms to create a cube.

• Discuss the idea that 3-dimensional shapes can be put together to make other 3-dimensional shapes.

▶ **Mathematical Discourse**

2 *Where in your home might someone have put together shapes to make new shapes?*
Children might suggest tile in bathrooms or kitchens, brickwork on a pathway, or fabric pieces to make a quilt.

👥 **Guided Practice**

Step By Step

- Discuss each Connect It problem as a class using the discussion points outlined below.

Analyze

- Cut out the pieces from Activity Sheet 32 (Shapes 2) and distribute to children.

- Tell children that each of the rectangles is formed by several triangles, but they will have to combine these triangles at times to decompose each shape into the given number of shapes. You may want to demonstrate one of the shapes with the class.

- Suggest that children use different colors to show each smaller shape. Encourage them to outline the shapes before coloring to clearly see the sides of the individual shapes used to make the composite shape.

- If children have difficulty starting the activity, remind them of ways in which they combined shapes previously in the lesson.

- Invite children to describe the ways that they decomposed each rectangle. Encourage children to share different solutions.

SMP TIP Use Tools

Allowing children to use shape pieces of different colors to compose rectangles enables them to view situations in which tools can help solve a problem. Encourage children to continue to use concrete models to solve other geometry problems. *(SMP 5)*

Create

- One way to approach Problem 4 is to rearrange the smaller shapes from the rectangles in Problem 3 to create a trapezoid.

- Invite children to share their drawings. Encourage them to comment on the drawings and explanations of others.

- Ask children to explain how they solved this problem. Some children may start with a

---

Connect It

Understand Putting Shapes Together

③ **Analyze** Color to show how to make this rectangle.

Use 2 shapes.   Use 3 shapes.

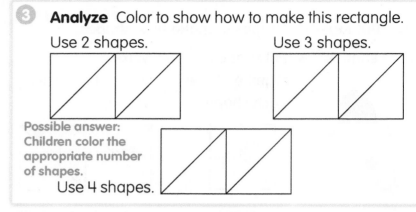

Possible answer: Children color the appropriate number of shapes.

Use 4 shapes.

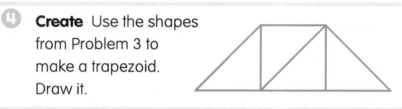

④ **Create** Use the shapes from Problem 3 to make a trapezoid. Draw it.

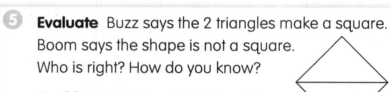

⑤ **Evaluate** Buzz says the 2 triangles make a square. Boom says the shape is not a square. Who is right? How do you know?

Possible answer: I agree with Buzz. The triangles make a square that is turned.

182

---

rectangle in the center and add the two outside triangles. Others may start with the triangles and put them together in different ways until they form the trapezoid.

Evaluate

- Ask children to talk with a partner about the problem. After a few minutes, start a class discussion about the shape.

  Misconception Alert This problem focuses on a common misconception that children have about shapes in different positions.

- Hold up a square pattern block and have children identify it as a square. Rotate the square so that it is oriented like the shape on the student page. Guide children to see that the shape is still a square.

Ready Mathematics
PRACTICE AND PROBLEM SOLVING

Assign *Practice and Problem Solving* **pages 255–256** after students have completed this section.

Show What I Know
Understand Putting Shapes Together

6 **Think about how to put shapes together.**

A: Use 4 or more shapes to make 2 new shapes. Draw them.

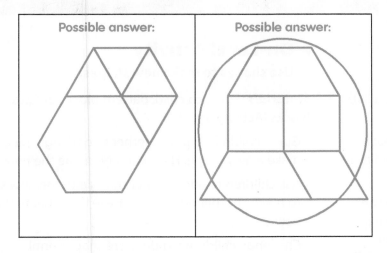

Possible answer: Possible answer:

183

B: Circle one shape above. Write how many of each shape you used.

Possible answer:

 ___0___   ◢ ___1___

 ___2___

 ___2___   ⬡ ___0___

Step By Step

- Read the directions aloud, making sure children understand what they are expected to do. Allow children to use pattern blocks as they work independently to solve the problems.
- In Part A, children use four or more small shapes to make and draw two different composite shapes.
- In Part B, children identify and count the smaller shapes that were used in one of the composite shapes they drew.
- Observe children as they work. Ask questions, such as the following, to encourage thinking and problem-solving strategies:

  How do you know that you have followed the directions?

  How can you easily show the different shapes that you used in each new shape?

  How can you tell that you have recorded all the shapes in Part B?

Scoring Rubrics

	Expectations for 4–3 Points
Points	**Expectations**
4	The child: • accurately uses four or more shapes to make two new shapes and draws the new composite shapes, showing how they're made up of the smaller shapes. • circles one composite shape, and accurately counts and identifies the number of smaller shapes in the composite shape.
3	The child: • may make two new shapes, but may not use four or more smaller shapes for each composite shape or does not indicate the smaller shapes in the composite shape. • may identify the shapes used in the composite shape, but may identify some shapes incorrectly or miscount the number of smaller shapes used.

	Expectations for 2–0 Points
Points	**Expectations**
2	The child: • may make a composite shape, but does not use four or more smaller shapes or does not make two composite shapes. • identifies only a few of the shapes used in the composite shape.
1	The child: • attempts to make two different composite shapes, but there is no evidence of understanding either problem.
0	The child: • does not attempt to solve the problems.

Differentiated Instruction

▶ Intervention Activity

Match shapes to outlines.

Materials For each child: Pattern Blocks (Activity Sheet 33), pattern blocks

• Have children place actual pattern blocks within each shape on the activity sheet, naming the shapes and the number of sides.

• Have children remove the pattern blocks. Point to the rhombus. Instruct children to make the rhombus shape with pattern blocks other than the rhombus. Allow children time to experiment with different shapes until they find a combination that works.

• Guide children to continue working through the shapes, placing different pattern blocks within the outlines to see which pattern blocks can be combined to create each shape on the activity sheet.

▶ On-Level Activity

Use shapes to make new shapes.

Materials For each child: pattern blocks or Pattern Blocks (Activity Sheet 33)

• Guide children to put together two triangle pieces to make a new shape. Have children name the new shape.

• Ask children to add another triangle to the new shape to make another new shape. Have them name that new shape.

• Challenge children to add more shapes until they have formed a hexagon. Encourage some children to try to make a hexagon that looks different than the pattern block hexagon.

• Invite children to share the work they did and name all the shapes they used to make the hexagon.

▶ Challenge Activity

Make pictures with shapes.

Materials For each child: tangram pictures, 7 tangram pieces or Tangram Pieces (Activity Sheet 44)

• Display pictures made from tangram pieces. Challenge children to make their own tangram puzzles or pictures.

• Encourage children to use all seven pieces in their pictures. Have children make their pictures on a sheet of paper. Once the picture is made, children trace around their pictures to make an outline.

• Allow children to trade papers. See if another child can recreate the picture by placing the tangram pieces within the outline.

Teacher Notes

Teacher-Toolbox.com

Overview

Assign the Lesson 27 Quiz and have children work independently to complete it.

Use the results of the quiz to assess children's understanding of the content of the lesson and to identify areas for reteaching. See the Lesson Pacing Guide at the beginning of the lesson and the Differentiated Instruction activities for suggested instructional resources.

Tested Skills

Assesses 1.G.A.2

Problems on this quiz require children to be able to compose two-dimensional shapes to create a composite shape and compose two-dimensional shapes to create the same composite shape in more than one way. Children will also need to be familiar with identifying squares, circles, triangles, rectangles, hexagons, trapezoids, and rhombuses.

Ready® **Mathematics**

Lesson 27 Quiz Answer Key

Name _____

Materials: Shapes cut out from page 3 of the quiz.

Solve.

1 Show 2 different ways to put together shapes to make a circle. *Possible answer:*

2 Show 3 different ways to put together shapes to make a rectangle. *Possible answer:*

Common Misconceptions and Errors

Errors may result if children:

- confuse shapes and their names and/or attributes.
- cannot identify a known shape when shown in a different orientation.
- cannot use the required number of shapes to make a composite shape.

Name _____

Solve.

3 Use 2 shapes to make the trapezoid.
Color to show how to make it.

Possible answer:

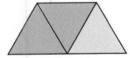

4 Use 3 or more triangles to make a shape. Draw it.

Possible answer:

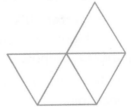

5 Use 2 or more shapes.
Make a new shape.

Possible answer:

CCSS Focus

Domain
Geometry

Cluster
A. Reason with shapes and their attributes.

Standard
1.G.A.3 Partition circles and rectangles into two and four equal shares, describe the shares using the words *halves*, *fourths*, and *quarters*, and use the phrases *half of*, *fourth of*, and *quarter of*. Describe the whole as two of, or four of the shares. Understand for these examples that decomposing into more equal shares creates smaller shares.

Standards for Mathematical Practice (SMP)
2 Reason abstractly and quantitatively.

3 Construct viable arguments and critique the reasoning of others.

4 Model with mathematics.

6 Attend to precision.

7 Look for and make use of structure.

Lesson Objectives

Content Objectives
- Divide circles and rectangles into two and four equal parts.
- Identify the number of equal parts in a divided shape.
- Name the parts as *halves*, *fourths*, and *quarters*.
- Understand that if a whole is divided into more parts, the parts get smaller.

Language Objectives
- Fold or draw lines on paper shapes to show either two or four equal parts.
- Recognize when a folded or divided shape is NOT divided into equal parts and tell why.
- Use the key vocabulary terms *equal parts*, *halves*, *fourths*, and *quarters* in discussions with a partner.

Prerequisite Skills

- Identify circles, squares, and rectangles.
- Compose and decompose shapes.
- Draw shapes.

Lesson Vocabulary

- **equal parts** parts that cover an equal amount of space.
- **fourths, fourth** four equal parts; one of four parts of a whole.
- **halves, half** two equal parts; one of two equal parts of a whole.
- **quarters, quarter** four equal parts; one of four parts of a whole.
- **unequal parts** parts of a whole that are not the same size.
- **whole** all of an object, a group of objects, shape, or quantity.

Learning Progression

In Kindergarten children discuss shape and orientation. They also put shapes together to compose other shapes.

In Grade 1 children develop their understanding of shapes, including defining and non-defining attributes and composing and decomposing shapes.

In this lesson children decompose simple shapes into equal shares of halves and fourths. They describe the relationships between the equal shares and the whole, and between the halves and fourths. This lesson is a foundational building block of fractions, which will be extended in future grades.

In Grade 2 children partition circles and rectangles into two, three, or four equal shares and recognize that equal shares of identical wholes need not have the same shape.

Lesson Pacing Guide

Whole Class Instruction

Day 1
45–60 minutes

Introduction
Use What You Know
- Explore It *25 min*
- Try It *20 min*

Day 2
45–60 minutes

Modeled Instruction
Explore Together
- Opening Question *5 min*
- Think *15 min*
- Talk About It *10 min*
- Hands-On Activity *15 min*

Practice and Problem Solving
Assign pages 259–260.

Day 3
45–60 minutes

Guided Instruction
Explore Together
- Hands-On Problem *5 min*
- Problems 1–2 *15 min*
- Talk About It *10 min*
- Concept Extension *15 min*

Practice and Problem Solving
Assign pages 261–262.

Day 4
45–60 minutes

Guided Practice
Connect It
- Problems 3–5 *15 min*

Independent Practice
Show What I Know
- Problem 6 *15 min*
- Intervention, On-Level, or Challenge Activity *15 min*

Practice and Problem Solving
Assign pages 263–264.

Teacher-Toolbox: Lesson Quiz
Lesson 28 Quiz

Materials for Lesson Activities

Per child: 10 rectangular sheets of paper, scissors, 2 paper plates
Activity Sheet 32*, Activity Sheet 33, Activity Sheet 45

Per pair: geoboard and rubber bands

For display: none

*Used for more than one activity.

Small Group Differentiation

Teacher-Toolbox.com

Reteach
Ready Prerequisite Lessons *45–90 min*

Grade K
- Lesson 30 Name Shapes
- Lesson 32 Build Shapes

Teacher-led Activities
Tools for Instruction *15–20 min*

Grade 1 *(Lesson 28)*
- Plane Figures: Making Equal Shares
- Shape and Position of Objects

Student-led Activities
Math Center Activities *30–40 min*

Grade K *(Lessons 30 and 32)*
- K.42 I Spy Shapes
- K.43 Shape Match
- K.44 Is It Flat or Solid
- K.45 Match and Name Shapes
- K.48 Match and Draw
- K.49 Shape Bingo
- K.50 Make a Shape
- K.51 Shape Shift

Grade 1 *(Lesson 28)*
- 1.43 Parts of Shapes Match
- 1.44 Draw to Show Parts

Personalized Learning

i-Ready.com

Independent
i-Ready Lessons* *10–20 min*

Grade 1 *(Lesson 28)*
- Fraction of a Whole: Halves and Fourths
- Fraction Concepts: Part of a Whole

i-Ready lessons may be updated during the 2016–2017 school year. Updated references will be on the Teacher-Toolbox.

👥 Introduction

Activity Fold Paper into Equal Parts

Objective

Explore equal shares of shapes.

Materials for each child

• rectangular sheet of paper

• Circle (Activity Sheet 45)

Overview

Children explore equal shares by folding paper rectangles and circles into halves and fourths. Children observe the change in size of the parts as more parts are made.

Step By Step

Explore It

Pose the problem.

• Invite two children to come to the front of the class. Hold up a large rectangular sheet of paper. Say: *These two friends want to share a sheet of paper so that they each have the same amount of paper. How can they share the paper?*

Explore halves.

• Distribute rectangular sheets of paper to pairs of children. Have them determine how to share the paper so that each child has an equal part.

• After a few minutes, allow pairs to share their strategies. Some children may fold the paper in half, matching sides and corners. Others may simply draw a line down what they approximate to be the middle of the paper.

• Discuss with the class how to determine if the parts are equal. Encourage partners to see if the two parts match exactly.

• Have children draw a line on the first rectangle on the Student Book page to record how they divided their sheet of paper into two equal parts. Encourage children who are having difficulty showing equal parts to refold their papers to use as a guide.

G Explore It

Draw to show how you found 2 equal parts.

Possible answer:

Draw to show how you found 4 equal parts.

Possible answer:

184

Explore fourths.

• Pose a similar problem. Say: *Four friends want to share a sheet of paper. How can they share the paper?*

• Distribute another rectangular sheet of paper to each pair of children. Guide them to use the strategy of folding and aligning the sides of the paper to make the parts equal.

• Again, have children share their strategies and compare their equal parts. Look for partners who divided the paper differently and discuss how the equal parts can look different but still be equal parts of the whole piece of paper.

• Have children draw lines on the second rectangle on the Student Book page to record how they divided their sheet of paper into four equal parts. Again, encourage children who are having difficulty showing equal parts to refold their papers to use as a guide.

Compare halves and fourths.

• Ask children to compare their two sheets of paper. Note that one sheet shows two equal parts while the other sheet shows four equal parts.

• Have children observe and discuss the size of one part on each sheet of paper. Guide children to see that the sheet with more parts has smaller parts.

>> **Try It**

Draw to show how you found 4 equal parts.

Possible answer:

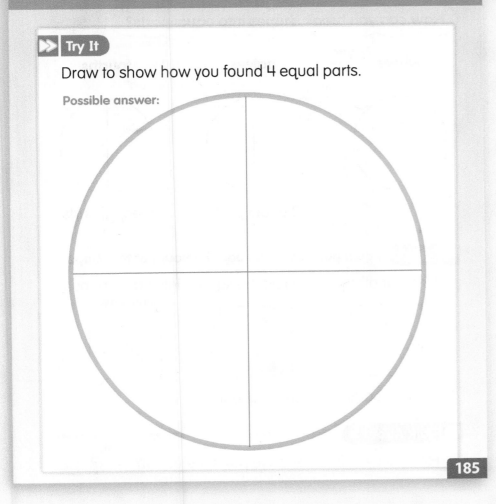

185

Try It

Pose the problem.

- Use the activity sheets to cut out and distribute paper circles to each child.

- Tell children that the circle represents a pie. Ask them to show how four friends can equally share the pie.

Solve the problem.

- Encourage children to fold the circle to find a way to divide the circle into 4 equal-sized parts.

- Ask children to share their strategies and compare their equal parts.

- Have children draw lines on the circle on the Student Book page to record how they divided their circle into four equal parts. Suggest to children who are having difficulty showing equal parts to refold their papers to use as a guide.

- Look for children who divided the paper into parts that are not equal-sized.

- If children struggle with completing the task, they will have opportunities to develop understanding as they work through the activities of the lesson.

Modeled Instruction

Step By Step

- Introduce the question at the top of the page. Then direct attention to the circles. Invite children to describe how the pictures remind them of what they did in the Activity in the Introduction.

- Discuss how a shape that shows 2 equal parts shows *halves* and one part is *half of* the whole. Then help children make the connection between the number *four* and the word *fourths* as you discuss one of 4 equal parts being a *fourth of* the whole.

▶ **English Language Learners**

Think

- Read Think with children. Have them imagine that the squares on the page are pieces of paper or sandwiches that are being shared. Guide children to compare the squares. Ask: *How do you know the parts are not equal?* [They do not cover an equal amount of the shape.]

Talk About It

- Present Talk About It. Encourage discussion by asking questions, such as: *How can you tell if the parts shown at the top of the page are equal?* Encourage children to share many different ideas.

▶ **Mathematical Discourse 1**

▶ **Hands-On Activity**

> **SMP TIP Model with Mathematics**
> Solving real-life problems with models helps children develop mathematical proficiency. Ask children to routinely interpret their mathematical results in the context of a situation and see if the results make sense. *(SMP 4)*

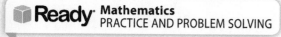 **Ready** Mathematics
PRACTICE AND PROBLEM SOLVING

Assign *Practice and Problem Solving* **pages 259–260** after students have completed this section.

Explore Together
Understand Breaking Shapes into Parts

How can you break shapes into equal parts?

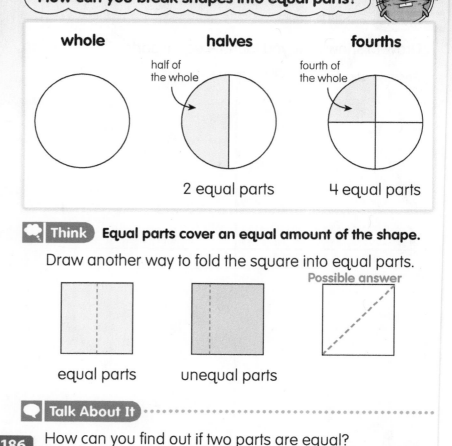

whole   halves   fourths

half of the whole

fourth of the whole

2 equal parts   4 equal parts

Think Equal parts cover an equal amount of the shape.

Draw another way to fold the square into equal parts.

Possible answer

equal parts   unequal parts

Talk About It ·

186 How can you find out if two parts are equal?

▶ **Mathematical Discourse**

1 *If you can't fold a shape in half, how can you be sure that you are breaking it into equal parts?*

Look for responses that include using what they know about the attributes of a shape, or knowing the smaller shapes that can be put together to create a larger shape.

▶ **English Language Learners**

Some languages do not include the "th" sound. When you introduce "fourth" and "fourths," emphasize the "th" ending and contrast the words "four" and "fourth." Allow children to practice pronouncing the words and hearing the difference.

▶ **Hands-On Activity**

Show equal parts on a geoboard.

Materials For each pair: geoboard and rubber bands

- Have partners stretch a rubber band on the geoboard to form a square and then use another rubber band to break the square into two equal parts.

- Encourage children to use the pegs on the geoboard to help them find the middle of one side of the shape. Guide them to anchor the rubber band on that peg and stretch it to the opposite side of the square.

- Then have children suggest how to divide the square into four equal parts. As children share their work, discuss whether they have made equal parts.

Explore Together
Understand Breaking Shapes into Parts

✋ **Fold shapes into equal parts.**

| Fold each shape. → | Draw equal parts. → | Circle the word that describes the parts. |

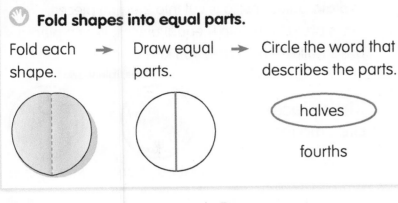

halves

fourths

❶ **Draw 4 equal parts.**
Possible answer:

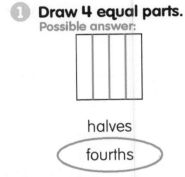

halves

(fourths)

❷ **Draw 4 equal parts.**

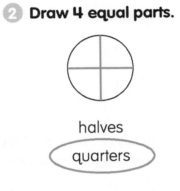

halves

(quarters)

💬 **Talk About It**

Look at a half of a circle. Look at a fourth of the same circle. Which part is larger?

187

▶ **Concept Extension**
Fold other shapes into equal parts.

Materials For each child: Pattern Blocks (Activity Sheet 33)

Cut out and distribute the paper shapes. Have children fold the shapes into two equal parts. Then ask children to try to divide each shape into four equal parts. Discuss the results. Children should discover that not all of the shapes can be divided into four equal parts.

▶ **Mathematical Discourse**

2 *How did you decide if a half of a circle or a fourth of the same circle is larger?*
Some children might have used the parts of the folded shapes, while others may have used the pictured halves and fourths on the page. Encourage several children to share their strategies.

Step By Step

- Cut out the large circle and square from Activity Sheet 32 (Shapes 2) and distribute to each child. Review the directions at the top of the page.

- Have children follow the model by folding the paper circle to show two equal parts. Help them make the connection between the fold line and the line in the second circle that makes equal parts. Ask children why the word *halves* is circled.

- Allow children time to complete Problems 1 and 2. Check that they fold the paper correctly to show equal parts. Encourage children to replicate the fold lines by drawing lines in the shapes on the page.

- Remind children to circle the word that describes the parts. When children get to Problem 2, review that *quarters* is another word that is used to describe four equal parts and means the same thing as *fourths*.

Talk About It

- Read aloud the Talk About It question. Encourage children to justify their answers.

▶ **Mathematical Discourse 2**

▶ **Concept Extension**

📦 **Ready** **Mathematics**
PRACTICE AND PROBLEM SOLVING

Assign *Practice and Problem Solving* **pages 261–262** after students have completed this section.

👥👥 Guided Practice

Step By Step

Discuss each Connect It problem as a class using the discussion points outlined below.

Explain

- This problem focuses on the understanding that decomposing into more equal parts creates smaller parts.

- Suggest that children refer to other places in the lesson where they have divided circles into equal parts.

- Ask questions such as: *How can you tell whose pizza has smaller pieces? How does the size of a part change when there are more parts?*

> **SMP TIP Construct Arguments**
> Asking children to show how they found an answer provides an opportunity for children to construct a viable argument. Encourage children to use concrete referents, such as drawings or diagrams, to make their arguments. *(SMP 3)*

Identify

- In previous problems, the number of equal parts is given. This problem focuses on children's ability to describe the number of equal parts in the whole.

- Suggest that children mark each part as they count the number of equal parts. They might also label each part with a consecutive counting number.

- Ask children what each of the equal parts of this shape is called. [A fourth or a quarter.]

Analyze

- This problem features the meaning of a *quarter* as well as the importance of dividing into equal parts when showing a quarter.

---

3 Explain Jake's pizza is cut into 2 equal pieces. Kim's pizza is cut into 4 equal pieces. Which pieces are smaller? Show how you know.

Possible work:

Kim's pieces are smaller.

Jake's pizza   Kim's pizza

4 Identify Write how many equal parts.

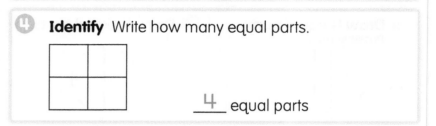

___4___ equal parts

5 Analyze Buzz says that he shaded a quarter of this shape. Do you agree? Why or why not?

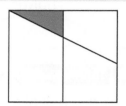

Possible answer: I do not agree. The parts are not equal.

188

- Ask children to talk with a partner about the problem. After a few minutes, start a class discussion about how to know what a quarter of a shape is.

- Ask questions, such as: *How many parts do you make to divide a shape into quarters? How can you tell if the shape is divided correctly?*

- After children share their answers, you may want to draw similar rectangles on the board and invite volunteers to show how to correctly divide the shape into quarters.

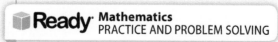 **Ready** **Mathematics**
PRACTICE AND PROBLEM SOLVING

Assign *Practice and Problem Solving* **pages 263–264** after students have completed this section.

Show What I Know
Understand Breaking Shapes into Parts

6 Think about breaking shapes into equal parts.

A: Ben has these cookies.

He shares the cookies with a friend.
They each get equal parts.
Color what Ben gets.
Sample shading:

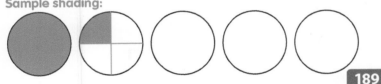

B: 4 friends share the cookies.
Color what Ben gets.
Sample shading:

189

Step By Step

- Read the directions aloud, making sure children understand what they are expected to do.

- Tell children that they will complete this page independently.

- In Part A, 5 cookies need to be shared equally between 2 friends. Children identify that Ben will get some whole cookies and half of one cookie or that Ben will get half of each cookie.

- In Part B, 5 cookies need to be shared equally among 4 friends. Children identify that Ben will get a whole cookie and one-fourth of one cookie or that Ben will get one-fourth of each cookie.

- Observe children as they work. Ask questions such as the following to encourage thinking and problem-solving strategies:

When Ben shares the cookies with one friend, how many equal shares will there be?

Could Ben and his friend each get any whole cookies? How many?

How can Ben and his friend equally share the remaining cookie?

When Ben shares the cookies with three friends, how many equal shares will there be?

If each friend gets one whole cookie, how can they share the remaining cookie?

Scoring Rubrics

Expectations for 4–3 Points

Points	Expectations
4	The child: • accurately shades Ben's share of the cookies in each situation.
3	The child: • may shade a partial cookie in each situation, but does not accurately shade the whole cookies.

Expectations for 2–0 Points

Points	Expectations
2	The child: • may shade more than one cookie in each situation, but does not accurately shade all wholes or parts.
1	The child: • may shade some of the cookies, but there is no evidence of understanding of the problems.
0	The child: • does not attempt to solve the problems.

Differentiated Instruction

▶ Intervention Activity
Match and make halves and fourths.

Materials For each child: 4 sheets of paper, scissors

- Cut one sheet of paper into two equal parts and label each part with the word *half*. Cut a second sheet into four equal parts and label each part with the word *fourth*.

- Have children match the fractional puzzle pieces to a whole rectangular piece of paper, placing them on top of the paper to check that they match.

- Have children fold, cut, and label the unmarked sheets of paper to show halves and fourths.

- You may want to follow up with a discussion about the idea that fourths of the same shape are smaller than halves.

▶ On-Level Activity
Show halves and fourths.

Materials For each child: 2 sheets of paper, 2 paper plates

- Distribute the materials to each child. Have children fold one sheet of paper to show two equal parts. Then have children label each part with the word *half*.

- Have children fold the other sheet of paper to show four equal parts. Have children label each part with the word *fourth*. Discuss with children that the word *quarter* can also be used to describe each part.

- Invite children to repeat the process with the paper plates, showing both halves and fourths.

▶ Challenge Activity
Make more equal parts.

Materials For each child: 3 or 4 pieces of paper

Distribute paper. Challenge children to fold each piece of paper to show a different number of equal parts. Tell them to try to make more than four equal parts with each piece of paper. Have children share their results with the class. You may wish to identify the various numbers of equal parts and ask children to suggest what these parts might be called.

Teacher Notes

Teacher-Toolbox.com

Overview

Assign the Lesson 28 Quiz and have children work independently to complete it.

Use the results of the quiz to assess children's understanding of the content of the lesson and to identify areas for reteaching. See the Lesson Pacing Guide at the beginning of the lesson and the Differentiated Instruction activities for suggested instructional resources.

Tested Skills

Assesses 1.G.A.3

Problems on this quiz require children to be able to decompose shapes into two and four equal parts, name these parts as halves and fourths or quarters, and recognize that the more equal parts a whole is divided into, the smaller each part is. Children will also need to be familiar with identifying circles, squares, and rectangles and composing and decomposing shapes.

Ready® **Mathematics**

Lesson 28 Quiz Answer Key

Name _____

Solve.

1 Show two different ways to draw 2 equal parts.

2 Show 2 equal parts in one circle.
Show 4 equal parts in the other circle.
Color the circle that shows fourths.

3 Write how many equal parts.
Circle the names for the parts.

__4__ equal parts

(fourths)   halves

Common Misconceptions and Errors

Errors may result if children:

- cannot distinguish between equal and unequal parts.
- do not know how to divide a shape into equal-sized parts.
- think that decomposing into more parts results in larger parts.
- do not recognize the relationship between equal shares and the whole or the relationship between halves and fourths.

Lesson 28 Quiz Answer Key continued

Name _____

Solve.

4 Write how many equal parts.
Circle the name for the parts.

__2__ equal parts

fourths   (halves)

5 Break each shape into equal parts to match the word below it.
Which parts are smaller? Circle the word.

Possible drawings:

halves   (quarters)

Assessment

Step By Step

- Have children solve the problems individually and show their work. Emphasize that children are free to use whatever way helps them solve the problems.

- Circulate and observe children as they work. Children should be able to identify shapes and their distinguishing attributes such as number of sides.

- You may want to distribute cutout shapes from Shapes 2 *(Activity Sheet 32)* and Pattern Blocks *(Activity Sheet 33)* for children to use as templates for tracing or as models for drawing shapes. The distinguishing attributes should be visible in the shapes that the children draw.

Unit 6 Review

Solve the problems.

1 How many equal parts are there?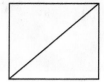

___2___ equal parts

---

2 This circle shows
<u>fourths or quarters</u>

This circle shows
<u>halves</u> .

Which circle has larger parts? Color it.

---

3 Draw a trapezoid.
Possible answer:

4 How many triangles?

___4___

---

5 Circle the rectangle.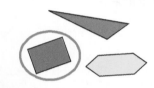

6 Break the shape into
1 ▰ and 1 ▲.

Teacher Notes

7 What shape is this? __triangle__

Put two of these shapes together. Draw.
What shape do they make?

Possible answer:

The two __triangles__ make a __rhombus__.

Step By Step

• For Problem 7, you may want to encourage
children to use the cutout shapes (from the
activity sheets) as templates for tracing or as
models for drawing shapes. The
distinguishing attributes should be visible in
the shapes that the children draw.

8 Circle the words that describe a rhombus.

3 sides

(4 sides the same length)

1 square corner

(opposite sides the same length)

6 sides

191

Teacher Notes

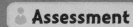
Assessment

Step By Step

Put It Together

- On this page, children draw a shape that is made up of two or four triangles. Then they use this to create a new composite shape. They name the composite shape and identify the equal parts.

- Read the directions and task aloud. Make sure children understand what they need to do to complete the task.

- Direct children to complete problem 9 on their own.

- As children work on their own, observe their progress and understanding. Respond to their questions and provide additional support as needed.

- Have children share their finished drawing with the class. Ask them to name the number of parts their first shape is divided into. [2 or 4].

- Have children point to and identify the shapes they used to make the second composite shape.

- Have children return to the Unit Opener page and complete the *After* column of the progress chart.

Put It Together

9 **Make shapes.**

Put together 2 or 4 triangles like this .

Make a shape with 4 sides. Describe the shape.

The shape is a ___rectangle___.
It has __4__ equal parts.

Circle the word that describes the equal parts.

halves   (fourths)

Possible answer:

Use the shape you made.
Add some other shapes
to make a new shape.

Draw the new shape.

Possible answer:

192

Teacher Notes

192   **Unit 6** Review

Scoring Rubric

Points	Expectations
4	The child: • draws a composite shape using two or four triangles. • identifies the number of equal parts and the fractional name. • identifies all the shapes in the composite shape.
3	The child: • draws a composite shape using two or four triangles. • identifies the number of equal parts and/or the fractional name. • identifies most of the shapes in the composite shape.
2	The child: • may use two or four triangles, but the drawing does not align corresponding sides. • identifies the number of equal parts or the fractional name, but not both. • identifies some of the shapes in the composite shape.
1	The child: • may not use the correct number of triangles and the drawing does not align corresponding sides. • incorrectly identifies the number of equal parts and/or the fractional name. • incorrectly identifies most or all of the shapes in the composite shape.
0	The child: • does not attempt to complete the task.

Which lessons are students building upon?

Kindergarten, Lesson 26
Compare Length
K.MD.A.1, K.MD.A.2

Kindergarten, Lesson 27
Compare Weight
K.MD.A.1, K.MD.A.2

Kindergarten, Lesson 28
Sort Objects
K.MD.B.3

Kindergarten, Lesson 26
Compare Length
K.MD.A.1, K.MD.A.2

Kindergarten, Lesson 27
Compare Weight
K.MD.A.1, K.MD.A.2

Kindergarten, Lesson 26
Compare Length
K.MD.A.1, K.MD.A.2

Kindergarten, Lesson 26
Compare Length
K.MD.A.1, K.MD.A.2

Unit 7

Lesson 29
Sort and Count
1.MD.C.4

Lesson 30
Compare Data
1.MD.C.4

Lesson 31
Order Objects by Length
1.MD.A.1

Lesson 32
Compare Lengths
1.MD.A.1

Lesson 33
Understand Length Measurement
1.MD.A.2

Lesson 34
Tell Time
1.MD.B.3

Which lessons are students preparing for?

Grade 2, Lesson 23
Draw and Use Bar Graphs and Picture Graphs
2.MD.D.10

Grade 2, Lesson 20
Compare Lengths
2.MD.A.4

Grade 2, Lesson 23
Draw and Use Bar Graphs and Picture Graphs
2.MD.D.10

Grade 2, Lesson 16
Understand Length and Measurement Tools
2.MD.A.1

Grade 2, Lesson 17
Measure Length
2.MD.A.1

Grade 2, Lesson 17
Measure Length
2.MD.A.1

Grade 2, Lesson 20
Compare Lengths
2.MD.A.4

Grade 2, Lesson 19
Understand Estimating Length
2.MD.A.3

Grade 2, Lesson 20
Compare Lengths
2.MD.A.4

Grade 2, Lesson 24
Tell and Write Time
2.NBT.A.2, 2.MD.C.7

©Curriculum Associates, LLC   Copying is not permitted

Unit 7 How Many? How Much? How Long? **193b**

Unit 7
How Many? How Much? How Long?

Unit 7 – Measurement and Data
How Many? How Much? How Long?

Sara has pencils of different lengths. She wants to know the lengths of the pencils. What math questions could Sara ask about the pencils?

In this unit, you will learn how to sort objects, tell time, and measure length. Then you will be able to solve problems like Sara's.

✓ Self Check

Check off the skills you know now. Then see how many more you can check off after each lesson!

I can:	Before this unit	After this unit
sort and count objects.	☐	☐
compare data.	☐	☐
order objects by length.	☐	☐
compare lengths of objects.	☐	☐
measure lengths of objects.	☐	☐
tell time to the hour and half-hour.	☐	☐

▣ Ready Mathematics
PRACTICE AND PROBLEM SOLVING

Practice and Problem Solving Resources

Use the following resources from *Practice and Problem Solving* to engage students and their families and to extend student learning.

- **Family Letters** Send Family Letters home separately before each lesson or as part of a family communication package.

- **Unit Games** Use partner Unit Games at classroom centers and/or send them home for play with family members.

- **Unit Practice** Assign Unit Practice as homework, as independent or small group practice, or for whole class discussion.

- **Fluency Practice** Assign Fluency Skills Practice and Fluency Repeated Reasoning Practice worksheets throughout the unit.

At A Glance

- This page introduces children to the general ideas behind counting, sorting, and measuring objects and telling time.
- The checklist allows them to see what skills they will be learning and take ownership of their progress.

Step By Step

- Explain to children that they are going to begin a new unit of lessons. Tell them that in all the lessons in this unit they will be learning how to sort objects, tell time, and measure length.

- Read the introduction to the unit together as a class. Invite children to suggest questions that could be asked about the problem situation. Discuss the questions children pose without the expectation that they are to solve them.

- Then take a few minutes to have each child independently read through the list of skills.

- Ask children to consider each skill and check the box in the *Before* column if it is a skill they think they already have. Remind children that these skills are likely to all be new to them, but it's still possible some children have some of the skills.

- Engage children in a brief discussion about the skills. Invite children to comment on which ones they would most like to learn, or which ones seem similar or related to something they already know. Remind them that the goal is to be able to check off all the skills they have learned by the end of the unit.

- At the end of the unit, have children complete the *After* column. As time allows, pose questions about the problem situation at the top of the page and solve as a class.

©Curriculum Associates, LLC Copying is not permitted

Unit 7 How Many? How Much? How Long? **193**

CCSS Focus

Domain
Measurement and Data

Cluster
C. Represent and interpret data.

Standard
1.MD.C.4 Organize, represent, and interpret data with up to three categories; ask and answer questions about the total number of data points, how many in each category, and how many more or less are in one category than in another.

Additional Standards
1.G.A.1, 1.G.A.2 (See page B3 for full text.)

Standards for Mathematical Practice (SMP)
2 Reason abstractly and quantitatively.
3 Construct viable arguments and critique the reasoning of others.
4 Model with mathematics.
6 Attend to precision.

Lesson Objectives

Content Objectives

- Define meaningful categories for a given set of objects and sort the objects according to the categories.
- Count to find the number of objects in each category.
- Represent categorical data using tally charts, charts with numbers, and picture graphs.

Language Objectives

- Identify and describe the sorting rule or categories used when given objects are sorted into different groups.
- Interpret data to complete tally charts, charts with numbers, and picture graphs.
- Recognize and list more than one way to sort a group of objects.

Prerequisite Skills

- Count up to 20 objects.
- Identify geometric shapes.

Lesson Vocabulary

- **data** numerical information about a set of objects, usually gathered through observation, surveys, or measurement.
- **picture graph** a data display in which pictures are used to represent the number of data in each category.
- **sort** to group or organize objects by shared attributes.
- **tally chart** a data display in which tally marks are used to represent the number of data in each category.
- **tally marks** marks used to show pieces of data being counted.

Learning Progression

In Kindergarten children classify objects into categories. They count collections of objects and compare sets of objects.

In Grade 1 children begin to organize and represent categorical data in various ways. They ask and answer questions about data, using what they know about addition and subtraction.

In this lesson children sort objects into categories and begin to understand the benefits of organizing and representing such data. They represent categorical data in tally charts, in charts with numbers, and in picture graphs. They count the objects in each category and begin to explore categorical information.

In Grade 2 children make picture graphs and bar graphs to represent data sets with up to four categories. They solve simple put-together, take-apart, and compare problems using information presented in the graphs. Children's work with categorical data in early grades prepares them for later work with bivariate categorical data—data that are categorized according to two attributes.

Lesson Pacing Guide

Whole Class Instruction

Day 1
45–60 minutes

Introduction
Use What You Know
• Explore It *25 min*
• Try It *20 min*

Day 2
45–60 minutes

Modeled Instruction
Explore Together
• Example Problem *5 min*
• Model It *20 min*
• Hands-On Activity *20 min*

Practice and Problem Solving
Assign pages 275–276.

Day 3
45–60 minutes

Guided Instruction
Learn Together
• Example Problem *5 min*
• Model It *15 min*
• Talk About It *10 min*
• Concept Extension *15 min*

Practice and Problem Solving
Assign pages 277–278.

Day 4
45–60 minutes

Guided Practice
Practice Together
• Example Problem *5 min*
• Problems 1–2 *25 min*
• Concept Extension *15 min*

Practice and Problem Solving
Assign pages 279–280.

Day 5
45–60 minutes

Independent Practice
Practice by Myself
• Problems 3–4 *15 min*
• Fluency Practice *5 min*
• Quick Check and Remediation *10 min*
• Hands-On or Challenge Activity *15 min*

Teacher-Toolbox: Lesson Quiz
Lesson 29 Quiz

Materials for Lesson Activities

Per child: 20 connecting cubes, 15 two-color counters, pattern blocks
Activity Sheet 33, Activity Sheet 34

Per pair: 30 connecting cubes (10 each in three different colors), pattern blocks, colored strips of paper in different pre-measured lengths
Activity Sheet 33, Activity Sheet 35

For display: tally chart containing information about favorite colors
Activity Sheet 23

Small Group Differentiation

Teacher-Toolbox.com

Reteach
Ready Prerequisite Lessons *45–90 min*

Grade K
• Lesson 28 Sort Objects

Teacher-led Activities
Tools for Instruction *15–20 min*

Grade 1 *(Lesson 29)*
• Sorting in Two Ways

Student-led Activities
Math Center Activities *30–40 min*

Grade K *(Lesson 28)*
• K.38 Sort Objects
• K.39 Look for Attributes

Grade 1 *(Lesson 29)*
• 1.45 Make a Tally Chart

Personalized Learning

i-Ready.com

Independent
i-Ready Lessons* *10–20 min*

Grade 1 *(Lesson 29)*
• Counting Objects in a Set
• Sorting and Counting

* i-Ready lessons may be updated during the 2016–2017 school year. Updated references will be on the Teacher-Toolbox.

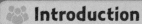

Introduction

Activity Understanding Sorting and Counting

Objective

Identify the rule, or attribute, for a given sorting procedure.

Materials for each child

- 20 connecting cubes (10 each in two different colors)
- 15 two-color counters (optional)

Overview

Children explore the concept of organizing, or sorting, data by categories as they try to determine the rule and predict how each item will be sorted.

Step By Step

Explore It

Pose the problem.

- Distribute up to 10 connecting cubes of one color and up to 10 connecting cubes of another color to each child.
- Instruct the children to use the workmat on the Student Book page to sort the cubes into two groups by color.
- Ask: *What rule did you use to sort the cubes?* [color]

Pose a second problem.

- Explain to children that now you are going to sort the class into two groups and it is their job to figure out the sorting rule.

Sort the children.

- Decide on a sorting rule—striped clothing, for example—but do not share the rule with the class.
- Have children come up to the front of the room one by one, and guide them to the left (striped) or right (not striped).
- After several children have been sorted, ask the class to predict which side the next child will go to.
- Continue sorting, asking children to predict which group each child belongs to.

Sort and Count

Explore It

How can you sort the cubes?

194

Identify the rule.

- After several predictions, have children state what they think the sorting rule is. Keep a list of ideas to discourage repeats.
- If children are unable to figure out the rule, provide some hints. For example: *What do you notice that is the same about everyone in this group?* Or get more specific, such as: *What is the same about everyone's clothing in this group?*
- Once the rule is identified, have children sort a few more classmates. Then discuss their observations about the two groups.

Talk about sorting rules.

- Ask: *What other sorting rules could you use?* Elicit the idea that there are many different ways to sort a group of children, for example, by hair color or gender. Challenge children to look around the room and suggest other sorting rules for different classroom objects.
- As children give their ideas for a sorting rule, listen for evidence that they understand the purpose of sorting: to differentiate objects according to their attributes. Be alert for children who think there is only one way to sort a group.

Use What You Know
Sort and Count

>> Try It

How can you sort the fish?

195

Step By Step

Try It

Pose the problem.

- Direct children's attention to the picture of the fish tank on the Student Book page.

- Ask: *What are some different ways you could sort the fish?*

- Have children work in pairs to discuss ways the fish could be sorted.

Talk about sorting rules.

- Ask: *What sorting rules could you use?*

- Have children share the ways they think the group could be sorted. Some possible answers include: by size, by having stripes or dots, by whether the fish has bubbles coming out of its mouth, by color, by the direction the fish is facing.

- Make sure children understand that there are many ways to sort this group. Ask: *What would happen if I asked you to sort the group of fish by how many of their eyes you can see?* [You'd have only one group of fish, since all fish have the same number of eyes showing.]

Sort the fish.

- Have children sort the fish by size (large fish and small fish), and count how many there are of each type. [5 large, 6 small]

- Some children may benefit from using manipulatives to help them avoid double counting. Provide counters as needed and suggest that children place counters of one color over the large fish and counters of another color over the small fish, then count how many counters of each color.

- Have children sort the fish by another attribute, then count and tell how many fish are in each group.

Modeled Instruction

Step By Step

- Read the questions at the top of the page.

- Explain that to answer these questions, you have to sort the shapes. That means making groups that include all the same shapes. Use the Hands-On Activity to introduce the sorting process or provide practice.

▶ **Hands-On Activity**

Model It

- Read Model It with children. Point out that the tally chart uses tally marks to represent each object that fits the sorting category. Guide children to identify the sorting categories as triangle, square, and trapezoid.

- Have children count the triangles, making sure that they keep track of them as they count. Ask Mathematical Discourse question 1 to emphasize the importance of organization and tracking.

▶ **Mathematical Discourse 1**

- Compare children's counts with the number of tally marks in the triangle row.

- Tell children to complete the tally chart by counting the squares and then the trapezoids. As they count and keep track of each shape above, children make a tally mark in the chart below.

- Ask children to verify that the tallies are correct for each shape. Then ask them to complete the second chart with the appropriate numbers for each category.

Ready· Mathematics
PRACTICE AND PROBLEM SOLVING

Assign *Practice and Problem Solving* **pages 275–276** after students have completed this section.

Explore Together
Sort and Count

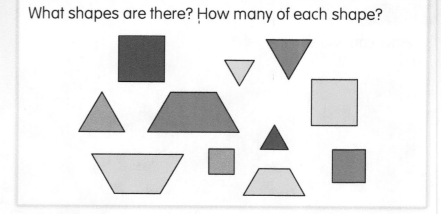

What shapes are there? How many of each shape?

▮ **Model It** Make a chart.

Sort by shape. You can make a tally chart to count.
You can also make a chart with numbers.

Shapes	How Many
△	IIII
☐	IIII
▱	III

Shapes	How Many
△	4
☐	4
▱	3

196

▶ **Mathematical Discourse**

1 *How can you keep track of the objects as you count them?*
Some children may cover the shapes with their fingers. Others might make a mark on each as they count. Children should be able to explain their method and show that there is a one-to-one correspondence between tally marks and the actual number of items in any category.

▶ **Hands-On Activity**

Sort shapes.

Materials For each pair: pattern blocks or Pattern Blocks (Activity Sheet 33)

- Have children work in pairs. Give them about 10–12 pattern blocks with three different shapes.

- Have children sort the blocks into groups and explain their sorts to the class. Ask how many pattern blocks are in each category.

Learn Together
Sort and Count

What color are the pencils?

How many of each color?

⊞ Model It Make a picture graph.

Sort and count.

Pencils	How Many
✏️	IIII
✏️	III
✏️	III

Use circles to show how many.

Pencils	How Many
✏️	OOOO
✏️	OOO
✏️	OOO

💬 Talk About It Do you agree? Why or why not?

Buzz says he can sort the pencils by size.

197

▶ Concept Extension
Sort by two attributes.

• Review that the pencils can be sorted by color or by length. Then explain that they can be sorted by both color and length.

• Ask: *How many pencils are both yellow and short?* [2] *How many are yellow and long?* [2] Continue with the other colors.

• After counting the pencils that belong in each of these groups, ask children to find the total number of pencils and verify that it is the same as in the sorting by color.

• You may want to have children revisit the picture of the fish from the Activity in the Introduction, and have them sort the fish using two attributes.

▶ Mathematical Discourse

2 *How are the tally chart and picture graph alike? How are they different?*

Children should understand that both the tally chart and the picture graph show how many of each color pencil there are. The tally chart uses tally marks to stand for each pencil and the picture graph uses circles.

Step By Step

• Read the questions at the top of the page. Be sure children understand that they need to sort by color. You may want to give pairs colored strips of paper in lengths that match the pencils in the problem to allow them to do a physical sort.

Model It

• Have children work with a partner to verify the number of yellow pencils. One child counts and marks the yellow pencils while the other counts the tally marks. Guide children to recognize that the number of tally marks in each row matches the number of circles in the picture graph.

• Instruct partners to complete the tally chart and picture graph, taking turns counting and making tally marks and circles. Encourage them to check their work.

▶ **Mathematical Discourse 2**

Talk About It

• Read Talk About It. Discuss that the pencils are different lengths and can also be sorted into groups of short pencils and long pencils. Clear up the misconception that there is only one way to sort a group of objects.

▶ **Concept Extension**

> **SMP TIP Model with Mathematics**
> As children organize and display data—sorting, counting, making picture graphs, etc.—they make connections between different models. To support this emerging understanding, ask children to explain how a tally chart or picture graph helps them see patterns in the data. (*SMP 4*)

 Ready Mathematics
PRACTICE AND PROBLEM SOLVING

Assign *Practice and Problem Solving* **pages 277–278** after students have completed this section.

👥 Guided Practice

Step By Step

- Direct attention to the picture of the balls at the top of the page. Tell children that they will sort the balls into groups of footballs, kickballs, and soccer balls. Then they will make a tally chart and picture graph to show how many of each kind of ball there are.

- You may want to make copies of the picture and cut out the individual balls so children can use them to complete the sorting process.

- Put children in pairs to complete the tally chart. One partner can count the balls while the other makes tally marks. Together, partners check their work and make sure their tally charts are complete.

- Direct attention to Problem 2. Guide children to see that the column headings and the categories match those in the tally chart. Have children complete the picture graph independently.

- Compare completed graphs as a class and allow children to make corrections as needed.

▶ **Mathematical Discourse 1**

▶ **Concept Extension**

SMP TIP Attend to Precision
Children attend to precision as they communicate with each other to carefully count and precisely record each piece of data. When they check their work, children make sense of the symbols (tally marks) they used to record the data. *(SMP 6)*

 **Mathematics**
PRACTICE AND PROBLEM SOLVING

Assign *Practice and Problem Solving* **pages 279–280** after students have completed this section.

Practice Together
Sort and Count

How many of each kind of ball are there?

You can make a tally chart.
You can make a picture graph.

1 Complete the tally chart.

Ball	How Many
🏈	|||
🔴		
⚽	||||

2 Complete the picture graph.

Ball	How Many
🏈	○ ○ ○
🔴	○
⚽	○ ○ ○ ○

198

▶ **Mathematical Discourse**

1 *What pictures are used in the picture graph to show how many of the different kinds of balls there are? Why do you think these pictures are used?*
Children might recognize that the pictures of circles resemble the shape of the balls and realize that circles are easy to draw.

▶ **Concept Extension**

Discuss how graphs can be used.

- Discuss with children how graphs display data that has been counted and sorted. This allows people who were not involved in the sorting and counting to see what the results are.

- Explain that graphs can be used to ask and answer questions about the data. Ask questions, such as the following, and have children explain how the graph can be used to find the answer: *What kind of balls are there the most of? The fewest? How many more soccer balls than footballs are there? How many balls are there in all?*

Practice by Myself
Sort and Count

Use the data.

Favorite Fruit

❸ Make a tally chart.   Make a chart with numbers.

Favorite Fruit	How Many
🍎	卌卌 I
🍌	卌
🍐	III

Favorite Fruit	How Many
🍎	6
🍌	5
🍐	3

❹ Make a picture graph.

Favorite Fruit	How Many
🍎	☺ ☺ ☺ ☺ ☺ ☺
🍌	☺ ☺ ☺ ☺ ☺
🍐	☺ ☺ ☺

199

Step By Step

- Cut the data cards from Activity Sheet 34 (Data Cards) and distribute a set to each child.

- Read each problem aloud, then have children work independently to solve.

- Pose a data collection situation. Say: *A teacher has cards with pictures of apples, pears, and bananas. She asks some children to pick the card that shows the fruit that they like best. She collects the cards they pick. The picture at the top of the page and the cards that you have show their choices.*

- Tell children that they need to sort the fruit cards and make a tally chart, a chart with numbers, and a picture graph. Make sure children understand that the same data is used for each of the displays.

- Observe children as they work to make sure they are sorting correctly. Suggest that they choose a picture that is easy to draw to make the picture graph.

- Ask Mathematical Discourse question 2 to check that children understand the process used for collecting and displaying data.

▶ **Mathematical Discourse 2**

▶ **Fluency Practice**

▶ **Fluency Practice**

Count by 1s, 2s, and 5s.

Materials For display: 120 Chart (Activity Sheet 23)

Display the 120 chart. Have the class count on by 1, 2, and 5, using examples like the following:

- count by 1:
  start at 22 and end at 40
  start at 46 and end at 60

- count by 2:
  start at 12 and end at 40
  start at 68 and end at 90

- count by 5:
  start at 25 and end at 120
  start at 55 and end at 100

▶ **Mathematical Discourse**

2 *Why do you think you were asked to make a tally chart first? Which chart or graph do you think shows the data best?*

Children might recognize that they first have to sort and count the data and that the tally chart helps with the counting process. Some children may prefer the chart with numbers as a data display since there is no need to count. Others might prefer the picture graph since it is more illustrative and concrete.

Differentiated Instruction

▶ Quick Check and Remediation

Materials For display: tally chart containing information about favorite colors: 5 blue, 6 green, 4 yellow.

• Show children the tally chart. Have them make a picture graph to display the data.

• For children who are still struggling, use the chart below to guide remediation.

• After providing remediation, check children's understanding by changing the numbers and/or colors used in the chart, and asking children to create a picture graph using the new data.

If the error is . . .	Children may . . .	To remediate . . .
the pictures do not correspond to the number of people	not understand how to count tally marks.	Explain that each line stands for one person who picked that color. Point out that a diagonal line is used to make a group of 5. Ask children to count the tallies again and fix their graphs.
labels are missing or inaccurate	not recognize the importance of appropriate labels or know how to write them.	Ask children to describe in words what the categories represent. Have children write their description in the appropriate position on the graph. Discuss how someone who hasn't studied the data would not know what the pictures mean if they are not labeled.

▶ Hands-On Activity

Build tally charts one category at a time.

Materials For each pair: two copies of Chart Template (Activity Sheet 35), 30 connecting cubes (10 each in three different colors)

• Give pairs of children a few connecting cubes that are all the same color and the chart templates. Direct their attention to the first blank chart. Have them write the color in the first column and write tally marks in the second column as they count the cubes. Discuss.

• Collect the connecting cubes. Give pairs 2 colors of connecting cubes and direct their attention to the next blank chart. Elicit that they need to sort the cubes before counting and writing tally marks. Have children complete the task.

• Collect the connecting cubes. Give pairs 3 colors of connecting cubes and direct their attention to a third chart. Have children describe what they need to do: sort, count, tally. Have them complete the task and then verify their tallies.

▶ Challenge Activity

Create pattern block pictures and make a tally chart.

Materials For each child: pattern blocks or Pattern Blocks (Activity Sheet 33)

• Have children create a picture using at least a dozen of the pattern block shapes. Encourage them to combine multiple pieces together so that the picture is made up of pattern block shapes touching. You may want to model an example.

• Once the children have created their pictures, have them trace one shape at a time before removing it from the design. Then have the children create a tally chart of the shapes they used.

• Children may wish to swap tally charts with a partner and gather the blocks that the tally chart specifies. Then each child can attempt to follow the traced diagram to make their partner's pattern block picture.

Teacher Notes

Lesson 29
Sort and Count

Teacher-Toolbox.com

Overview

Assign the Lesson 29 Quiz and have children work independently to complete it.

Use the results of the quiz to assess children's understanding of the content of the lesson and to identify areas for reteaching. See the Lesson Pacing Guide at the beginning of the lesson and the Differentiated Instruction activities for suggested instructional resources.

Tested Skills

Assesses 1.MD.C.4

Problems on this quiz require children to be able to sort objects into categories, count the number of objects in each category, and represent the categorical data using tally charts, charts with numbers, and picture graphs. Children will also need to be familiar with counting up to 20 objects and identifying geometric shapes.

Ready **Mathematics**

Lesson 29 Quiz Answer Key

Name _____

Solve.

How many of each kind of beach toy are there?

1 Make a tally chart.

Beach Toy	How Many
🩴	|
🏐	||||
🪣	||

2 Make a chart with numbers.

Beach Toy	How Many
🩴	1
🏐	4
🪣	2

3 Make a picture graph.

Beach Toy	How Many
🩴	◯
🏐	◯ ◯ ◯ ◯
🪣	◯ ◯

Grade 1 **Lesson 29** Sort and Count

 1

©Curriculum Associates, LLC
Copying permitted for classroom use.

Common Misconceptions and Errors

Errors may result if children:

- do not understand tally marks or how to count them.
- do not recognize the importance of accurate labels or know how to interpret them.
- do not understand the sorting categories.

Name _____

Solve.

Use the data. **Favorite Animal**

4 Make a tally chart.

Favorite Animal	How Many
🐭	⊍⊍⊍
🐟	IIII
🐰	⊍⊍⊍ I

5 Make a picture graph.

Favorite Animal	How Many
🐭	◯ ◯ ◯ ◯ ◯
🐟	◯ ◯ ◯ ◯
🐰	◯ ◯ ◯ ◯ ◯ ◯

©Curriculum Associates, LLC
Copying permitted for classroom use.

2

LESSON OVERVIEW

Lesson 30
Compare Data

CCSS Focus

Domain
Measurement and Data

Cluster
C. Represent and interpret data.

Standard
1.MD.C.4 Organize, represent, and interpret data with up to three categories; ask and answer questions about the total number of data points, how many in each category, and how many more or less are in one category than in another.

Additional Standards
1.OA.A.1, 1.OA.C.6 (See page B3 for full text.)

Standards for Mathematical Practice (SMP)

1 Make sense of problems and persevere in solving them.

2 Reason abstractly and quantitatively.

4 Model with mathematics.

5 Use appropriate tools strategically.

7 Look for and make use of structure.

Lesson Objectives

Content Objectives

• Answer questions about data in charts and graphs.

• Compare quantities represented in charts and graphs.

Language Objectives

• Read data in a tally chart or picture graph and tell what it represents.

• Record answers to comparison questions (more and fewer) about data in a tally chart or picture graph.

• Listen to the ideas of others about how to make sense of the data in tally charts or picture graphs and compare their strategies.

Prerequisite Skills

• Read a tally chart or picture graph.

• Compare quantities within 20.

Lesson Vocabulary

There is no new vocabulary. Review the following key terms.

• **compare** to decide if amounts or sizes are greater than, less than, or equal to each other.

• **data** numerical information about a set of objects, usually gathered through observation, surveys, or measurement.

• **picture graph** a data display in which pictures are used to represent the number of data in each category.

• **tally chart** a data display in which tally marks are used to represent the number of data in each category.

• **tally marks** marks used to show pieces of data being counted.

Learning Progression

In Kindergarten children classify objects into categories. They work with data by counting and making comparisons.

In Grade 1 children sort and count to organize and represent categorical data in various ways. They work with up to three categories.

In this lesson children build their repertoire of analytical skills through comparing categorical data in charts and graphs. They ask and answer questions about data, using what they know about addition, subtraction, and comparison.

Using categorical data builds skills with real-world problem solving.

In Grade 2 children draw picture graphs and bar graphs to represent data sets with up to four categories. They solve simple put-together, take-apart, and compare problems using information presented in the graphs. Children's work with categorical data in early grades prepares them for later work with bivariate categorical data—data that are categorized according to two attributes.

Lesson Pacing Guide

Whole Class Instruction

Day 1
45–60 minutes

Introduction
Use What You Know
• Explore It *25 min*
• Try It *20 min*

Day 2
45–60 minutes

Modeled Instruction
Explore Together
• Example Problem *5 min*
• Model It *25 min*
• Fluency Practice *15 min*

Practice and Problem Solving
Assign pages 283–284.

Day 3
45–60 minutes

Guided Instruction
Learn Together
• Opening Question *5 min*
• Model It *15 min*
• Talk About It *10 min*
• Hands-On Activity *15 min*

Practice and Problem Solving
Assign pages 285–286.

Day 4
45–60 minutes

Guided Practice
Practice Together
• Example Problem *5 min*
• Problems 1–2 *25 min*
• Visual Model *15 min*

Practice and Problem Solving
Assign pages 287–288.

Day 5
45–60 minutes

Independent Practice
Practice by Myself
• Problems 3–4 *10 min*
• Concept Extension *10 min*
• Quick Check and Remediation *10 min*
• Hands-On or Challenge Activity *15 min*

Teacher-Toolbox: Lesson Quiz
Lesson 30 Quiz

Materials for Lesson Activities

Per child: 16 connecting cubes, assortment of 3 kinds of small objects (such as pattern blocks, buttons, and dried beans)
Activity Sheet 35, Activity Sheet 36

Per pair: none

Per group of 3: 45 connecting cubes (15 each in 3 different colors)

For display: 12 pieces of tape
Activity Sheet 46

Small Group Differentiation

Teacher-Toolbox.com

Reteach
Ready Prerequisite Lessons 45–90 min

Grade K
• Lesson 26 Compare Length
• Lesson 27 Compare Weight

Teacher-led Activities
Tools for Instruction 15–20 min

Grade 1 *(Lesson 30)*
• Representing Data: Tally Charts
• Counting Up to 20 Objects
• Sorting in Two Ways

Student-led Activities
Math Center Activities 30–40 min

Grade K *(Lessons 26 and 27)*
• K.34 Length Vocabulary
• K.35 Compare Lengths
• K.36 Which Weighs More?
• K.37 Heavier or Lighter?

Grade 1 *(Lesson 30)*
• 1.46 Picture Graph Questions

Personalized Learning

i-Ready.com

Independent
i-Ready Lessons* 10–20 min

Grade 1 *(Lesson 30)*
• Subtraction Concepts: Comparison
• Picture Graphs
• Comparing Sets
• Sorting and Counting

* i-Ready lessons may be updated during the 2016–2017 school year. Updated references will be on the Teacher-Toolbox.

👥 Introduction

Activity Compare Data

Objective
Collect and display categorical data, and describe features of the data set.

Materials for display
- 12 pieces of tape
- Shape Cards (Activity Sheet 46)

Overview
Children collect and use categorical data to answer a question. They describe the data, noting particular aspects such as total number of responses and which categories have the most/least responses.

Step By Step

Explore It

Pose the problem.
- Distribute one shape card to each of 12 children. Tell children to look at the shape on their own card, but not to show their card to anyone else.
- Say: *Some children have a shape card. What shapes are on the cards? How many of each type of shape are there?* Ask children to discuss reasons why someone might want to know this information. Reasons may include "simple curiosity."

Organize a data display.
- Say: *Let's make a picture graph to show the number of different shapes.*
- Draw the outline of a picture graph on the board. Include the column headings *Shape* and *Number of Shapes*.
- Enlist children's help in determining the types of shape to show in each row. Have children holding a shape card name their shape. Write the name of each shape in a row of the picture graph on the board: *Triangle, Circle, Square*

Use What You Know
Compare Data

◯ Explore It

Make a picture graph. Sample answer:

Shape	Number of Shapes
Triangle	◺ ◺ ◺ ◺ ◺ ◺
Circle	◯ ◯
Square	▢ ▢ ▢ ▢

What does the picture graph show?

Gather and display the data.
- Tell the children to count the number of sides their shape has and recall the name of the shape.
- Invite each child with a shape card to come up to the display, show their card to the class, tell the name of the shape, and tape their shape card in the appropriate row for that shape.
- Tell children to place each card right next to any others that are already in the row, without overlapping. This creates a picture graph, with one card for each child's shape. [6 triangles, 2 circles, 4 squares]

Draw the picture graph.
- Have children draw pictures to record the number of shapes for each category in the picture graph on the Student Book page.

>> **Try It**

Write about the picture graph.

Number of responses in all _____ 12 _____

Shape with most responses _____ triangle _____

Shape with fewest responses _____ circle _____

There are more _____ triangles _____ than squares.

A question I can ask about our picture graph is:

Answers will vary. _____

_____

_____

_____ .

201

Step By Step

Try It

Describe the data.

- When children have completed their picture graphs, tell them that they are now ready to describe the data. Give children time to study the graph.

- Read aloud the question in the thought bubble on the previous page: *What does the picture graph show?* Guide children to see that the picture graph shows all the shapes they had on their cards.

- Ask: *How many responses are there in all? How can you find out?* Children may add the number of shapes in each row or count all.

- Ask which category has the most responses, which has the fewest, and which category has more responses than the squares category. Have children record their answers on the Student Book page.

- Encourage children to think about other questions they can ask and answer about the graph. Have children write a question on the Student Book page. Invite volunteers to share their questions and have the class find an answer.

- Have children look for interesting differences and similarities between the categories and offer explanations for why they think the data came out this way.

Summarize the data.

- Have children work in small groups to prepare a report that summarizes the information they have found. Reports might explain how the data was gathered and summarize the key features of the data.

Modeled Instruction

Step By Step

- Begin by asking children what they have learned or remember from the Activity in the Introduction. Explain that picture graphs are one way to organize and display data so others can understand what it is about.

- Read the description at the top of the page and go over the parts of the picture graph: the title, the categories, the pictures.

- Ask: *What are you trying to find out?* [How many children have dogs or cats.] Use the Mathematical Discourse questions to discuss the meaning of the data.

▶ **Mathematical Discourse 1 and 2**

Model It

- Explain that Model It shows one way to answer the question. Read the information. Have children point to each picture and count it. Ask: *Why don't you just count everything together?* [We are not looking for the total number of children.] Ask: *Why do you start at "1" for each row?* [Each row tells the number of children who have one kind of pet.]

- Have children tap each smile face and count them out loud for dogs and cats.

- Have children complete the addition statement and answer the question.

▶ **Fluency Practice**

SMP TIP Use Tools

Show children how picture graphs are a tool for solving data problems. Present the data shown in the picture graphs as scattered words on the board. Discuss how the graph organizes the data and makes it much easier to answer questions, like those in the Mathematical Discourse. (SMP 5)

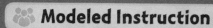 **Ready** Mathematics
PRACTICE AND PROBLEM SOLVING

Assign *Practice and Problem Solving* **pages 283–284** after students have completed this section.

Explore Together
Compare Data

Children name their pets. They make a picture graph with the data. How many have dogs or cats?

Our Pets

Bird	☺ ☺
Dog	☺ ☺ ☺ ☺ ☺ ☺ ☺
Cat	☺ ☺ ☺ ☺

Model It Find how many children have dogs or cats.

Each picture shows 1 child. Count the pictures for dogs. Count the pictures for cats. Then add.

Our Pets

Bird	☺ ☺	
Dog	① ② ③ ④ ⑤ ⑥ ⑦	_7_ dogs
Cat	① ② ③ ④	_4_ cats

$7 + 4 = \underline{11}$

202 $\underline{11}$ **children have dogs or cats.**

▶ **Mathematical Discourse**

1 *What information does this picture graph give us? What do the pictures stand for?*

Children should be able to recognize that the picture graph tells what pets a group of children have. Each picture represents one child who has a pet.

2 *What other questions could you ask and answer about this data?*

Children might suggest questions that involve comparisons, such as the most, the fewest, or how many more. Other questions might ask about the total number of data items in two or all three of the categories.

▶ **Fluency Practice**
Practice adding three numbers.

Materials For each child: Practice Adding Three Numbers (Activity Sheet 36)

Distribute Activity Sheet 36 (Practice Adding Three Numbers). Explain that children need to add each group of numbers and show their work. Have children work independently.

Learn Together
Compare Data

How many more 🍐 than 🍎 ?

Favorite Fruits	How Many
🍐	14
🍌	8
🍎	12

▦ Model It

Color the squares to show how many.

14 is how many more than 12?

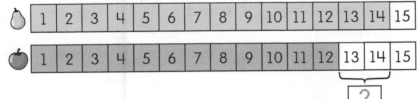

🍐 | 1 | 2 | 3 | 4 | 5 | 6 | 7 | 8 | 9 | 10 | 11 | 12 | 13 | 14 | 15

🍎 | 1 | 2 | 3 | 4 | 5 | 6 | 7 | 8 | 9 | 10 | 11 | 12 | 13 | 14 | 15

2

There are __2__ more 🍐 than 🍎 .

💬 Talk About It

Look at the chart. What other questions can you ask?
What answers can you find?

203

▶ Hands-On Activity

Build a data set from information in a table.

Materials For each group: 45 connecting cubes (15 each in three different colors)

- Mention that, in the past, the class has sorted and counted objects to make charts or graphs. This time, they will use the information in the table on the Student Book page to make a collection of objects.

- Have children choose one color of connecting cubes to represent each fruit.

- Children work in groups of three to assemble "fruit bars" with connecting cubes to represent the numbers shown in the table. Each child makes a bar for one fruit.

▶ Mathematical Discourse

3 *What are some other ways you can compare?*

Children might mention various methods they have used, such as comparing actual objects, using bar models, matching one-to-one, counting on, etc.

▶ English Language Learners

Discuss the use of the word *table*. Explain that when information is organized into rows and columns, that is often called a table. This is not a tally chart, because it does not have tally marks, and it is not a picture graph because it does not use pictures to represent the data, only numbers. In fact, the tally charts and picture graphs are special kinds of tables. Ask children what other meanings they know for the word *table*.

Step By Step

- Read the question aloud. Discuss the difference between the table shown here and the picture graph on the previous page; the table shows numeric values rather than pictorial representations of quantities.

▶ English Language Learners

- Discuss the meaning of the table and that each number indicates how many people chose that fruit as their favorite. Ask: *Why might someone want to compare favorite fruits?*

Model It

- Have children examine Model It. Point out that the number paths are another way to show how many of each kind of fruit. Discuss this as a method for comparing quantities. Use Mathematical Discourse question 3 to relate to other ways of comparing.

▶ Mathematical Discourse 3

- Have children complete the comparison and discuss.

Talk About It

- Ask children to discuss the Talk About It questions with a partner. Encourage each pair to ask and answer two questions about the data. Circulate to monitor discussions.

> **SMP TIP Use Structure**
> While children are discussing the Talk About It questions, they are making use of the structure provided by the displays of data and building a foundation for future data representations. Ask them which representations best help them answer their questions and why. (SMP 7)

▶ Hands-On Activity

Ready Mathematics
PRACTICE AND PROBLEM SOLVING

Assign *Practice and Problem Solving* **pages 285–286** after students have completed this section.

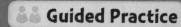
Guided Practice

Step By Step

- Read the directions to the example problem. Ask children to describe how the graph shows that more children like grapes than strawberries or apples. Explain that *most* means *more than anything else*. Ask Mathematical Discourse question 1 to encourage children to think about the process used in analyzing data.

▶ **Mathematical Discourse 1**

- Discuss Problem 1 with children. Have them tell what is being asked. Ask them to describe the table, identify the three kinds of blocks, and tell what the numbers mean. Discuss approaches for solving and have children find the total.

- Discuss Problem 2 with children. Review the convention for grouping tally marks in groups of 5. Have the children describe what the tally chart represents. [The number of markers Ms. Lee has.] Elicit that the questions ask for *how many more* and *how many fewer* comparisons. Have children work in pairs to answer the questions and then explain their solutions to the class.

▶ **Visual Model**

Ready Mathematics
PRACTICE AND PROBLEM SOLVING

Assign *Practice and Problem Solving* **pages 287–288** after students have completed this section.

Compare Data

Circle the fruit that the most children like.

Fruit	Number of Children
🍎	☺ ☺ ☺ ☺ ☺ ☺
🍓	☺ ☺ ☺ ☺ ☺
🍇	☺ ☺ ☺ ☺ ☺ ☺ ☺ ☺

1 Children counted their blocks. How many blocks did they count in all?

They counted __19__ blocks in all.

Blocks	How Many
◆	9
▽	4
△	6

2 The tally chart shows Ms. Lee's markers.

Marker	Tally Marks
Blue	|||| |||| ||
Red	|||| |||
Yellow	|||| |||| ||||

How many more yellow than red? __7__

How many fewer red than blue? __4__

204

▶ **Mathematical Discourse**

1 *When you look at data in a table, chart, or graph, what do you look for first, and why?*

Children can learn from listening to each other's strategies for making sense of data. Listen for those who may be focusing on peripheral attributes of the display rather than the important parts. Also listen for indications that children are seeking the meaning in a data display rather than just seeing an assemblage of pictures or numbers.

▶ **Visual Model**

Make a picture graph from tally marks or a data table.

- A picture graph is a visual model of data. Have children make their own picture graphs based on the data representations in Problem 1 or Problem 2. Children may work alone or with a partner.

- For the data in these problems, pictures of smile faces or stick figures don't make sense. Discuss what kinds of pictures, or symbols, would be appropriate. For example, children might use circles or check marks to represent the shapes in Problem 1 and might use simple illustrations of a marker or perhaps rectangles to represent the markers in Problem 2.

Practice by Myself
Compare Data

3 The tally chart shows what children like best.
Write the number for each object.
Circle the one that the most children like.

 _12_

 _8_

  _18_

Object	Tally Marks
	⊪⊪ ⊪⊪ ||
	⊪⊪ |||
	⊪⊪ ⊪⊪ ⊪⊪ |||

4 Circle what more children like.
Write how many more.

(boots) or slippers   _4_ **more**

Circle what fewer children like.
Write how many fewer.

sneakers or (boots)   _6_ **fewer**

205

Step By Step

- Before children work on this page, review the different data displays presented in this lesson.
- Read each problem aloud, then have children work independently to solve.
- For Problem 3, observe to see if children are able to connect the context—liking something best—to the tally chart. They then have to find the object that *most* children like *best*.
- Problem 4 asks children to make comparisons based on the data in Problem 3. Observe to ensure that children understand the meaning of *more* and *fewer*. Ask children to explain the strategies they used to solve.
- Ask Mathematical Discourse question 2 to show the connection between data analysis and problem solving.

▶ **Mathematical Discourse 2**

▶ **Concept Extension**

▶ **Concept Extension**

Write a number sentence to compare.

- Display the tally chart and solution to Problem 3. Write the following statement on the board to compare boots and slippers: "4 more children like boots best than like slippers best."

- Say: *This is a word sentence that compares the data. Let's write a number sentence.* Point out that 8 children like slippers best and 12 like boots best.

- Ask: *Which is greater?* [12] *How can you tell?* [There are more tally marks for boots than for slippers.] Say: *You know that 8 plus some more is equal to 12.* Write "8 + ___ = 12" and ask for a volunteer to solve.

- Next, write the following to compare sneakers and boots: "6 fewer children like boots best than like sneakers best." Point out that this time the question is "how many fewer." Have children describe how to write a missing addend number sentence and solve.

▶ **Mathematical Discourse**

2 *How can you check your work when you compare data?*

Listen for multiple strategies for solving problems and verifying that the answers are correct. Encourage children to solve a problem one way and then check it using a different approach. For example, if a child uses subtraction to determine that 4 more children like boots than slippers, they might line up counters to verify their answer.

Differentiated Instruction

▶ Quick Check and Remediation

Materials For each child: 16 connecting cubes

- Ask children to look at a picture graph showing number of rainy (3), cloudy (9), and sunny (13) days and tell how many more days were sunny than rainy. [10]
- For children who are still struggling, use the chart below to guide remediation.
- After providing remediation, check children's understanding by having them look at a picture graph showing number of rainy (8), cloudy (14), and sunny (11) days and tell which kind of weather occurred on the most days and how they know. [Cloudy, because there were 3 more cloudy days than sunny days and 6 more cloudy days than rainy days.]

If the error is . . .	Children may . . .	To remediate . . .
3 or 13	not understand how to compare and gave one of the quantities instead.	Explain that this is the number of rainy (or sunny) days. Have children count the pictures for rainy days and for sunny days. Ask if there are more sunny days or more rainy days. [Sunny.] Have them use the method of their choice to compare the quantities.
16	not understand how to compare and gave the sum instead.	Have children line up connecting cubes to represent the rainy and sunny days. Point out how the cubes and the rows of pictures in the picture graph look similar. Allow children to match the connecting cubes or use another strategy to compare.
6 or 12	be trying to compare rainy and cloudy days.	Have children point to the items they are comparing; correct any misunderstanding.

▶ Hands-On Activity

Make a picture chart.

Materials For each child: assortment of small objects of 3 kinds (pattern blocks, buttons, dried beans, etc.), Chart Template (Activity Sheet 35)

- Give each child a handful of the mixed objects. Have them sort their objects directly onto a blank picture graph template.
- Have children label each row, and then remove their objects one by one, replacing each one with a picture. Then have children count pictures in each row.
- Invite children to display their picture graphs and describe the data, giving at least one comparison.

▶ Challenge Activity

Survey the class and report the results.

- Have children work in pairs or small groups to create a categorical question to ask their classmates. Each group surveys the class and records the data with a tally chart.
- Groups use the tally chart to make either a picture graph or a numeric table. Each group presents their results to the class, along with information about the total number of responses, which categories had the most and fewest responses, and any other information they found interesting.
- Display the results in the classroom.

Teacher Notes

Teacher-Toolbox.com

Overview

Assign the Lesson 30 Quiz and have children work independently to complete it.

Use the results of the quiz to assess children's understanding of the content of the lesson and to identify areas for reteaching. See the Lesson Pacing Guide at the beginning of the lesson and the Differentiated Instruction activities for suggested instructional resources.

Tested Skills

Assesses 1.MD.C.4

Problems on this quiz require children to be able to compare and interpret data in charts and graphs and answer questions about the data. Children will also need to be familiar with reading a tally chart or picture graph and comparing quantities within 20.

Ready® **Mathematics**

Lesson 30 Quiz Answer Key

Name _____

Solve.

1 The picture graph shows what toy children like best.
Write the number for each toy.
Circle the toy that the most children like.

 9

 7

 5

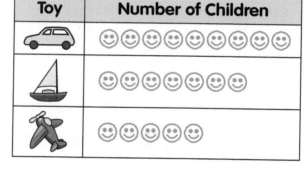

Toy	Number of Children
🚗	☺☺☺☺☺☺☺☺☺
⛵	☺☺☺☺☺☺☺
✈	☺☺☺☺☺

2 Circle the toy that more children like.
Write how many more.

 or __2__ more

Circle the toy that fewer children like.
Write how many fewer.

 or __4__ fewer

Grade 1 **Lesson 30** Compare Data   1   ©Curriculum Associates, LLC
Copying permitted for classroom use.

Common Misconceptions and Errors

Errors may result if children:

• do not or cannot compare quantities and instead give one of the quantities or the sum of the quantities as an answer.

• compare the incorrect quantities.

• confuse more and fewer.

• do not understand tally marks or how to count them.

Name _____

Solve.

3 The tally chart shows what farm animal children like best. Write the number for each animal. Circle the animal that the most children like.

 ___13___

 ___7___

 ___15___

Animal	Tally Marks
	卌 卌 |||
	卌 ||
	卌 卌 卌

4 Circle the animal that more children like. Write how many more.

 or ___6___ more

Circle the animal that fewer children like. Write how many fewer.

or ___8___ fewer

2

CCSS Focus

Domain
Measurement and Data

Cluster
A. Measure lengths indirectly and by iterating length units.

Standard
1.MD.A.1 Order three objects by length; compare the lengths of two objects indirectly by using a third object.

Standards for Mathematical Practice (SMP)

3 Construct viable arguments and critique the reasoning of others.

6 Attend to precision.

7 Look for and make use of structure.

Lesson Objectives

Content Objectives
• Order three objects by length.

Language Objectives
• Order three classroom objects by length (shortest to longest or longest to shortest).
• Orally explain why one end of all the objects being ordered by length must be aligned.
• Draw a line that is shorter or longer than two given objects.

Prerequisite Skills

• Compare quantities within 10.
• Describe measurable attributes of objects, such as length.

Lesson Vocabulary

• **length** the distance from one point to another.
• **longer** describes the greater length of two objects being compared.
• **longest** greatest in distance.
• **shorter** describes the lesser length or height of two objects being compared.
• **shortest** least in distance or height.
• **taller** describes the greater height of two objects being compared.
• **tallest** describes the greatest height when ordering three or more objects by height.

Review the following key term.

• **compare** to decide if amounts or sizes are greater than, less than, or equal to each other.

Learning Progression

In Kindergarten children begin to describe measurable attributes, such as length. They directly compare two objects to see which object is longer or shorter.

In Grade 1 children compare and order objects by length. They use a non-standard reference unit to measure objects by laying multiple copies of a shorter object end to end. They understand that the number of such reference objects is the length measurement of the item being measured.

In this lesson children compare the lengths of three objects, lining them up so that one end is aligned, and put the items in order by length. They identify the shortest and longest objects.

In Grade 2 children come to understand the need for standard units of measurement and begin using standard tools to measure objects and compare length.

Lesson Pacing Guide

Whole Class Instruction

Day 1
45–60 minutes

Introduction

Use What You Know
- Explore It *25 min*
- Try It *20 min*

Day 2
45–60 minutes

Modeled Instruction

Explore Together
- Example Problem *20 min*
- Model It *25 min*

Practice and Problem Solving
Assign pages 291–292.

Day 3
45–60 minutes

Guided Instruction

Learn Together
- Example Problem *5 min*
- Model It *10 min*
- Talk About It *15 min*
- Hands-On Activity *15 min*

Practice and Problem Solving
Assign pages 293–294.

Day 4
45–60 minutes

Guided Practice

Practice Together
- Example Problem *5 min*
- Problems 1–2 *25 min*
- Fluency Practice *15 min*

Practice and Problem Solving
Assign pages 295–296.

Day 5
45–60 minutes

Independent Practice

Practice by Myself
- Problems 3–5 *10 min*
- Concept Extension *10 min*
- Quick Check and Remediation *10 min*
- Hands-On or Challenge Activity *15 min*

Teacher-Toolbox: Lesson Quiz
Lesson 31 Quiz

Materials for Lesson Activities

Per child: 1 book, 20 connecting cubes (10 each in two different colors), 3 objects of 3 different lengths, 3 objects of 3 different heights Activity Sheet 37

Per pair: 3 pencils of 3 different lengths, 3 pieces of straws of 3 different lengths, 4 or 5 objects of different heights or lengths

Per group of 3: connecting cubes (a different color and number for each child)

For display: none

Small Group Differentiation

Teacher-Toolbox.com

Reteach
Ready Prerequisite Lessons *45–90 min*

Grade K
- Lesson 26 Compare Length

Teacher-led Activities
Tools for Instruction *15–20 min*

Grade 1 *(Lesson 31)*
- Describing Length
- Measuring Height and Length

Student-led Activities
Math Center Activities *30–40 min*

Grade K *(Lesson 26)*
- K.34 Length Vocabulary
- K.35 Compare Lengths

Grade 1 *(Lesson 31)*
- 1.47 Use Vocabulary for Length

Introduction

Activity Compare Length and Height

Objective
Compare lengths of three objects.

Materials for each pair
- 3 pencils of 3 different lengths
- 3 pieces of straw of 3 different lengths

Overview
Children develop a process for comparing the lengths of three objects.

Step By Step

Explore It

Pose the problem.
- Show children a short pencil and a box of pencils of various lengths. Say: *I got this pencil from a board game. I want to save all our short pencils to use in our classroom games. Let's compare the length of some pencils and find which ones are the shortest.*

Set up the problem.
- Take 3 pencils of similar lengths from the box and distribute to 3 children who are not sitting near each other.
- Have children stand and hold up their pencils.
- Ask: *Can you tell which is shortest?* [No]
- Ask: *What should you do to compare the lengths of these pencils?* Guide children to recognize that they can lay the pencils side by side.

Solve the problem.
- Emphasize the importance of aligning one end of the pencils (use the eraser or flat end).
- Have children point out which is longest and shortest. Set aside the shortest pencil for use in classroom games.

Solve a similar problem.
- Distribute 3 pencils of 3 different lengths to each pair of children.

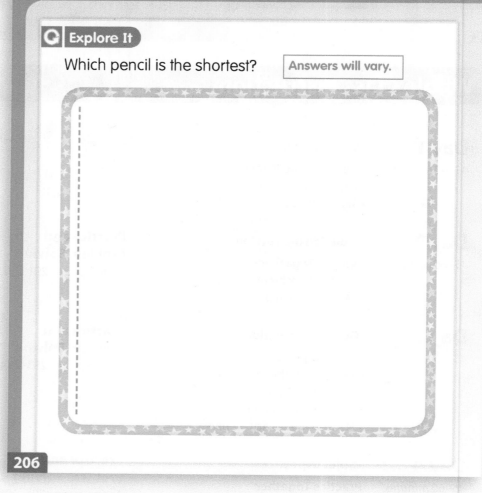

Explore It

Which pencil is the shortest?   Answers will vary.

206

- Ask children to put the 3 pencils in order from shortest to longest, aligning one end with the dashed line at the left of the workmat shown on the Student Book page. Have children explain to their partner how they decided.
- Watch for misalignment of the objects and for children who don't understand that the shortest one is the one that "sticks out" a lesser distance than all the others.
- Once children have ordered the pencils by length, you may want to have them record their work by tracing around the pencils on their workmats.

Discuss.
- Ask: *How can you tell which is shortest?* [The other pencils "stick out" farther.]
- Reiterate the importance of aligning one end of the objects.

Use What You Know
Order Objects by Length

>> Try It

Which straw is the tallest? | Answers will vary. |

207

Step By Step

Try It

Pose another problem.

- Explain that you don't usually say *length* when you measure objects that are positioned up and down; you say *height* and *how tall*. Call a child to the front of the room and say: *Let's compare my height to the height of [child's name].*

- Have the class determine who is taller and who is shorter.

- Have children work in pairs. Distribute 3 pieces of straws of 3 different lengths to each pair.

- Ask children to put the pieces of straw in order from tallest to shortest.

Solve the problem.

- Watch for misalignment of the objects. Encourage children to use the dashed line at the bottom of the workmat on their Student Book page to help them align their straws.

- Once children have ordered the pieces of straw by height, ask them to tell which is tallest.

- You may wish to have children record their work by drawing a line on their workmats that is the same height as each piece of straw.

Lead the class in discussion.

- Invite children to share how comparing the pencils and the pieces of straw were the same and how they were different.

Modeled Instruction

Step By Step

- Begin by asking children what they have learned or remember from the Activity in the Introduction. Review the idea of lining up objects to compare length.

▶ **English Language Learners**

- Read the example problem aloud. Discuss with the class how they would compare the length of the collars. Elicit that you can't always tell just by looking.

Model It

- Point out that, in Model It, the collars are off the dogs' necks and are stretched out to their full length. Also point out the dashed line that indicates the collars are properly lined up. Ask: *What would happen if one of the collars was bent or twisted?* [We couldn't measure accurately.]

> **SMP TIP Attend to Precision**
> Encourage children to attend to precision by questioning them about how and why to align the end points of objects. The procedures children learn in this lesson form the foundation for future work with measurement, including assigning an appropriate number to a measurement. (SMP 6)

- Have children run their fingers along each collar and compare them visually. Ask children which collar is longest and tell them to complete the first sentence.

- Repeat with the shortest collar and have children complete the second sentence. Ask: *How do you know?*

▶ **Mathematical Discourse 1**

Assign *Practice and Problem Solving* **pages 291–292** after students have completed this section.

Order Objects by Length

Three dogs with collars.
Which collar is the longest?

▦ **Model It** Compare lengths. ··························

Lay the collars on a table.
Line up one end.
Put them in order from shortest to longest.

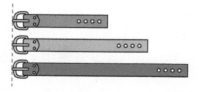

The ___blue___ collar is the longest.

208 The ___pink___ collar is the shortest.

▶ **Mathematical Discourse**

1 *What other measurements could you compare in this picture?*
Children should use the language of measurement to talk about the height of the dogs and the length of the dogs or their tails. Some may even mention width. Have children clarify how they would compare these dimensions, and address any misconceptions or misuse of terminology.

▶ **English Language Learners**

Help children distinguish among the many terms for measuring and comparing length: *length, height, width, long, tall, wide, short*. Discuss the comparative forms such as *longer* and *shorter*; these are used to compare two objects. When comparing three objects, teach children to use the superlative *est* forms—*longest, tallest, shortest*—to tell which object is the most long/tall/short of all.

Learn Together
Order Objects by Length

Ron puts books on a shelf.
He wants to order them
from shortest to tallest.
Which book is shortest?

▦ Model It **Order the books from shortest to tallest.** ·········

Stand the books on a shelf.
Circle the shortest.
Put an X on the tallest.

💬 Talk About It **Do you agree? Why or why not?** ·········

Boom says the red flower is the shortest.

Possible answer: I don't agree. The stem of
the red flower is not lined up with the other
stems. It looks like the yellow one is the
shortest.

209

▶ Hands-On Activity
Compare the widths of books.

Materials For each child: 1 book

- Have children stand their books up to
show the direction for measuring the
book's height (up and down). Then have
them indicate the direction for
measuring the book's width (across).

- Organize children in groups of three.
Have them compare the widths of their
books, put the books in order from
narrowest to widest, and identify the
widest book.

- Circulate to monitor and provide
guidance. Ask: *What edge of the books
did you line up to compare widths?* [The
edge of the spine, or possibly the edge
of the side opposite the spine. All three
books should be aligned along the
same edge.]

▶ Mathematical Discourse

2 *How would you help Boom find the
shortest flower?*

Children's responses should indicate
that one end of all three flowers must
be aligned before they can compare
and find the shortest. Some children
may be tempted to guess. Press them
to verify their answers; "just knowing"
is not enough in math. They need to be
able to explain their reasoning.

Step By Step

- Read the problem aloud. Ask: *Are you
comparing the length, width, or height of the
books? How do you know?* [Height; *shortest*
and *tallest* are words that describe height.]

- Have children hold up a book and indicate
which sides are used to measure its height.
Invite a volunteer to describe how you
might compare the heights of these books.

Model It

- Direct children's attention to Model It. Ask:
*How do you know the books are lined up
properly?* [They are all on the same shelf.]
Point out that they are all aligned the same
way as well, with the binding side out.

- Have children mark the books as indicated.
Check that they are correctly choosing the
shortest and tallest book.

Talk About It

- Read Talk About It aloud. Have children
discuss the problem in pairs. Then discuss
as a class. Elicit that only two of the three
flowers are aligned on the dashed line.

▶ **Mathematical Discourse 2**

▶ **Hands-On Activity**

Ready. **Mathematics**
PRACTICE AND PROBLEM SOLVING

Assign *Practice and Problem Solving*
pages 293–294 after students have
completed this section.

👥👥 Guided Practice

Step By Step

- Read through the problem with the class. Point out the use of the word *shorter* to compare the top worm with the bottom worm. Guide children to recognize that all three worms are aligned, so they can easily compare lengths.

- For Problem 1, have children explain how they determined the shortest and the longest pencil.

- Read Problem 2 with the class. Use the Mathematical Discourse question to guide discussion. Elicit children's ideas about how to approach the problem and encourage flexible thinking.

▶ **Mathematical Discourse**

- Reinforce the use of the words *shorter, longer, shortest,* and *longest* by asking children to compare the lengths of the worms, pencils, and dogs in as many ways as they can.

▶ **Fluency Practice**

📦 **Ready**· **Mathematics**
PRACTICE AND PROBLEM SOLVING

Assign *Practice and Problem Solving* **pages 295–296** after students have completed this section.

Practice Together
Order Objects by Length

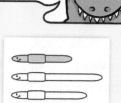

Color the worm that is the shortest.
The middle worm is longest.
The top worm is shorter than
the bottom worm.

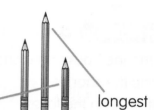

1 Draw lines to show
which pencil is longest
and which is shortest.

shortest   longest

2 Read the clues.
Then color the dogs.

The red dog is longest.

The blue dog is shorter
than the yellow dog.

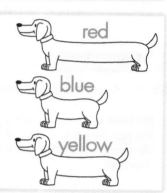

red

blue

yellow

210

▶ **Mathematical Discourse**

- *How do you know which dog to start with?*

Listen for evidence of logical reasoning. Since all three dogs are aligned, the first sentence tells you that the top dog should be red. According to the second sentence, you can compare the two remaining dogs and color the shorter one blue.

▶ **Fluency Practice**

Make a ten with connecting cubes.

Materials For each child: Practice Making a Ten to Add (Activity Sheet 37), 20 connecting cubes (10 each in two different colors)

- Distribute connecting cubes and Activity Sheet 37 (Practice Making a Ten to Add).

- Children model the addition facts using two colors of connecting cubes. Then they decompose one addend, compose a ten with the other addend, find the sum, and write the new addition sentence.

- Model the example problem $5 + 8 = \underline{\quad}$. Make trains of 5 and 8 connecting cubes. Break apart the 5-cube train and place 2 of the cubes on the 8-cube train to make 10. Relate this action to the number sentences shown in the example problem.

Practice by Myself
Order Objects by Length

3 Read the clues.
Then color the bats.

The green bat is shortest.
The red bat is longer than
the blue bat.

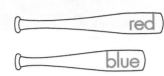

4 Circle the word that makes the
sentence true.

The green balloon is (shorter) / longer
than the orange balloon.

5 Draw a line that is taller than both rectangles.
Possible answer:

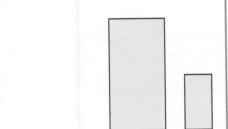

211

Step By Step

- Before children work on this page, review the length comparison words used throughout the lesson.

- Read each problem aloud, then have children work independently to solve.

- Problem 3 requires children to use logical reasoning to determine which color to use for each bat.

- Problem 4 has the children identify the attribute of the object rather than look for the object with a given attribute. Ask children how they determined the answer.

- Problem 5 provides an open-ended opportunity for children to draw their own image of something that is taller than the given rectangles. Ask children to describe to you how they know their line is the tallest. Watch that children are comparing height rather than width.

▶ **Concept Extension**

SMP TIP Look for Structure
As children gain practice in making length comparisons, they focus on the measurable attribute of length and gain a better understanding. Encourage children to remember the structure of these problems as they approach new measurement challenges. *(SMP 7)*

▶ **Concept Extension**
Order four or five objects by length or height.

Materials For each pair: 4 or 5 objects of different heights or lengths

Give pairs of children four or five objects and have them put the objects in order by length (or height) from longest (or tallest) to shortest. Have each group describe how they solved the problem and explain their answer.

Differentiated Instruction

▶ Quick Check and Remediation

Materials For each child: 3 objects of 3 different lengths, 3 objects of 3 different heights

- Ask children to put three objects in order from shortest to longest.
- For children who are still struggling, use the chart below to guide remediation.
- After providing remediation, check children's understanding using by asking them to identify the tallest and shortest item in a set of three objects.

If the error is . . .	Children may . . .	To remediate . . .
reverse order	not understand that the order matters.	Have children point to the shortest and the longest. If these are incorrect, place the shortest object on the left and say: *What comes next?* Continue in this manner.
an order of short, long, medium or long, short, medium	not have aligned one end of each object or compared the other ends incorrectly.	Guide children to align one end of each object. Then have them lightly trace to the end of each object with a finger. Ask: *Which object sticks out the farthest?* Guide children to identify this as the longest object. Ask: *Which one is next longest?* Then elicit that the remaining object is the shortest.
objects jumbled or piled	not understand the task.	Pick up the objects and hold them so that they are almost aligned. Point out that some objects stick up farther than the others. Explain that these are longer. Help children align the objects correctly. Then have them lightly trace each object. Ask: *Which object sticks out the farthest?* Guide children to identify this as the longest object. Then ask: *Which one is next longest?* Then elicit that the remaining object is the shortest.

▶ Hands-On Activity

Compare heights of connecting cube towers.

Materials For each group of 3: connecting cubes (a different color and number for each child)

- Group three children together. Have each child build a tower out of connecting cubes, all the same color.
- Tell groups to order the towers from shortest to tallest.
- Tell one child from each group to add 3 cubes to their towers. Allow the group to re-order their towers if needed.

▶ Challenge Activity

Line up from shortest to tallest.

Put children in groups of three or four. Say: *Your task is to line up in order from shortest to tallest, without talking. You may use gestures, but you cannot speak.* Have other children check to see if the group lined up correctly.

Teacher Notes

Teacher-Toolbox.com

Overview

Assign the Lesson 31 Quiz and have children work independently to complete it.

Use the results of the quiz to assess children's understanding of the content of the lesson and to identify areas for reteaching. See the Lesson Pacing Guide at the beginning of the lesson and the Differentiated Instruction activities for suggested instructional resources.

Tested Skills

Assesses 1.MD.A.1

Problems on this quiz require children to be able to order three objects by length, identify the longest and shortest objects, and draw a line that is longer or shorter than all given objects. Children will also need to be familiar with describing measurable attributes of objects, such as length.

Ready® **Mathematics**

Lesson 31 Quiz Answer Key

Name _____

Solve.

1 Read the clues.

Then color the flowers.

The red flower is the tallest.
The blue flower is shorter than the yellow flower.

blue red yellow

2 Read the clues.

Then color the rectangles.

The blue rectangle is the shortest.
The yellow rectangle is longer than the green rectangle.

green

blue

yellow

3 Circle the word that makes the sentence true.

The gray pencil is shorter/longer than the white pencil.

Grade 1 **Lesson 31** Order Objects by Length   1   ©Curriculum Associates, LLC
Copying permitted for classroom use.

Common Misconceptions and Errors

Errors may result if children:

- do not align one end of each object before drawing to compare.
- do not understand (or confuse) the order and put objects in reverse order.
- confuse *longer* with *shorter* or *longest* with *shortest*.
- do not reason logically.

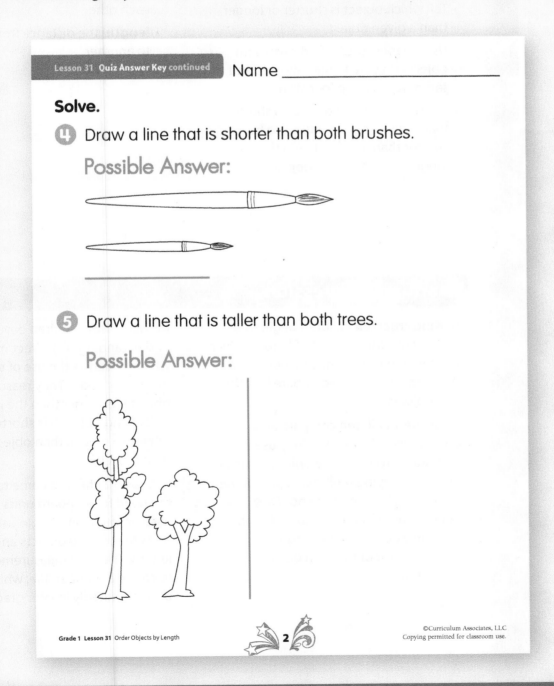

CCSS Focus

Domain
Measurement and Data

Cluster
A. Measure lengths indirectly and by iterating length units.

Standard
1.MD.A.1 Order three objects by length; compare the lengths of two objects indirectly by using a third object.

Standards for Mathematical Practice (SMP)
3 Construct viable arguments and critique the reasoning of others.

5 Use appropriate tools strategically.

6 Attend to precision.

7 Look for and make use of structure.

Lesson Objectives

Content Objectives
- Recognize that sometimes it is not possible to compare length directly.
- Compare two objects by comparing their lengths to a third, reference, object.
- Use logical reasoning to indirectly compare the lengths of objects.

Language Objectives
- Tell which object is shorter or longer than a given object.
- Use a paper strip to find classroom objects that are longer, shorter, and the same size as the paper strip.
- Describe why an item that is shorter than a given object must also be shorter than a second item that is longer than the given object.

Prerequisite Skills
- Compare the lengths of two objects.
- Compare and order quantities within 10.

Lesson Vocabulary
There is no new vocabulary. Review the following key terms.
- **compare** to decide if amounts or sizes are greater than, less than, or equal to each other.
- **length** the distance from one point to another.

Learning Progression

In Kindergarten children begin to understand the concept of length, which is a core measurement concept. They use direct comparison to compare lengths of two objects.

In Grade 1 children compare and order objects by length. They use a non-standard reference unit to measure objects by laying multiple copies of the reference object end to end. They understand that the number of such reference objects is the length measurement of the item being measured.

In this lesson children develop an understanding of indirect measurement, which underlies the use of standard measuring tools. They reason that if object A is longer than the reference object and object B is shorter than the reference object, then object A is longer than object B.

In Grade 2 children come to understand the need for standard units of measurement and begin using standard tools to measure objects and compare length. They use measurement concepts to create a number line, which is a model used repeatedly in later grades.

Lesson Pacing Guide

Whole Class Instruction

Day 1 45–60 minutes	**Introduction** **Use What You Know** • Explore It 25 min • Try It 20 min	
Day 2 45–60 minutes	**Modeled Instruction** **Explore Together** • Example Problem 5 min • Model It 25 min • Visual Model 15 min	**Practice and Problem Solving** Assign pages 299–300.
Day 3 45–60 minutes	**Guided Instruction** **Learn Together** • Example Problem 5 min • Model It 10 min • Talk About It 15 min • Hands-On Activity 15 min	**Practice and Problem Solving** Assign pages 301–302.
Day 4 45–60 minutes	**Guided Practice** **Practice Together** • Example Problem 5 min • Problems 1–2 20 min • Concept Extension 20 min	**Practice and Problem Solving** Assign pages 303–304.
Day 5 45–60 minutes	**Independent Practice** **Practice by Myself** • Problems 3–5 10 min • Fluency Practice 10 min • Quick Check and Remediation 10 min • Hands-On or Challenge Activity 15 min	
	Teacher-Toolbox: Lesson Quiz Lesson 32 Quiz	

Materials for Lesson Activities

Per child: 6 connecting cubes, unsharpened pencil, strip of paper, assortment of classroom items, heavy paper strip, 2 different pieces of pre-measured string, 3 index cards (labeled *Pam, Joe,* and *Robin*)

Per pair: 10 connecting cubes, clay, 2 index cards (labeled *longer* and *shorter*) Activity Sheet 38

For display: strip of paper, box of objects of different lengths, a reference object, masking tape

Small Group Differentiation

Teacher-Toolbox.com

Reteach **Ready Prerequisite Lessons** 45–90 min

Grade K • Lesson 26 Compare Length

Teacher-led Activities **Tools for Instruction** 15–20 min

Grade 1 *(Lesson 32)* • Describing Length • Measuring Height and Length

Student-led Activities **Math Center Activities** 30–40 min

Grade K *(Lesson 26)* • K.34 Length Vocabulary • K.35 Compare Lengths

Grade 1 *(Lesson 32)* • 1.48 Shorter or Longer Objects

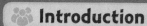

Introduction

Activity Compare Lengths

Objective
Use a reference object to sort other objects as *taller* or *shorter*.

Materials for each child
- one strip of paper (cut so each child's strip is a different length, with about half longer, half shorter, and one or two the same length as the benchmark strip)
- new, unsharpened pencil
- assortment of classroom items

Materials for display
- benchmark strip of paper that is 3 inches long

Overview
Children sort strips of paper into *taller* and *shorter* groups by comparing each paper strip to a benchmark strip. They then draw lines that are shorter or longer than a given length of pencil.

Step By Step

Explore It

Pose the problem.
- Distribute paper strips to children. Ask: *How can we figure out who has a strip of paper that is taller than my strip, and who has one that is shorter?*

Sort the children.
- One by one, invite children to the front of the room and have them compare their strip to the displayed benchmark strip, held vertically. This will serve as the reference. Remind children of the importance of aligning one end of objects when comparing height.
- Have children with shorter strips form one group and children with taller strips form another. Children whose strips are the same length as the benchmark strip can return to their seats.

Use What You Know
Compare Lengths

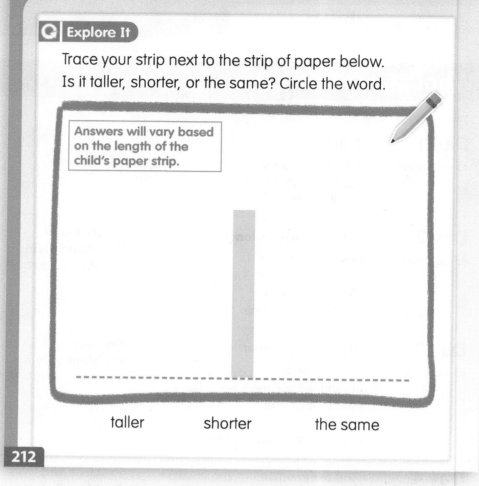

Explore It

Trace your strip next to the strip of paper below. Is it taller, shorter, or the same? Circle the word.

Answers will vary based on the length of the child's paper strip.

taller   shorter   the same

212

Compare the two groups.

- Point to the *shorter* group. Ask: *What can you say about this group?* Guide children to recognize that they all have strips of paper that are shorter than the benchmark strip and thus shorter than all the strips in the *taller* group.

- Point to the *taller* group. Ask: *What can you say about this group?* Elicit that they all have strips that are taller than the benchmark strip and thus taller than all of those in the *shorter* group.

- Have one child from each group step forward. Ask: *Without measuring, tell me whether [child from taller group]'s strip is taller or shorter than [child from shorter group]'s strip. How do you know?*

- Don't accept responses such as *his/her strip looks taller*. Lead children to the understanding that the child from the *taller* group's strip is taller than the benchmark strip, which is taller than everyone's strip in the *shorter* group. So, the child from the *taller* group has a taller strip of paper than the child from the *shorter* group.

Make a record.

- Have each child trace his or her strip of paper next to the strip of paper on the Student Book page. Then have them circle if their strip is *taller*, *shorter*, or *the same*.

Use What You Know
Compare Lengths

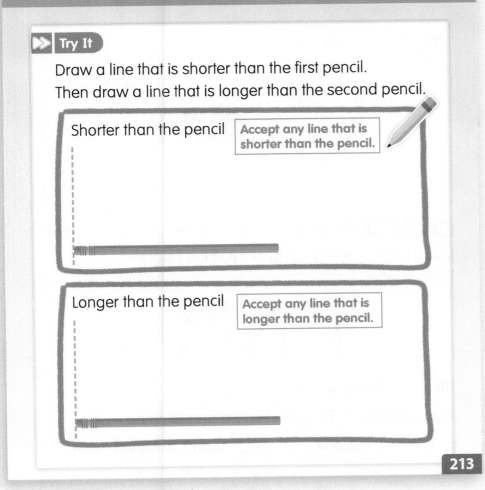

>> Try It

Draw a line that is shorter than the first pencil.
Then draw a line that is longer than the second pencil.

Shorter than the pencil
| Accept any line that is shorter than the pencil. |

Longer than the pencil
| Accept any line that is longer than the pencil. |

213

Step By Step

Try It

Compare other items using a reference object.

- Give each child a new, unsharpened pencil.

- Have them search the room for one object that is longer than the pencil and one that is shorter.

- As children find a shorter and a longer object, ask them to compare the lengths of the two found objects and determine, without measuring, which object is shorter based on their comparison to the pencil. Take note of which children have not yet grasped the idea of indirect comparison.

Draw a line to show shorter and longer.

- Direct children's attention to the top section of the Student Book page. Ask them to draw a line that is shorter than the pencil. Then have children draw a line that is longer than the pencil in the next section.

- Have children look at the two lines they drew. Ask them to explain which of the two lines they drew is longer. Listen for children who use the given pencil on the page in their explanations.

Modeled Instruction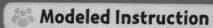

Step By Step

- Read the problem at the top of the page aloud. Explain that the tables are too big to move next to each other and compare directly. Ask: *What if you had a long piece of string? How could you use it to compare the lengths of the tables?* Discuss all ideas.

Model It

- Direct attention to Model It, pointing out that the same piece of yellow string is laid along the length of each table.

- Ask: *Which table is longer than the string?* [the gray table] *Which table is shorter than the string?* [the brown table] *So, which table is the longer table?* [the gray table]

- Have children complete the Model It sentences and discuss their conclusions. Discuss Mathematical Discourse question 1.

▶ **Mathematical Discourse 1**

- Use the visual model to show logical reasoning about the relationship between the lengths.

▶ **Visual Model**

Ready Mathematics
PRACTICE AND PROBLEM SOLVING

Assign *Practice and Problem Solving* **pages 299–300** after students have completed this section.

Compare Lengths

Which table is longer?

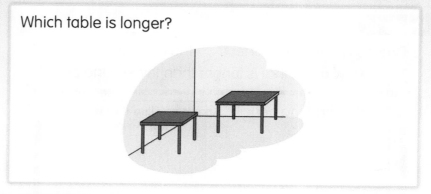

 **Model It** Compare lengths. ·····························

Use a piece of string. Compare it to the length of each table.

The gray table is longer than the string.

The brown table is ___shorter___ **than the string.**

So the gray table is ___longer___ **than the brown table.**

214

▶ **Mathematical Discourse**

1 *What is the order of these three objects from shortest to longest? How does this help you compare the lengths of the tables?*

Children should be able to name the objects from shortest to longest: brown table, string, gray table. Children might recognize that the object that was used as the reference object ended up in the middle. This is why the string can be used to indirectly compare the length of the two tables.

▶ **Visual Model**

Model the logic of indirect comparison.

Draw the following diagram on the board. Discuss with children how it models the problem on the student page.

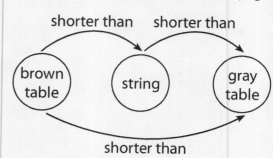

Learn Together
Compare Lengths

Which object is shorter?

 Model It Use a paper strip.

Compare each object to the paper. Write shorter or longer.

shorter

longer

The shoe is ___shorter___ than the spoon.

 Talk About It Do you agree? Why or why not?

Chris is shorter than Amy.
Ray is taller than Amy.
Boom says Chris is taller than Ray.

215

▶ **Hands-On Activity**

Compare lengths of classroom objects.

Materials For each child: strip of heavy paper

Give each child a strip of heavy paper to use as a reference unit. Have children find at least three objects in the classroom that are the same length as the reference unit, at least three objects that are longer than the reference unit, and at least three objects that are shorter than the reference unit.

▶ **Mathematical Discourse**

2 *How did you decide if Boom is correct?*
Look for explanations that show evidence of logical reasoning. One person is taller than Amy and the other is shorter. So, logically, Amy is in between, and the taller person is taller than the one who is shorter than Amy.

Step By Step

- Read the question at the top of the page. Ask: *How can you compare the lengths of the shoe and the spoon?* Introduce the idea of using a strip of paper.

- Show children a strip of paper, and ask how it is like the piece of string used to compare the tables on the previous page. Then model how to use the paper to compare the length of two classroom objects.

Model It

- Read Model It and ask children which object is longer than the paper and which one is shorter. Then ask them to fill in the blanks.

  Error Alert Children who write *longer* below the shoe and *shorter* below the spoon may be comparing the strip of paper to each object, instead of comparing each object to the paper. Ask them to describe each situation with a complete sentence, such as: *The shoe is shorter than the paper.*

Talk About It

- Talk About It focuses on reasoning about indirect measurement. Read the problem with the class.

- Have children work in pairs to draw their response. Circulate and monitor their work. Some children may be able to answer without drawing, but encourage them to make a drawing to justify their conclusions.

- Invite partners to share their drawings with the class. Ask Mathematical Discourse question 2 to focus on the error in logic that Boom made. Challenge children to correct Boom and make a true statement.

▶ **Mathematical Discourse 2**

▶ **Hands-On Activity**

 **Mathematics**
PRACTICE AND PROBLEM SOLVING

Assign *Practice and Problem Solving* **pages 301–302** after students have completed this section.

👥👥 Guided Practice

Step By Step

- The example problem guides children to make a superlative comparison: finding the longest snake. Discuss with the class and ask children to explain the conclusion.

- For Problem 1, guide children to compare the heights of the rectangle and the triangle. Then have them complete the problem. Discuss their rationale for their answer. Encourage children to make a variety of comparison statements using all three objects.

- Problem 2 focuses on reasoning related to indirect measurement. Have children discuss this in pairs. Circulate and support their discussions. For those who struggle, remind them of the Visual Model they saw earlier in the lesson or have them draw an illustration of the problem situation.

> **SMP TIP Use Structure**
> Children use transitivity when they indirectly compare lengths of multiple objects. Encourage them to state their logic in an order that makes sense and follows the structure of the problem. For example: *My string is longer than the pencil. My string is shorter than the book. That means the book is longer than the pencil. (SMP 7)*

- Ask Mathematical Discourse question 1 to encourage more in-depth thinking about indirect measurement.

▶ **Mathematical Discourse 1**

▶ **Concept Extension**

Ready Mathematics
PRACTICE AND PROBLEM SOLVING

Assign *Practice and Problem Solving* **pages 303–304** after students have completed this section.

Practice Together
Compare Lengths

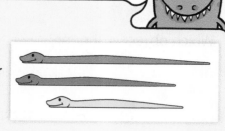

The red snake is longer than the blue snake.

The blue snake is longer than the yellow snake.

The <u>   red   </u> **snake is the longest.**

---

1 Draw a line that is shorter than the triangle. Circle the tallest object.

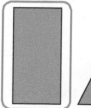

---

2 The crayon is shorter than the pencil.
The pencil is shorter than the notebook.

The crayon is <u> shorter </u> than the notebook.

216

▶ **Mathematical Discourse**

1 *Suppose I have two objects and they are both shorter than a third object. Can I tell which one is shorter or longer than the other? Why or why not? What can I do if I need to compare their lengths but I can't compare them side by side?*

If both objects are shorter than the reference object, then you cannot compare their lengths using that reference object. To compare their lengths, you need to find a reference object that is longer than one of the objects and shorter than the other object.

▶ **Concept Extension**

Sort objects by length.

Materials For display: box containing 10–12 objects of differing lengths, a reference object

Have children sort objects in the box as shorter, the same length as, or longer than the reference object. Then choose one of the "longer" objects as a reference object and have children further sort these as shorter, the same length as, or longer than the new reference object. Discuss how the "longer" group can now be classified as "a little bit longer," "longer," and "a lot longer."

Practice by Myself
Compare Lengths

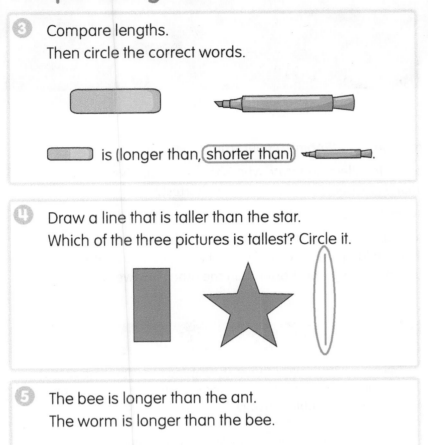

③ Compare lengths.
Then circle the correct words.

⬚ is (longer than, (shorter than)) ◁▭.

④ Draw a line that is taller than the star.
Which of the three pictures is tallest? Circle it.

⑤ The bee is longer than the ant.
The worm is longer than the bee.

The ant is ___shorter___ than the worm.

217

Step By Step

- Before children work on this page, review the models and tools used in this lesson. Emphasize that children are free to use whatever way helps them solve the problem.

- Read each problem aloud, then have children work independently to solve.

- For Problem 3, you may want to provide children with a piece of string that is longer than the picture of the eraser but shorter than the picture of the marker. You may want to challenge some children to create their own tool or strategy to compare the lengths.

- Monitor children's work on Problem 4 to ensure that they understand the directions. Have them explain their rationale. Elicit that you can't always tell "just by looking."

- For children who still struggle with Problem 5, have them use connecting cubes to model each object. Then discuss the reasoning.

▶ **Mathematical Discourse 2**

▶ **Fluency Practice**

▶ **Fluency Practice**
Practice writing true number sentences.

Materials For each pair: Make Equal Facts (Activity Sheet 38)

Have children work in pairs to complete Activity Sheet 38 (Make Equal Facts). Each partner can complete one side of the number sentence for each problem.

▶ **Mathematical Discourse**

2 *In Problem 5, what is the answer if the bee is shorter than the ant and the worm is shorter than the bee? How can you tell?*

The ant is longer than the worm. Children should show evidence of logical reasoning in their response. The bee is still the reference object, but the lengths of the other objects have been reversed. Consider providing cards with the names of the objects on them to help children reorganize their thinking.

Differentiated Instruction

▶ Quick Check and Remediation

Materials For each child: 3 index cards (labeled "Pam", "Joe", and "Robin"), paper strip

- Ask children to put the cards in order by height, shortest to tallest, and state who is the shortest. Give the following rules: *Pam is taller than Joe. Robin is taller than Pam.* [Joe, Pam, Robin; Joe is shortest.]

- For children who are still struggling, use the chart below to guide remediation.

- After providing remediation, give each child a strip of paper, an object that is longer than the paper strip, and an object that is shorter than the paper strip. Check children's understanding by having them use the paper strip to measure and state which of the two objects is longer or shorter than the other. [Answer will vary depending on the objects given.]

If the error is . . .	Children may . . .	To remediate . . .
Robin, Joe, Pam	have focused on the first comparison and then placed Robin incorrectly.	Read the first sentence and verify that Joe and Pam are in correct relation to each other. Read the second sentence and have the children place Robin correctly.
Pam, Robin, Joe	have focused on the second comparison and then placed Joe incorrectly.	Read the second sentence and verify that Pam and Robin are in correct relation to each other. Read the first sentence and have the children place Joe correctly.
Robin, Pam, Joe	have put the cards in order from tallest to shortest.	Remind children that the shortest goes on the left. Have children start with Pam. Read the first sentence and place Joe accordingly. Read the second sentence and place Robin accordingly.

▶ Hands-On Activity

Compare lengths of clay snakes to a cube tower.

Materials For each pair: clay, 10 connecting cubes, 2 index cards (labeled *longer* and *shorter*)

- Children work in pairs to make a cube tower.

- One child takes the card that says *longer* and the partner takes the card that says *shorter*. The child with the card labeled *longer* makes a clay snake that is longer than the cube tower and the partner makes a clay snake that is shorter than the cube tower.

- Each child compares his/her snake to the tower. Children make statements such as: *My snake is longer than the cube tower and your snake is shorter than the cube tower. So my snake is longer than your snake.*

- Partners switch cards and repeat the activity.

▶ Challenge Activity

Compare lengths of irregular paths, using string.

Materials For display: masking tape; for each child: string

- Use masking tape to mark three crooked paths from various spots in the classroom to the door. One path should be longer than a piece of pre-measured string and two should be shorter.

- Ask children how to determine which path is the shortest. One way is to use the piece of string as a reference object.

- Give children the piece of string and have them lay it along each path and state whether the string is shorter or longer than the path. Ask: *How can you tell?* [Either the path extends past the end of the string or the string extends past the end of the path.]

- Ask: *How can you now find the shortest path?* [One way would be to use a shorter string. Another would be to mark on the string itself where each path ends.]

Teacher Notes

Teacher-Toolbox.com

Overview

Assign the Lesson 32 Quiz and have children work independently to complete it.

Use the results of the quiz to assess children's understanding of the content of the lesson and to identify areas for reteaching. See the Lesson Pacing Guide at the beginning of the lesson and the Differentiated Instruction activities for suggested instructional resources.

Tested Skills

Assesses 1.MD.A.1

Problems on this quiz require children to be able to compare length indirectly by using a reference object and logical reasoning. Children will also need to be familiar with comparing the length of two objects and ordering objects by length.

Ready **Mathematics**

Lesson 32 Quiz Answer Key

Name _____

Solve.

1. Compare the lengths.
   Circle the correct words.

   _____ is (**longer than**, shorter than) _____.

2. Draw a line that is taller than the bag of cups.
   Which of the three pictures is tallest? Circle it.

   Possible Answer:

Grade 1 **Lesson 32** Compare Length   1

©Curriculum Associates, LLC
Copying permitted for classroom use.

Common Misconceptions and Errors

Errors may result if children:

- make an error in logic.
- focus on the comparison of only two objects when three are being compared.
- do not understand (or confuse) the order and put objects in reverse order.
- confuse *longer* with *shorter* or *longest* with *shortest*.

Name _____

Solve.

3 Compare lengths. Then circle the correct words.

The white bat is (longer than, (shorter than)) the gray bat.

4 The pen is longer than the pencil.
The pencil is longer than the crayon.

The pen is ___longer___ than the crayon.

5 Kuri is shorter than Rob.
Cam is shorter than Kuri.

Rob is ___taller___ than Cam.

Lesson 33
Understand Length Measurement

CCSS Focus

Domain
Measurement and Data

Cluster
A. Measure lengths indirectly and by iterating length units.

Standard
1.MD.A.2 Express the length of an object as a whole number of length units, by laying multiple copies of a shorter object (the length unit) end to end; understand that the length measurement of an object is the number of same-size length units that span it with no gaps or overlaps. *Limit to contexts where the object being measured is spanned by a whole number of length units with no gaps or overlaps.*

Standards for Mathematical Practice (SMP)

2 Reason abstractly and quantitatively.

3 Construct viable arguments and critique the reasoning of others.

5 Use appropriate tools strategically.

6 Attend to precision.

7 Look for and make use of structure.

Lesson Objectives

Content Objectives

- Measure a length using non-standard units of measure.
- Understand that the number of iterated units from end to end is a measure.
- Iterate units with no gaps or overlaps.
- Understand that *unit* implies uniformity in length.

Language Objectives

- Lay same-sized objects end-to-end without gaps or overlaps to measure the length of a given object.
- Draw an object, measure it with two different units, and record the number of units used.
- Listen to the ideas of others when measuring an object using two different sized units, and discuss whether more or fewer of the larger unit will be used to measure the object.

Prerequisite Skills

- Order objects by length.
- Compare lengths of up to three objects.

Lesson Vocabulary

- **measure** the process of finding a number that shows the size or quantity.
- **unit** that which is used to measure the height or length of an object.

Review the following key term.

- **length** the distance from one point to another.

Learning Progression

In Kindergarten children compare lengths of objects and describe them in terms of taller, longer, shorter, more, or less.

In Grade 1 children compare lengths of two objects to a third object, building the concept of measurement as the act of comparing a length to a series of other lengths.

In this lesson children iterate non-standard units to equal the length of another object, recognizing that the number of units iterated represents the length of the object. They explore how different-sized units affect the numerical representation of length and analyze the importance of using units of uniform length with no gaps or overlaps in measuring an object.

In Grade 2 children build on the concept of measurement using standard units, describing the measure in terms of the unit name. The concept of unit is further developed as children measure an object using two different units, recognizing that the numerical representation is dependent upon the unit.

Lesson Pacing Guide

Whole Class Instruction

Day 1
45–60 minutes

Introduction
Use What You Know
- Explore It *25 min*
- Try It *20 min*

Day 2
45–60 minutes

Modeled Instruction
Explore Together
- Opening Question *5 min*
- Think *10 min*
- Talk About It *15 min*
- Hands-On Activity *15 min*

Practice and Problem Solving
Assign pages 307–308.

Day 3
45–60 minutes

Guided Instruction
Explore Together
- Hands-On Problem *10 min*
- Problem 1 *10 min*
- Talk About It *10 min*
- Hands-On Activity *15 min*

Practice and Problem Solving
Assign pages 309–310.

Day 4
45–60 minutes

Guided Practice
Connect It
- Problems 2–4 *15 min*

Independent Practice
Show What I Know
- Problem 5 *15 min*
- Intervention, On-Level, or Challenge Activity *15 min*

Practice and Problem Solving
Assign pages 311–312.

Teacher-Toolbox: Lesson Quiz
Lesson 33 Quiz

Materials for Lesson Activities

Per child: 30 centimeter cubes, 30 connecting cubes, 15 toothpicks, objects to use as units of measure, string or yarn, classroom objects to measure Activity Sheet 39*

Per pair: 12-15 four-inch straws, 30 centimeter cubes, 30 connecting cubes, 30 toothpicks, 30 paper clips, classroom objects to measure

For display: 5 centimeter cubes, 5 connecting cubes

*Used for more than one activity.

Small Group Differentiation

Teacher-Toolbox.com

Reteach
Ready Prerequisite Lessons *45–90 min*

Grade K
- Lesson 26 Compare Length

Teacher-led Activities
Tools for Instruction *15–20 min*

Grade 1 *(Lesson 33)*
- Measuring Length
- Describing Length
- Measuring Height and Length

Student-led Activities
Math Center Activities *30–40 min*

Grade K *(Lesson 26)*
- K.34 Length Vocabulary
- K.35 Compare Lengths

Grade 1 *(Lesson 33)*
- 1.49 Measure Length
- 1.50 Measure the Path

👥 Introduction

Activity Measure Me

Objective
Explore the concept of measurement.

Materials for each pair
- 12–15 straws, each 4 inches in length
- various classroom objects to measure

Overview
Children use a non-standard unit to measure each other and a given length of string, describing height and length in terms of the unit.

Step By Step

Explore It

Pose the problem.
- Tell pairs of children they are to find the number of straws that will line up to match each of their heights.

Measure each other.
- Instruct one of the children in each pair to lay flat on the floor while the partner finds the number of straws tall they are. They record the number on the Student Book page and then reverse roles.
- Let children measure without intervention. Note how they iterate the straws. Do they lay the straws end to end or orient them in varied ways? Do they overlap or leave gaps between the straws? Use these observations to guide later discussion.

Compare measurements.
- Allow each pair to tell how many straws tall they are. Ask who is taller, who is shorter, and how they know. Encourage them to use the number of straws as the means of comparison. This may create confusion for some children who are close in height.
- Have children describe how they measured their partner. Ask questions such as: *What did you do if the last straw didn't get all the way to the top of the head or if it was a little longer than the top of the head?*

Answers will vary depending on children's height.

🔄 Explore It

Write the number of straws used to measure the height of each partner.

Name _____

about _____ straws tall

Name _____

about _____ straws tall

Who is taller? How do you know?

218

- Reinforce the concept that measurement is an approximation by having two children of almost the same height stand next to each other. Discuss that the number of straws used was the same even though they are not exactly the same height, so we say they are *about [number] straws tall*.

Explore unit iteration.

- Address the concept of unit iteration with the questions: *Why did you lay the straws in a straight line? What would happen if you left out some of the straws?*

- Have children of two obviously different heights lay on the floor. Line up straws in a straight line next to the taller child and in a zigzag pattern next to the shorter child, so the same number of straws is used for each one. Ask: *Does it make sense that both [child's name] and [child's name] are [number of straws used] straws tall? Why not? Why is it important to line up the straws in a straight line to measure?*

- Repeat this activity, but this time correctly line up straws next to the shorter child. Leave gaps between the straws as you line them up next to the taller child, so the same number of straws is used for each child. Ask: *Why is it important to line up the straws without leaving gaps between them? What do you think might happen if I lined up the straws so that they were overlapping?*

>> **Try It**

Measure the length of the string using straws.
Write how many straws long it is.

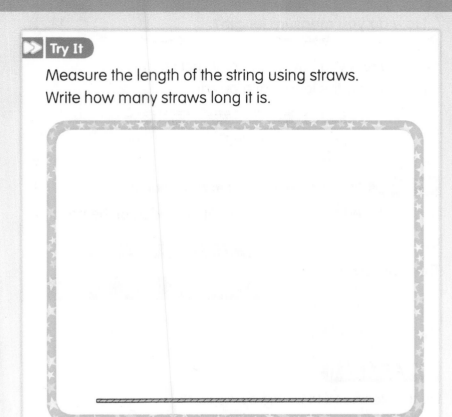

about ___1___ straw long

219

Try It

Measure a given object.

• Have children use their straws to measure the length of the string on the Student Book page and write about how about many straws long it is.

• Invite children to demonstrate how they lined up the straws to measure.

Check understanding.

• Have children use straws to measure the length or width of another object in the classroom.

• Observe methods children use without expectation of complete accuracy at this time. Take note of children who may need additional assistance during the lesson.

Modeled Instruction

Step By Step

- Read aloud the question and information at the top of the page.

- Review the important aspects of measuring explored during the Activity in the Introduction. Discuss how the straw did not closely match up with the string. Tell children that there are many other kinds of objects you can use to measure that might match up more closely.

Think

- Cut out the small-square strips from Activity Sheet 39 (Measuring Tools) and distribute. Read the first 2 sentences of Think aloud. Then have children place a strip of tiles on the picture of tiles used to measure the pencil. Discuss how the picture of tiles represents the object. Review the way the tiles are lined up and iterated from end to end. Then have children count the tiles and complete the sentence.

Talk About It

- Allow children time to discuss the Talk About It questions with a partner. Let children share ideas with the class and then ask them to measure the bottom length of their book with the strip of small square tiles.

- Iterate a combination of centimeter cubes and connecting cubes along the bottom length of the book, telling children your measure. Discuss why your measure is different from theirs, emphasizing the need to measure in same-size units.

▶ **Mathematical Discourse 1 and 2**

▶ **Hands-On Activity**

 **Ready** Mathematics
PRACTICE AND PROBLEM SOLVING

Assign *Practice and Problem Solving* **pages 307–308** after students have completed this section.

Explore Together
Understand Length Measurement

> How do you measure length?

Length tells you how long an object is.
You can find the length of a pencil.

|— Length —|

💬 **Think** You can use tiles to measure length. ················

Line up the edge of the first tile with the edge of the pencil.

Count the tiles.

There are 10 tiles.

The pencil is _10_ tiles long.

💬 **Talk About It** ···

Do the tiles need to be the same size?
Why or why not?

220

▶ **Mathematical Discourse**

1 *Would it make more sense to measure the length of a table with straws or tiles? Why?*

Some children may respond that straws are easier to use since the table is big and not as many are needed. Others may respond that by using the tiles, there is a better chance that the tiles will line up along the table.

2 *Why is it important to line up the first tile with one end of the object whose length you are measuring?*

Children should respond that the tiles need to match up with the object so they are the same size. If you don't line up the first tile, you won't be measuring the whole length of the object.

▶ **Hands-On Activity 1**
Practice making approximate measurements.

Materials For each pair: 30 centimeter cubes, 3 four-inch straws, classroom objects to measure that are less than 30 cm long (such as crayons, markers, books, pencil boxes, etc.)

Put children in pairs to measure the length of 3 or 4 items, using both straws and cubes. Tell children to describe the measure in terms of each one, using "about" for approximate measures. Discuss whether it is easier to measure the length of the items with straws or cubes and why.

Explore Together
Understand Length Measurement

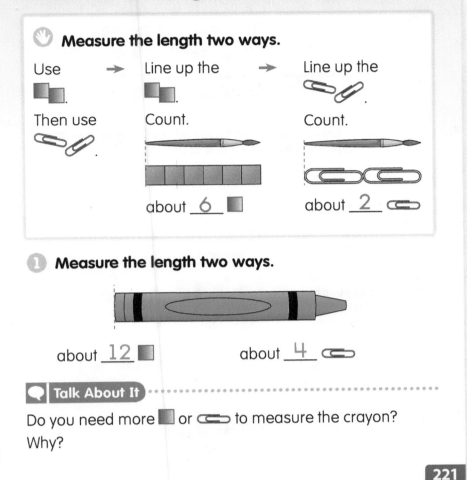

✋ **Measure the length two ways.**

Use 🔲. → Line up the 🔲. → Line up the 📎.

Then use 📎. Count. Count.

about __6__ 🔲   about __2__ 📎

① **Measure the length two ways.**

about __12__ 🔲   about __4__ 📎

💬 **Talk About It**

Do you need more 🔲 or 📎 to measure the crayon? Why?

221

Step By Step

- Explain to children that there are many units that can be used to measure. Ask them to list things that might be used as a measuring tool. Emphasize that each unit must be the same size.

- Draw attention to the units shown on this page. Have children compare the units and observe the pictures of the measurements.

- Ask: *How is measuring with tiles and paper clips the same? How is it different?* [Both are placed touching end to end from left to right along the entire length of the paintbrush. The units are different sizes.]

- Cut out the small-square strips and paper clip strips from Activity Sheet 39 (Measuring Tools) and distribute. Read the directions for Problem 1 and have children measure the crayon using the small-square strip and then the paper clip strip. Circulate and help children with the measuring process as necessary.

- Invite children to share their measurements. Discuss and resolve any discrepancies.

Talk About It

- Have children discuss Talk About It in pairs, and then discuss as a class how the size of the unit used affects the numerical measure.

▶ **Mathematical Discourse 3**

▶ **Hands-On Activity 2**

**Ready**® **Mathematics**
PRACTICE AND PROBLEM SOLVING

Assign *Practice and Problem Solving* **pages 309–310** after students have completed this section.

▶ **Hands-On Activity 2**
Use different units to measure.

Materials For each child: objects that can be used as units of measure (such as unused pencils, toothpicks, craft sticks, etc.)

- Have children use each of the "units" to measure the length or width of objects at their desks, such as: the length or width of the desktop, a book, a piece of paper, etc.

- Discuss the measures, checking to ensure children are iterating from one end of the object to the other and describing their measure numerically with the unit name.

- Ask: *How can the width of your desk have a measure of both _____ and _____ ?* Emphasize that the number represents the number of units, which is determined by the size of the unit used.

▶ **Mathematical Discourse**

3 *Why is it important to know how to measure something?*

Children may think of situations such as measuring the length and width of their foot to buy the right size of shoe, measuring the length and width of a toy to make sure you have the right size box or bag to store it in, etc. (You may need to make suggestions to jump-start children's ideas.)

👥 **Guided Practice**

Step By Step

- Discuss each Connect It problem as a class using the discussion points outlined below.

Explain

- Present the problem and have children compare the way the string is measured to the way items were measured on previous pages. Guide them to recognize that two different sizes of paper clips are used.

- Discuss the problems that occur when measuring with different size units. Ask: *Suppose you need a string the same length as the one Buzz has. He tells you it is 8 paper clips long. Do you think you would cut a piece of string the same length as the one Buzz measured? Explain.*

- Have children measure the length of the string using centimeter cubes and then using connecting cubes, recording each measure. Share results, emphasizing the uniformity in the measures.

- Then tell children to use different combinations of the two kinds of cubes and record the number of units used. Children should discover that the numerical measure is not consistent among everyone.

Reason

- Ask children how this way of measuring length is similar to the problem Buzz had with the paper clips. Lead them to see that by overlapping the squares, some of the units are smaller than others. It is like measuring with different sizes of units.

- Emphasize that measurement is a comparison of one object to another. Aligning the objects carefully and exactly results in more accurate measures.

Analyze

- Discuss the reasons Boom may have left gaps between the paper clips as shown.

Connect It
Understand Length Measurement

② **Explain** Buzz says this string is 8 long. Boom says that is wrong. How does Boom know?

Possible answer: Buzz uses large and small paper clips. The paper clips need to be the same size.

③ **Reason** Boom uses 8 squares to measure a ribbon. Did Boom measure the right way? Why or why not?

Possible answer: No, Boom has some squares that are on top of each other. The squares need to touch but cannot be on top of each other.

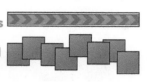

④ **Analyze** Boom says that his leaf is 4 long. Do you agree? Why or why not?

Possible answer: No, the paper clips are lined up but do not touch each other.

222

SMP TIP Attend to Precision
Measure the length of an object that is not an exact number of paper clips long. Explain that, even if the last clip doesn't reach the end of the object, they all still must be placed end to end to get the most accurate measure as possible. Emphasize the importance of measuring as accurately as possible. *(SMP 6)*

- Display objects that are non-linear in shape like the leaf. Point out that the length of an object is determined by the longest part of the object. Have the children place toothpicks vertically on each side of the leaf where the paper clips begin and end.

📦 **Ready**· Mathematics
PRACTICE AND PROBLEM SOLVING

Assign *Practice and Problem Solving* **pages 311–312** after students have completed this section.

Show What I Know
Understand Length Measurement

(5) **Think about measuring length.**

A: Use  and ▮. Circle the correct answer.

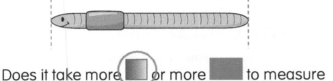

Does it take more ▢ or more ▮ to measure the worm?

Does it take fewer ▮ or fewer ▢ to measure the ladybug?

B: Draw a pencil. Measure it with ▢ and ▮.

Possible answer: Children may draw a pencil about 9 centimeters long, with a length of 9 squares and a length of 6 rectangles.

about __9__ ▢   about __6__ ▮

223

Step By Step

- Read the problems aloud and allow children to respond independently. Make sure children understand that they need to measure the length of the objects.

- Distribute the small-rectangle and small-square strips from Activity Sheet 39 (Measuring Tools).

- As children complete the tasks, support them with the following questions:

  How might the size of the squares and rectangles help you decide which one takes more?

  What does "fewer" mean? How is it different from "more"?

  Where do you think you should begin measuring the length of the pencil you drew? How might toothpicks help you know where to begin and end measuring?

  Think about what Buzz and Boom did wrong when they measured. How can you make sure you are measuring properly?

- As you circulate, ask children to justify the choices they make in Part A.

Scoring Rubrics

Expectations for 4–3 Points

Points	Expectations
4	The child: • selects the unit that answers each question without measuring. • accurately measures the length of the pencil drawn, recording the number of each unit used.
3	The child: • selects the unit that answers each question but needs to measure. • accurately measures the length of the pencil drawn, recording the number of each unit used.

Expectations for 2–0 Points

Points	Expectations
2	The child: • selects the opposing units for each question, justifying that the larger unit represents "more." • measures the length of the pencil drawn but may have minor errors such as small gaps or the unit extended slightly beyond the left side of the figure.
1	The child: • may circle one of the units shown but is unable to give a reason for the choice. • may draw a pencil and attempt to iterate but uses a combination of units with gaps and overlaps and no numerical recording.
0	The child: • does not attempt to answer the questions or draw and measure a pencil.

Differentiated Instruction

▶ Intervention Activity
Measure objects with cubes.

Materials For each child: 25 connecting cubes, 2 toothpicks, classroom objects to measure with lengths that are less than 18 inches

- Provide children with several objects in which to measure length and a set of connecting cubes.

- Place a toothpick vertically on the left side of the item to serve as a guide.

- Instruct children to connect or place cubes side by side from the toothpick to the end of the object. Then have them count cubes and record the measure.

▶ On-Level Activity
Measure around the room.

Materials For each pair: 30 centimeter cubes, 30 connecting cubes, 15 toothpicks, 30 paper clips (same size)

- Distribute materials. Explain that children will use these items as units of measure. Have each pair make a recording sheet by folding a sheet of paper into fourths and labeling each section with the name of one of the units.

- Have pairs select and measure the length or width of an object in the classroom. Encourage them to select an object whose length or width is easy to measure with each unit listed on their paper.

- After children measure a dimension of the object with each unit, they record the measurement in the appropriate box.

- Discuss which units children needed more of and fewer of to measure the length or width of the object.

▶ Challenge Activity
Find ways to measure odd-shaped objects.

Materials For each child: string or yarn, classroom objects to measure, objects to use as units of measure

Challenge children to find ways of measuring a non-straight dimension of an item, such as the distance around a globe/ball or the distance around (perimeter) odd-shaped objects, like their hand or foot, bulletin board letters, etc.

Children must:

- select a method that will help them measure as accurately as possible.

- choose a unit that will give the most accurate measure. (Encourage them to try a variety of units.)

- describe the strategy, unit used, and the number of units needed to measure the selected dimension of each item.

Teacher Notes

Teacher-Toolbox.com

Overview

Assign the Lesson 33 Quiz and have children work independently to complete it.

Use the results of the quiz to assess children's understanding of the content of the lesson and to identify areas for reteaching. See the Lesson Pacing Guide at the beginning of the lesson and the Differentiated Instruction activities for suggested instructional resources.

Tested Skills

Assesses 1.MD.A.2

Problems on this quiz require children to be able to iterate a non-standard unit of measure with no gaps or overlaps end to end to measure the length of an object and recognize that it takes more smaller-sized units than larger-sized units to measure the same object. Children will also need to be familiar with ordering objects by length and comparing lengths of up to three objects.

Ready® Mathematics

Lesson 33 Quiz Answer Key

Name _____

Materials: 2 tile strip cutouts from page 3 of the quiz.

Solve.

1. Use ▢ and ▢. Circle the correct answer.

   Does it take more (▢) or more ▢ to measure the bat?

2. Measure the length with ▢ and ▢.

   about __12__ ▢   about __8__ ▢

Grade 1 **Lesson 33** *Understand* Length Measurement   1

Common Misconceptions and Errors

Errors may result if children:

- have gaps and overlaps when measuring.
- think it would take more larger-sized units than smaller-sized units to measure an object.
- do not recognize that the number of iterated non-standard units represents the length of an object.
- do not understand that "unit" implies uniformity in length.

Lesson 33 Quiz Answer Key continued

Name _____

Solve.

3 Circle the correct way to measure the length of the worm.

4 Pam and Jan measured the length of the same book. Pam got 10 units and Jan got 15 units.

Which unit did Pam use?

Which unit did Jan use?

2

Lesson 34
Tell Time

CCSS Focus

Domain
Measurement and Data

Cluster
B. Tell and write time.

Standard
1.MD.B.3 Tell and write time in hours and half-hours using analog and digital clocks.

Standards for Mathematical Practice (SMP)

6 Attend to precision.

7 Look for and make use of structure.

Lesson Objectives

Content Objectives

- Tell time to the hour and half hour, using analog and digital clocks.
- Write the time to the hour and half hour.
- Understand that 30 minutes is the same as a half hour.

Language Objectives

- Draw the hour hand on an analog clock to show a given time to the hour.
- Tell time to the half hour more than one way using words and numbers.
- Show the same time on an analog clock (draw) and a digital clock (write).

Prerequisite Skills

- Understand that when an object is divided into two equal parts, the parts are called halves.
- Count from 1 to 20.

Lesson Vocabulary

- **analog clock** a clock that uses hour and minute hand positions to show time.
- **digital clock** a clock that uses the number of hours and minutes to show time.
- **half hour** 30 minutes, or a unit of time that is half as long as one hour.
- **half past** a way of referring to the time that is one half hour after a given hour (e.g., half past 3 is the same as 3:30).
- **hour** a unit of time equal to 60 minutes.
- **hour hand** the shorter indicator (or hand) on an analog clock, which shows the hours.
- **minute** a unit of time equal to 60 seconds.
- **minute hand** the longer indicator (or hand) on an analog clock, which shows the minutes.
- **o'clock** literally means *of the clock*; used to tell that the current time is a particular hour.

Learning Progression

In Kindergarten children do not directly address telling time, but teachers often talk about the rhythms of the school day and times to do certain activities.

In Grade 1 children begin reading digital and analog clocks.

In this lesson children learn to tell time to the hour and half hour. They relate their concept of one-half to measuring an intangible item: time. They learn to recognize minutes and hours on analog and digital clocks and to read and write time to the hour and half hour.

In Grade 2 children extend their understanding of how to tell time to include time to the nearest 5 minutes. They also learn the meaning of AM and PM and use them along with the numerical time.

Lesson Pacing Guide

Whole Class Instruction

Day 1 *45–60 minutes*	**Introduction** **Use What You Know** • Explore It *25 min* • Try It *20 min*	
Day 2 *45–60 minutes*	**Modeled Instruction** **Explore Together** • Example Problem *10 min* • Model It *15 min* • Fluency Practice *20 min*	**Practice and Problem Solving** Assign pages 315–316.
Day 3 *45–60 minutes*	**Guided Instruction** **Learn Together** • Example Problem *5 min* • Model It *15 min* • Talk About It *10 min* • Concept Extension *15 min*	**Practice and Problem Solving** Assign pages 317–318.
Day 4 *45–60 minutes*	**Guided Practice** **Practice Together** • Example Problem *5 min* • Problems 1–2 *20 min* • Hands-On Activity *20 min*	**Practice and Problem Solving** Assign pages 319–320.
Day 5 *45–60 minutes*	**Independent Practice** **Practice by Myself** • Problems 3–5 *15 min* • Quick Check and Remediation *15 min* • Hands-On or Challenge Activity *15 min*	

Teacher-Toolbox: Lesson Quiz
Lesson 34 Quiz

Small Group Differentiation

Teacher-Toolbox.com

Teacher-led Activities
Tools for Instruction *15–20 min*

Grade 1 *(Lesson 34)*
• Telling Time to the Hour and Half Hour

Student-led Activities
Math Center Activities *30–40 min*

Grade 1 *(Lesson 34)*
• 1.51 Vocabulary for Time
• 1.52 Tell Time

Materials for Lesson Activities

Per child:	28 toothpicks, cardstock, 12 small sticky notes, 1 round-head fastener Activity Sheet 16, Activity Sheet 17, Activity Sheet 18, Activity Sheet 20, Activity Sheet 40*, Activity Sheet 45
Per pair:	none
For display:	demonstration clock, round-head fastener, heavy-stock paper or cardboard Activity Sheet 40*

*Used for more than one activity.

👥 Introduction

Activity **Tell Time**

Objective

Understand how the hour hand and minute hand move on a clock.

Materials for display

- demonstration clock or Clock Face (Activity Sheet 40)
- heavy-stock paper or cardboard
- round-head fastener

Overview

Children observe and demonstrate the movement of the minute hand completely around the clock as the hour hand moves from one number to the next.

Step By Step

Explore It

Prepare for the activity.

- Display the demonstration clock for the class. If one is not available, you can copy and cut out the Clock Face activity sheet and glue it on heavy-stock paper or cardboard. Punch a hole through the hands and the center of the clock face and attach the hands with a round-head fastener.

Investigate the hour hand.

- Tell children that clocks have two hands. Discuss how the hands look different.

- Explain that telling time includes a number for the hour and a number for the minutes. Tell children that when the time is exactly on an hour, the hour hand points right at the hour number and the minute hand points at 12. Explain that at 12 o'clock, the hour hand and the minute hand point right at 12. Show on the demonstration clock.

Use What You Know
Tell Time

🅖 Explore It

Show 4 o'clock.

Show 7 o'clock.

Show 10 o'clock.

Show 2 o'clock.

224

- Direct attention to the hour hand on the demonstration clock. Slowly turn the hour hand so that it points to 1, 2, and 3. Have children state the time as it points to each number.

- Ask: *How can we show that it is 4 o'clock?* Invite a volunteer to place the hour hand in the correct position on the demonstration clock. Then have children record this by drawing the hour hand to show 4 o'clock on the first clock on the Student Book page. Repeat for the other times shown.

- Remind children that the hour hand is shorter than the minute hand, so each hour hand they draw should be shorter than the minute hand that is already pointing to the 12.

>> Try It

Possible answer:

_7_ o'clock

225

Try It

Investigate the minute hand.

- Point to the minute hand on the demonstration clock. Tell children that the minute hand starts at 12 and moves completely around the clock in the same time that it takes the hour hand to move from one number to the next.

- Invite a child to move the minute hand around the clock once. As he or she does this, slowly move the hour hand from 2 to 3.

- Explain that on an actual clock, it would take 60 minutes, or 1 hour, for the minute hand to move completely around the clock and for the hour hand to move from one number to the next.

- It may be helpful to provide familiar benchmarks for 60 minutes (1 hour), such as *about how long soccer practice is* or *a little bit longer than math period.*

Practice placing the hands.

- Remind children that the minute hand is longer than the hour hand, and always points to 12 at the start of each hour.

- Ask several children to tell where the hour hand points for various "on the hour" times. Evaluate their responses for accuracy and understanding.

- Direct attention to the Student Book page. Have children to draw an hour and minute hand to show an "on the hour" time and write the time below the clock.

👥 Modeled Instruction

Step By Step

- Cut out the hands and clock face from Activity Sheet 40 (Clock Face) and distribute to each child.

- Explain that the flat part of an analog clock is called its face. Discuss why it might be called a face. Review the terms *minute hand* and *hour hand*. Have children hold up each hand.

▶ **English Language Learners**

- Ask children to describe situations when they might want to know what time it is. Explain that *o'clock* is a word that is used after a number to name the time in hours.

- Show 6 o'clock on the demonstration clock. Explain that the hour hand points directly at 6 and the minute hand points to 12.

- Read the text at the top of the page. Explain that this page shows only what the hour hand looks like at different times and that you'll study the minute hand later.

Model It

- Direct children's attention to Model It. Ask them to describe the position of the hour hand on the first clock and model it on their clock faces. Elicit that the first clock shows the hour hand pointing exactly at the 2. Explain that this means it's exactly 2 o'clock.

- Ask children to describe the position of the hour hand on the second clock and model it on their clock faces. Help them see that it points a little past the 2. Remind them that the hour hand moves very slowly, so this clock shows that it's just past 2 o'clock.

▶ **Mathematical Discourse 1**

- Have children model and then draw the hour hand at almost 3 o'clock. Discuss.

▶ **Fluency Practice**

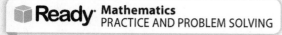

Mathematics
PRACTICE AND PROBLEM SOLVING

Assign *Practice and Problem Solving* **pages 315–316** after students have completed this section.

Tell Time

It is 2 o'clock.

Next, it is just past 2 o'clock.

Then it is almost 3 o'clock.

Where is the **hour hand** at each time?

hour

⊞ Model It Show the hour hand. ⋯⋯⋯⋯⋯⋯

Draw the **hour hand** to show the time.

2 o'clock   just past 2 o'clock   almost 3 o'clock

226

▶ **Mathematical Discourse**

1 *How does the hour hand move on a clock as the time goes from 2 o'clock to 3 o'clock? Why?*

Children should recognize that, over the course of an hour, the hour hand moves very slowly from one number to the next.

▶ **Fluency Practice**

Practice addition and subtraction within 10.

Materials For each child: Facts Practice 1, 2, 3, or 4 (Activity Sheet 16, 17, 18, or 20)

- Select one of the Facts Practice activity sheets for children to complete.

▶ **English Language Learners**

Discuss multiple English meanings of the words *hand* and *face*.

- Children know what their face is and they have learned what a clock face is. Discuss similarities and differences.

- Children know what hands are. The fingers on their hands can point to things like the hands on a clock point to the numbers.

Learn Together
Tell Time

What time do these clocks show?

🔲 **Model It** Read the time.

The **minute hand** is halfway around the clock.
The hour hand is halfway between 9 and 10.

It is half past __9__.

It is 30 minutes after __9__.

It is __9__:30,
or nine thirty.

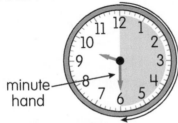

minute hand

💬 **Talk About It** Do you agree? Why or why not?

Buzz says 9:30 is halfway between 9:00 and 10:00.
So, 30 minutes is the same as a half hour.

227

Step By Step

- Read the question at the top of the page. Discuss the two types of clocks. Point out the hour hand and the part of the digital display that shows the hour. Point out the minute hand and the part of the digital display that shows the minutes.

▶ **Mathematical Discourse 2**

- Have children look at the hour hand and describe its position relative to the hours 9 and 10. Guide them to recognize that it is about halfway between 9 and 10.

Model It

- Read Model It aloud. Reiterate that the hour hand is halfway between 9 and 10. Relate this to the position of the minute hand, halfway around the clock.

- Ask: *Is it before or after 9 o'clock?* [after] *How can you tell?* [The hour hand is past the 9.]

▶ **Mathematical Discourse 3**

- Have children complete Model It on their own. Discuss how the written time, 9:30, looks the same as the time on the digital clock. Show children that times on the hour, such as 4 o'clock and 9 o'clock, include two zeros for minutes as in 4:00 and 9:00.

Talk About It

- Read Talk About It. Discuss with the class. Explain that there are 60 minutes in 1 hour. Use Mathematical Discourse question 4 to explore the idea of "half of 60."

▶ **Mathematical Discourse 4**

▶ **Concept Extension**

📦 **Ready** **Mathematics**
PRACTICE AND PROBLEM SOLVING

Assign *Practice and Problem Solving*
pages 317–318 after students have completed this section.

 ▶ **Concept Extension**

Relate half hours to halves of shapes.

Materials For each child: Clock Face (Activity Sheet 40)

- Have children draw a line from 12 to 6 and shade the right half of the clock face. Review that the two equal-size parts of a whole circle are halves.

- Ask children to use their fingers to show how the minute hand moves from the 12 to the 6 in a half hour. Relate the half-hour time period to half of the clock.

▶ **Mathematical Discourse**

2 *When the hour hand on an analog clock shows that the time is almost 3 o'clock, what hour does a digital clock show?*

Make sure children understand that *almost 3 o'clock* means it is still *2 something*. The hour on the digital clock won't switch to 3 until it is exactly 3 o'clock.

3 *At 9:00 the minute hand was on the 12. How far around the circle did the minute hand travel to get to the 6? How do you know?*

Help children understand that the minute hand traveled halfway around the clock and that's why the hour hand is halfway between 9 and 10.

4 *30 + 30 is 60. How does this relate to minutes and hours?*

Guide children to understand that double 30 is 60, so 30 is half of 60. Since there are 60 minutes in 1 hour, 30 minutes is half of 1 hour. That's why the digital clock shows ":30" when the minute hand points to 6.

Guided Practice

Step By Step

- Read the example problem. Remind children that the minute hand points straight up, toward 12, at the start of the hour. Guide them to recognize that the hour hand points directly at 7, so this clock face shows 7 o'clock.

- Discuss the differences and similarities between the analog and digital clock. Point out the stylized numbers on digital clocks. Use the Hands-On Activity to familiarize children with SSD (seven-segment display) numbers.

▶ **Hands-On Activity**

- Read each problem aloud. Then have children complete the problems and discuss.

- In Problem 1, ensure that children recognize the correct placement of the minute hand and the hour hand. Have them say the time out loud: *4 o'clock.*

- In Problem 2, have children describe what they have drawn. Listen for understanding of the differences between the minute and hour hands—their lengths, what they mean, and how they move. Ensure that children can translate from *half past 3* to the numeric version *3:30.*

▶ **Mathematical Discourse 1**

> **SMP TIP Attend to Precision**
> Encourage children to use precise language when stating the time and when discussing their mathematical reasoning related to time. Language should include terms such as: *hour, half hour, about, o'clock, past,* and ___ *thirty. (SMP 6)*

 **Mathematics**
PRACTICE AND PROBLEM SOLVING

Assign *Practice and Problem Solving* **pages 319–320** after students have completed this section.

Tell Time

These clocks show the same time.

What time is it?

It is __7__ **o'clock.**

① Circle the clock that shows 4:00.

② It is half past 3. Draw the time on these clocks.

228

▶ **Mathematical Discourse**

1 *Boom drew half past 3 by pointing a small hand to the 6 and a long hand to the 3. Is this correct? Why or why not? How would you fix it?*

   Children should recognize that Boom switched the hands. The long hand should be on the 6 and the short hand should be on the 3.

▶ **Hands-On Activity**

Construct a digital clock face.

Materials For each child: cardstock, 28 toothpicks

- Have children draw a colon in the middle of the cardstock to create their own digital clock display.

- Ask children to make an "8" using exactly seven toothpicks. Demonstrate how to make the other digits (0–7, 9) by removing specific toothpicks from the 8. Allow time for children to practice.

- Have children divide their toothpicks into four groups of seven. Explain that each group of seven toothpicks will be used for one of the digits on their digital clock.

- Have children use toothpicks to form the numbers to display 12:30 on their digital clocks. Give children various other "on the hour" and "half past" times and have them use toothpicks to show them.

Practice by Myself
Tell Time

3 Read the digital clock. Draw the hands to show the time.

4 Circle the clock that shows 11:00.

5 It is eight thirty. Draw the times on these clocks.

229

Step By Step

- Before children work on this page, review the key concepts in the lesson.

- Read each problem aloud, then have children work independently to solve.

- For Problem 3, ensure that children are drawing the hands so that it is clear that the minute hand is longer than the hour hand. The hour hand should be between 12 and 1, not on the 12.

- In Problem 4, 11:00 and 1:00 are mirror images. Make sure that children do not get the two times confused.

- Problem 5 requires reading and modeling both digital and analog clocks. Check that children write the hour to the left of the colon and the minutes to the right.

▶ **Mathematical Discourse 2**

SMP TIP Use Structure
Children use the structures inherent in the clock face and the digital time display when they tell time. They can use their knowledge of halves of a circle to help them read and write time to the half hour. They recognize that the colon on the digital clock separates the hours and minutes, and use this information to correctly place the hour hand and minute hand. *(SMP 7)*

▶ **Mathematical Discourse**

2 *How would you explain to someone who can't tell time how to read these clocks [show a digital and analog clock]?*

Listen for children's understanding of hours and minutes and how each kind of clock differentiates hours and minutes. Children should be able to discuss the colon on the digital clock and the size/shape of the hands on an analog clock as well as the different speeds at which the hands move. Some children might explain the meaning of ":30" and "half past." Others might tell how to read the hour from an analog clock, by the placement of the hour hand.

Differentiated Instruction

▶ Quick Check and Remediation

Materials For display: demonstration clock or Clock Face (Activity Sheet 40)

• Ask children to state the time for analog clocks showing 1:30, 3:00, and 8:30.

• For children who are still struggling, use the chart below to guide remediation.

• After providing remediation, check children's understanding using the following problem: *Draw the time shown on this digital clock (digital clock shows 6:00)*. [Child draws an analog clock with the hour hand pointing to 6 and the minute hand pointing to 12.]

If the error is . . .	Children may . . .	To remediate . . .
2:30 or 9:30	not understand that the hour is the one that has been passed, not the one that is upcoming.	Ask: *Where is the hour hand pointing?* [in between two numbers] Explain that the time doesn't say the next number until the hour hand points to it or passes it. Elicit that the time is half past 1 or half past 8, which is the same as 1:30 or 8:30.
3:30 instead of 3:00	not recognize the placement of the minute hand.	Cover up the clock face except for the area from 1 to 4. Have children identify where the hour hand points [directly at 3]. State that the hour hand points directly at the number at the start of the hour. Ask: *Where does the minute hand point at the start of an hour?* [straight up to 12] Reveal the whole clock.
other errors	be confused about minutes and hours.	Cover up the clock face except for the area around the hour hand. Guide children to determine the correct hour or the hour that the time is just past. Reveal the whole clock. Discuss the placement of the minute hand.

▶ Hands-On Activity
Construct a clock face.

Materials For each child: 12 small sticky notes, Circle (Activity Sheet 45)

• Distribute sticky notes and Activity Sheet 45 (Circle). Then have children write the numbers 1 through 12 on sticky notes.

• Children discuss in small groups how to place the numbers onto their clock faces.

• When everyone has made their clock face, discuss how these are like actual clocks and how they are different. Have children draw hands on their analog clock faces to show a time (to an hour or half hour).

▶ Challenge Activity
Solve simple time problems.

Materials For each child: 1 round-head fastener, Clock Face (Activity Sheet 40)

• Cut out and assemble analog clock faces and distribute to children.

• Pose very simple problems, such as: *3 hours past 4:00* or *a half hour past 1:00* or *a half hour past 8:30*. Problems should involve only adding hours within 12, or adding a half hour onto a given time.

• Have children respond to each prompt by moving the hands on their clock models to show the new time, or writing the numbers as if on a digital clock face.

• Ask children to explain how they determined the time.

Teacher Notes

Teacher-Toolbox.com

Overview

Assign the Lesson 34 Quiz and have children work independently to complete it.

Use the results of the quiz to assess children's understanding of the content of the lesson and to identify areas for reteaching. See the Lesson Pacing Guide at the beginning of the lesson and the Differentiated Instruction activities for suggested instructional resources.

Tested Skills

Assesses 1.MD.B.3

Problems on this quiz require children to be able to tell and write time to the hour and half hour using analog and digital clocks. Children will also need to be familiar with counting from 1 to 20 and know that when an object is divided into two equal parts, the parts are called halves.

Ready® **Mathematics**

Lesson 34 **Quiz Answer Key**

Name _____

Solve.

1 Read the digital clock. Draw the hands to show the time.

2 Read the digital clock. Draw the hands to show the time.

3 Circle the clock that shows 1:30.

Grade 1 **Lesson 34** Tell Time

1

©Curriculum Associates, LLC
Copying permitted for classroom use.

Common Misconceptions and Errors

Errors may result if children:

- think the hour is the number that the hour hand is approaching and not the number just passed on an analog clock.

- do not understand how to read or place the minute hand on an analog clock.

- confuse the minute hand and the hour hand on an analog clock.

- confuse minutes and hours.

Name _____

Solve.

④ It is two thirty.

Draw the time on these clocks.

⑤ Jay eats dinner at 6:00.

Circle the clock that shows when Jay eats dinner.

Assessment

Step By Step

- Have children solve the problems individually and show their work. Emphasize that children are free to use whatever way helps them solve the problems.

- Observe as children work. For Problem 1, ask children to explain how they know which belt is shorter and which is longer.

- For Problem 2, be alert for children who have difficulty distinguishing the hour hand and minute hand on the analog clock.

Unit 7 Review

Solve the problems.

1. The blue belt is ___longer___ than the orange belt.

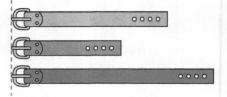

2. It is eight o'clock. Show the time on these clocks.

8:00

3. Make a tally chart and a chart with numbers. Then fill in the blanks.

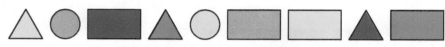

Shapes	How Many
△	|||
▭	||||
○	||

Shapes	How Many
△	3
▭	4
○	2

230 ___2___ more ▭ than ○   ___1___ fewer ○ than △

Teacher Notes

④ Read the clues.
Then color the dogs.

The blue dog is shortest.

The yellow dog is longer
than the red dog.

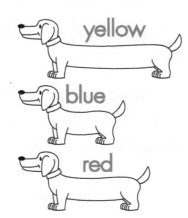

Step By Step

• For Problem 5, be alert for children who
have difficulty distinguishing the hour hand
and minute hand on the analog clock.

⑤ It is half past 7.

It is __30__ minutes after __7__ o'clock.

Show the time on these clocks.

231

Teacher Notes

Assessment

Step By Step

Put It Together

- On this page, children compare the lengths of objects, then use two different units to measure one of object. Distribute the strips of squares and rectangles from Activity Sheet 39 (Measuring Tools).

- Read the directions and task aloud. Make sure children understand what they need to do to complete the task. Then direct children to complete problem 6 on their own.

- Look for evidence that children know how to use a reference unit to measure an object: they line up the edge of the object with the edge of the first unit and align the reference units so that they touch but do not overlap.

- If children struggle, ask questions such as: *Where will you start measuring?* or *How do you know how many squares or rectangles to count to find the length?*

- Have children share their measurements with the class. Ask them to explain why it takes more squares than rectangles to measure the pencil.

- Have children return to the Unit Opener page and complete the *After* column.

Put It Together

6 **Compare and measure.**

Color the longest pencil red.
Color the shortest pencil blue.

Measure the length of the longest pencil.
Use ▦ and ▬ .

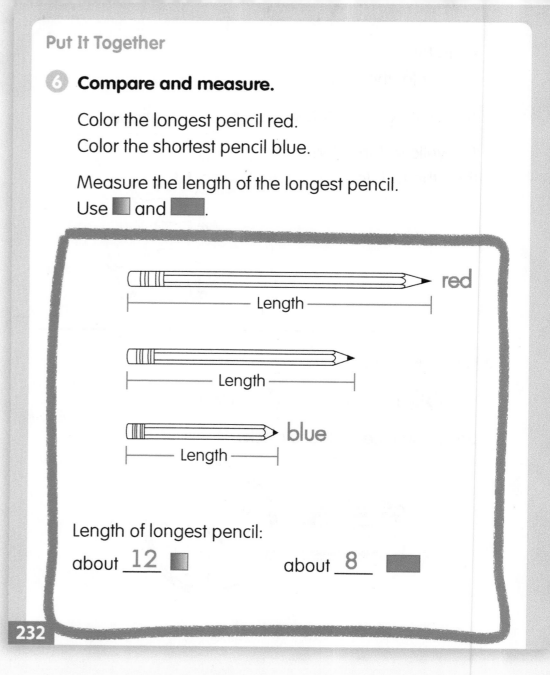

Length of longest pencil:

about __12__ ▦   about __8__ ▬

232

Teacher Notes

Scoring Rubric

Points	Expectations
4	The child: • identifies the shortest and longest pencils. • accurately measures the longest pencil using both squares and rectangles.
3	The child: • identifies the shortest and longest pencils. • accurately measures the longest pencil with one of the units and is close with the second unit.
2	The child: • identifies either the longest or shortest pencil correctly, but not both. • accurately measures the longest pencil with one of the units but not both.
1	The child: • is unable to identify the shortest and longest pencils. • fills in length measurements, but both numbers are inaccurate.
0	The child: • does not attempt to complete the task.

Content Emphasis in the Common Core Standards

Major Areas of Emphasis

Not all of the content in a given grade is emphasized equally in the Common Core Standards. Some clusters of the standards require greater emphasis than others. This greater emphasis may be based on the depth of the ideas, the time that students need to master the concepts, the content's importance to future mathematics topics, or a combination of some or all of these. A greater focus on the most critical material at each grade allows for lessons to go more in-depth and for students to have more time to master concepts and mathematical practices.

The tables on these two pages identify the Major Clusters emphasized by the Common Core Standards and assessments and those that are Supporting and Additional Clusters, In addition, the *Ready*® lessons that correspond to these clusters are also identified.

Use the tables on these pages to help inform instructional decisions regarding the amount of time spent on clusters of varying degrees of emphasis. If you are using *Ready*® as a supplement with another program, you may want to spend more time with the *Ready*® lessons connected to clusters with a major emphasis.

The table below indicates the clusters of Major Emphasis in the Common Core Standards.

Standard Clusters with Major Emphasis	Standards	*Ready*® Lesson(s)
Operations and Algebraic Thinking		
Represent and solve problems involving addition and subtraction.	1.OA.A.1, 1.OA.A.2	3, 5, 15
Understand and apply properties of operations and the relationship between addition and subtraction.	1.OA.B.3, 1.OA.B.4	4, 8
Add and subtract within 20.	1.OA.C.5, 1.OA.C.6	1, 2, 6, 9, 11, 13, 14, 16
Work with addition and subtraction equations.	1.OA.D.7, 1.OA.D.8	7, 10
Number and Operations in Base Ten		
Extend the counting sequence.	1.NBT.A.1	18
Understand place value.	1.NBT.B.2, 1.NBT.B.3	12, 17, 21, 22
Use place value understanding and properties of operations to add and subtract.	1.NBT.C.4, 1.NBT.C.5, 1.NBT.C.6	19, 20, 23, 24, 25
Measurement and Data		
Measure lengths indirectly and by iterating length units.	1.MD.A.1, 1.MD.A.2	31, 32, 33

Supporting and Additional Areas of Emphasis

Although some clusters have greater emphasis in the Common Core Standards, this does not mean that standards within the clusters identified as Supporting or Additional can be neglected during instruction. Neglecting material will leave gaps in students' skills and understanding and may leave students unprepared for the challenges of a later grade. Standards for topics that are not major emphases are written in such a way as to support and strengthen the areas of major emphasis. This allows for valuable connections that add coherence to the grade.

In addition, the Supporting and Additional clusters provide students with understanding that is essential for success on the Common Core assessments, though they are not a major focus of the assessments. The Common Core assessments will mirror the emphasis developed by the Common Core and highlighted here. Major clusters will represent the majority of the questions on the Common Core assessments, but it is important to note that items identified as being Supporting or Additional will also be included.

The table below indicates the clusters with Supporting or Additional Emphasis in the Common Core Standards.

Standard Clusters with Supporting or Additional Emphasis	Standards	Ready® Lesson(s)
Measurement and Data		
Tell and write time.	1.MD.B.3	34
Represent and interpret data.	1.MD.C.4	29, 30
Geometry		
Reason with shapes and their attributes.	1.G.A.1, 1.G.A.2, 1.G.A.3	26, 27, 28

Additional Resources

For more information on Content Emphases, see these helpful resources.

http://www.corestandards.org/other-resources/key-shifts-in-mathematics/

www.parcconline.org/parcc-model-content-frameworks

www.smarterbalanced.org/wordpress/wp-content/uploads/2011/12/Math-Content-Specifications.pdf

engageny.org/resource/math-content-emphases/

Correlations

Common Core State Standards Coverage by *Ready® Instruction*

The table below correlates each Common Core State Standard to the *Ready®* Common Core Instruction lesson(s) that offer(s) comprehensive instruction on that standard. Use this table to determine which lessons your students should complete based on their mastery of each standard.

Common Core State Standards for Grade 1 Mathematical Standards	Content Emphasis	*Ready®* Lesson(s)
Operations and Algebraic Thinking		
Represent and solve problems involving addition and subtraction.		
1.OA.A.1 Use addition and subtraction within 20 to solve word problems involving situations of adding to, taking from, putting together, taking apart, and comparing, with unknowns in all positions, e.g., by using objects, drawings, and equations with a symbol for the unknown number to represent the problem.	Major	3, 5
1.OA.A.2 Solve word problems that call for addition of three whole numbers whose sum is less than or equal to 20, e.g., by using objects, drawings, and equations with a symbol for the unknown number to represent the problem.	Major	15
Understand and apply properties of operations and the relationship between addition and subtraction.		
1.OA.B.3 Apply properties of operations as strategies to add and subtract. *Examples: If 8 + 3 = 11 is known, then 3 + 8 = 11 is also known. (Commutative property of addition.) To add 2 + 6 + 4, the second two numbers can be added to make a ten, so 2 + 6 + 4 = 2 + 10 = 12. (Associative property of addition.)*	Major	8
1.OA.B.4 Understand subtraction as an unknown-addend problem. *For example, subtract 10 − 8 by finding the number that makes 10 when added to 8.*	Major	4
Add and subtract within 20.		
1.OA.C.5 Relate counting to addition and subtraction (e.g., by counting on 2 to add 2).	Major	1, 18
1.OA.C.6 Add and subtract within 20, demonstrating fluency for addition and subtraction within 10. Use strategies such as counting on; making ten (e.g., 8 + 6 = 8 + 2 + 4 = 10 + 4 = 14); decomposing a number leading to a ten (e.g., 13 − 4 = 13 − 3 − 1 = 10 − 1 = 9); using the relationship between addition and subtraction (e.g., knowing that 8 + 4 = 12, one knows 12 − 8 = 4); and creating equivalent but easier or known sums (e.g., adding 6 + 7 by creating the known equivalent 6 + 6 + 1 = 12 + 1 = 13).	Major	2, 6, 9, 11, 13, 14, 16
Work with addition and subtraction equations.		
1.OA.D.7 Understand the meaning of the equal sign, and determine if equations involving addition and subtraction are true or false. *For example, which of the following equations are true and which are false? 6 = 6, 7 = 8 − 1, 5 + 2 = 2 + 5, 4 + 1 = 5 + 2.*	Major	10
1.OA.D.8 Determine the unknown whole number in an addition or subtraction equation relating three whole numbers. *For example, determine the unknown number that makes the equation true in each of the equations 8 + ? = 11, 5 = □ − 3, 6 + 6 = □.*	Major	7

Common Core State Standards for Grade 1 Mathematical Standards	Content Emphasis	Ready® Lesson(s)
Number and Operations in Base Ten		
Extend the counting sequence.		
1.NBT.A.1 Count to 120, starting at any number less than 120. In this range, read and write numerals and represent a number of objects with a written numeral.	Major	18
Understand place value.		
1.NBT.B.2 Understand that the two digits of a two-digit number represent amounts of tens and ones. Understand the following as special cases:		
1.NBT.B.2a 10 can be thought of as a bundle of ten ones—called a "ten."	Major	12, 17, 21
1.NBT.B.2b The numbers from 11 to 19 are composed of a ten and one, two, three, four, five, six, seven, eight, or nine ones.		
1.NBT.B.2c The numbers 10, 20, 30, 40, 50, 60, 70, 80, 90 refer to one, two, three, four, five, six, seven, eight, or nine tens (and 0 ones).		
1.NBT.B.3 Compare two two-digit numbers based on meanings of the tens and ones digits, recording the results of comparisons with the symbols $>$, $=$, and $<$.	Major	22
Use place value understanding and properties of operations to add and subtract.		
1.NBT.C.4 Add within 100, including adding a two-digit number and a one-digit number, and adding a two-digit number and a multiple of 10, using concrete models or drawings and strategies based on place value, properties of operations, and/or the relationship between addition and subtraction; relate the strategy to a written method and explain the reasoning used. Understand that in adding two-digit numbers, one adds tens and tens, ones and ones; and sometimes it is necessary to compose a ten.	Major	23, 24, 25
1.NBT.C.5 Given a two-digit number, mentally find 10 more or 10 less than the number, without having to count; explain the reasoning used.	Major	19
1.NBT.C.6 Subtract multiples of 10 in the range 10-90 from multiples of 10 in the range 10-90 (positive or zero differences), using concrete models or drawings and strategies based on place value, properties of operations, and/or the relationship between addition and subtraction; relate the strategy to a written method and explain the reasoning used.	Major	20

Ready® Mathematics Standards Correlations

Common Core State Standards Coverage by *Ready® Instruction,* *continued*

Common Core State Standards for Grade 1 Mathematical Standards	Content Emphasis	*Ready®* Lesson(s)
Measurement and Data		
Measure lengths indirectly and by iterating length units.		
1.MD.A.1 Order three objects by length; compare the lengths of two objects indirectly by using a third object.	Major	31, 32
1.MD.A.2 Express the length of an object as a whole number of length units, by laying multiple copies of a shorter object (the length unit) end to end; understand that the length measurement of an object is the number of same-size length units that span it with no gaps or overlaps. *Limit to contexts where the object being measured is spanned by a whole number of length units with no gaps or overlaps.*	Major	33
Tell and write time.		
1.MD.B.3 Tell and write time in hours and half-hours using analog and digital clocks.	Supporting/ Additional	34
Represent and interpret data.		
1.MD.C.4 Organize, represent, and interpret data with up to three categories; ask and answer questions about the total number of data points, how many in each category, and how many more or less are in one category than in another.	Supporting/ Additional	29, 30
Geometry		
Reason with shapes and their attributes.		
1.G.A.1 Distinguish between defining attributes (e.g., triangles are closed and three-sided) versus non-defining attributes (e.g., color, orientation, overall size); build and draw shapes to possess defining attributes.	Supporting/ Additional	26
1.G.A.2 Compose two-dimensional shapes (rectangles, squares, trapezoids, triangles, half-circles, and quarter-circles) or three-dimensional shapes (cubes, right rectangular prisms, right circular cones, and right circular cylinders) to create a composite shape, and compose new shapes from the composite shape.	Supporting/ Additional	27
1.G.A.3 Partition circles and rectangles into two and four equal shares, describe the shares using the words *halves, fourths,* and *quarters,* and use the phrases *half of, fourth of,* and *quarter of.* Describe the whole as two of, or four of the shares. Understand for these examples that decomposing into more equal shares creates smaller shares.	Supporting/ Additional	28

Unit Review Correlations

Standards Coverage by *Ready® Instruction*

The table below shows the standard(s) addressed for the items in the Interim Assessments, and the corresponding *Ready® Instruction* lesson(s) being assessed by each item. Use this information to adjust lesson plans and focus remediation.

Question	Standard(s)	Ready® Lesson(s)
Unit 1: Operations and Algebraic Thinking—Add and Subtract		
1	1.OA.A.1, 1.OA.C.5, 1.OA.C.6	2, 3
2	1.OA.A.1, 1.OA.C.5, 1.OA.C.6	1, 3
3	1.OA.C.5, 1.OA.C.6, 1.OA.D.8	2
4	1.OA.C.5, 1.OA.C.6, 1.OA.D.8	1
5	1.OA.C.5, 1.OA.C.6, 1.OA.D.8	2
6	1.OA.C.5, 1.OA.C.6, 1.OA.D.8	1
7	1.OA.A.1, 1.OA.C.6, 1.OA.D.8	3, 5
8	1.OA.A.1, 1.OA.B.4, 1.OA.C.6, 1.OA.D.8	3, 4
9	1.OA.A.1, 1.OA.C.6	3
Unit 2: Operations and Algebraic Thinking—Learn Facts to 10		
1	1.OA.C.6, 1.OA.D.8	6, 9, 11
2	1.OA.C.6, 1.OA.D.8	7, 11
3	1.OA.C.6, 1.OA.D.7	8, 10, 11
4	1.OA.C.6, 1.OA.D.8	9, 11
5	1.OA.C.6, 1.OA.D.8	7, 11
6	1.OA.B.3, 1.OA.C.6, 1.OA.D.7	8, 10, 11
7	1.OA.B.3, 1.OA.C.6, 1.OA.D.7, 1.OA.D.8	7, 10, 11
8	1.OA.B.3, 1.OA.C.6, 1.OA.D.8	9, 11
9	1.OA.C.6, 1.OA.D.7, 1.OA.D.8	8, 10, 11

Unit Review Correlations, *continued*

Question	Standard(s)	*Ready*® Lesson(s)
Unit 3: Operations and Algebraic Thinking and Number and Operations in Base Ten—Add and Subtract to 20		
1	1.OA.B.3, 1.OA.C.6, 1.NBT.B.2a, 1.NBT.B.2b	12, 13, 14
2	1.OA.B.3, 1.OA.C.6	16
3	1.OA.A.2, 1.OA.B.3, 1.OA.C.6	15
4	1.OA.B.3, 1.OA.C.6	16
5	1.NBT.B.2a, 1.NBT.B.2b	12
6	1.OA.B.3, 1.OA.C.6, 1.NBT.B.2a, 1.NBT.B.2b	13, 14
7	1.OA.A.2, 1.OA.B.3, 1.OA.C.6, 1.NBT.B.2a, 1.NBT.B.2b	12, 13, 14, 15
8	1.OA.C.6, 1.NBT.B.2a, 1.NBT.B.2b	12, 13
9	1.OA.C.6, 1.NBT.B.2a, 1.NBT.B.2b	12, 16
Unit 4: Number and Operations in Base Ten—Tens		
1	1.OA.C.5, 1.NBT.A.1, 1.NBT.C.4	18
2	1.OA.C.5, 1.NBT.A.1, 1.NBT.C.5	18, 19
3	1.OA.C.5, 1.NBT.C.5	19
4	1.OA.C.5, 1.NBT.C.6	19, 20
5	1.OA.C.5, 1.NBT.A.1	18
6	1.NBT.B.2a, 1.NBT.B.2c	17
7	1.OA.C.5, 1.NBT.C.4, 1.NBT.C.6	19
8	1.NBT.B.2a, 1.NBT.B.2c, 1.NBT.C.4, 1.NBT.C.6	17, 20

Unit Review Correlations, *continued*

Question	Standard(s)	*Ready®* Lesson(s)
Unit 5: Number and Operations in Base Ten—Tens and Ones		
1	1.NBT.B.2a, 1.NBT.B.2c, 1.NBT.B.3	22
2	1.NBT.B.2a, 1.NBT.C.4	21, 23, 24
3	1.NBT.B.2a, 1.NBT.B.2c	21
4	1.NBT.B.2a, 1.NBT.B.2c, 1.NBT.C.4	21, 23
5	1.NBT.B.2a, 1.NBT.B.2c, 1.NBT.B.3	22
6	1.NBT.B.2a, 1.NBT.B.2c, 1.NBT.C.4	24
7	1.NBT.B.2a, 1.NBT.B.2c, 1.NBT.B.3	22
8	1.NBT.B.2a, 1.NBT.B.2c, 1.NBT.C.4	25
9	1.NBT.B.2a, 1.NBT.B.2c, 1.NBT.C.4	21, 23, 24, 25
Unit 6: Geometry—Shapes		
1	1.G.A.3	28
2	1.G.A.3	28
3	1.G.A.1	26
4	1.G.A.2	27
5	1.G.A.1	26
6	1.G.A.2	27
7	1.G.A.1, 1.G.A.2	26, 27
8	1.G.A.1	26
9	1.G.A.1, 1.G.A.2, 1.G.A.3	26, 27, 28

Unit Review Correlations, *continued*

Question	Standard(s)	*Ready*® Lesson(s)
Unit 7: Measurement and Data—How Many? How Much? How Long?		
1	1.MD.A.1	31
2	1.MD.B.3	34
3	1.MD.C.4, 1.OA.A.1, 1.OA.C.6	29, 30
4	1.MD.A.1	31, 32
5	1.MD.B.3	34
6	1.MD.A.1, 1.MD.A.2	31, 32, 33

Supporting Research

References

Ball, D. L., Ferrini-Mundy, J., Kilpatrick, J., Milgram, R. J., Schmid, W., & Schaar, R. (2005). Reaching for common ground in K–12 mathematics education. *Notices of the American Mathematical Society,* 52(9).

Beed, P. L., Hawkins, E. M., & Roller, C. M. (1991). Moving learners toward independence: The power of scaffolded instruction. *The Reading Teacher*, 44(9), 648–655.

Eastburn, J. A. (2011). The effects of a concrete, representational, abstract (CRA) instructional model on tier 2 first-grade math students in a response to intervention model: Educational implications for number sense and computational fluency. Dissertation. *ProQuest Information & Learning*, AAI3408708.

Furner, J. M., Yahya, N., & Duffy, M. L. (2005). 20 Ways to teach mathematics: strategies to reach all students. *Intervention in School and Clinic*, 41(1).

Hall, T., Strangman, N., & Meyer, A. (2003). Differentiated instruction and implications for UDL implementation. National Center on Accessing the General Curriculum. Accessed at: *http://aim.cast.org/learn/historyarchive/backgroundpapers/differentiated*

Hess, K. K., Carlock, D., Jones, B., & Walkup, J. R. (2009). *What exactly do "fewer, clearer, and higher standards" really look like in the classroom? Using a cognitive rigor matrix to analyze curriculum, plan lessons, and implement assessments.* Accessed at: *http://www.nciea.org/cgi-bin/pubspage.cgi?sortby=pub_date.*

National Council of Teachers of Mathematics. (2007). Effective strategies for teaching students with difficulties in mathematics.

———. (2008). Teaching mathematics to English language learners.

National Governors Association Center for Best Practices and Council of Chief State School Officers. (2010). Common Core *State Standards for Mathematics*. Accessed at: *http://www.corestandards.org/the-standards.*

———. (2012). *Publisher's Criteria for the Common Core State Standards in Mathematics, K–8.* Accessed at: *http://www.corestandards.org/resources.*

National Mathematics Advisory Panel. (2008). Foundations for success: The final report of the National Mathematics Advisory Panel. Accessed at: *http://www2.ed.gov/about/bdscomm/list/mathpanel/index.html.*

National Research Council. (2001). *Adding it Up: Helping Children Learn Mathematics.* Mathematics Learning Study Committee: Kilpatrick, J., Swafford, J., & Findell, B. (eds.). Washington, D.C.: National Academy Press.

Partnership for Assessment of Readiness for College and Careers. (2011). *PARCC model content frameworks: English language arts/literacy grades 3–11.* Accessed at: *http://www.parcconline.org/parcc-model-content-frameworks.*

Pashler, H., Bain, P., Bottge, B., Graesser, A., Koedinger, K., McDaniel, M., & Metcalfe, J. (2007). *Organizing instruction and study to improve student learning* (NCER 2007–2004). Washington, D.C.: National Center for Education Research, Institute of Education Sciences, U.S. Department of Education. Retrieved from *http://ies.ed.gov/ncer.*

Robertson, K. (2009). Math instruction for English language learners. *Colorìn Colorado!* Accessed at: *http://www.colorincolorado.org/article/30570/.*

Schmidt,W., Houang, R., & Cogan, L. (2002). A coherent curriculum, *American Educator,* Summer, 2002.

Seethaler, P. M., Fuchs, L. S., Fuchs, D., & Compton, D. L. (2012). Predicting first graders' development of calculation versus word-problem performance: the role of dynamic assessment. *Journal of Educational Psychology* 104(1), 224–234.

Smarter Balanced Assessment Consortium. (2012). *General Item Specifications.* Accessed at: *http://www. smarterbalanced. org/wordpress/wp-content/uploads/2012/05/TaskItemSpecifications/ItemSpecifications/GeneralItemSpecifications.pdf.*

Activity Sheets

These Activity Sheets are provided for use with a variety of activities found in the **Ready**® Teacher's Resource Book. These activity masters may be photocopied for classroom use. Refer to the activity in the lesson for a full list of materials and instructions.

Activity Sheets (continued)

Name _____

1	2	3	4	5	6	7	8	9	10

1	2	3	4	5	6	7	8	9	10

1	2	3	4	5	6	7	8	9	10

1	2	3	4	5	6	7	8	9	10

1	2	3	4	5	6	7	8	9	10

Number Bond Recording Sheet

Number Bond Mat

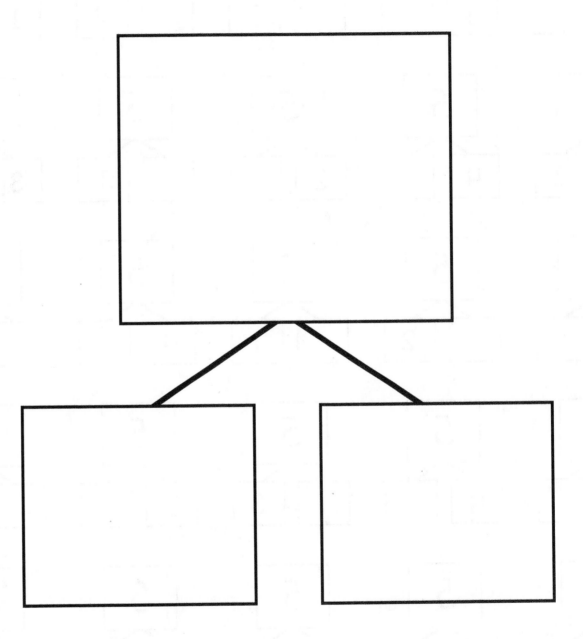

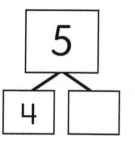 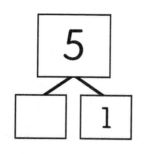 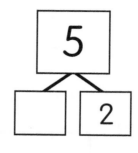 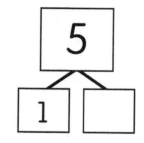 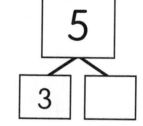

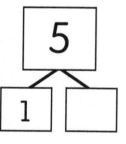 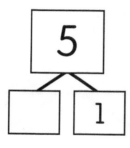 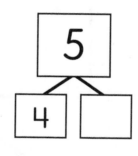 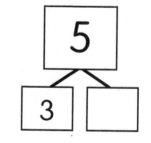 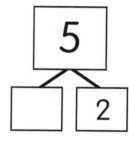

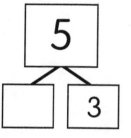 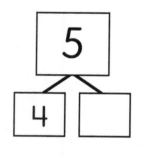 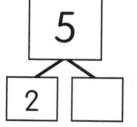 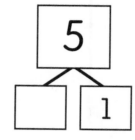 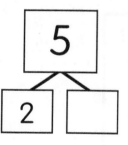

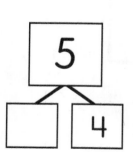 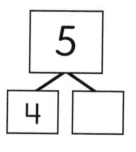 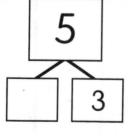 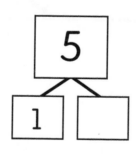 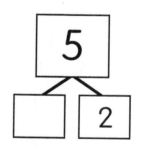

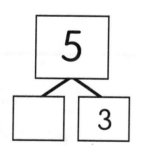 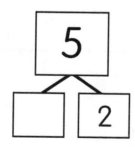 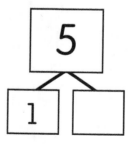

Name _____

Addition Table 1

0 + 0 ___	0 + 1 ___	0 + 2 ___	0 + 3 ___	0 + 4 ___	0 + 5 ___
1 + 0 ___	1 + 1 ___	1 + 2 ___	1 + 3 ___	1 + 4 ___	1 + 5 ___
2 + 0 ___	2 + 1 ___	2 + 2 ___	2 + 3 ___	2 + 4 ___	2 + 5 ___
3 + 0 ___	3 + 1 ___	3 + 2 ___	3 + 3 ___	3 + 4 ___	3 + 5 ___
4 + 0 ___	4 + 1 ___	4 + 2 ___	4 + 3 ___	4 + 4 ___	4 + 5 ___
5 + 0 ___	5 + 1 ___	5 + 2 ___	5 + 3 ___	5 + 4 ___	5 + 5 ___

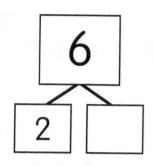
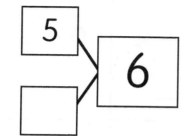
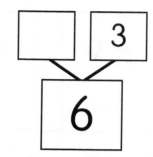

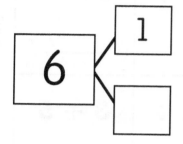
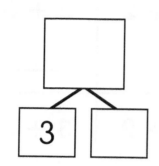
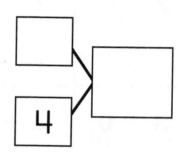

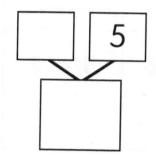
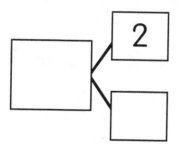
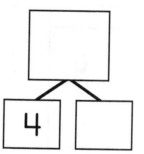

Name _____

Partners for 7 Practice

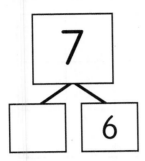

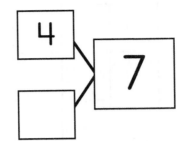

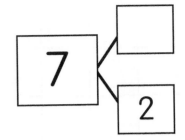

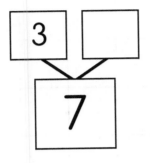

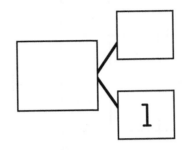

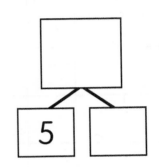

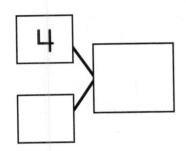

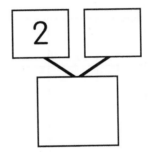

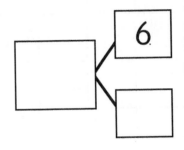

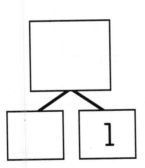

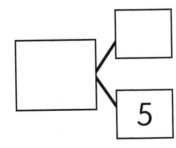

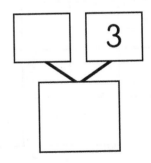

Grid Paper

Partners for 8 Practice

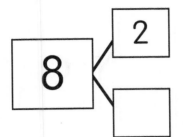

2 + ____ = 8

8 = ____ + 2

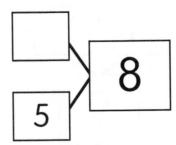

____ + 5 = 8

8 = 5 + ____

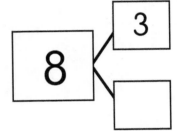

7 + ____ = 8

8 = ____ + 7

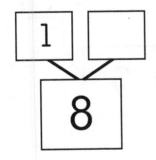

1 + ____ = 8

8 = ____ + 1

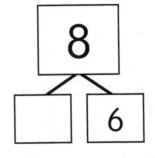

____ + 6 = 8

8 = 6 + ____

3 + ____ = 8

8 = ____ + 3

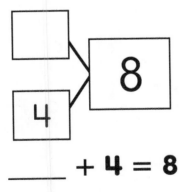

____ + 4 = 8

8 = 4 + ____

Partners for 9 Practice

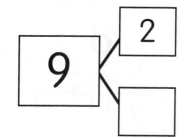

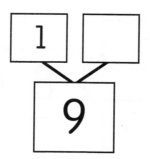

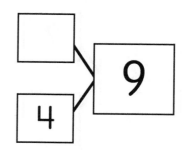

2 + ____ = 9

9 = ____ + 2

1 + ____ = 9

9 = ____ + 1

____ + 4 = 9

9 = 4 + ____

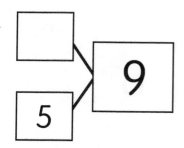

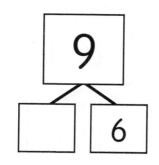

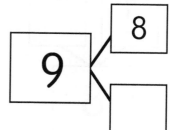

____ + 5 = 9

9 = 5 + ____

____ + 6 = 9

9 = 6 + ____

8 + ____ = 9

9 = ____ + 8

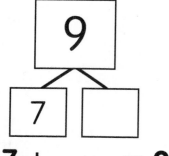

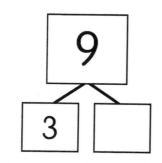

7 + ____ = 9

9 = ____ + 7

3 + ____ = 9

9 = ____ + 3

Name _____

Partners for 10 Practice

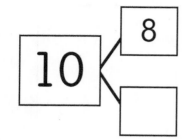

8 + _____ = 10

10 = _____ + 8

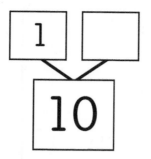

1 + _____ = 10

10 = _____ + 1

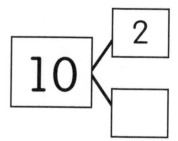

_____ + 4 = 10

10 = 4 + _____

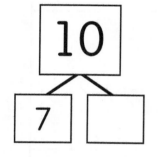

7 + _____ = 10

10 = _____ + 7

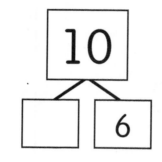

_____ + 6 = 10

10 = 6 + _____

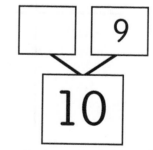

2 + _____ = 10

10 = _____ + 2

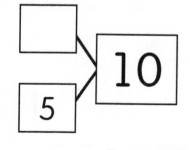

_____ + 5 = 10

10 = 5 + _____

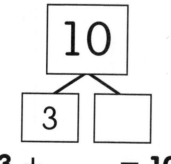

3 + _____ = 10

10 = _____ + 3

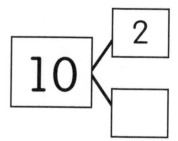

1 + _____ = 10

10 = _____ + 1

True and Untrue Number Sentences

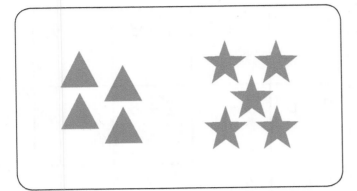

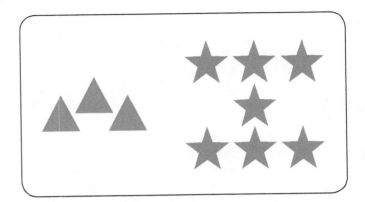

_____ + _____ = _____ + _____

_____ + _____ = _____ + _____

Name _____

1 + 1	1 + 2	1 + 3	1 + 4	1 + 5	1 + 6	1 + 7	1 + 8	1 + 9
2 + 1	2 + 2	2 + 3	2 + 4	2 + 5	2 + 6	2 + 7	2 + 8	
3 + 1	3 + 2	3 + 3	3 + 4	3 + 5	3 + 6	3 + 7		
4 + 1	4 + 2	4 + 3	4 + 4	4 + 5	4 + 6			
5 + 1	5 + 2	5 + 3	5 + 4	5 + 5				
6 + 1	6 + 2	6 + 3	6 + 4					
7 + 1	7 + 2	7 + 3						
8 + 1	8 + 2							
9 + 1								

Name _____

Addition Table 3

1 + 1	1 + 2	1 + 3	1 + 4	1 + 5	1 + 6	1 + 7	1 + 8	1 + 9
2	3	4	5	6	7	8	9	10
2 + 1	2 + 2	2 + 3	2 + 4	2 + 5	2 + 6	2 + 7	2 + 8	
3	4	5	6	7	8	9	10	
3 + 1	3 + 2	3 + 3	3 + 4	3 + 5	3 + 6	3 + 7		
4	5	6	7	8	9	10		
4 + 1	4 + 2	4 + 3	4 + 4	4 + 5	4 + 6			
5	6	7	8	9	10			
5 + 1	5 + 2	5 + 3	5 + 4	5 + 5				
6	7	8	9	10				
6 + 1	6 + 2	6 + 3	6 + 4					
7	8	9	10					
7 + 1	7 + 2	7 + 3						
8	9	10						
8 + 1	8 + 2							
9	10							
9 + 1								
10								

Facts Practice 1

1 + ___ = 6	___ − 5 = 1	8 − ___ = 7	___ = 5 + 4
10 − 8 = ___	___ = 9 − 2	___ + 1 = 9	0 + ___ = 6
___ + 0 = 8	10 − ___ = 4	6 − 4 = ___	9 + ___ = 10
2 + ___ = 6	___ = 10 + 0	___ − 0 = 7	7 − 6 = ___
3 = 8 − ___	3 + 3 = ___	9 − ___ = 1	7 + 0 = ___
___ + 4 = 10	9 − ___ = 0	3 + 5 = ___	___ = 10 − 7
3 + ___ = 9	8 = 10 − ___	4 + ___ = 8	___ − 6 = 3
6 + ___ = 7	9 − 5 = ___	___ = 6 + 2	___ + 9 = 9
___ = 10 − 9	___ + 3 = 10	7 − 4 = ___	5 + ___ = 10

Facts Practice 2

___ = 4 + 2	9 + ___ = 10	___ + 2 = 9	8 − 7 = ___
___ − 1 = 9	7 + ___ = 8	___ = 1 + 6	9 − 3 = ___
8 − ___ = 4	___ + 10 = 10	0 + 8 = ___	___ = 6 − 2
5 + ___ = 6	___ − 3 = 4	___ = 3 + 4	10 − 4 = ___
___ = 1 + 8	8 − ___ = 6	___ + 2 = 7	0 + ___ = 7
7 − 1 = ___	___ + 6 = 8	7 = 6 + ___	___ = 4 + 5
___ + 7 = 10	5 = 10 − ___	9 + 0 = ___	___ − 5 = 2
6 + ___ = 9	2 + 8 = ___	9 = 2 + ___	___ − 0 = 6
___ = 5 + 3	10 − 3 = ___	9 − ___ = 5	4 + ___ = 10

___ + 3 = 6	9 − ___ = 0	___ = 7 + 3	8 + ___ = 10
0 = ___ − 6	___ + 3 = 7	10 − 0 = ___	6 − ___ = 3
8 − 0 = ___	___ + 7 = 9	___ = 2 + 5	___ − 8 = 0
10 = ___ + 9	___ = 1 + 7	10 − ___ = 8	6 + ___ = 6
7 − 7 = ___	___ + 0 = 10	8 − ___ = 5	8 − ___ = 6
___ − 7 = 2	___ = 10 − 0	6 = 1 + ___	7 + ___ = 7
___ + 9 = 9	___ − 6 = 2	9 − ___ = 4	6 + 3 = ___
7 = 6 + ___	7 − 2 = ___	___ + 5 = 10	10 − ___ = 3
___ = 9 − 0	5 + 4 = ___	10 − ___ = 10	___ − 8 = 0

Name _____

1	2	3	4	5	6	7	8	9	10
11	12	13	14	15	16	17	18	19	20
21	22	23	24	25	26	27	28	29	30
31	32	33	34	35	36	37	38	39	40
41	42	43	44	45	46	47	48	49	50
51	52	53	54	55	56	57	58	59	60
61	62	63	64	65	66	67	68	69	70
71	72	73	74	75	76	77	78	79	80
81	82	83	84	85	86	87	88	89	90
91	92	93	94	95	96	97	98	99	100

Name _____

How many ways can
you make 7?

___ + ___ = 7   ___ + ___ = 7

7 = ___ + ___   7 = ___ + ___

___ + ___ = 7   ___ + ___ = 7

How many ways can
you make 8?

___ + ___ = 8   ___ + ___ = 8

8 = ___ + ___   8 = ___ + ___

___ + ___ = 8   ___ + ___ = 8

8 = ___ + ___

How many ways can
you make 9?

___ + ___ = 9   ___ + ___ = 9

9 = ___ + ___   9 = ___ + ___

___ + ___ = 9   ___ + ___ = 9

9 = ___ + ___   9 = ___ + ___

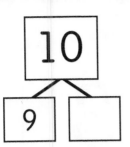

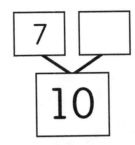

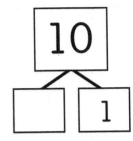

10 / 9, ☐

10 → ☐, 4

7, ☐ / 10

10 / ☐, 1

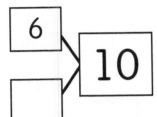

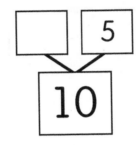

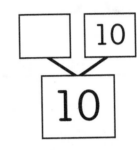

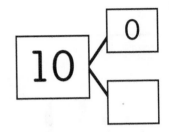

6, ☐ → 10

8, ☐ / 10

10 / 2, ☐

10 → 0, ☐

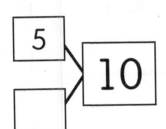

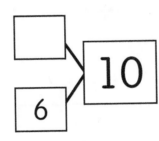

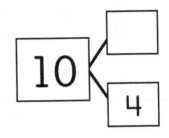

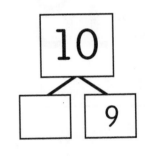

5, ☐ → 10

☐, 5 / 10

☐, 10 / 10

3, ☐ → 10

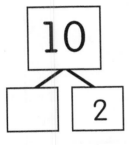

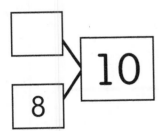

10 / ☐, 2

☐, 6 → 10

10 → ☐, 4

10 / ☐, 9

☐, 8 → 10

10 → 3, ☐

5, ☐ / 10

10 / 1, ☐

Name _____

Teen Number Cards

	11	12	13
14	15	16	17
18	19	+	–
=	<	>	□

120 Chart

1	2	3	4	5	6	7	8	9	10
11	12	13	14	15	16	17	18	19	20
21	22	23	24	25	26	27	28	29	30
31	32	33	34	35	36	37	38	39	40
41	42	43	44	45	46	47	48	49	50
51	52	53	54	55	56	57	58	59	60
61	62	63	64	65	66	67	68	69	70
71	72	73	74	75	76	77	78	79	80
81	82	83	84	85	86	87	88	89	90
91	92	93	94	95	96	97	98	99	100
101	102	103	104	105	106	107	108	109	110
111	112	113	114	115	116	117	118	119	120

Name _____

	10	20	30
40	50	60	70
80	90	+	−
=	<	>	☐

Name _____

100	110	120	130
140	150	160	170
180	190	200	

Number Cards 0 to 11

0	1	2	3
4	5	<u>6</u>	7
8	<u>9</u>	10	11
=	<	>	☐

10 More, 10 Less

20 + 10 = _____	40 − 10 = _____
10 + 10 = _____	20 − 10 = _____
30 + 10 = _____	60 − 10 = _____
40 + 10 = _____	30 − 10 = _____
20 + 10 = _____	70 − 10 = _____
50 + 10 = _____	50 − 10 = _____
70 + 10 = _____	80 − 10 = _____
10 + 10 = _____	90 − 10 = _____
80 + 10 = _____	40 − 10 = _____
40 + 10 = _____	70 − 10 = _____
60 + 10 = _____	20 − 10 = _____
50 + 10 = _____	60 − 10 = _____
90 + 10 = _____	50 − 10 = _____
30 + 10 = _____	90 − 10 = _____
80 + 10 = _____	30 − 10 = _____

Place-Value Mat

Tens	Ones

Name _____

	My Work
60 + 35 = _____	
_____ = 27 + 20	
_____ = 10 + 19	
16 + 40 = _____	
50 + 21 = _____	
_____ = 44 + 30	
23 + 70 = _____	
_____ = 10 + 72	
18 + 20 = _____	
10 + 52 = _____	

Name _____

Practice Adding Tens and Ones

	My Work
14 + 22 = ____	
____ = 74 + 14	
35 + 21 = ____	
43 + 24 = ____	
____ = 85 + 12	
51 + 23 = ____	
21 + 25 = ____	
63 + 22 = ____	
____ = 17 + 11	
31 + 42 = ____	

Name _____

Practice Regrouping to Add

	My Work
18 + 38 = _____	
29 + 28 = _____	
36 + 47 = _____	
47 + 25 = _____	
58 + 36 = _____	
21 + 19 = _____	
38 + 27 = _____	
48 + 43 = _____	
29 + 29 = _____	

rectangle	**triangle**	**hexagon**
4 sides 4 square corners opposite sides equal	3 sides 3 corners	6 sides 6 corners
Any shape with 4 sides and 4 corners	**square** 4 equal sides 4 square corners	**rhombus** 4 equal sides 4 corners

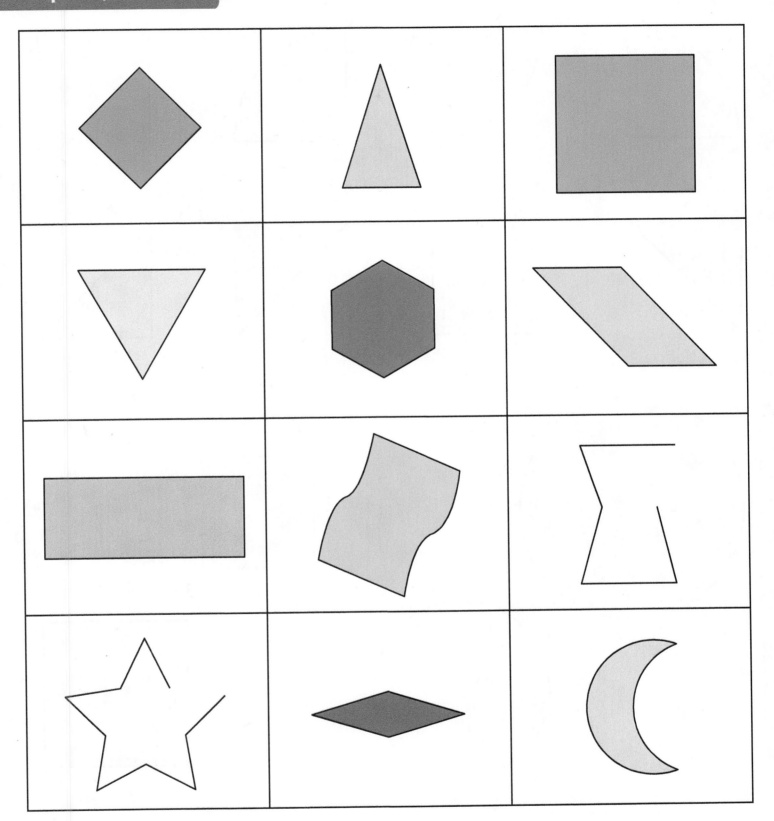

Name _____

  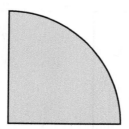 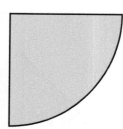

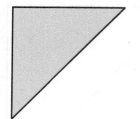 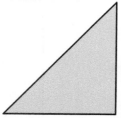 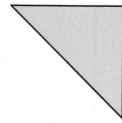 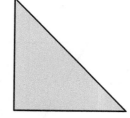

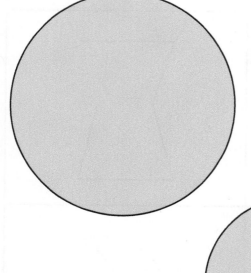 

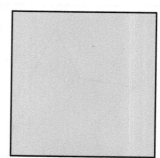

Name _____

 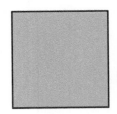

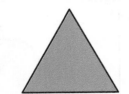 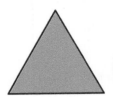

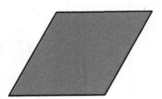 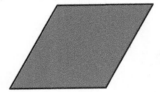

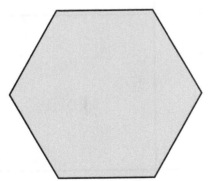 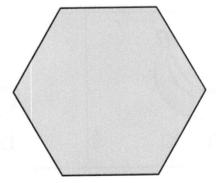

Data Cards

apple	apple	apple
apple	apple	apple
pear	pear	pear
banana	banana	banana
banana	banana	

Name _____

Name _____

Practice Adding Three Numbers

	My Work
4 + 5 + 6 = ____	
8 + 4 + 2 = ____	
5 + 7 + 5 = ____	
3 + 9 + 7 = ____	
6 + 4 + 6 = ____	
9 + 7 + 1 = ____	
2 + 8 + 8 = ____	
5 + 3 + 5 = ____	
9 + 2 + 1 = ____	
7 + 7 + 6 = ____	

Name _____

Practice Making a Ten to Add

Change each number sentence to have 10 as one addend. Write the totals.

Example:

5 + 8 = _13_

_3_ + _10_ = _13_

9 + 6 = _____ ____ + ____ = _____	7 + 9 = _____ ____ + ____ = _____
8 + 4 = _____ ____ + ____ = _____	6 + 8 = _____ ____ + ____ = _____
9 + 9 = _____ ____ + ____ = _____	8 + 7 = _____ ____ + ____ = _____
4 + 7 = _____ ____ + ____ = _____	9 + 8 = _____ ____ + ____ = _____

Name _____

Write numbers in the boxes to make true number sentences.

Example:

$$13 = 13$$

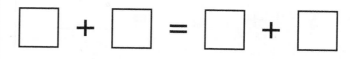

$$\boxed{6} + \boxed{7} = \boxed{8} + \boxed{5}$$

$$13 = 13$$

$$\square + \square = \square + \square$$

$$12 = 12$$

$$\square + \square = \square + \square$$

$$16 = 16$$

$$\square + \square = \square + \square$$

$$10 = 10$$

$$\square + \square = \square + \square$$

$$8 = 8$$

$$\square + \square = \square + \square$$

$$6 = 6$$

$$\square + \square = \square + \square$$

$$7 = 7$$

$$\square + \square = \square + \square$$

$$9 = 9$$

$$\square + \square = \square + \square$$

Measuring Tools

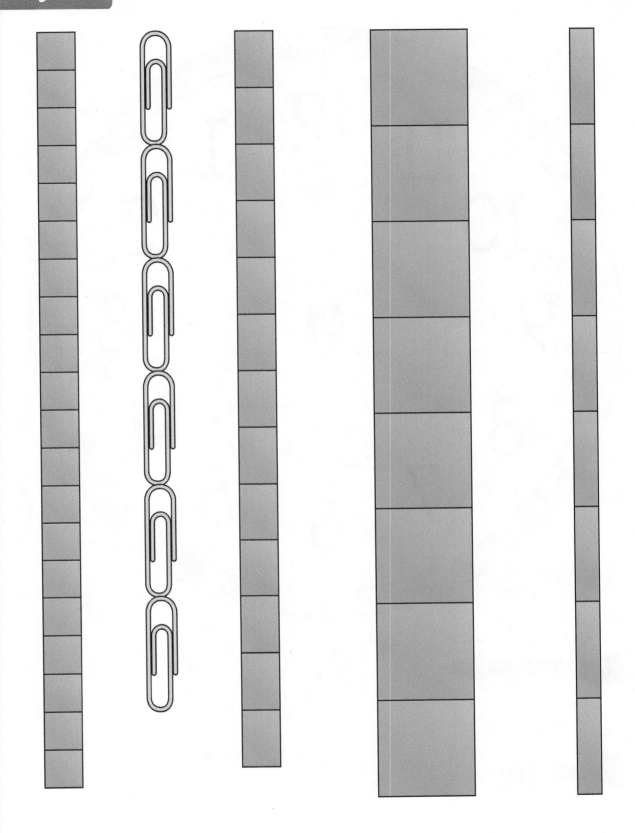

Name _____

Name _____

1 + 9	2 + 8	3 + 7	4 + 6
1 + 8	2 + 7	3 + 6	4 + 5
1 + 7	2 + 6	3 + 5	4 + 3
1 + 6	2 + 5	3 + 4	4 + 2

9 + 1	8 + 2	7 + 3	6 + 4
8 + 1	7 + 2	6 + 3	5 + 4
7 + 1	6 + 2	5 + 3	3 + 4
6 + 1	5 + 2	4 + 3	2 + 4

Dot Cards—Small

10 more

10 less

Name _____

Two-Digit Number Mats

1	0	2	0
3	0	4	0
5	0	6	0
7	0		

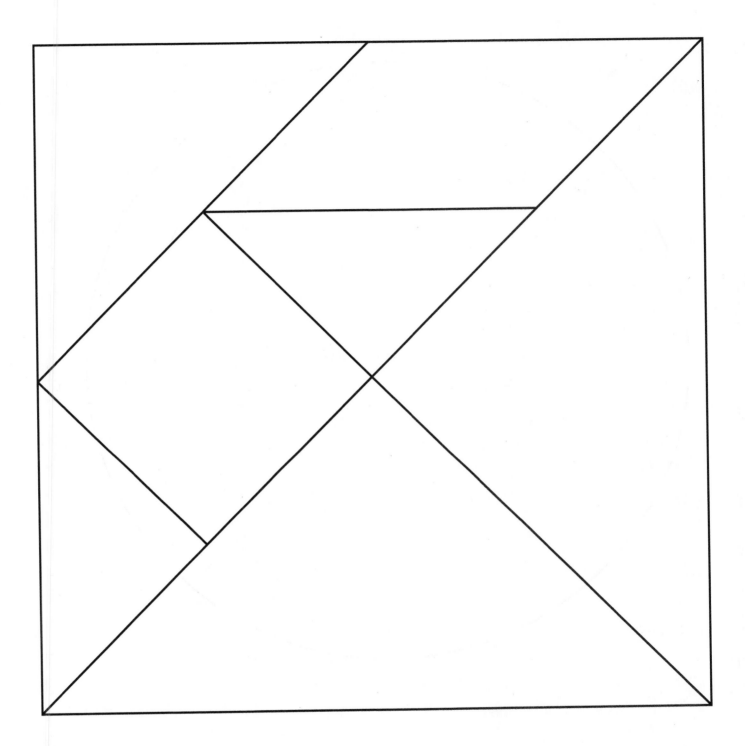

Name _____

Name _____

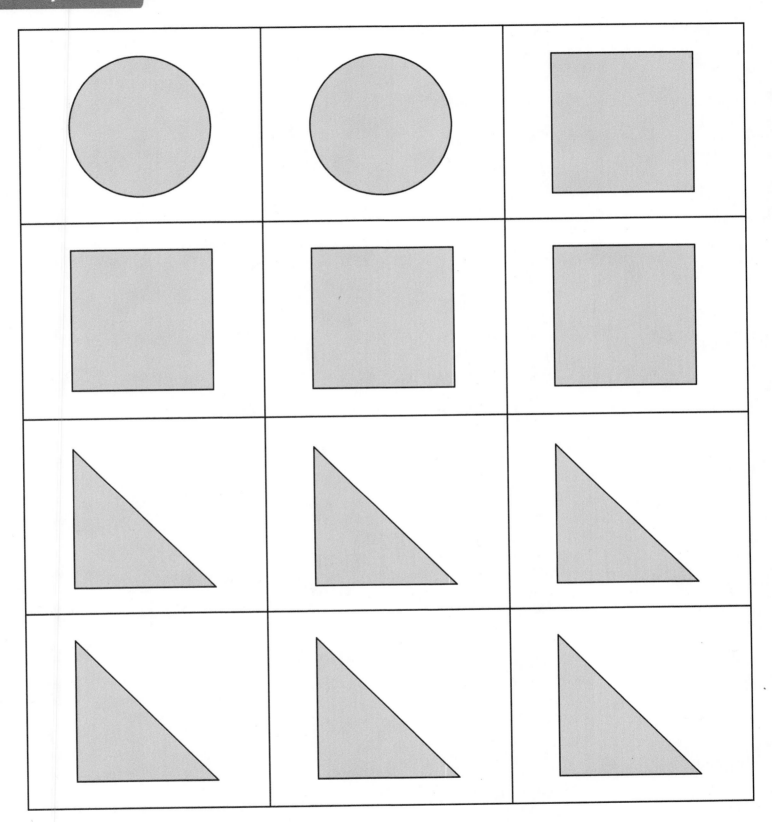